# *Principles of* GENETICS

*Principles of*

# GENETICS

THIRD EDITION

ELDON J. GARDNER

*Utah State University*

JOHN WILEY & SONS, INC.

*New York / London / Sydney / Toronto*

10 9 8 7 6 5 4 3

Library of Congress Catalog Card Number: 67-30462
SBN 471 29125 0
Printed in the United States of America

# *Preface*

This edition has been completely revised and rewritten with many new examples, illustrations, and problems. The material has been organized into three parts: I, Basic Genetics; II, Nature and Function of Genetic Material; and III, Population Genetics and Evolution.

Some teachers prefer to discuss the chemistry of the genetic material (DNA) at the beginning and thus to provide a modern, dynamic setting for the course. Other teachers follow the more traditional approach through cells and Mendelian genetics. The instructors who prefer to deal with biochemical aspects early may introduce Chapter 12 at the beginning, immediately after Chapter 1 or following Chapter 6. In the first draft of this edition, biochemical material was placed in position as Chapter 2. After careful consideration, it was removed to Chapter 12 to give unity to Part II of the three-part book. It is recognized that each teacher may have his own preference in the sequence of topics that he presents in the classroom. The chapters are prepared as units and may be discussed in different order with a little attention to continuity on the part of the teacher. For example, new terms are defined when first introduced. With appropriate comment from the teacher or reference to the glossary, the student should have little difficulty in accommodating a change in the sequence of chapters.

Full chapter status has been given to Cytoplasmic Inheritance and Maternal Effects (Chapter 11), Developmental and Behavior Genetics (Chapter 16), and Genetics of Race and Species Formation (Chapter 19), thus increasing the number of chapters from 18 in the second edition to 21 in this edition. To make room for new material, much of the history (including several portraits of early geneticists) has been eliminated. The glossary has been extended to include terms that are new to this edition. Answers to half of the problems are included in the text. The other half are printed in an answer book for instructors. It is the prime aim of this edition (as in the previous editions) to present the basic principles of genetics in their modern context and as a unified whole.

Several colleagues, graduate students, and friends have assisted in the present revision of this book. I express deepest appreciation to all who have contributed in any way. I am especially indebted to my colleague John R.

Simmons who read most of the chapters and suggested improvements. Others who read chapters or gave assistance in their special fields are Larre N. Egbert, W. S. Boyle, G. Albin Matson, James T. Bowman, Wade Dewey, Hugh P. Stanley, Wendell Gardner, and Keith L. Dixon. Lois Cox gave editorial assistance. Portraits were drawn by Professor Everett Thorpe.

Credits for tables, illustrations, and quotations from other publications are given in the legends according to the wishes of the author or publisher. I am indebted to the Literary Executor of the late Sir Ronald A. Fisher, F.R.S., and to Oliver & Boyd Ltd., Edinburgh, for their permission to reprint Tables 3 and 4 from their book *Statistical Methods for Research Workers.*

*Logan, Utah*
*August 1967*

*Eldon J. Gardner*

# *Preface to Second Edition*

Those investigators in the vanguard are currently advancing the frontiers of genetics with relentless vigor. Their phenomenal progress is at once awe inspiring and problematical to an author of a genetics textbook. This second edition of *Principles of Genetics* has been revised with an acute awareness that many of its revisions may be doomed to be only of historical interest by the time they reach print.

Space considerations have dictated representative rather than exhaustive chapter bibliographies. The glossary which has been added as an appendix takes definitions from within the text and makes them more readily available as references. In the interest of presenting comprehensively updated material, much of the history included in the first edition has been eliminated and some chapters have been combined and shortened.

The present dynamic state of the science of genetics still has its foundation, however, in previously established (though admittedly not immutable) basic tenets. The prime aim of this book continues to be to present these basic principles in their modern context and as a unified whole.

Many colleagues and friends have assisted in the revision of this book for the second edition. To all who have contributed in any way, I express deepest appreciation. I am especially indebted to C. M. Woolf of the University of Utah who read the manuscript and suggested improvements. My colleagues Lois Cox, John R. Simmons, James W. Edwards, Larry L. Cox, and Gwen Haws have rendered valuable assistance. W. S. Boyle has provided a number of excellent photographs. The portraits of geneticists were drawn by Everett Thorpe. Wilma Turpen and Chrystal Christensen typed the manuscript.

Credits for tables, illustrations, and quotations from other publications are given in the legends according to the wishes of the author or publisher. I am indebted to Professor Sir Ronald A. Fisher, Cambridge, and to Messrs. Oliver and Boyd Ltd., Edinburgh, for permission to abridge tables 3 and 4 from their book *Statistical Methods for Research Workers*. Several illustrations have been redrawn from the National Pigeon Association Booklet.

*Logan, Utah*
*January, 1964*

*Eldon J. Gardner*

# *Contents*

# I

## *Basic Genetics (Mendelian and NonMendelian)*

# *Mendelian Genetics* | 1

Early observations on plants and animals suggested that underlying natural laws could account for heredity and variation. Investigators were unsuccessful in trying to unravel the basic principles, however, until the beginning of the twentieth century, when an adequate scientific foundation was available. By effectively applying the scientific method, many investigators working with various plants and animals accumulated and organized a vast body of facts concerning the mechanisms of heredity and variation. It gradually became obvious that the same basic principles could be applied to plants, animals, and man.

Tigers beget little tigers and not elephants or representatives of some other species because specific physical elements (genes) are transmitted from parents to offspring through the gametes, that is, eggs and sperm. Pine trees give rise to other pine trees because their pollen and eggs carry determiners that control developmental processes that ultimately give rise to more pine trees. Thus, the distinguishing characteristics of a given species are maintained generation after generation.

All characteristics of any organism, however, have hereditary and environmental components, although some traits are more immediately influenced by the environment than others. Whereas the basic biological pattern is set by heredity, the development of the individual is affected by the environment. Some genes respond differentially to a wide range of conditions. Others are far more precise and restricted in their effects.

## HISTORICAL SETTING

Practical accomplishments with some genetic overtones occurred in remote periods of history. Tablets of stone prepared by the Babylonians 6000 years ago show pedigrees of several successive generations of horses, suggesting a conscious effort toward improvement. Other stone carvings of the same period illustrate the artificial cross-pollination of date palms practiced by early Babylonians. Many years before the Christian era, Chinese farmers were improving varieties of rice by selecting seed from plants that had the most desirable characteristics. Maize was cultivated and improved in the Western Hemisphere before the Neolithic era. Selection and hybridization were undoubtedly employed by early plant and animal breeders, although these people were not even vaguely aware of the principles of genetics.

Hippocrates, Aristotle, and other Greek philosophers made observations and engaged in speculations that suggested genetic principles. Their elements of truth, however, were vague and interspersed with error. Stories of unusual hybrids initiated by the Greeks were repeated with imaginative flourishes by Pliny (79–23 B.C.), Gesner (1516–1565), and other Hellenistic and Medieval writers. These tales were perpetuated for about 2000 years following the Greek period. The giraffe was supposed to be a hybrid between the camel and the leopard. The two-humped camel was thought to have resulted from a cross between a camel and a boar. When the camel mated with the sparrow an ostrich was imagined to appear. Plants were also imagined to be capable of remarkable hybridizations. Banana trees were said to arise from hybridization between acacia and palm trees. Although many of these tales persisted, little information existed before the seventeenth century that contributed to the science of genetics. Fantastic explanations of the mechanism of reproduction and of sex determination were associated with these stories.

### *Sexual Reproduction in Animals and Plants*

Much of the speculation of the ancients represented a sincere attempt to explain biological phenomena but, in the absence of facts, curious and more or less superstitious men resorted to imagination. A new era was introduced in the latter part of the seventeenth century by the development of the microscope and its effective use. Many years before the eggs and sperm of mammals were observed, however, William Harvey (1578–1657) had speculated that all animals arise from eggs and that semen plays a vitalizing role in the process. Only after the microscope made possible the discovery of the details of sexual reproduction, however, could the genetic mechanism be discovered.

Although general knowledge about sexual reproduction in plants and animals was accumulated in the eighteenth century, actual fertilization was not observed until 1855 when N. Pringsheim first saw nuclear fusion in green algae (Vaucheria). In 1875, O. Hertwig observed the entrance of the sperm into the sea urchin egg. A single sperm was found to penetrate a single egg. This established a firm cytological basis for inheritance.

## GREGOR MENDEL AND HIS EXPERIMENTS

Because of his experiments with garden peas (*Pisum sativum*), Gregor Mendel (1822–1884: Fig. 1.1) is appropriately called the "father of genetics." His experiments were elegant and his conclusions constitute the foundation of the modern science of genetics.

Throughout his life, Mendel showed great interest in living things. His home community in Austria was a gardening and fruit-growing area, and he was raised on a small fruit farm. Mendel's father had a great love for plants, especially fruit trees, and undoubtedly influenced his son

**Fig. 1.1** Gregor Mendel, Austrian monk whose experiments with garden peas laid the foundation for the science of genetics.

as they worked together in the garden and orchard. As Mendel grew older, he became intensely interested in plant hybridization, and during his life he made crosses between varieties of many different plants and between a few varieties of animals.

Mendel received his early schooling in his home community and later attended a preparatory school. Overexertion and privation led to an illness that delayed his completion of the course and impaired his health. After he had recovered sufficiently, he completed a two-year university course in philosophy. He then entered Altbrünn Monastery, an Augustinian religious community near Brünn, Austria (now Brno, Czechoslovakia). It was customary, in these communities, for men to carry on creative work, either scientific or artistic, along with their religious duties. Mendel was therefore encouraged to continue the work of his major interest: the hybridization of plants.

In 1849 Mendel obtained a temporary position as teacher in a preparatory school. After a successful year of teaching, he attended the University of Vienna where he took formal course work in science and mathematics. His university experience provided him with a sound scientific background and aroused an interest in precise experimental work which he pursued after returning to the monastery.

**Fig. 1.2** Garden at Altbrünn. Monastery garden where Mendel's experiments on garden peas were conducted. (Photograph by Professor Dr. Ing. Jaroslav Kříženecky.)

Again in 1854 Mendel was employed as a teacher and, for the next fourteen years, he continued as a temporary substitute teacher, giving courses in physics and natural history. He had time for experiments, especially during summer vacations, and was allowed a limited space in the monastery garden (Fig. 1.2). These were the most pleasant and productive years of his life. His garden-pea experiments were carried out during the years 1856 to 1864.

Mendel was not the first to perform hybridization experiments, but he was the first to consider their results in terms of single traits. He designed appropriate experiments and actually counted and classified the peas that resulted from the crosses. Then he compared the proportions with mathematical models. His predecessors had considered the whole organism, which incorporated a nebulous complex of traits and, thus, they were able to observe only that differences occurred among parents and progeny. Mendel, on the other hand, discovered a precise pattern in these differences. On the basis of preliminary experiments and hypotheses, he could predict results for various crosses. Through appropriate tests he subsequently verified the predictions.

### *Choice of Material*

Mendel chose the garden pea as his experimental material because it was an annual plant that had well-defined characteristics, and it could be grown and crossed easily. Moreover, garden peas have perfect flowers (Fig. 1.3) containing both female

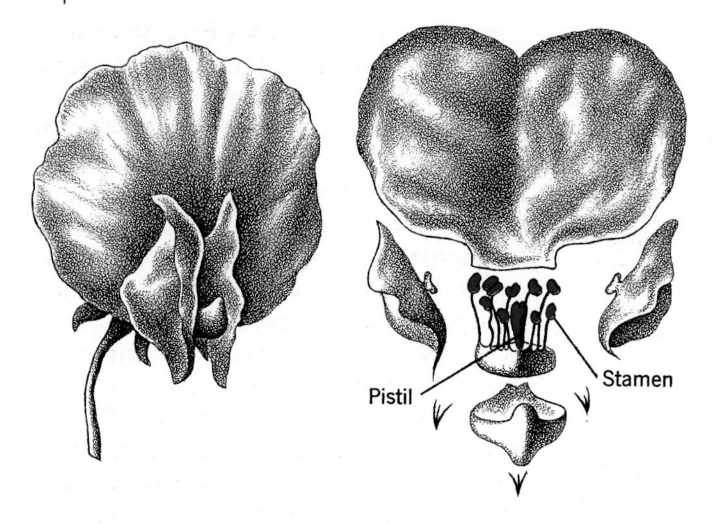


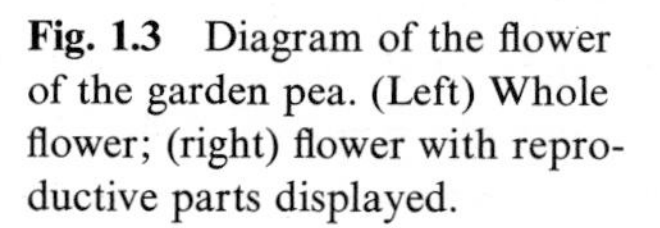

**Fig. 1.3** Diagram of the flower of the garden pea. (Left) Whole flower; (right) flower with reproductive parts displayed.

and male (pollen-producing) parts, and they are ordinarily self-fertilized. Pollen from another plant can be introduced to the stigma by an experimenter, but cross-pollination does not occur to any great extent without man's intervention.

Good fortune as well as wise judgment attended Mendel's choice, because other properties of garden peas, unknown to Mendel, were important for his experiments. Through many generations of natural self-fertilization, garden peas had developed into pure lines. Single alterations of traits were demonstrated by visible differences in varieties. Furthermore, in the traits Mendel chose to study, one manifestation was dominant over a well-defined contrasting or alternative trait.

Seven pairs of contrasting traits were chosen for study. Vines were either tall or dwarf; unripe pods were green or yellow and inflated or constricted between the seeds; flowers were either distributed along the stem (axial) or bunched at the top (terminal); nutritive parts of the ripe seeds were green or yellow; the outer surface of the seed was smooth or deeply wrinkled; and the seed coats were either white or gray. Flower color was positively correlated with this last trait: seeds with white seed coats were produced by plants that had white flowers, and those with gray seed coats came from plants that had violet flowers. Much of Mendel's success in his first experiments may be attributed to his good judgment in making crosses, as far as possible, between parents that differed in only one trait. When this was not feasible, he considered only one trait at a time.

### *Mechanics of Crossing*

Crosses were made with great care when the peas were in blossom. To prevent the possibility of self-fertilization, the anthers were removed from the plants chosen as seed parents before their pollen-receiving parts were fully mature. Pollen from the plant chosen as the pollen parent was transferred at the appropriate time to the stigma of the seed-parent flower. Seeds were allowed to mature on the vines. When a trait such as seed color was studied, classification could be made immediately; but before other traits, such as plant size, could be classified, the seeds had to be planted in the next season and the plants raised to maturity. The hybridization experiments were carried through several generations, and backcrosses were made to pure parent varieties.

*Data and Conclusions*

Mendel visualized clearly each problem to be solved and designed the experiment to that end. He conducted his experiments, classified the plants resulting from the crosses, and recorded data with great accuracy, care, and objectivity. The data and conclusions drawn from the experimental results were set forth in a paper entitled *Experiments in Plant Hybridization,* which was read before the Brünn Natural History Society in 1865 and published in the proceedings of that society in 1866.

Mendel's paper is a classic in biology for its elegance and simplicity. In addition to the statement of the problem, experimental design, data, and conclusions, the paper includes Mendel's hypothesis concerning the hereditary mechanism. Unfortunately, the paper was prepared as a lecture rather than as a scientific publication. The raw data were not included and therefore the crosses cannot be followed in detail. Mendel did not say how he arrived at the idea from which the hypothesis was developed. More information than that contained in the paper is now available from his surviving letters, but many questions remain unanswered. We may never know how his brilliant idea was conceived.

## PRINCIPLE OF SEGREGATION

When flowers of a tall strain of peas were fertilized with their own pollen, the offspring were all tall. When a dwarf variety was selfed (that is, was allowed to be self-fertilized), it produced only dwarfs. Mendel observed that weather, soil, and moisture conditions affected the growth characteristics of the peas, but heredity was the main limiting factor under the conditions of his experiments. In a given environment, tall plants were 6 to 7 feet high, whereas dwarfs measured from 9 to 18 inches. No dwarfs ever turned into tall plants and no tall plants became dwarfs.

In one experiment, Mendel raised separately, and then crossed, tall and dwarf varieties of garden peas. All of the offspring in the first ($F_1$) generation (F symbolized filial from the Latin, meaning progeny) were tall. The dwarf trait had disappeared in the $F_1$ progeny. When the tall hybrid plants were fertilized by their own pollen (selfed) and the progeny (second generation, or $F_2$) were classified, the missing trait appeared again. Some progeny were tall and some were dwarfs. Careful classification of the plants showed that when large numbers were considered, about three-fourths of the plants were tall and one-fourth were dwarfs. To be exact, from a total of 1064 $F_2$ "grandchildren" from the original (P) plants, 787 were tall and 277 were dwarfs. The actual results were compared with the calculated figures based on a 3:1 ratio; that is, 798 tall and 266 dwarfs. This type of cross between parents, differing in only one trait, or in which only one trait is considered, is a monohybrid cross.

Another monohybrid cross was executed between plants with green seeds and plants with yellow seeds. The resulting $F_1$ seeds were all yellow. From a total of 8023 $F_2$ seeds harvested from 258 plants, 6022 were yellow and 2001 were green, again approximately a 3:1 ratio.

The experiment could have been concluded at this point, but to test his hypothesis further, Mendel predicted what would occur in the $F_3$ generation and planted the $F_2$ seeds to test this prediction. On the basis of his hypothesis he predicted that about one-third of the yellow $F_2$ seeds would produce only yellow seeds, whereas two-thirds would produce both yellow and green seeds. The green $F_2$ seeds were expected to produce all green. From a total of 519 yellow $F_2$ seeds planted, 353 of the plants were found to produce both yellow and green seeds in the proportion of about three yellow to one green, and 166 had only yellow seeds. As expected, only plants producing green seeds were obtained from the green $F_2$ seeds.

In other monohybrid crosses, the remaining five of the seven pairs of contrasting characters originally selected were studied. One member of each pair seemed to dominate the other in the same way as the tall dominated the dwarf. This member Mendel identified as dominant in contrast to the other recessive member. Mendel's conclusions from the monohybrid crosses were based on his concept of unit characters, which was in marked contrast to the belief in blending inheritance which was common at the time. The physical elements (genes) were visualized (in pairs) on the basis of good experimental evidence. These determiners for unit characters could be dominant or recessive with respect to each other and the members of pairs were capable of segregation. Mendel called this separating process the "splitting of hybrids."

The most significant deduction from Mendel's results of monohybrid crosses was the separation of pairs of alleles resulting in the "purity of gametes." The concept of segregation has been identified as Mendel's first principle.

## SYMBOLS AND TERMINOLOGY

Letters of the alphabet were used by Mendel as symbols for pairs of hereditary elements. Capitals (for example, *A*) signified the dominant, and lower case (for example, *a*) the recessive member of the pair. Mendel considered the elements now called genes to be abstract units, any one of which could be symbolized by *A* or *B* or some other letter. Now many genes are known and several may be involved in the same series of experiments. To avoid confusion as to which particular gene is indicated, appropriate letters are chosen to represent particular genes. The mutant trait that deviates from the ancestral type is usually chosen as the basis for the symbol. This is usually the recessive member of the pair because most mutations occur as recessives. Some mutant genes, however, such as the gene (*W*) for wrinkled wings in the fruit fly, are dominant.

The rule is most easily applied if the history of the organism under investigation is well enough known to suggest which member of the contrasting pair (for example, tall or dwarf in peas) represents the mutant character. World collections of the species of peas show no dwarfs in natural populations. They occur only in certain cultivated stocks that have been developed by man. Dwarf is probably the mutant; and tall, the wild type. Therefore, *d* is used to symbolize the gene for dwarf and *D* for tall. With the aid of these symbols, Mendel's experiment (Fig. 1.4) may be reconstructed in steps. The parents (P), each with two genes representing a pair, are symbolized as follows:[1]

| Tall parent | | Dwarf parent |
|---|---|---|
| | × | |
| *DD* | | *dd* |

The tall parent (from the variety that produced only tall peas) carried two genes for tallness (*DD*), whereas the dwarf parent had two recessive genes (*dd*) for dwarfness.

Segregation, the separation of the pairs of determiners or genes, occurs in the formation of mature reproductive cells or gametes. Each gamete produced by the tall parent carries only one *D* gene, and each gamete from the dwarf parent carries only one *d* gene. Therefore, the fertilized egg (or zygote), which results from the fusion of the male and female gametes, must have one gene of each kind (*Dd*). Because the *D* was always present, the $F_1$ plants (first-

[1] In diagrams of crosses, the female or seed parent is always written first.

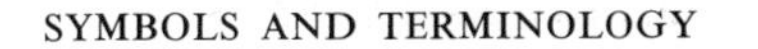

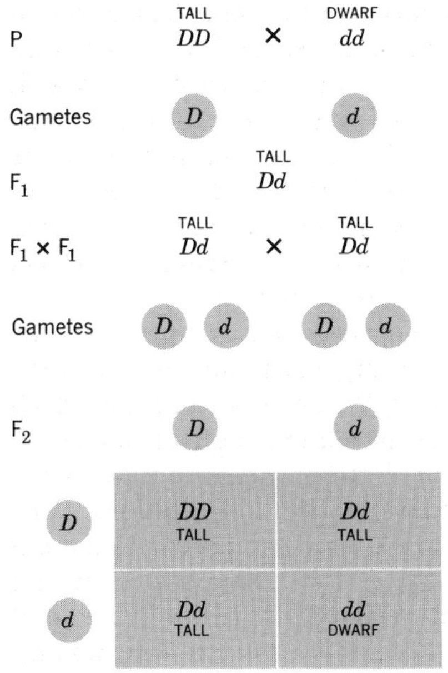

P: TALL *DD* × DWARF *dd*

Gametes: (*D*) (*d*)

$F_1$: TALL *Dd*

$F_1 \times F_1$: TALL *Dd* × TALL *Dd*

Gametes: (*D*) (*d*) (*D*) (*d*)

$F_2$:

| | (*D*) | (*d*) |
|---|---|---|
| (*D*) | *DD* TALL | *Dd* TALL |
| (*d*) | *Dd* TALL | *dd* DWARF |

**SUMMARY CHART**

| Phenotypes | Genotypes | Genotypic Frequency | Phenotypic Ratio |
|---|---|---|---|
| Tall | *DD* | 1 | 3 |
| | *Dd* | 2 | |
| Dwarf | *dd* | 1 | 1 |

**Fig. 1.4** Diagrammatic representation of Mendel's cross between tall and dwarf garden peas and summary of phenotypic and genotypic results.

generation progeny) were all tall. When the $F_1$ tall (*Dd*) plants resulting from this cross were selfed, separation of gene pairs of both the seed- and pollen-producing parts of the flowers occurred. Half of the gametes carried the *D* gene and half the *d* gene. The results of selfing the $F_1$ indicated to Mendel that the genes were entirely separate from each other.

When the $F_1$ plants from Mendel's experiments were crossed back to the recessive (dwarf) variety, half of the progeny were tall and half dwarf, as illustrated in Fig. 1.5. This result demonstrated further the principle of segregation, but the separation, of paired genes could be detected in only one parent. Both genes were alike in the dwarf parent.

Special terms (see the glossary) used to identify various aspects of monohybrid crosses are also useful for describing more complex crosses. Genetics is a young science which has a vocabulary of its own. Gene symbols represented in pairs designate zygotes and the individual plants or animals that have arisen from zygotes. Members of the gene pairs are represented separately to designate mature germ cells or gametes, either eggs or sperm. Circles or brackets placed around gamete symbols indicate mature germ cells, not plants or animals. A female and a male gamete combine in fertilization to produce a zygote. Zygotes or individual organisms carrying similar genes (such as *DD* or *dd*) are *homozygous,* and those with unlike genes (such as *Dd*) are *heterozygous.* Two other useful terms, *phenotype* and *genotype,* distinguish the visible expression or trait from the actual gene constitution. Obviously, genes do not have tall vines, blue eyes, or curly hair; they are submicroscopic units of a complex chemical substance known, in most organisms, as deoxyribonucleic acid (DNA); genes of some other organisms are

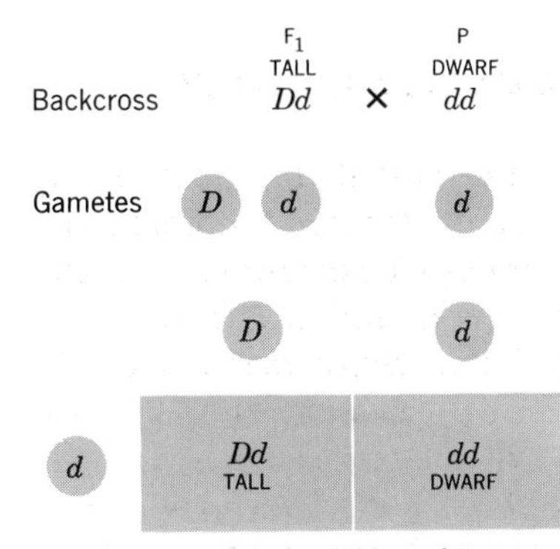


**Fig. 1.5** Diagram of backcross between $F_1$ tall garden pea and dwarf parent variety from cross illustrated in Fig. 1.4.

composed of a different chemical, ribonucleic acid (RNA). This nucleic acid also serves other important functions in determining traits of individuals (as shown in Part II of this book).

Letter symbols are used exclusively to represent genotypes. Another useful term is *allele,* an abbreviation of allelomorph (from the Greek word meaning one form or the other), which identifies members of a gene pair producing contrasting phenotypes. An allele of a particular gene is its partner gene. In the foregoing example, *d* is an allele of *D* and vice versa.

## PRINCIPLE OF INDEPENDENT COMBINATIONS

Mendel also crossed plants that differed in two pairs of alleles; that is, he made a dihybrid cross to clarify the relation and action of pairs of alleles. In this experiment he crossed plants having round, yellow seeds with plants having wrinkled, green seeds. Genes for both round and yellow were known from previous studies to be dominant over their respective alleles producing wrinkled and green seeds.

All the $F_1$ seeds resulting from the cross were round and yellow as expected. When the $F_1$ hybrid seeds were planted and the plants were allowed to self-fertilize, four $F_2$ phenotypes were observed in a definite pattern. From a total of 556 seeds the following distribution was obtained: 315 round, yellow; 108 round, green; 101 wrinkled, yellow; and 32 wrinkled, green. When reduced to lowest terms, these results were found to fit very nearly a ratio of 9:3:3:1, which Mendel recognized as the result of two monohybrid crosses, each expected to result in a 3:1 ratio, operating together. The product of the two monohybrid ratios (3:1 or $3 + 1$) was equal to the dihybrid ratio (9:3:3:1 or $9 + 3 + 3 + 1$), thus conforming to the law of probability which states: *the chance of two or more independent events occurring together is the product of the chances of their separate occurrences.*

The results were those expected from the assortment of two independent pairs of elements, each showing dominance of one member. Not only did the members of pairs of alleles segregate, but also one pair behaved independently with respect to another pair. Thus, Mendel could draw another conclusion which involved the independent combinations of different pairs of alleles, or *independent assortment.* This concept is sometimes referred to as Mendel's second principle.

The principle of independent combinations has a practical application in plant and animal breeding. It is possible to combine desirable traits carried in different varieties and to maintain these traits in the same individuals. For example, a variety of barley resistant to rust was needed in a rust-infested area in the United States. The best available rust-resistant variety, however, like most barley varieties, had hulls on the seeds and did not thresh well. Another variety had no hulls and threshed out clean, like wheat, but had poor rust resistance. These two varieties were combined by appropriate crosses and a valuable new strain with rust resistance and no hulls was obtained.

### *Dihybrid Ratios*

The basic mechanics of genetics were postulated and later established from particular ratios such as 3:1 and 9:3:3:1. The ratios in themselves are not important; they merely represent the groupings expected when particular conditions are met. Common patterns such as the 9:3:3:1 ratio do, however, serve as models for analyzing results of experiments. When such a ratio is obtained from an actual cross in which the parental genotypes are not known, the geneticist may postulate that two independent pairs of alleles are involved, and that one member of each pair is completely dominant over its allele. Mendel's dihybrid cross between plants with round, yellow seeds and those with wrinkled, green seeds is represented diagrammatically in Fig. 1.6 as a pattern for analyzing other crosses. Parents (P) are represented by letter symbols for the two pairs of genes under consideration. The next step is to show the kinds of gametes that each parent can produce. The yellow, round seed parent produces only one kind [*GW*]. Each egg must carry only one member of each pair of alleles. Likewise, all gametes of the pollen parents will carry one member of each pair [*gw*]. The brackets and single members of the pairs remind us that these are gametes and not pea plants. Fertilization or fusion of the gametes occurs next in the natural reproductive cycle. $F_1$ plants resulting from fertilization are represented by the genotype *GgWw*. These plants are heterozygous for both pairs of alleles.

When the $F_1$ plants were selfed by Mendel (that is, pollen and eggs from the same plant were united), four kinds of gametes were produced by the male parts and four by the female parts of the $F_1$. At the top of the checkerboard (Fig. 1.6) the four kinds of gametes from the seed parent are shown. The four possible gametes from the pollen parent are represented at the left. This checkerboard is merely a geometrical device for bringing together all possible combinations of male and female gametes in the formation of zygotes. It is valuable as a learning exercise but will be replaced later with less time-consuming methods. Letter symbols in the sixteen squares in the checkerboard represent combinations of independent genes brought together by the fusion of gametes. When these are collected according to the phenotypes represented, the 9:3:3:1 ratio becomes apparent. The completed summary chart illustrates the $F_2$ results of the cross in tabular form.

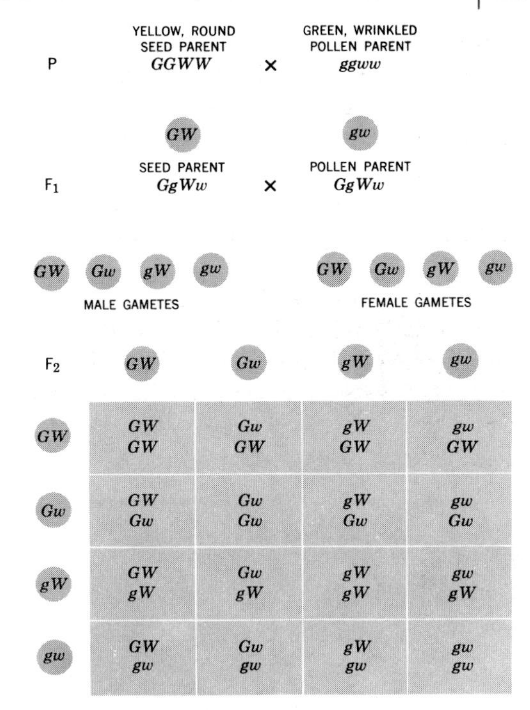


**SUMMARY CHART**

| Phenotypes | Genotypes | Genotypic Frequency | Phenotypic Ratio |
|---|---|---|---|
| Yellow, round | *GGWW* | 1 | 9 |
| | *GGWw* | 2 | |
| | *GgWW* | 2 | |
| | *GgWw* | 4 | |
| Yellow, wrinkled | *GGww* | 1 | 3 |
| | *Ggww* | 2 | |
| Green, round | *ggWW* | 1 | 3 |
| | *ggWw* | 2 | |
| Green, wrinkled | *ggww* | 1 | 1 |

**Fig. 1.6** Diagram and summary of a cross between a variety of garden peas with yellow, round seeds and a variety with green, wrinkled seeds.

The 1:1:1:1 ratio is expected from a dihybrid backcross to the recessive parent; that is, a cross between an $F_1$ that carries

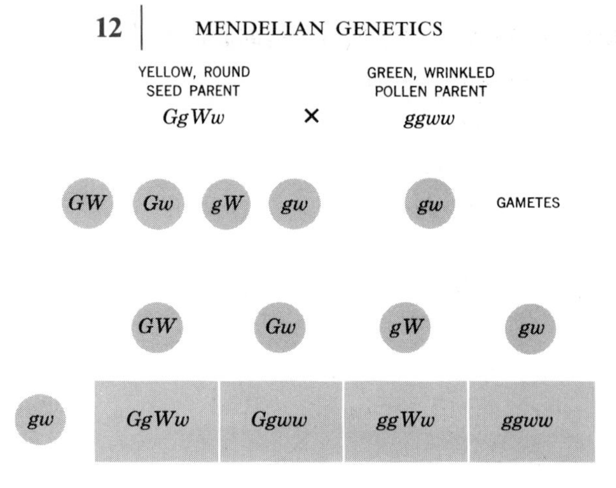


**SUMMARY CHART**

| Phenotypes | Genotypes | Genotypic Frequency | Phenotypic Ratio |
|---|---|---|---|
| Yellow, round | *GgWw* | 1 | 1 |
| Yellow, wrinkled | *Ggww* | 1 | 1 |
| Green, round | *ggWw* | 1 | 1 |
| Green, wrinkled | *ggww* | 1 | 1 |

**Fig. 1.7** Diagram and summary of a cross between an $F_1$ garden pea with yellow, round seeds and the fully recessive parent type with green, wrinkled seeds.

two heterozygous pairs of genes and a parent type with the full recessive combination for these two gene pairs. This type of cross is illustrated in Fig. 1.7. A cross of this type (called a test cross) is used in practical breeding to determine the genotype of an individual that may carry recessive genes, the expressions of which are obscured by dominant alleles.

### *Trihybrid Ratios*

Virtually all cross-fertilizing plants or animals differ in more than one or two pairs of alleles. Therefore, matings in natural breeding populations usually involve new combinations of many genes. Genetic analysis of such crosses may be complicated. In many cases, however, complex combinations can be simplified by resolving them into monohybrid crosses, or by making use of formulas devised to handle several factors in the same problem. Crosses between parents that differ in three characters (that is, trihybrid crosses) are combinations of three monohybrid crosses operating together.

What results might be expected from a cross between two varieties of garden peas differing in three characters: (1) in the $F_1$, (2) in the backcross to the fully recessive parent, and (3) in the $F_2$? We may diagram the cross in which the seed parent is homozygous for the genes producing a tall vine and yellow, round seeds (*DDGGWW*), and the pollen parent has a dwarf vine and green, wrinkled seeds (*ddggww*). All three characters represented in the seed parent are known from previous experiments to depend on dominant genes. The first generation cross may be illustrated as follows:

| | | | |
|---|---|---|---|
| *DDGGWW* | × | *ddggww* | P |
| *DGW* | | *dgw* | gametes |
| | *DdGgWw* | | $F_1$ |

When the $F_1$ plants are crossed with the full recessive type, *DdGgWw* × *ddggww*, eight kinds of gametes (*DGW*, *DGw*, *DgW*, *Dgw*, *dGW*, *dGw*, *dgW*, *dgw*) are produced by the $F_1$ parent and only one kind, *dgw*, by the full recessive parent. As a result of fertilization, eight kinds of peas are expected in equal proportion. Thus, the trihybrid backcross ratio of 1:1:1:1:1:1:1:1 is explained by the fertilization of eight different kinds of gametes from the $F_1$ by the one kind of gamete from the fully recessive parents. The sequence involved in this backcross and the summarized results are illustrated in Fig. 1.8.

When the $F_1$ plants were selfed (that is, *DdGgWw* × *DdGgWw*) eight kinds of gam-

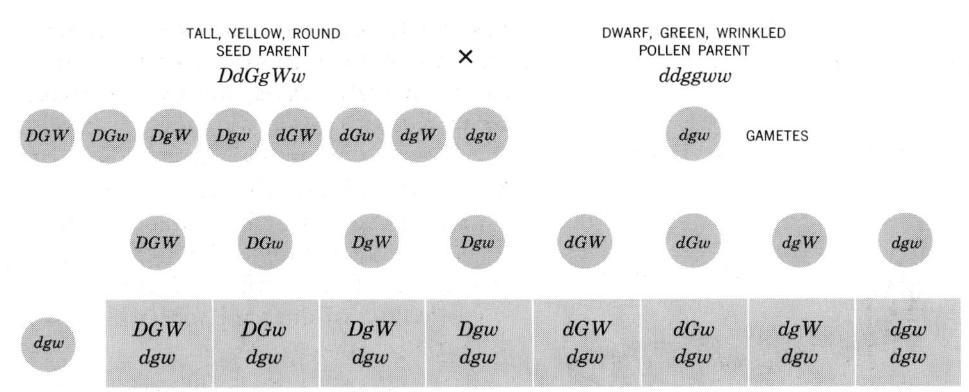


**SUMMARY CHART**

| Phenotypes | Genotypes | Genotypic Frequency | Phenotypic Ratio |
|---|---|---|---|
| Tall, yellow, round | *DdGgWw* | 1 | 1 |
| Tall, yellow, wrinkled | *DdGgww* | 1 | 1 |
| Tall, green, round | *DdggWw* | 1 | 1 |
| Tall, green, wrinkled | *Ddggww* | 1 | 1 |
| Dwarf, yellow round | *ddGgWw* | 1 | 1 |
| Dwarf, yellow wrinkled | *ddGgww* | 1 | 1 |
| Dwarf, green, round | *ddggWw* | 1 | 1 |
| Dwarf, green, wrinkled | *ddggww* | 1 | 1 |

**Fig. 1.8** Diagram and summary of a cross between $F_1$ garden peas with tall vines, yellow and round seeds, and the fully recessive parental type with dwarf vines, green and wrinkled seeds.

etes, *DGW, DGw, DgW, Dgw, dGW, dGw, dgW, dgw*, were produced from both the male and female parts. These gametes represent all combinations. If the $F_1 \times F_1$ cross were represented by a checkerboard, 64 squares would be required. A less time-consuming method for determining the results of complex combinations is illustrated in the next section.

## FORKED-LINE METHOD OF SOLVING GENETIC PROBLEMS

A method for bringing the combinations of a trihybrid cross together may be illustrated as follows: first visualize the trihybrid cross as three monohybrid crosses, that is, *Dd* × *Dd*, *Gg* × *Gg*, and *Ww* × *Ww*, operating together. If one member of each pair is dominant, a 3:1 ratio might be predicted from each monohybrid cross. Since the three pairs are independent, each monohybrid segregant may occur with any combination possible from any other pair of alleles. The combinations, therefore, can be systematically arranged together. The 3:1 ratio from *Dd* × *Dd* may be combined with the 3:1 ratios from each of the other two monohybrid crosses, *Gg* × *Gg* and *Ww* × *Ww*, as shown in Fig. 1.9.

Usually the genotypes as well as the phenotypes are necessary for the complete solution of such a problem. The same forked-line system may be employed to represent and combine genotypes expected from monohybrid crosses. From each monohybrid cross in the example a genotypic frequency of 1:2:1 may be predicted.

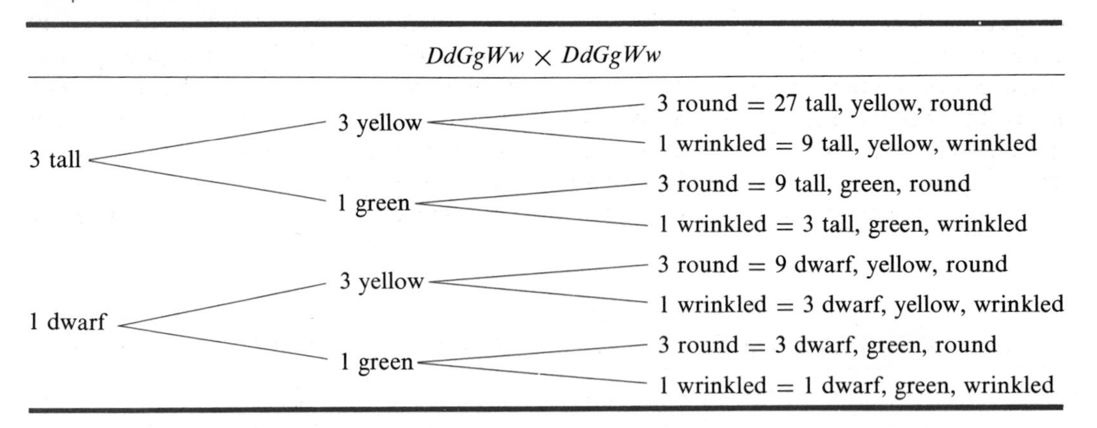


**Fig. 1.9** Diagram illustrating the forked-line method for solving genetic problems in which independent combinations are involved. Genotypes of parents are given, but only phenotypes of progeny are listed in this example.

The three monohybrid units may be combined as shown in Fig. 1.10. The forked-line system is merely a device for bringing together the results of monohybrid crosses, which may be summarized in the same manner as those obtained from the alternative checkerboard method.

## INTERMEDIATE INHERITANCE

In the absence of dominance, every genotype may have a distinguishable phenotype. The ratio for the monohybrid cross becomes 1:2:1 instead of 3:1; the dihybrid ratio, when the two pairs of alleles are intermediate, is 1:2:1:2:4:2:1:2:1.

In snapdragons, for example, intermediate-size leaves are produced by a heterozygous gene combination (*BB′*). Plants with broad leaves and narrow leaves have the homozygous gene arrangements, *BB* and *B′B′*, respectively. Likewise, pink flowers are controlled by a heterozygous (*RR′*) pair, and red (*RR*) and white (*R′R′*) by the corresponding homozygotes. From a cross between plants with broad leaves and red flowers (*BBRR*) and those with narrow leaves and white flowers (*B′B′R′R′*), all the $F_1$ progeny (*B′BR′R*) had intermediate leaves and pink flowers. The $F_2$ were classified into nine phenotypic classes corresponding with the genotypic combinations as illustrated in Fig. 1.11. The 9:3:3:1 dihybrid ratio was thus replaced by the 1:2:1:2:4:2:1:2:1 ratio, as expected in the absence of dominance.

## MODERN EVALUATIONS OF MENDEL'S CONCLUSIONS

New interpretations are inevitable in scientific disciplines as additional data accumulate. Mendel considered a single gene to be responsible for a single trait. It is now known that many genes are involved in the production of some traits, although single gene substitutions can influence basic biochemical reactions and thus be responsible for alternative end products. Furthermore, it is the genes and not the traits that are inherited. Genes behave as separate units, whereas traits may result from complex interactions involving many genes.

Complete dominance was indicated in all seven allelic pairs that Mendel reported. It was natural, therefore, for him to consider dominance as an inherent property of genes. When sweet peas and snapdragons were studied, shortly after the discovery of Mendel's paper, intermediate traits were observed in hybrids (as we saw in Fig. 1.11). Crosses between homozygous snapdragons with red flowers and those with white flowers resulted in $F_1$ progeny with pink flowers. Heterozygotes could thus be distinguished phenotypically from both parents. Dominance has now been shown to be influenced by factors in the external, internal (hormonal), and genetic environment. Therefore, Mendel's view of dominance as a fundamental inherent

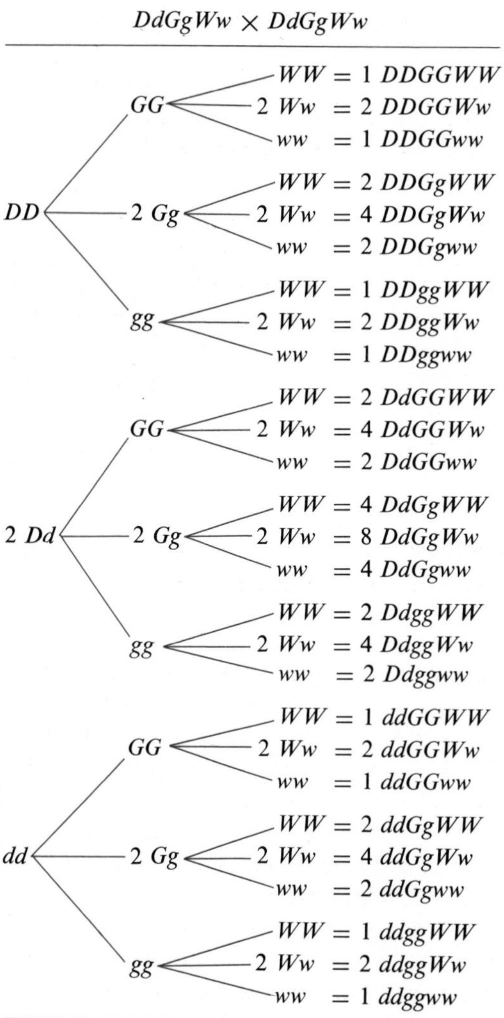

*DdGgWw* × *DdGgWw*

| | | | |
|---|---|---|---|
| *DD* | *GG* | *WW* | = 1 *DDGGWW* |
| | | 2 *Ww* | = 2 *DDGGWw* |
| | | *ww* | = 1 *DDGGww* |
| | 2 *Gg* | *WW* | = 2 *DDGgWW* |
| | | 2 *Ww* | = 4 *DDGgWw* |
| | | *ww* | = 2 *DDGgww* |
| | *gg* | *WW* | = 1 *DDggWW* |
| | | 2 *Ww* | = 2 *DDggWw* |
| | | *ww* | = 1 *DDggww* |
| 2 *Dd* | *GG* | *WW* | = 2 *DdGGWW* |
| | | 2 *Ww* | = 4 *DdGGWw* |
| | | *ww* | = 2 *DdGGww* |
| | 2 *Gg* | *WW* | = 4 *DdGgWW* |
| | | 2 *Ww* | = 8 *DdGgWw* |
| | | *ww* | = 4 *DdGgww* |
| | *gg* | *WW* | = 2 *DdggWW* |
| | | 2 *Ww* | = 4 *DdggWw* |
| | | *ww* | = 2 *Ddggww* |
| *dd* | *GG* | *WW* | = 1 *ddGGWW* |
| | | 2 *Ww* | = 2 *ddGGWw* |
| | | *ww* | = 1 *ddGGww* |
| | 2 *Gg* | *WW* | = 2 *ddGgWW* |
| | | 2 *Ww* | = 4 *ddGgWw* |
| | | *ww* | = 2 *ddGgww* |
| | *gg* | *WW* | = 1 *ddggWW* |
| | | 2 *Ww* | = 2 *ddggWw* |
| | | *ww* | = 1 *ddggww* |

*A*

| Phenotypes | Genotypes | Genotypic Frequency | Phenotypic Ratio |
|---|---|---|---|
| Tall, yellow, round | *DDGGWW* | 1 | 27 |
| | *DDGGWw* | 2 | |
| | *DDGgWW* | 2 | |
| | *DDGgWw* | 4 | |
| | *DdGGWW* | 2 | |
| | *DdGGWw* | 4 | |
| | *DdGgWW* | 4 | |
| | *DdGgWw* | 8 | |
| Tall, yellow, wrinkled | *DDGGww* | 1 | 9 |
| | *DDGgww* | 2 | |
| | *DdGGww* | 2 | |
| | *DdGgww* | 4 | |
| Tall, green, round | *DDggWW* | 1 | 9 |
| | *DDggWw* | 2 | |
| | *DdggWW* | 2 | |
| | *DdggWw* | 4 | |
| Tall, green, wrinkled | *DDggww* | 1 | 3 |
| | *Ddggww* | 2 | |
| Dwarf, yellow, round | *ddGGWW* | 1 | 9 |
| | *ddGGWw* | 2 | |
| | *ddGgWW* | 2 | |
| | *ddGgWw* | 4 | |
| Dwarf, yellow, wrinkled | *ddGGww* | 1 | 3 |
| | *ddGgww* | 2 | |
| Dwarf, green, round | *ddggWW* | 1 | 3 |
| | *ddggWw* | 2 | |
| Dwarf, green, wrinkled | *ddggww* | 1 | 1 |

*B*

**Fig. 1.10** *A*, diagram of a cross between two $F_1$ garden peas of the genotype *DdGgWw*. The forked-line method is employed and the genotypes are illustrated. These results represent the $F_2$ of a trihybrid cross similar to those obtained from the checkerboard method involving 64 squares. *B*, summary of $F_2$ from trihybrid cross resulting in a 27:9:9:9:3:3:3:1 phenotypic ratio.

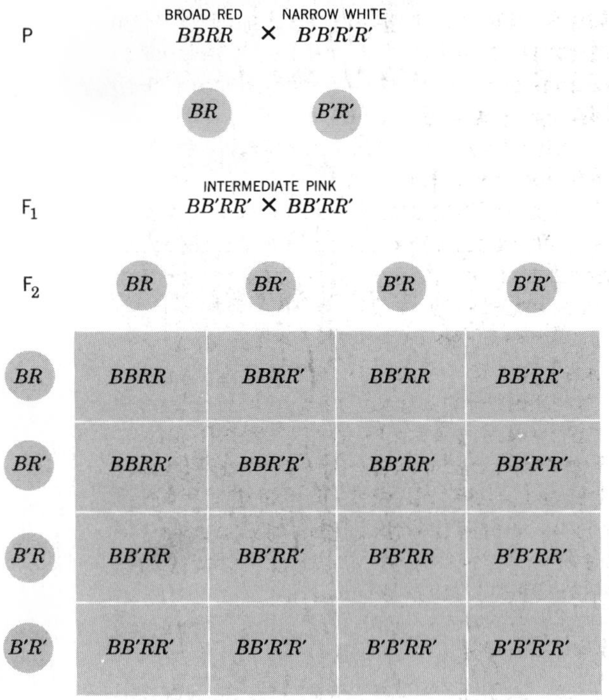

P BROAD RED *BBRR* × NARROW WHITE *B'B'R'R'*

*BR* *B'R'*

F1 INTERMEDIATE PINK *BB'RR'* × *BB'RR'*

F2

| | *BR* | *BR'* | *B'R* | *B'R'* |
|---|---|---|---|---|
| *BR* | *BBRR* | *BBRR'* | *BB'RR* | *BB'RR'* |
| *BR'* | *BBRR'* | *BBR'R'* | *BB'RR'* | *BB'R'R'* |
| *B'R* | *BB'RR* | *BB'RR'* | *B'B'RR* | *B'B'RR'* |
| *B'R'* | *BB'RR'* | *BB'R'R'* | *B'B'RR'* | *B'B'R'R'* |

**SUMMARY OF $F_2$ EXPECTED RESULTS**

| Phenotypes | Genotypes | Genotypic Frequency | Phenotypic Ratio |
|---|---|---|---|
| Broad red | *BBRR* | 1 | 1 |
| Broad pink | *BBRR'* | 2 | 2 |
| Broad white | *BBR'R'* | 1 | 1 |
| Int. red | *BB'RR* | 2 | 2 |
| Int. pink | *BB'RR'* | 4 | 4 |
| Int. white | *BB'R'R'* | 2 | 2 |
| Narrow red | *B'B'RR* | 1 | 1 |
| Narrow pink | *B'B'RR'* | 2 | 2 |
| Narrow white | *B'B'R'R'* | 1 | 1 |

**Fig. 1.11** Diagram and summary of a cross between snapdragons with broad leaves and red flowers and those with narrow leaves and white flowers, illustrating intermediate inheritance.

property of the gene itself is no longer tenable for all cases. Dominance of some genes may eventually be explained on the basis of modifier genes that are present in the genetic environment. In other cases, dominance may depend on the quantity or activity of enzymes that are gene controlled.

The most important concepts that Mendel interpreted from his experiments were: (1) segregation, which describes the separation of alleles resulting in pure gametes; and (2) independent assortment or the independent combinations of different pairs of alleles. These principles are the basic foundation of Mendelian heredity. A physical basis for these principles has been discovered in the process through which mature germ cells are developed (Chapter 2). Since Mendel's time, these principles have been found to apply not only to garden peas but also to virtually all plants and animals in which sexual reproduction occurs. It is now known, however, that genes are in chromosomes and that some groups of genes do not assort independently (Chapter 6).

## NEGLECT AND DISCOVERY OF MENDEL'S WORK

Mendel's garden pea experiments, significant as they were, had no immediate influence on science or practical breeding. In fact, the results remained virtually unknown for 34 years after their publication in 1866. During that period only a few people knew of the experiments, and it is safe to say that no one really understood them. Two biologists, W. O. Focke and Karl Nägeli, cited Mendel's experiments during this period; Focke in 1881 made several references to Mendel. From the letters now available, it is known that Nägeli was informed of Mendel's work, but was not impressed. He considered the experiments to be unfinished and in need of further verification. Nägeli's great prestige indirectly weighed against the recognition of Mendel's garden pea experiments. Various other explanations have been offered to account for this neglect; most important was the fact that the conclusions were too original to find acceptance. In 1866 knowledge about the structural and functional biological unit, the cell, was meager indeed. Cell division was not understood, and the sequence through which mature reproductive cells developed was entirely unknown. Without this basic knowledge it was impossible to appreciate the significance of Mendel's results.

Another reason for lack of recognition was Mendel's own uncertainty concerning the significance of his results. After his experiments with garden peas, he crossed other plants, but was unable to confirm his earlier results. When he crossed varieties of hawkweeds, Hieracium, the progeny did not show evidence of segregation of genes from both parents, but rather, were all like their mothers. These plants are now known to be apomictic, or capable of reproduction without fertilization. The plants that Mendel considered to be hybrids were thus not hybrids at all. He did not know whether his earlier results on garden peas reflected significant principles or merely peculiarities of garden peas. His uncertainty, along with his innate modesty, prevented him from advertising his own work. An understanding and appreciation of Mendel's results may also have been retarded by the great interest then current in Darwin's work, *On the Origin of Species* (1859), published while Mendel's pea experiments were in progress. Mendel was deeply interested in the *Origin of Species* and hoped that his experiments would give information about evolution. Darwin's later book, *Variation of Animals and Plants under Domestication* (1868), emphasized gradual changes and continuous variation in animals and plants, which seemed to be in conflict with the abrupt discontinuous variation indicated from Mendel's crosses. One of the tragedies of the 19th century was that Darwin did not know of Mendel's work. Darwin would surely have been impressed with the results of Mendel's experiments and genetics might have been several years ahead.

Also, there is reason to believe that Mendel used his data merely to illustrate his theory. Mendel probably worked with some twenty or thirty different characteristics, but he only reported on seven that behaved similarly. The probability of picking at random seven different characteristics (genes) of the pea (which has seven chromosome pairs), each on a different chromosome, is very low. It is quite possible, however, that the seven were selected because they behaved alike. Some of Mendel's "good fortune" in the choice of characteristics may have come from insight gained in preliminary work.

In 1900, Mendel's paper was discovered simultaneously by three men: Hugo de Vries, a Dutch biologist, known for his mutation theory and studies on the evening primrose and maize; Carl Correns, a German botanist who studied maize, peas, and beans; and Erich von Tschermak-Seysenegg, an Austrian botanist who worked with several plants, including garden peas. All three investigators approached Mendel's principles independently from their own studies, recognized their significance, and found and cited his work in their publications. Genetics developed rapidly after 1900 and soon earned a place among the biological sciences.

## TODAY'S GENERAL TECHNIQUES

In exploring the mechanisms of heredity and variation, researchers in the field of genetics utilize many techniques. The direct approach, through experimental breeding, is widely used whenever possible. In human genetics, however, methods such as studies of twins, pedigree analyses, and statistical procedures are more appli-

**Fig. 1.12** A family of mice. The family consists of a father and mother and seven young mice. (Photograph by W. P. Nye.)

cable. Cytological investigation of the cell and its parts is practiced on human material and extensively among experimental animals and plants. On an even more fundamental level, researchers are using biochemical and biophysical techniques in trying to discover and delineate what the gene is and how it functions. These basic techniques warrant preliminary consideration at this point.

### *Experimental Breeding*

When an investigator is free to choose his material for experimental breeding, he generally tries to make sure that it fulfills at least four critical conditions: (1) it has a short life cycle; (2) it has abundant progeny; (3) it incorporates clearly distinguishable variations; and (4) it is convenient to maintain.

Since the same basic principles (at least, as far as they concern gene action) seem to apply to all organisms, the investigator tries to choose a material that is especially suitable for his particular investigation. Mice (Fig. 1.12) are useful as research subjects because they require only about 2½ months between generations and produce families of six or seven. Their patterns of structure and reaction can be readily observed, and they can be maintained in research institutes and most university animal quarters. Insects, molds, bacteria, and viruses are favorable for research and teaching because they have even shorter life cycles, more abundant progeny, readily distinguishable hereditary differences, and can be cultured conveniently in almost any genetics laboratory.

Different expressions of a trait in a population (variability) are necessary for genetical analysis. The barley plant is represented by many strains that show considerable variation and, as a result, it has been widely used in genetic investigations. Some variations in barley heads which depend on single gene differences are shown in Fig. 1.13.

The "vinegar" fly, particularly *Drosophila melanogaster* (Fig. 1.14), fulfills all four of the criteria for a good experimental material. This organism is used extensively by genetics students and research workers. Geneticists commonly call this insect a "fruit" fly, but entomologists use the term for another group of flies. Drosophila has been and perhaps still is the most widely used single material for original investigations and learning exercises for genetics students. With the present emphasis on population genetics and evolution, Drosophila promises to occupy a place of even greater importance in the genetics laboratories and field studies of the future.

## *Investigations Involving Twins*

Identical or one-egg (monozygotic) twins (Fig. 1.15) develop from a common source (a single fertilized egg) and, therefore, both twins have identical genes. Differences between such a pair may be attributed primarily to environmental influences, and thus the relative importance of heredity and environment on the expression of various traits can be investigated. Fraternal (dizygotic) twins come from separate fertilized eggs and are no more closely related genetically than ordinary brothers and sisters (sibs). In twin studies designed to investigate the incidence of certain characteristics, fraternal twins may serve as a valuable control. On the average, one in

**Fig. 1.13** Variations in barley heads. *A*, black, two-rowed, awned; *B*, black, six-rowed, awned; *C*, black, two-rowed, hooded; *D*, yellow, six-rowed, hooded; *E*, yellow, two-rowed, awned, kernels alternate; *F*, yellow, two-rowed, awned, kernels opposite; *G*, yellow, clustered, awned; *H*, yellow, extreme clustered.

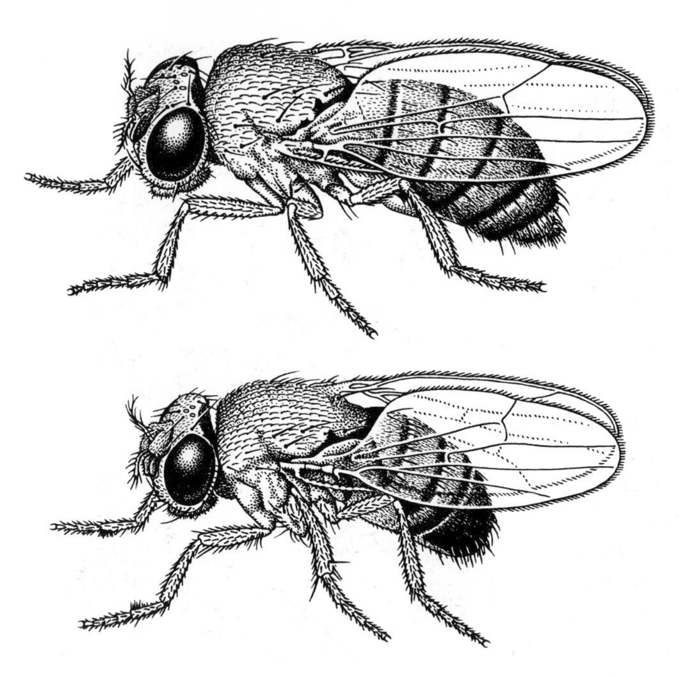

**Fig. 1.14** Lateral view of two flies, *Drosophila melanogaster*. (Upper) Female; (lower) male.

**Fig. 1.15** Twins which are much alike and probably identical. Strickler from Monkmeyer Photo Press Service.

every 86 births is a twin birth. Thus, two of 86 or about one in 43 babies born are twins. Despite the limitations of infrequent occurrence and the difficulty of distinguishing between monozygotic and dizygotic twins, studies of twins represent the most reliable method now available to researchers in human genetics.

*Pedigree*

The pedigree method consists of analyzing, for a particular trait, the results of mating already made. Diagrams or charts are usually constructed to symbolize individuals and illustrate relationships among them. From the data obtained, attempts are made to detect patterns of inheritance. This is the oldest method of genetic investigation and was used before the time of Christ. It is still widely used in studies of human inheritance and is also applied to animal breeding.

**Fig. 1.16** Sir Francis Galton, English biometrician of the last century who studied human inheritance.

*Statistics*

Sir Francis Galton (1822–1911; Fig. 1.16), a geneticist and biometrician of the last century, employed statistical tools extensively for human inheritance studies. His work was critical and well designed, but unfortunately it was done before the foundation of Mendelian genetics was established. A large part of it, therefore, has required reinterpretation. Galton deserves much credit for pioneering in the use of mathematical tools that are now considered necessary for any research dealing with quantitative data. Use of statistical methods by geneticists to control experiments and analyze results has been revitalized by recent developments in population genetics. This has led to new applications of genetics to practical aspects of plant and animal breeding.

*Cytology*

Cytological studies have been invaluable in establishing the physical basis of heredity and in discovering the nature and role of the nucleus, cytoplasm, and gene. Much interest has been centered around germ cells and their behavior. The geneticist, who deals mainly with genes, which cannot be seen, is much more secure in his conclusions and confident of the validity of his results if he can point to physical, microscopically observable structures that are related to hereditary processes. The parallel between the mechanism postulated by the geneticist to account for his results and the observable cycle of the germ cells was a major factor in establishing the foundation of genetics.

At present, genetic theory is considerably ahead of cytological verification in all organisms, but particularly in bacteria and viruses. Elaborate genetic evidence has been established for recombination and other genetic mechanisms in some groups of bacteria and viruses and physical verification is now being obtained. New methods and new tools must be devised to probe more deeply into these chemical and physical relationships. Studies on these organisms have been especially fruitful in exploring the relations between genes and traits.

### *Biochemical and Biophysical Investigations of Genes*

Special techniques involving chemistry and physics have been applied to bacteria and other microorganisms with the objective of analyzing gene chemistry and gene action in relatively simple organisms. *Escherichia coli* (the common colon bacillus), pneumococcus (the pneumonia organism), and several other bacteria have been useful in biochemical genetics studies. Viruses, particularly bacteriophages (the type of virus that infects bacteria), are used for studies of the fine structure of the gene and gene action. Modern tools such as electron microscopes and methods such as autoradiographs (images on photographic emulsions produced by the variable distribution of radioactive material in a specimen) have aided greatly in studies of chromosomes and genetic material.

## SUMMARY

Genetics is the science of heredity and variation. Its scientific roots are deeply embedded in the past, but the science itself is a product of the present century. Mendel's recognition of physical elements as determiners of hereditary characteristics and his principles of segregation and independent assortment formed the basis for the science. Presumably, the hereditary mechanism operates in nearly all animal and plant groups, but some lend themselves better than others to investigation. For breeding experiments, organisms with short life cycle, abundant progeny, and distinct variations are usually chosen. It is desirable but not always possible to work with a material that can be maintained conveniently. Methods that apply to human genetics as well as to experimental organisms are: pedigree analysis, statistical studies, cytological observations, and biochemical and biophysical investigations.

## REFERENCES

Bateson, W. 1909. *Mendel's principles of heredity.* The University Press, Cambridge.

Dunn, L. C. (ed.) 1951. *Genetics in the 20th century.* The Macmillan Co., New York. (Chapters 1–4 are especially appropriate for this discussion.)

Dunn, L. C. 1965. *A short history of genetics.* McGraw-Hill Book Co., New York.

Gardner, E. J. 1965. *History of biology.* Burgess Publishing Co., Minneapolis.

Iltis, H. 1932. *Life of Mendel.* (Translated by E. and C. Paul.) W. W. Norton and Co., New York.

Křiženecký, J., and B. Němec. 1965. *Fundamenta Genetica.* Brno, Czechoslavakia. (Papers of Mendel and others who contributed to the foundation of genetics. Prepared for the Mendel Centennial at Brno.)

Mendel, G. 1866. "Versuche über pflanzen-hybriden." (Available in the original German in *J. Hered.,* **42**, 1–47.) English translation under the title "Experiments in plant hybridization." Harvard University Press, Cambridge, Mass. This is Mendel's paper describing his garden pea experiments and presenting the Mendelian principles. It was prepared as a lecture and delivered before the Brünn Natural History Society in two installments, on February 8 and March 8, 1865, and published in the proceedings of the Society in 1866.)

Stern, C. (ed.) 1950. "The birth of genetics." (Supplement of *Genetics.*) **35(5)**, part 2. (English translations of letters from Mendel to Nägeli and the papers of de Vries, Correns, and Tschermak, the three men who discovered Mendel's papers in 1900.)

Stern, C., and E. R. Sherwood (eds.) 1966. *The Origin of Genetics.* A Mendel Source Book. W. H. Freeman and Co., San Francisco. New evidence and new interpretation of Mendel's work and its discovery in 1900.

Sturtevant, A. H. 1965. *A history of genetics.* Harper and Row, New York.

Tschermak-Seysenegg, E. von. 1951. "The rediscovery of Gregor Mendel's work." *J. Hered.,* **42,** 163–171.

## Problems

**1.1** How and when did the field of genetics become qualified as a science?

**1.2** Give evidence that applications of genetics were made in remote periods of early history.

**1.3** Why was the discovery of sexual reproduction in plants a valuable milestone in the history of genetics?

**1.4** When, where, and under what circumstances did Gregor Mendel make his contribution to genetics?

**1.5** In what ways was Mendel wise and fortunate in his choice of experimental material?

**1.6** On the basis of Mendel's hypothesis and observations, predict the results from the following crosses in garden peas: (a) a tall (dominant and homozygous) variety crossed with a dwarf variety; (b) the progeny of (a) selfed; (c) the progeny from (a) crossed with the original tall parent: (d) the progeny from (a) crossed with the original dwarf parent variety.

**1.7** Mendel crossed pea plants producing round seeds with those producing wrinkled seeds. From a total of 7324 $F_2$ seeds, 5474 were round and 1850 were wrinkled. Using the symbols *W* and *w* for genes, (a) symbolize the original P cross; (b) the gametes; and (c) $F_1$ progeny. (d) Represent a cross between two $F_1$ plants (or one selfed); (e) symbolize the gametes; and (f) summarize the expected $F_2$ results under the headings phenotypes, genotypes, genotypic frequency, and phenotypic ratio.

**1.8** (a) Diagram a cross between a homozygous pea plant that produced yellow seeds (*GG*) and one that produced green seeds (*gg*). Carry to the $F_2$ and summarize the expected results under the following headings: phenotypes, genotypes, genotypic frequency, and phenotypic ratio. (b) From a total of 8023 $F_2$ seeds, Mendel classified 6022 yellow and 2001 green. Compare the observed and calculated results in a tabulation chart under the headings phenotypes, observed, calculated, deviations.

**1.9** The French biologist Cuénot crossed wild, gray-colored mice with white (albino) mice. In the first generation all were gray. From many litters he obtained in the $F_2$, 198 gray, and 72 white mice. (a) Propose a hypothesis to explain these results. (b) On the basis of the hypothesis, diagram the cross and compare the observed results with those expected.

**1.10** A woman has a rare abnormality of the eyelids called ptosis, which makes it impossible for her to open her eyes completely. The condition has been found to depend on a single dominant gene (*P*). The woman's father had ptosis, but her mother had normal eyelids. Her father's mother had normal eyelids. (a) What are the probable genotypes of the woman, her father and mother? (b) What proportion of her children will be expected to have ptosis if she marries a man with normal eyelids?

**1.11** In pigeons, the checkered pattern is dependent on a dominant gene *C* and plain on the recessive allele *c*. Red color is controlled by a dominant gene *B* and brown by the recessive allele *b*. Diagram completely a cross between homozygous checkered, red; and plain, brown birds. Summarize the expected $F_2$ results.

**1.12** Male checkered, red birds with the genotype *CcBb* were mated with females with the following genotypes: (a) *CCBB;* (b) *Ccbb;* (c) *ccBB;* (d) *ccbb.* Summarize the expected first generation results of each cross.

**1.13** A checkered, brown female mated with a plain, red male produced 2 checkered, red; 2 plain, red; and 1 checkered, brown offspring. Give the probable genotypes of the parents.

**1.14** Give the probable genotypes of the parents in the following (each represents several successive matings); (a) a checkered, brown bird mated with a plain, brown, produced 13 checkered brown, and 15 plain brown; (b) checkered brown, and plain, red produced 19 checkered, red; (c) checkered, brown, and plain, red produced 9 checkered, brown; 8 checkered, red; 7 plain, brown; and 1 plain, red; (d) checkered, red, and plain, red produced 14 checkered, red; 4 checkered, brown; 16 plain, red; and 5 plain, brown; (e) plain, red, and plain, red produced 32 plain red; 12 plain brown.

**1.15** In mice, the gene (*C*) for colored fur is dominant over its allele (*c*) for white. The gene (*V*) for normal behavior is dominant over that (*v*) for waltzing. Give the probable genotypes of the parent mice (each pair was mated repeatedly and produced the following results): (a) colored, normal, mated with white, normal, produced 29 colored, normal, and 10 colored waltzers; (b) colored, normal mated with colored, normal produced 38 colored, normal; 15 colored, waltzers; 11 white, normal; and 4 white, waltzers; (c) colored, normal mated with white, waltzer, produced 8 colored, normal; 7 colored, waltzers; 9 white, normal; 6 white, waltzers.

**1.16** In rabbits, black fur is dependent on a dominant gene (*B*) and brown on the recessive allele (*b*). Normal length fur is determined by a dominant gene (*R*) and short (rex) by the recessive allele (*r*). (a) Diagram and summarize the results of a cross between a homozygous black rabbit with normal length fur and a brown, rex rabbit. (b) What proportion of the normal, black $F_2$ rabbits from the above cross may be expected to be homozygous for both gene pairs? (c) Diagram and summarize a backcross between the $F_1$ and the fully recessive brown, rex parent.

**1.17** In garden peas, the genes for tall vine (*D*), yellow seed (*G*), and round seed (*W*) are dominant over their respective alleles for dwarf (*d*), green (*g*), and wrinkled (*w*). (a) Symbolize a cross between a homozygous, tall, yellow, round plant and a dwarf, green, wrinkled plant. Represent the gametes possible from each parent and the $F_1$. (b) Symbolize a cross between two $F_1$ plants. Complete this cross by making use of the forked-line method and summarize the expected phenotypes. (c) Using the forked-line method, diagram a cross between the $F_1$ and the dwarf, green, wrinkled parent. Summarize the results for phenotypes, genotypes, genotypic frequency and phenotypic ratio.

**1.18** What phenotypes are expected and in what proportion from each of the following crosses:

(a) *DdGGww* × *DDGgWw*  (c) *DdGgWw* × *DdggWw*
(b) *ddggWw* × *DdGgww*  (d) *DDGgWW* × *DdGgWW*

**1.19** In snapdragons, flower color shows intermediate inheritance rather than dominance. Homozygous plants (*RR*) are red, heterozygous (*RR′*) pink, and homozygous (*R′R′*) white. Diagram a cross between a red and white plant and summarize the $F_2$ results under the headings phenotypes, genotypes, genotypic frequency, and phenotypic ratio.

**1.20** In shorthorn cattle, the gene (*R*) for red coat color is not dominant over white (*R'*). The heterozygous combination (*RR'*) produces roan. A breeder has white, red, and roan cows and bulls. What phenotypes might be expected from the following matings and in what proportions:

(a) red × red
(b) red × roan
(c) red × white
(d) roan × roan
(e) roan × white
(f) white × white

(g) Would it be easier to establish a true-breeding herd of red or a true-breeding herd of roan shorthorns? Explain.

**1.21** State and illustrate Mendel's principles of (a) segregation and (b) independent assortment.

**1.22** Give a modern evaluation of Mendel's conclusions, indicating which have remained firm and which require modification.

**1.23** Why did Mendel's work remain unappreciated for many years after its completion? By whom and under what circumstances was it discovered in 1900?

**1.24** What factors should be considered in choosing ideal materials for experimental breeding? List organisms that fit these requirements and organisms that do not.

**1.25** What techniques are available for studies in human genetics?

# *Cell Mechanics*

# 2

We shall now show how it was established that genes are in chromosomes and that chromosomes are intimately involved in the division cycles of individual cells as well as in the basic reproductive processes of entire organisms (animals and plants). The significance of chromosomes as complexes of hereditary determiners and their importance to the inheritance mechanism will be demonstrated.

Although cells vary widely in structure and function, they have some important properties in common, and all represent units of living material. The general structural characteristics of a cell are illustrated diagrammatically in Fig. 2.1. Great variation occurs among the cells of different organisms and among cells in different areas of the same organism. Plant cells differ from animal cells in shape and other characteristics, but plant and animal cells are essentially alike in terms of genes, chromosomes, and other structures and functions. The diagram represents only the general characteristics of a composite cell.

Cell division is the process through which cells reproduce themselves and multicellular organisms grow. When cells divide, each resultant part is a complete, although at first a smaller, cell. Immediately following division, the newly formed daughter cells grow rapidly, soon reaching the size of the original cell. Cell division is really a process of duplication or multiplication rather than of division in the usual sense.

Growth in higher organisms thus occurs through a combination of cell division and subsequent enlargement and differentiation of the cells produced. A man, for example, arises from a single fertilized cell or zygote, which develops eventually into an adult with more than a million billion cells. Most organisms with more than a single cell grow in this way. However, a few whole organisms (for example, rotifers) have a constant number of cells throughout adult life. Some tissues within other animals, such as the salivary glands of the larval fruit fly, grow by increase in the size of individual cells. In most animals, however, continued growth of individual cells is rare. Cell division (or duplication) is fundamental to the growth process of almost all higher organisms.

In unicellular animals, cell duplication equates with reproduction. Through this process, two new individuals are formed from the original parent. By contrast, the complex body of a multicellular organism arises from a single zygote through repeated divisions of the cells. Epithelial cells have a relatively short life span; replacements must be made continuously. Those in the lining of the respiratory, digestive, and urinary tracts, for example, are replaced within a few days. Some gland cells have a life span of only a few hours. Cells in

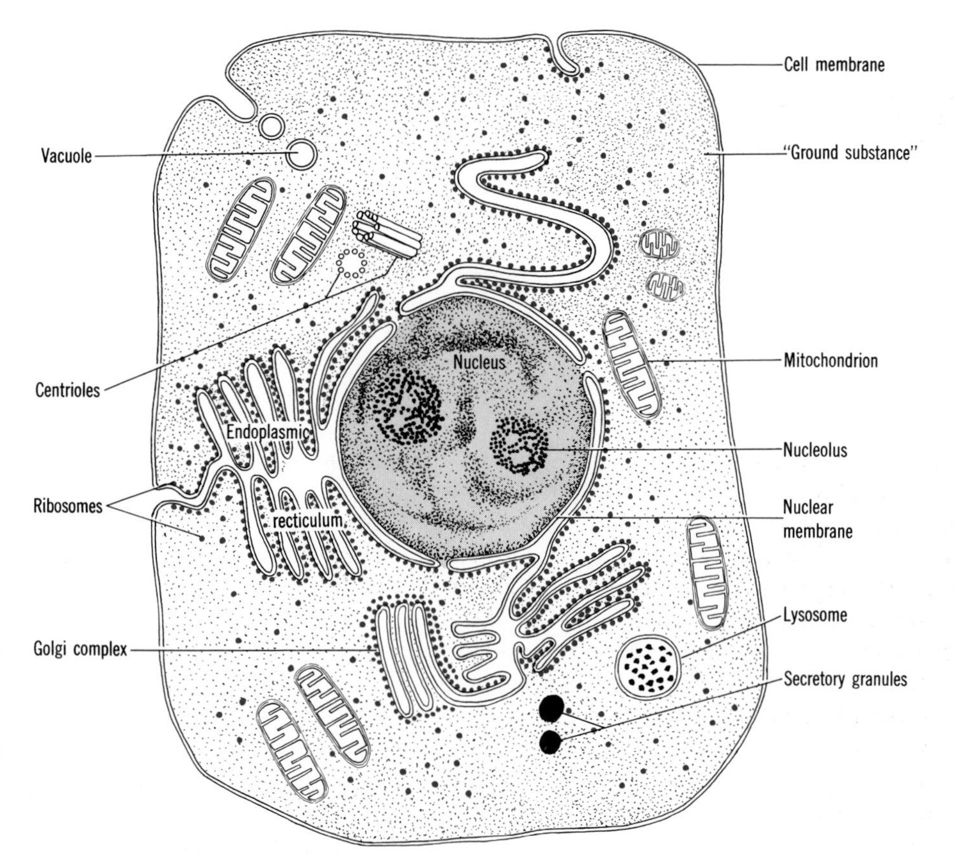


**Fig. 2.1** A schematic view of an animal cell, as it might be seen from electron micrographs. Although no single electron micrograph would reveal all structures shown, the diagram represents a composite of parts that many electron micrographs have shown to be in the organization of the cell.

particular parts of the nervous system, on the other hand, once established do not divide, and the number remains fairly constant through the mature life of the individual.

## MECHANICS OF CELL DIVISION

The mechanism by which equal products, both qualitatively and quantitatively, could result from a division process intrigued early investigators. Wilhelm Roux (1850–1924) speculated on this problem and constructed models to test his ideas. The only mechanism he could devise that would result in this kind of division required lining up the objects in a row and duplicating each exactly. He therefore suggested that the essential part of nuclear division or mitosis might be explained by visualizing strings of beadlike structures that line up and duplicate themselves. If cells really have such structures, he reasoned, such a model may illustrate the mechanics of cell division.

The detailed mechanism by which cells reproduce was elucidated in the latter part of the nineteenth century by Walther Flemming (1843–1915) and others. Two interrelated processes were found to be involved: (1) mitosis, the nuclear division;

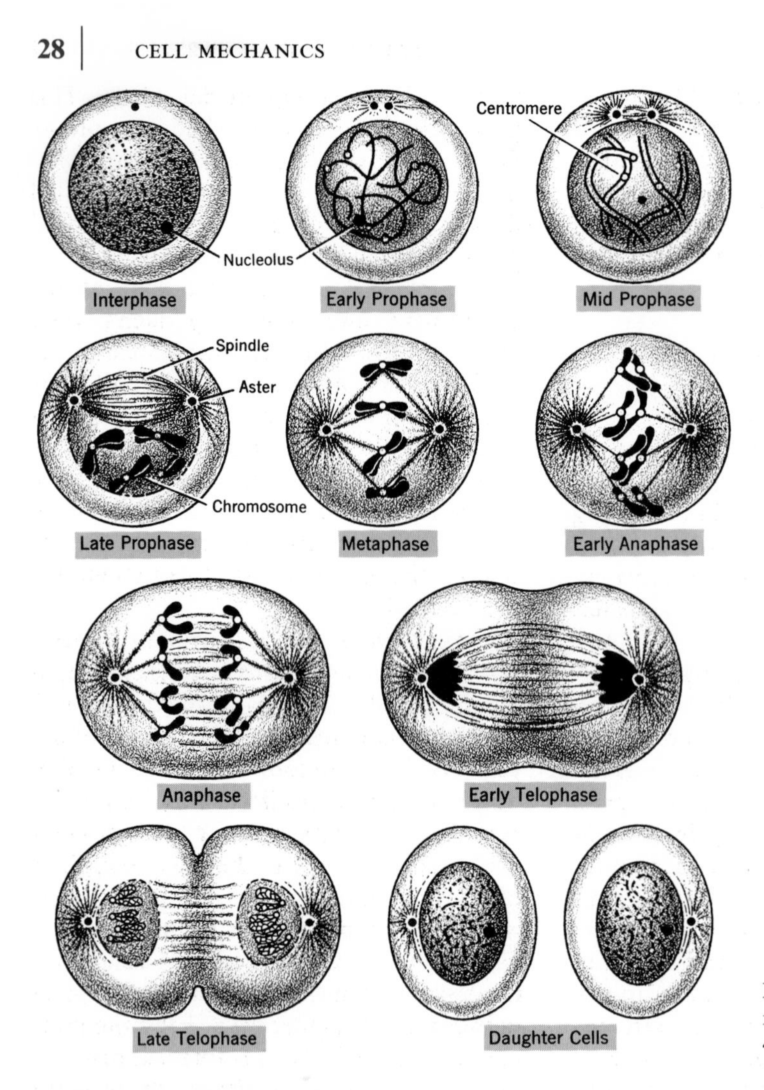


**Fig. 2.2** Schematic diagram of mitosis in an animal cell with 4 chromosomes.

and (2) cytokinesis, the changes in the cytoplasm, including the division of the cell proper. Figure 2.2 illustrates this process in animal cells. Since most of the classical work on mitosis was done with killed and stained preparations, questions persisted as to whether the objects observed in these preparations were artifacts or manifestations of living cell structures. The general process was verified by classical studies on living materials.

Variations of the squash or smear technique first developed by John Belling in the early 1930's have been used to spread living tissues on a microscope slide where they may be effectively compared before and after killing and staining. Such observations have demonstrated that the same structures observed in cells that were fixed and stained while undergoing cell division are present while the dividing cells are still alive. Belling's ingenious invention of a method of studying whole chromosomes has been a landmark for studies of chromosomes and cell division.

Modern tools like phase-contrast and electron microscopes have enabled more recent investigators to verify and photograph some structures observed in cell division. The basic process, however, was described by the classicists, Flemming, Edward Strasburger (1844–1912), Theodor Boveri (1862–1915), and their associates, at the turn of the century, and has been verified by more recent investigators using the ordinary light microscope.

## MITOSIS AND CYTOKINESIS

The names interphase, prophase, metaphase, anaphase, and telophase have been associated with the different stages of the mitotic cycle for convenience in describing the changes that occur. The prophase and telophase stages of mitosis are usually long and involved, whereas metaphase and anaphase are commonly brief.

In the beginning of the prophase, chromosomes appear thin, uncoiled, and filamentous, but they become increasingly coiled, shortened, and more distinct as the mitotic process progresses. The pronounced shortening is accomplished by decrease in the number of coils with a concomitant increase in the diameter of each coil. Eventually, in fixed and stained preparations, each whole chromosome appears solid and oval or rod shaped. Sometime during interphase or prophase, two strands (chromatids) become apparent in each chromosome unit. The chromatids can be observed in late prophase in many plant and animal materials that are favorable for chromosome observation. At this stage, the two chromatids of each chromosome are held together at a constricted area called the centromere (or kinetochore) which usually is the point of attachment for spindle tubules. Each of the two chromatids thus becomes connected to a different pole at the region of the centromere.

When the discrete chromosomes have been formed, the nuclear membrane gradually disappears and a spindle-shaped structure is formed. The chromosomes in the center or equatorial plane form a figure called an equatorial plate. This part of the cell cycle is called metaphase. During this stage, the chromosomes are particularly discrete and tightly coiled thus facilitating chromosome counts and gross structural comparisons.

The chromatids separate first at the centromere and ultimately along their whole length. This separation marks the beginning of anaphase. Each unit now has its own centromere and is a chromosome. The chromosomes elongate by changes in their coiling pattern and move to the respective poles of the spindle. In this duplication and separation of chromatids, the requirements of Roux's models are fulfilled.

During telophase, a nuclear membrane is reconstructed around each daughter nucleus. In the final stage (cytokinesis) of cell division, the cytoplasmic part of the cell divides. Animal cells with flexible outer layers accomplish this by a constriction that converges from the two sides and eventually separates the two daughter cells. The surface around the equator pushes in toward the center and pinches the cell into two parts. Plant cells with rigid walls form a partition or cell plate between the daughter cells. After the middle lamella (cell plate) is formed, primary walls are deposited on either side. In some plant cells, thick secondary walls of cellulose are later deposited.

In living material, the process (mitosis plus cytokinesis) of cell division is continuous from the time a cell first shows evidence of beginning to divide until the two daughter cells are completely formed. The entire procedure ordinarily requires a few hours to several days with variations dependent on the type of organism and environmental conditions. The mitosis (karyokinesis), and cytokinesis (cytoplasm division) phases are distinct but coordinated processes.

The actual mitotic sequence is illustra-

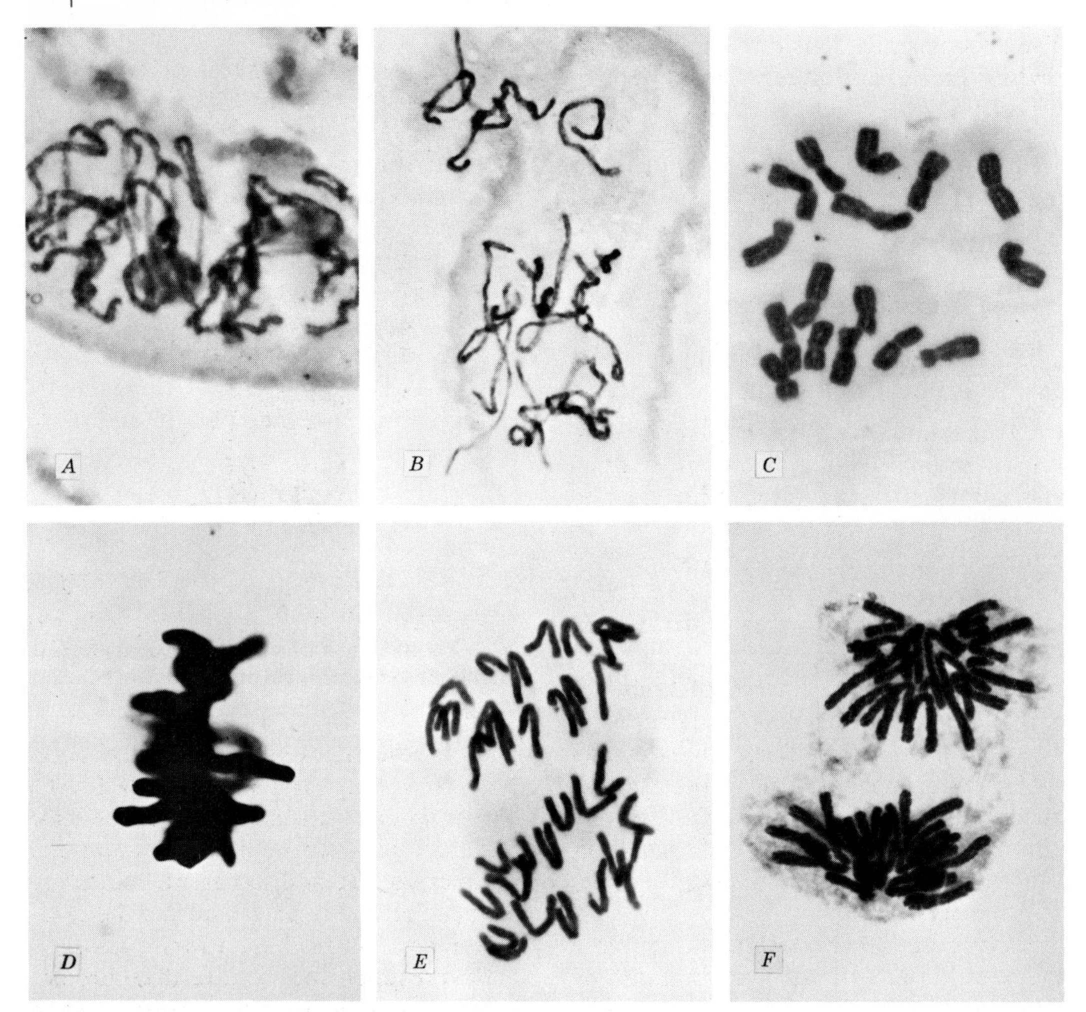


**Fig. 2.3** Photomicrographs representing major stages in the mitotic sequence of the onion, *Allium cepa,* root tip. This species has 16 chromosomes. *A*, early prophase; *B*, middle prophase; *C*, metaphase, polar view; *D*, metaphase, side view; *E*, anaphase showing separate chromosomes; *F*, telophase. All six photographs are made to the same scale. (Courtesy of W. S. Boyle.)

ted in Fig. 2.3 with a series of stages from the onion root tip, *Allium cepa.* In early prophase (*A*), the chromosomes are long, fine threads largely or completely uncoiled. More condensed chromosomes (*B*) represent a later prophase stage. The polar view (*C*, *D*) of metaphase shows the chromosomes on the equatorial plate. Each metaphase chromosome consists of two prominent chromatids, joined together at the centromere. The spindle apparatus is not visible with the stain utilized (aceto-carmine). The anaphase chromosomes (*E*) are shown approaching the poles. Each telophase (*F*) is followed by the reconstruction of the nuclear membranes around each group of chromosomes. Chromosomes cannot be seen after telophase, but electron microscope studies indicate that they retain their continuity through the interphase.

The cytoplasmic division completes the division process and gives rise to two daughter cells.

## CHROMOSOMES IN SEXUAL REPRODUCTION

Even before the full significance of mitosis was appreciated and before Mendel's work was discovered, sex cells (that is, eggs and sperm) were known to be involved in fertilization. Also, both parents were known ordinarily to transmit their characteristics to their progeny. It remained to be determined whether the whole cell or some part was primarily involved.

The German cytologist Eduard Strasburger observed that the egg carried more cytoplasm than the sperm. He made reciprocal crosses between different plant species and found that the results of the reciprocal crosses were similar. Since the egg and sperm were unequal with respect to size and amount of cytoplasm carried, he suggested that the cytoplasm was not ordinarily responsible for hereditary differences between species.

Early experiments designed to explore the question in animals were initiated by Theodor Boveri (Fig. 2.4) and continued by other cytologists. By shaking sea urchin eggs at a critical time in their development, Boveri produced some eggs without and some with nuclei. Each kind of egg was fertilized by normal sperm from another kind of sea urchin. Eggs lacking a nucleus produced larvae resembling the type from which the sperm were obtained, but those with nuclei developed into hybrids, showing the characteristics of both parental types. The cytoplasm in the two kinds of eggs had not been altered, and it was therefore presumed that the nucleus and not the cytoplasm was responsible for the transmission of hereditary traits.

Similar experiments were conducted by other investigators with types of tobacco, Nicotiana, using cytoplasm from the female parent and a sperm nucleus from the male parent. The offspring had characteristics peculiar to the pollen parent, indicating further that the nucleus and not the cytoplasm was responsible for inheritance.

**Fig. 2.4** Theodor Boveri, German cytologist and embryologist who made significant contributions to the chromosome theory of inheritance.

Boveri supported the idea that chromosomes contain genetic determiners, and he was largely responsible for developing the chromosome theory of inheritance. In 1902 a young American graduate student, W. S. Sutton (1876–1916) independently recognized a parallelism between the behavior of chromosomes and the Mendelian segregation of genes. He became the cofounder with Boveri of the chromosome theory. Later, several investigators observed that genes, as judged by the end products, behaved as they would be expected to behave if they were located in chromosomes. The next step was a detailed analysis of the process through which higher organisms reproduce themselves. Eggs and sperm in animals and comparable cells in plants were already known to be involved.

Reproduction in living organisms may be considered on different levels. The most obvious is the highly complex organismal level in which the whole animal or plant is reproduced. This is accomplished when individuals mate, and give rise to progeny representing their particular species. Another level centers on the formation of the sex cells on which reproduction of the organism is dependent. A third level of consideration emphasizes the activities of chromosomes and genes. The replication of genetic material is one of the most basic properties of the living entity.

## GAMETE FORMATION IN ANIMALS

All normal cells, with a few exceptions, can reproduce themselves. The sex cells or germ cells, however, are endowed with the capacity to initiate reproduction of the entire organism. A special sequence (gametogenesis, the origin of the gamete) results in the development of animal sex cells. Gametogenesis includes meiosis (from Greek, to reduce), a reduction process by which the chromosome number is reduced, and the development of characteristics of eggs and sperm that are necessary for their functioning. Eggs of animals usually accumulate nutrient materials that sustain the developing embryo for a brief period; sperm of most animal species develop a flagellum for independent motility.

It was Boveri who postulated that if different genes were in different chromosomes, completely independent of each other, the results of Mendel's dihybrid crosses could be explained. The theory, however, involved a number of steps, and several years were required for the evidence to accumulate. Four major questions required answers:

**1.** Are the chromosomes continuous from cell division to cell division?

**2.** Are the chromosomes qualitatively different, that is do they have their own individuality?

**3.** If so, is there a pairing process through which corresponding or homologous chromosomes come together, followed by a later separation of the members of pairs?

**4.** If the above three requirements are met, are chromosome pairs independent and capable of chance recombination?

A more detailed description of gametogenesis in animals as it is now understood will enable us to appreciate the past and current experimental attacks on the problem.

### *Spermatogenesis*

Sperm originate in the male reproductive organs or testes through a sequence called spermatogenesis (Fig. 2.5). Considered grossly, the process consists of a growth in cell size, two successive cell divisions, and a metamorphosis of the resulting cells from spherical static bodies to elongated, motile sperm. The process is initiated in diploid ($2n$) or unreduced germ cells that have the chromosome complement normal to the particular species. These cells, called spermatogonia, enlarge and become primary spermatocytes. The spermatocytes then divide, with each producing two secondary spermatocytes. In turn, each secondary spermatocyte divides into two spermatids. Each spermatid then changes shape, develops a motile organelle, and becomes a sperm. While the cells are dividing twice, the chromosomes undergo intricate and significant processes and duplicate themselves only once. Reduction in chromosome number is thus accomplished.

The chromosomes that appear as single threads in the early prophase of the first meiotic division represent the maternal and paternal chromosomes received by the individual (male or female) from the gametes of his parents. The number of chromosome threads ($2n$) is characteristic of

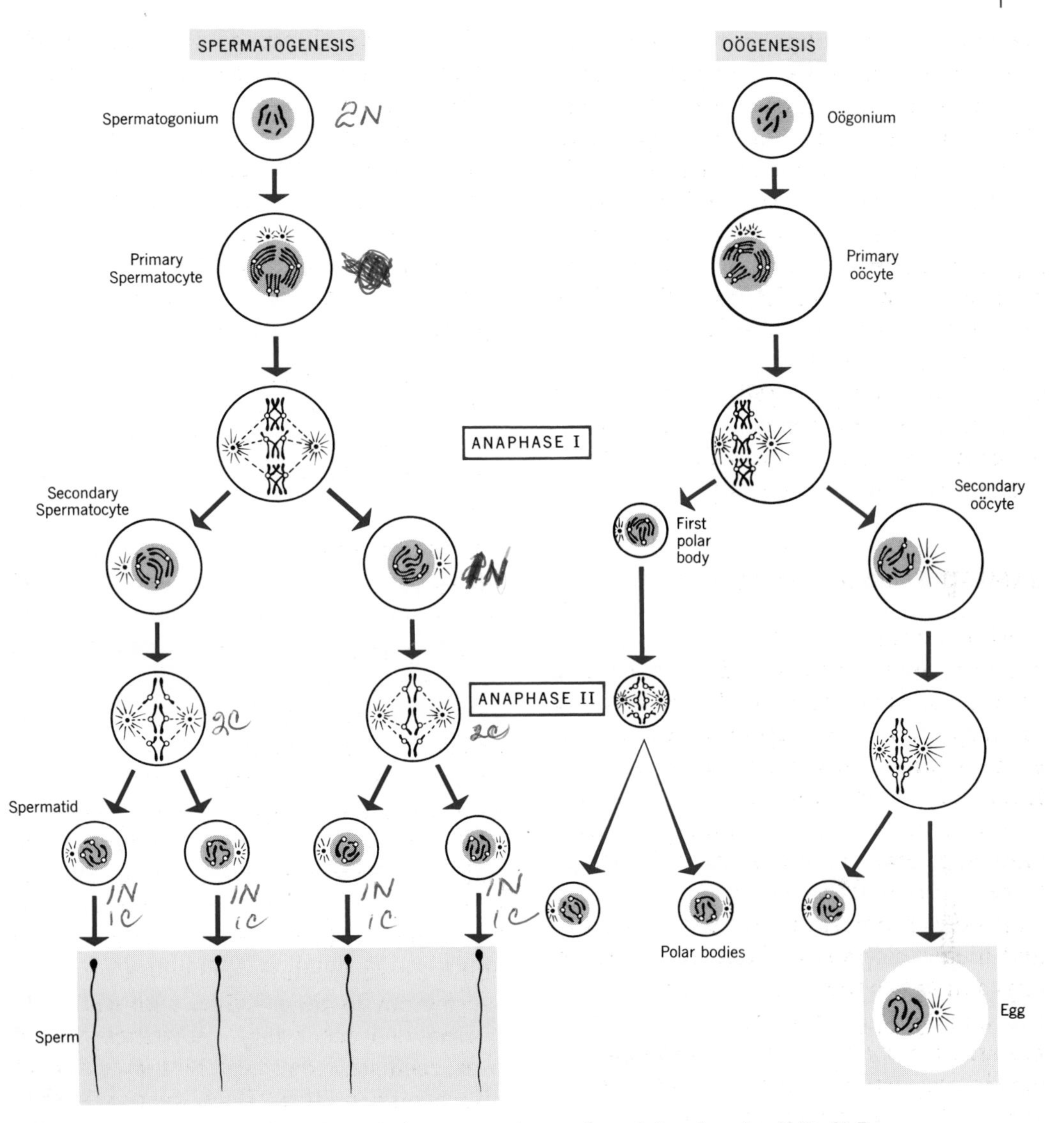


**Fig. 2.5** Diagram representing the meiotic sequence in a male and female animal. (Left) Process of spermatogenesis resulting in the formation of four sperm; (right) oögenesis resulting in the formation of one egg and three polar bodies.

the species to which the individual belongs. This preliminary stage of meiosis, in which the chromosomes appear as single thin filaments, is called the leptotene stage. During the zygotene stage, which follows, a pairing process called "synapsis" (from Greek, meaning conjunction or union) brings together maternal and paternal members of the same pair of chromosomes. Pairing is accomplished while the primary spermatocyte is enlarging. Not only do the corresponding maternal and paternal chromosomes come together, but each chromosome segment pairs with the appropriate segment on the homologous chromosome. The sequence of chromosome

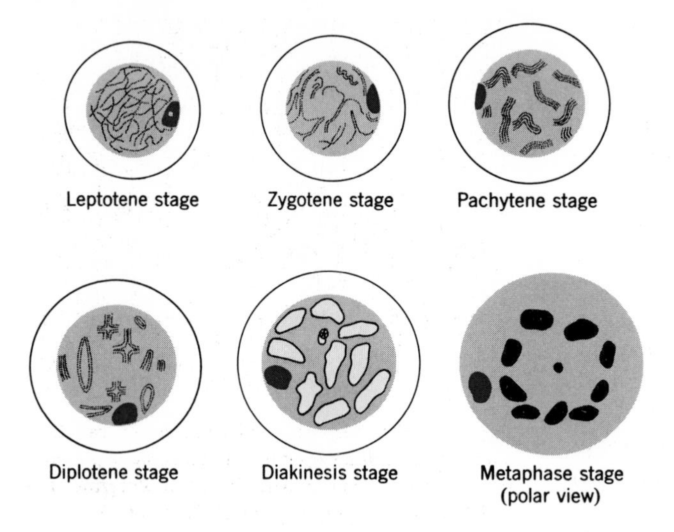


**Fig. 2.6** Diagram of the meiotic prophase of squash bug, *Anasa tristis,* illustrating chromosome pairing and duplication in the zygotene and pachytene stages, respectively. Bivalent appearance is lost in later prophase stages because of coiling and intense staining.

changes in the meiotic prophase is illustrated from the squash bug, *Anasa tristis* (Fig. 2.6).

When pairing is complete, the elongated, homologous chromosomes can be observed side by side in close association. This is the pachytene stage. Following pachynema, the chromosomes shorten, thicken, and become more distinct. In some preparations, the centromeres of paired chromosomes appear to repel each other, causing the strands to separate longitudinally in some areas and to form loops. This is the diplotene stage. In favorable preparations, four chromatids are visible. They are held together forming a tetrad or bivalent. At an earlier stage, in interphase, or early meiotic prophase, chromosome duplication is accomplished, but the four chromatids usually do not become visible until diplonema. Gene duplication, requiring the synthesis of new DNA, thus occurs long before the four chromatids are observable in microscope preparations.

In diplonema, the centromeres in each chromosome are not split and the longitudinal separation of the chromosomes is incomplete. Bivalents are held together at various places along their length because interchanges between chromatids (chiasmata) have occurred. From one to several chiasmata may be observed, depending on the length of the bivalent. Each chiasma apparently represents an exchange between nonsister chromatids. The point where the chiasma appears, however, is not necessarily where the chromatid exchange actually occurred, because chiasmata tend to slip along toward the ends of the bivalents and thus become terminalized as the meiotic prophase continues. Genetic implications of such exchanges or crossovers are discussed in detail in Chapter 6.

Shortening of the bivalents continues through the next stage, diakinesis, resulting in discrete units which, in favorable preparations, can be counted and found to represent half the $2n$ chromosome number as expected. As the meiotic prophase is completed, the bivalents become angular or oval in appearance, and take their place in the equatorial plane, forming the equatorial plate of metaphase I.

The first of the two cellular divisions in the meiotic sequence is the reduction division. In the anaphase of such a division, the original maternal and paternal chromosome (each composed of one centromere and two chromatids) separate. Thus, the number of chromosomes in each resultant cell is reduced from the original in the first division.

During the second cellular division, the centromeres of each bipartite chromosome divide, providing each new chromosome with its own centromere. Each chromosome moves to a pole of the spindle. The chromosome number in a spermatid is haploid ($n$), the same as in the secondary spermatocyte. However, the chromosomes of the spermatids are ostensibly unipartite whereas those of the secondary spermatocyte are bipartite, being composed of two chromatids. In other words, each spermatid nucleus has a single set of dissimilar chromosomes.

At the location of the centromeres, the second division is a type of mitotic division, called the equational division because it separates the duplicated chromatids. This division is in contrast to the reductional division in which the chromosomes that came together in synapsis separate. With respect to the distribution of genes, however, neither of the two divisions can be considered to be completely reductional or completely equational.

The terminal process in spermatogenesis is a complicated differentiation called spermiogenesis. Through a progressive sequence of changes, each of the comparatively large, spherical, nonmotile spermatids is metamorphosed into a small, elongated, motile sperm. In most animal species, spermatids begin this process by secretion of the apical body or acrosome and production of the flagellum from a centriole. Sloughing off of cytoplasm diminishes the overall size as the developing sperm changes from a spherical to an oval shape. The nucleus moves to one edge of the cell, becoming elongated and increasingly more compact. The acrosome, which is derived in part from Golgi material, takes its place around the anterior end of the sperm head as illustrated in Fig. 2.7. In some animals, the acrosome becomes

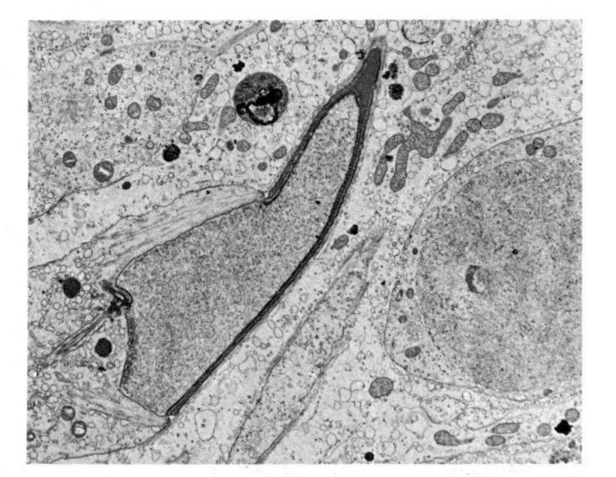

**Fig. 2.7** Electron photomicrograph of rat testis showing developing sperm. An acrosome is shown at the upper tip of sperm head in center. Magnification ×30,000. (Photograph by Hugh P. Stanley.)

pointed and facilitates the fusion between sperm and egg in fertilization. In other animals it has a chemical dissolving action.

The tail of the sperm is composed of two parts: the outer sheath, which is cytoplasmic in origin; and the axial filament inside the sheath which extends from the base of the head to the posterior end of the tail. The axial filament is formed from an elongation of part of one of the two centrioles of the spermatid. The remaining part of this centriole together with the other centriole and a group of modified mitochondria form a complex structure sometimes called the middle piece between the head and tail.

In most sexually mature male animals, spermatogenesis is constantly or periodically occurring in the testes and many millions of sperm are produced. Insects generally require only a few days to complete their cycle of spermatogenesis, but in mammals the cycle extends over weeks or months. In the mature human male, spermatogenesis occurs in the seminiferous tubules of the testes. Spermatogonia can be observed in cross sections of tubules at the periphery undergoing mitotic division. Those spermatagonia that appear to be in the innermost cell layer of the periphery enlarge and form primary spermatocytes with 23 bivalents. These spermatocytes undergo the two meiotic divisions in rapid succession and produce spermatids, which develop into sperm with single sets of 23 chromosomes. It should be noted that, although sperm cells develop in the testes of the male, they are not manufactured there. Rather, they result from a division process, originating from primordial cells which become established in the testes during early embryology.

The developmental time from primitive spermatogonia to mature human sperm is about 74 days. The change from primary spermatocytes in the preleptotene stage to mature sperm requires about 48 days. Radiation (approximately 300 roentgens (r) or units of X-rays) will inhibit spermatogenesis, resulting in temporary sterility. Spermatogonia are particularly susceptible to radiation damage. Radiation in larger amounts (400r or more) may result in prolonged or even permanent sterility in the human male. Genetic damage to genes and chromosomes following radiation will be discussed in Chapter 13.

*Oögenesis*

The process of gamete formation in the female animal (oögenesis, the origin of the egg) is also illustrated in Fig. 2.5. Oögenesis is essentially the same as spermatogenesis as far as the chromosome mechanism is concerned, but other aspects of the process are quite different. Much more nutrient material is accumulated during oögenesis than during spermatogenesis. This is particularly true of oviparous animals—those that lay eggs that hatch after removal from the body of the mother. These animals must provide yolk material for the nourishment of the developing embryo outside of the body. Even in viviparous animals, which retain and nourish the young inside the body of the mother, a considerable amount of nutrient material accumulates. Because of the accumulated nutrient material, an egg is usually considerably larger than a sperm of the same species.

In addition, the cells that result from divisions in oögenesis are of unequal size. Nutrient material in the primary oöcyte is not divided equally into four cells that result from the meiotic sequence. One large cell in each division (Fig. 2.5) contains essentially all of the yolk, while the polar bodies get very little. First and second polar bodies, however, receive the same chromosome complements as the secondary oöcytes and ova from the respective divisions, but they do not become functional sex cells. No stage in oögenesis is comparable to the spermatid stage in spermatogenesis, and no metamorphosis is necessary to make the egg functional.

In some animal species, oögenesis proceeds rapidly and continuously in sexually mature females and numerous eggs are produced. Usually, these eggs complete the second meiotic division and become mature before fertilization. In many other animals, including the mammals, the second meiotic division (equation division) does not occur until after sperm entry.

In man, for example, oögenesis begins before birth. Oögonia located in the follicles of cortical tissue in the fetal ovary begin to differentiate into primary oöcytes at about the third month of intrauterine development. At the time of birth of the female infant, the primary oöcytes are in the prophase of the first meiotic division. They remain in "suspended prophase" for many years until sexual maturity is reached. Then, as the ovarian follicles start to mature, the meiotic prophase is resumed. The first meiotic division for each developing egg is completed shortly before the time of ovulation for that egg. One cell, a secondary oöcyte, which results from this division, receives 23 chromosomes and most of the nutrient material accumulated in the primary oöcyte. The other cell, which is a polar body, also receives 23 chromosomes, but very little nutrient material.

The second meiotic division begins after the first is completed and is in progress when the developing egg is extruded from the ovary and passes into the Fallopian tube. This division is not completed, however, until after fertilization, which usually occurs in the tube. Fertilization is a random process in that any available sperm may fuse with any mature egg. If fertilization is accomplished, the secondary oöcyte divides and forms a mature ovum with a pronucleus containing a single set of 23 maternal chromosomes. The other cell resulting from this division is a second polar body, not capable of further development. The sperm head forms a pronucleus with 23 paternal chromosomes. When the two pronuclei fuse, a zygote with ($2n$) 46 chromosomes begins mitotic division or first cleavage, which results in the two-cell stage of a beginning embryo. Through continued mitotic divisions, an adult body is produced that contains more than a million billion cells.

## GAMETE FORMATION IN PLANTS

Gamete formation in plants, like that in animals, requires a reduction in chromosome number. The meiotic process itself is similar to that in animals, but the life cycle of plants is somewhat more complicated. Gamete formation usually does not follow meiosis directly. Gametogenesis in plants involves the formation of spores rather than sex cells. Gametes come from gametophytes in which the chromosome number is already reduced.

In most flowering plants, the flowers are bisexual; that is, they contain both stamens and pistils (Fig. 2.8). The anther portion of the stamen contains many pollen mother cells (microspore mother cells). As the flower matures, each pollen mother cell undergoes a meiotic division resulting in the production of 4 pollen grains (micro-

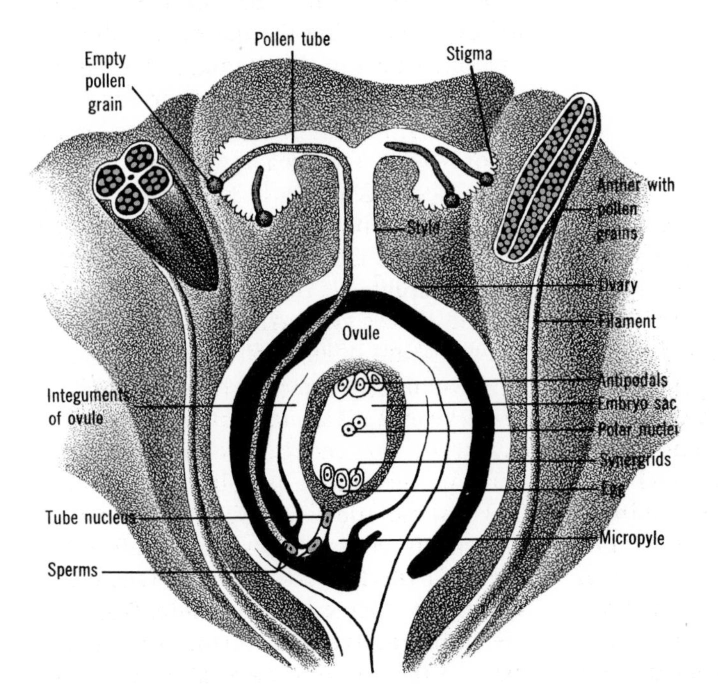


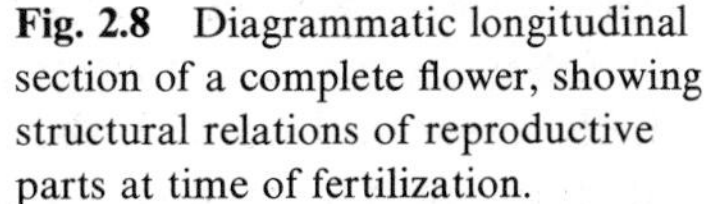

**Fig. 2.8** Diagrammatic longitudinal section of a complete flower, showing structural relations of reproductive parts at time of fertilization.

spores), all of which are functional. The haploid nucleus of each pollen grain then divides by mitosis to produce 2 nuclei, the generative and tube nuclei. In most plants, the pollen grains are released from the anther in this binucleate stage and may be transported to the stigma. After pollination, the generative nucleus divides by mitosis to produce 2 sperm nuclei, the male gametes. Each pistil contains one or more ovules. Each ovule contains one embryo-sac mother cell (megaspore mother cell). The embryo-sac mother cell divides by meiosis to produce 4 embryo-sac initials (megaspores), three of which die. The remaining haploid embryo-sac initial then undergoes a series of mitotic divisions resulting in an embryo sac containing 8 haploid nuclei. One of these 8 is the egg, the female gamete.

Plants such as squash, maize, oaks, and walnut are monoecious, with staminate and pistillate flowers on the same plant. Boxelders, willows, cottonwoods, and date palms are dioecious with staminate and pistillate flowers borne on separate plants.

### *Life Cycles*

An alternation of generations between a haploid gametophyte and diploid sporophyte phase of the cycle can separate gamete formation from other aspects of plant reproduction. This process characterizes virtually all plants, but the relative length of the two phases differs widely in different species. Diploid sporophytes bear spores with the reduced chromosome number. Spores grow into haploid gametophytes which ultimately produce gametes capable of fertilization. The resultant zygotes develop into sporophytes, completing the cycle. The sporophyte and gametophyte phases vary in length and importance in different plants.

In most green algae, meiosis occurs in the first two divisions of the fertilized egg. Thus, green algae have the haploid number of chromosomes throughout most of their life cycle. Meiosis in brown algae takes place at the other end of the cycle, immediately preceding the formation of gametes. The cells of the plant body are thus diploid and most of the life cycle is in the diploid phase. In mosses, the two types of generation are both conspicuous and the two phases of the cycle are more nearly equal. Among the seed plants, the gametophyte is considerably reduced. In the female it is the embryo sac and in the male it includes the pollen grain, pollen tube, and the three nuclei. One of these nuclei is the tube nucleus and two (those arising from mitotic division of the generative nucleus) are sperm.

The life cycle of a typical seed plant is illustrated in Fig. 2.9. Sporophyte ($2n$) germinal cells, in special parts of the flower, undergo a reduction division that produces haploid ($n$) cells. These divide and form the gametophyte. The sporophyte is reestablished from the zygote, which results from fertilization. In plants with perfect (bisexual) flowers, the formation of the male and female gametes may occur concomitantly in the respective staminate and pistillate parts. Diploid pollen mother cells undergo a meiotic sequence much like that described earlier for animals. Haploid microspores give rise to pollen grains. The nucleus of the pollen grain is duplicated by a mitotic-type division producing a tube nucleus and a generative nucleus. The generative nucleus divides to form two gametes. The pollen tube then grows down the style and enters the ovule, where fertilization occurs.

### *Meiosis*

The details of microsporogenesis, the development of the microspore, are illustrated (Fig. 2.10) with actual stages from living rye, *Secale cereale.* The zygotene stage of the meiotic prophase is shown in Fig. 2.10*A*.

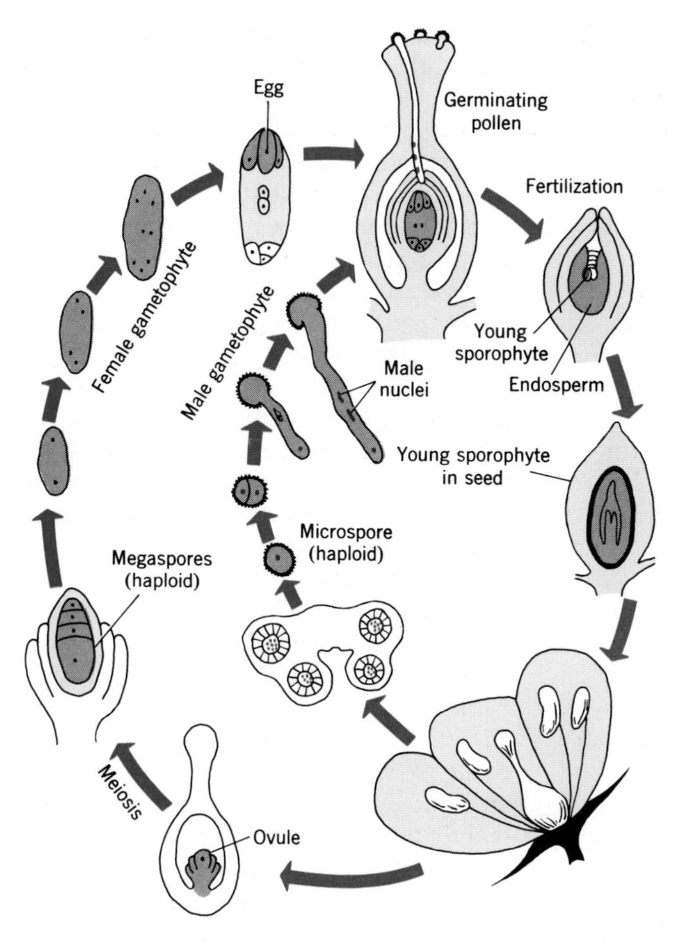


**Fig. 2.9** The life cycle of a seed plant.

Synapsis can be observed in progress in various parts of the chromosome configuration (see arrow). The diplotene stage is illustrated in Fig. 2.10*B*. In diakinesis and metaphase I (*C* to *E*), seven bivalents are visible. Later stages in the first and second divisions are shown (*F* to *H*) with the resulting four haploid sets of chromosomes. Following division of the cytoplasm, four independent microspores are formed. A pollen grain develops from each microspore.

The meiotic sequence of the female part (Fig. 2.10) begins in the nucleus of the developing embryo-sac mother cell. After the meiotic prophase, the mother cell divides twice to form four embryo-sac initials (megaspores). Three of these are reabsorbed and the one functional megaspore undergoes a series of mitotic divisions, eventually forming the embryo sac. One of the eight nuclei becomes the egg, two fuse to form a larger $2n$ nucleus that later gives rise to the endosperm nucleus (see below), and, in most seed plants, five nuclei are reabsorbed.

### *Fertilization*

The pollen tube contains three nuclei, the tube nucleus and two male gametes. Male gametes are carried through the micropyle into the embryo sac and accomplish the double fertilization process characteristic of the higher plants. One male

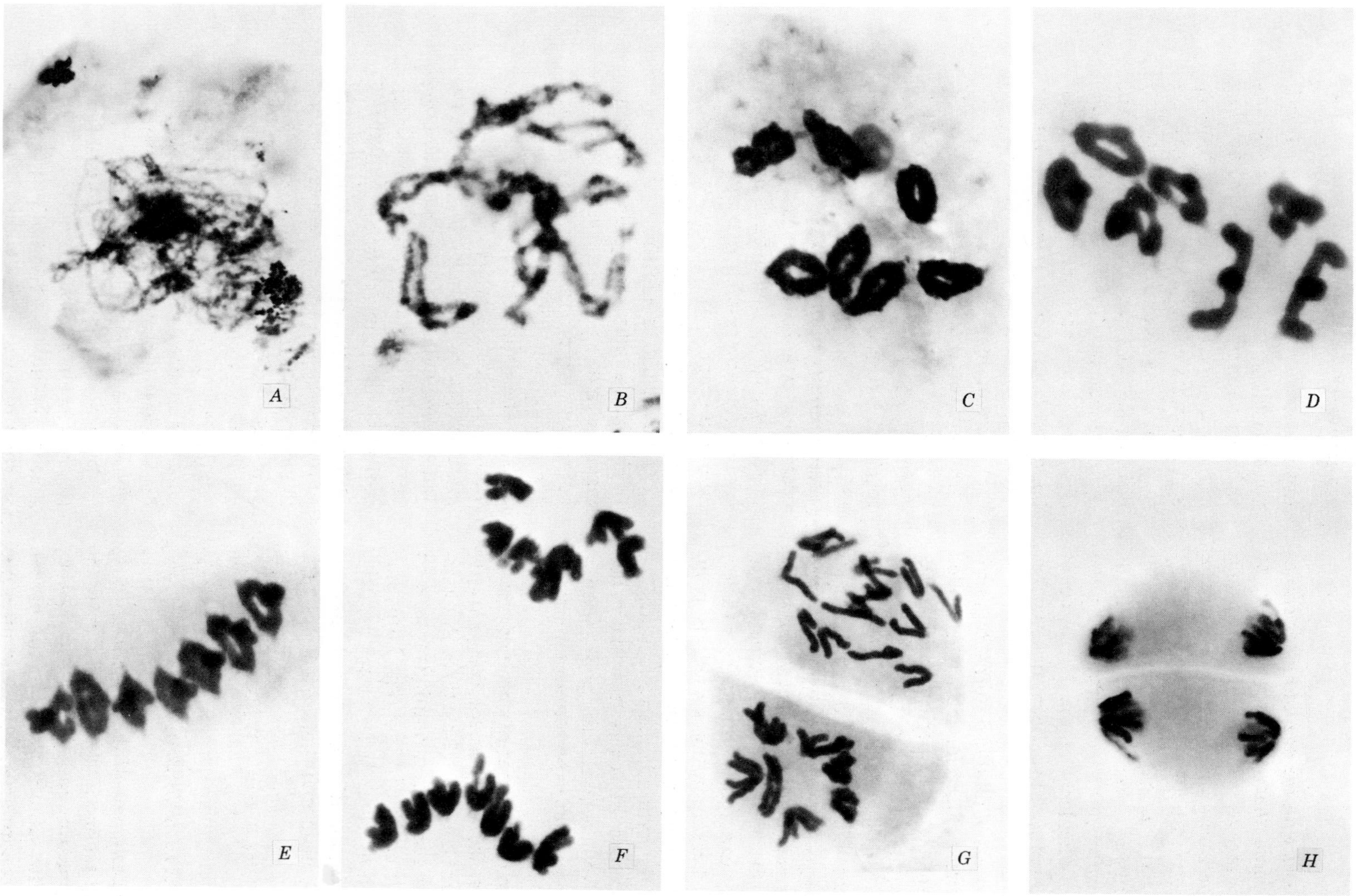

**Fig. 2.10** Successive stages of microsporogenesis in rye, *Secale cereale*. *A*, Zygotene stage, arrow shows synapsis in progress; *B*, diplotene stage; *C*, diakinesis, showing seven bivalents and nucleolus; *D*, *E*, metaphase I; *F*, telophase I; *G*, (lower figure) metaphase II and (upper figure) anaphase II; and *H*, telophase II. All 8 photographs are made to the same scale. (Courtesy of W. S. Boyle.)

gamete fuses with the egg and gives rise to the $2n$ zygote that divides repeatedly to form the embryo of the seed. The second male gamete unites with the $2n$ endosperm nucleus and forms the large triploid ($3n$) nucleus that divides repeatedly in typical seed plants to form the nutrient tissue (endosperm) of the seed. Variations in the process, particularly in the formation of the endosperm, have been observed in some plants.

The process of double fertilization introduces genetic material from the pollen parent into the endosperm tissue. Therefore, it might be expected that both maternal and paternal inheritance would be represented. This hereditary influence of the pollen parent genes on the endosperm is called xenia and has been shown to occur in the endosperm of some plants. When, for example, maize from a variety normally bearing white kernels is pollinated with yellow-kernel variety, the endosperm of the hybrid kernels is yellow. The dominant gene for yellow from the pollen comes to expression in the endosperm in the same manner expected for embryonic tissue.

The diploid number of chromosomes is restored in the fertilized cell that gives rise to the plant embryo. Thus, through fertilization, the genetic contributions from each parent are combined in a new individual that develops from the fertilized egg. Continuous mitotic division of cells and, in plants, some growth of individual cells result in a new individual, representative of the species to which the parents belong.

## CONTINUITY AND INDIVIDUALITY

In the early part of the present century, it was questioned whether the chromosomes appearing in a division stage were actually the same as those in the parent cell. In attempting to solve the problem, Boveri selected the round worm, *Ascaris megalocephala* (now *Parascaris equorum*), as his experimental material. The dividing zygotes and cells that resulted from the first cleavages had two pairs of large chromosomes, which could be followed readily through the division phases. Positions and appearances of the chromosomes were observed at metaphase, anaphase, and telophase, and the following prophase. Individual chromosomes were in the same arrangement in anaphase and telophase, giving characteristic shapes to the daughter nuclei. Some could be followed in similar position in the succeeding prophase stages. This observation was interpreted as substantiating the theory of continuity. The continuity of chromosomes has since been well established by more detailed comparisons of structural parts of chromosomes. Electron microscope pictures and autoradiographic studies have revealed identifiable chromosome threads in the interphase stage of mitosis.

The individuality and pairing of chromosomes required by the Mendelian hypothesis still had to be resolved. Early observations of chromosomes in the salamander and onion failed to show individuality of chromosomes. The chromosomes in these species appeared to be all alike. When observations were made on the grasshopper and other insects, however, individual chromosomes could be identified immediately by shape, size, and position. In mitotic figures, chromosomes were not in synapsis, but the two members of each pair were visible and identifiable in the dividing (metaphase) cells. The question of qualitative differences among chromosomes was resolved when actual pairing, or synapsis, was observed in a number of plant and animal materials.

By introducing sea urchin eggs into heavy suspensions of sperm, Boveri was able to induce double fertilization (dispermy) in some eggs. Some of these divided into three, and others into four blastomeres (cells making up an early embryo) at first cleavage. The 54 chromosomes resulting from double fertilization (18 from the egg nucleus and 18 from each sperm) duplicated themselves and formed various combinations in the cells because of irregular division. Some resultant cells had 18 chromosomes, which is the normal number for the sperm or egg, whereas some had 27 and others 36. Usually the whole unit of three or four blastomeres would disintegrate after the early cleavages. Boveri added calcium to the sea water in which the experimental embryos were kept and succeeded in separating the individual blastomeres before degeneration occurred. This made it possible to study individual isolated cells more critically.

Some of the cells that survived had 36 chromosomes, the normal $2n$ number for the sea urchin. Not all 36-chromosome cells survived, however, and Boveri postulated that certain combinations representing whole sets were necessary for survival. He prepared models that represented the combinations that might be expected from the irregular divisions. Those with 36 particular chromosomes, representing two sets of 18, were presumed to be the survivors. The chromosomes of the sea urchin are small and uniform in size, and thus Boveri was unable to distinguish the individual pairs of chromosomes with the microscope. He therefore calculated the expected proportions of combinations and compared the observed survivors with the expected normal combinations. The results were not entirely conclusive, but the studies indicated that chromosomes were qualitatively different and that complete sets were necessary for normal development.

The observation that, in certain insects, a particular chromosome was associated with sex determination provided further evidence for the qualitative differences among chromosomes. Sex thus became the first phenotype to be associated with a particular chromosome in animals (Chapter 4). Other genes were soon found to be located in the same chromosome that contained the sex determiners. These sex-linked genes, located in a particular observable chromosome, provided additional support for the chromosome theory. Genes associated with traits other than sex were found to be located on autosomes, that is, chromosomes not directly involved in sex determination. Of the 46 chromosomes in man, for example, 44 (22 pairs) are autosomes and 2 (1 pair) are sex determiners (see Chapter 4). Later studies on the plant genera Datura and Nicotiana (Chapter 10) showed that, when particular chromosomes were added to or removed from a normal set, characteristic and predictable phenotypic effects were produced. These data provided further verification of qualitative differences among chromosomes.

## INDEPENDENT COMBINATIONS OF GENES AND CHROMOSOME BEHAVIOR

If the genes are in chromosomes, the physical basis of independent assortment as well as that of segregation must be inherent in the chromosome mechanism at meiosis. To fit the Mendelian pattern, it was postulated that pairs of chromosomes were independent with respect to each other as Boveri (p. 32) had speculated. Testing this hypothesis required that the different pairs be distinguished from each other and that the members of the pair also be identified. A satisfactory demonstration was accomplished by E. E. Carothers in a study of grasshoppers. She observed that one member of one pair (chromosome I) in a certain grasshopper strain had a hook on the end which made it distinguishable from the other member of the pair. Two other pairs (VII and VIII) were also found to have structural features

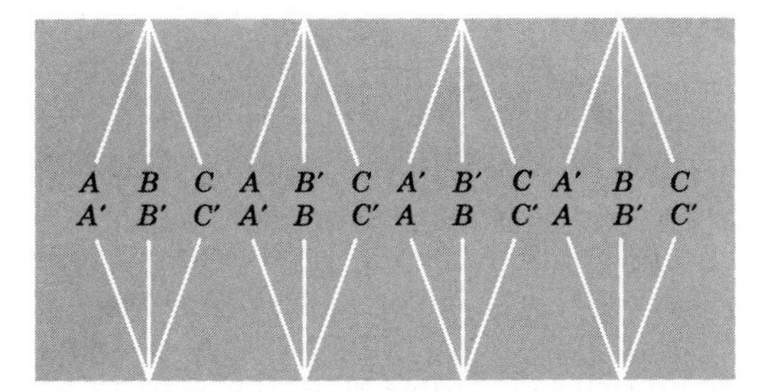


**Fig. 2.11** Diagram representing the arrangements of maternal and paternal chromosomes which could be identified in experiments with grasshoppers.

distinguishing the maternal from the paternal member of each pair.

By observing the marked chromosomes in reduction division, the maternal and paternal chromosomes could be followed. The three distinguishable pairs of maternal and of paternal chromosomes are symbolized AA′BB′CC′, and the various observed arrangements of the division spindle are illustrated in Fig. 2.11.

Miss Carothers then made crosses between different grasshoppers with marked chromosomes and observed the chromosome arrangements of hybrids in the meiotic process. She first made a control cross between grasshoppers that had three pairs of chromosomes exactly alike. Chromosomes of the progeny were like those of the parents, showing that the shapes and sizes remained constant from generation to generation. The grasshoppers with differently marked chromosomes were mated. The hybrids were raised to sexual maturity and the chromosomes were followed through the reduction division. Each chromosome paired with its homologue, and the three pairs remained distinct from one another.

The independence of the chromosome pairs, as they took their places on the equatorial plate in the reduction division, explained Mendel's second principle when a chance distribution of maternal and paternal chromosomes occurred in the two daughter cells. For example, the genes for vine height, seed color, and shape in the $F_1$ peas (described in Chapter 1) are located on separate homologous pairs. Gene *D* in the example is located on the maternal member of one pair while its allele *d* is in the corresponding position of the homologous (paternal) chromosome. Figure 2.12 shows diagrammatically six chromosomes representing three homologous pairs in unpaired condition, as would be expected during a mitotic division. Maternal and paternal members of each pair carrying their respective alleles are present in the same nucleus. At synapsis in meiosis each chromosome finds its mate, and presumably the alleles come together in corresponding positions, as illustrated in Fig. 2.13.

A particular maternal chromosome, for example, is equally likely to face one or the other pole of the spindle. Its paternal partner has the same 50-50 chance of being on one side or the other. The eight different meiotic metaphase arrangements that are possible and equally probable in the example (Fig. 2.13) are illustrated in Fig. 2.14. Once the bivalents take their places on the metaphase plate, their positions are fixed. In the anaphase, each chromosome moves to the nearest pole.

All chromosome pairs within a given species may be expected to assort them-

**Fig. 2.12** Diagram of a cell showing three chromosome pairs before synapsis has occurred.

**Fig. 2.13** Diagram of cell illustrating paired chromosomes after synapsis has occurred.

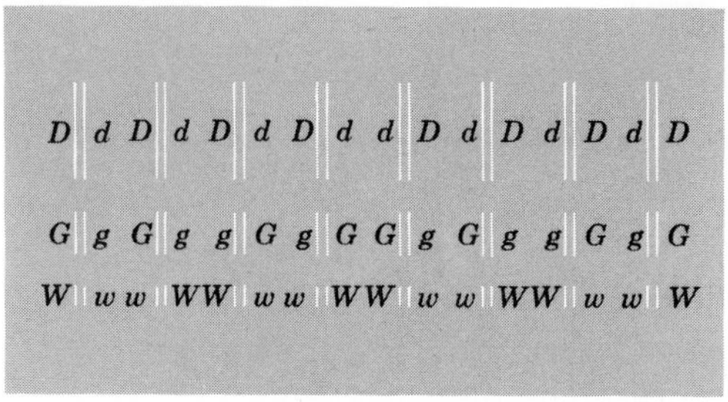

*D d D d D d D d d D d D d D d D*

*G g G g g G g G G g G g g G g G*

*W ww WW ww WW w w WW w w W*

**Fig. 2.14** Diagram illustrating the 8 possible arrangements of 3 independent chromosomes in metaphase I. The 8 different kinds of gametes are illustrated twice in the diagram to show the right and left positions which each member of each pair might take in the equatorial plate.

selves at random with respect to other pairs. It follows that genes located on different pairs of chromosomes distribute themselves independently. Had Mendel chosen two pairs of alleles that were in the same chromosome pair, the two pairs would probably not have behaved independently. He would have been unable to arrive at a general explanation to account for all his reported experimental results.

In animals and plants with a large number of chromosomes, an almost infinite number of possible combinations of chromosomes may be expected. For example, in organisms with 23 pairs of chromosomes, the probability that a gamete produced by an individual in the population will have any specific combination of chromosomes is $(½)^{23}$, which is in the order of one in eight million. This calculation excludes the possibility of any crossing over, which is another source of variability discussed in some detail in Chapter 6. Further increased numbers of gene combinations are possible in zygotes resulting from random fertilization. Much of the variation observed in natural populations can therefore be explained on the basis of the recombination of chromosomes and genes already present in the breeding population.

## SUMMARY

Genes are organized into complexes in chromosomes and are contained within the nuclei of living cells. They replicate in cell division and thus become a part of each new cell. Specialized sex cells can, after fertilization, initiate reproduction of an entire organism. These cells replicate and distribute their complement of genetic material to the cells of the organism through cell division. Genes determine the development, behavior, and characteristics of the individual in which they are carried. The mechanics of chromosome activities associated with meiosis provide the physical basis for Mendel's principles of segregation and independent assortment.

## REFERENCES


Belling, J. 1933. "Crossing over and gene rearrangement in flowering plants." *Genetics,* **18,** 388–413. (Critical chromosome study with demonstration and references on smear technique.)

Brachet, J., and A. E. Mirsky. (eds.) 1961. *The cell, biochemistry, physiology, morphology.* Academic Press, New York. (Vol. III deals with chromosomes, mitosis, and meiosis.)

Darlington, C. D. 1958. *The evolution of genetic systems,* 2nd ed. Basic Books, New York.

Darlington, C. D. 1965. *Cytology.* J. and A. Churchill, London. (Comprehensive treatment of cells and chromosome mechanics.)

Darlington, C. D., and L. F. LaCour. 1960. *The handling of chromosomes.* George Allen and Unwin, London.

Gross, P. R. (ed.) 1960. "Second conference on the mechanism of cell division." *Ann. New York Acad. Sci.,* **90,** 345–613.

McLeish, J., and B. Snoad. 1958. *Looking at chromosomes.* St. Martin's Press, New York. (Photomicrographs of stages in mitosis and meiosis.)

Sharma, A., and A. Sharma. 1965. *Chromosome techniques, theory and practice.* Butterworth and Co., Washington, D. C.

Swanson, C. P. 1957. *Cytology and cytogenetics.* Prentice-Hall, Englewood Cliffs, N. J.

Wallace, B. 1966. *Chromosomes, giant molecules, and evolution.* W. W. Norton and Co., New York.

## *Problems*

2.1 Mark the true statements with a + and the false with an o. (a) Skin cells and gametes of the same animal contain the same number of chromosomes. (b) Any chromosome may pair with any other chromosome in the same cell in meiosis. (c) The gametes of an animal may contain more maternal chromosomes than its body cells contain. (d) Of ten chromosomes in a mature sperm cell, five are always maternal. (e) Of 22 chromosomes in a primary oöcyte, 15 may be paternal. (f) Homologous parts of two chromosomes lie opposite one another in pairing. (g) A sperm has half as many chromosomes as a spermatogonium of the same animal.

2.2 In each somatic cell of a particular animal species there are 46 chromosomes. How many should there be in a (a) mature egg? (b) first polar body? (c) sperm? (d) spermatid? (e) primary spermatocyte? (f) brain cell (g) secondary oöcyte? (h) spermatogonium?

2.3 If spermatogenesis is normal and all cells survive, how many sperm will result from (a) 50 primary spermatocytes? (b) 50 spermatids?

2.4 In man, a type of myopia (an eye abnormality) is dependent on a dominant gene (*M*). Represent diagrammatically (on the chromosomes) a cross between a woman with myopia but heterozygous (*Mm*) and a normal man (*mm*). Show the kinds of gametes which each parent could produce and summarize the expected results from the cross.

2.5 Beginning with the myopic woman in Problem 2.4, diagram the oögenesis process producing the egg involved in the production of a child with myopia. Label all stages.

2.6 In what ways is cell division similar and different in animals and plants?

2.7 How does meiosis differ from mitosis? Consider differences in mechanism as well as end results.

2.8 How does gamete formation in higher animals differ from that in higher plants with reference to (a) gross mechanism, and (b) chromosome mechanism?

2.9 How is double fertilization accomplished in plants, and what is the fate of the egg and the endosperm nucleus?

2.10 In man, an abnormality of the large intestine called intestinal polyposis is dependent on a dominant gene *A*, and a nervous disorder called Huntington's chorea is determined by a dominant gene *H*. A man carrying the gene *A* (*Aahh*) married a woman carrying the gene *H* (*aaHh*). Assume that *A* and *H* are on nonhomologous chromosomes. Diagram the cross and indicate the proportions of the children that might be expected to have each abnormality, neither, or both.

2.11 Beginning with the oögonium in the woman described in Problem 2.10, diagram the steps in the process of oögenesis necessary for the formation of the egg which produced an *H* child. Label all stages.

2.12 Diagram completely the process of spermatogenesis involved in the production of the sperm in Problem 2.10 necessary for the production of an *A* child. Label all stages.

2.13 A man is heterozygous at two loci on different chromosomes (*AaBb*). What gene combinations are possible in his spermatozoa and in what proportions?

2.14 By observing the similarities and differences among members of the same families, what conclusions might be drawn as to the amount of heterozygosity in mankind? How much opportunity is apparently afforded for random combinations of genes?

2.15 How was it established that genes are in chromosomes?

2.16 Would greater variability be expected among asexually reproducing organisms, self-fertilizing organisms, or bisexual organisms? Explain.

2.17 If biopsies were taken from follicle tissues of the human ovary at the following developmental stages, what stages in the process of oögenesis might be observed: (a) fifth month of intrauterine development, (b) at birth, (c) 10 years of age, (d) 17 years of age?

# The Probability Factor in Genetics

# 3

Monohybrid crosses represent the basic unit for Mendelian genetics. The $AA \times AA$ and $aa \times aa$ monohybrid crosses show no genetic evidence of segregation. Segregation can be demonstrated, however, from four other monohybrid combinations: (1) $AA \times aa$, (in $F_2$); (2) $Aa \times Aa$; (3) $Aa \times AA$; and (4) $Aa \times aa$. Crosses (1) and (2) were described as parents for the $F_1$ and $F_2$ generations, respectively, in the crosses between tall and dwarf peas, whereas (3) and (4) are backcrosses between $F_1$ and dominant and recessive parent types, respectively (Chapter 1). Additional pertinent information about these four monohybrid combinations is summarized in Table 3.1. Genetic segregation is very nearly a universal process which occurs in all major groups of sexually reproducing organisms.

## DOMINANT GENES

If gene $A$ is completely dominant, $AA$ and $Aa$ individuals are alike phenotypically; but if $AA$ produces a more extreme or different expression than $Aa$, the inheritance is intermediate. In practice, phenotypes specified by single gene substitutions are called dominants, and those requiring homozygous combinations for expression are called recessives. Dominants are easier to detect than recessives; they are expressed when paired with either kind of allele. Criteria for identifying autosomal dominant genes from human pedigree studies are summarized as follows. (1) The trait is transmitted by an affected parent to about half of his or her children. If the families are large enough to include three or four children the trait usually occurs in every generation. (2) Persons who do not express the trait do not transmit it to their children. (3) Males and females are equally likely to express and to transmit the trait.

An example of dominant inheritance is illustrated by a study of the occurrence of brown teeth in a family group (Fig. 3.1). Most of the older family members who expressed the trait had lost their teeth at an early age because of extreme softness and tendency to decay. One compensating factor was that the people with brown teeth never had toothaches. A middle-aged woman whose teeth were worn completely to the gums reported that she had never felt pain from her teeth. The reason became evident when X-ray photographs of her teeth were examined. The central pulp cavity of each tooth was filled with dentine and no nerves entered the teeth, as illustrated (Fig. 3.2*A* to *D*) by X-ray films of her daughter who had a similar condition.

Dentists who worked with the family verified the observations of family members concerning the soft nature of the teeth and described their problems of filling

**TABLE 3.1 Monohybrid combinations, gametes, genotypic frequency of progeny, and phenotypic ratios for dominance and intermediate inheritance.**

| Combinations | Gametes | | Progeny | | |
|---|---|---|---|---|---|
| | First Parent | Second Parent | Genotypic Frequency | Phenotypic Ratio when Dominance Is: Complete | Phenotypic Ratio when Dominance Is: Intermediate |
| $AA \times aa$ | $A$ | $a$ | all $Aa$ | all dom. | all int. |
| $Aa \times Aa$ | $A$ $a$ | $A$ $a$ | $\frac{1}{4}AA$, $\frac{1}{2}Aa$, $\frac{1}{4}aa$ | 3:1 | 1:2:1 |
| $Aa \times AA$ | $A$ $a$ | $A$ | $\frac{1}{2}AA$, $\frac{1}{2}Aa$ | all dom. | 1:1 |
| $Aa \times aa$ | $A$ $a$ | $a$ | $\frac{1}{2}Aa$, $\frac{1}{2}aa$ | 1:1 | 1:1 |

and maintaining the teeth as extremely difficult and discouraging. Histological studies showed that the brown color was due to abnormal enamel formation. Dentine, which usually is completely covered, could be seen through the deficient enamel and this gave the teeth their brown appearance.

Among the descendants of II-1, sixteen people have brown teeth. In the families in which the trait occurs, seventeen individuals have white teeth. Thus, about half of the children who have one parent with brown teeth express the trait. This is expected from matings between heterozygous people with brown teeth and those who are homozygous for the recessive allele for white teeth. Among the descendants of those who have white teeth, no brown teeth have occurred. The trait is expressed in both males and females. Thus, the three criteria for identifying dominant genes were illustrated in this study. From the pattern of dominant inheritance and the probability factors involved, it might be predicted that in future generations those

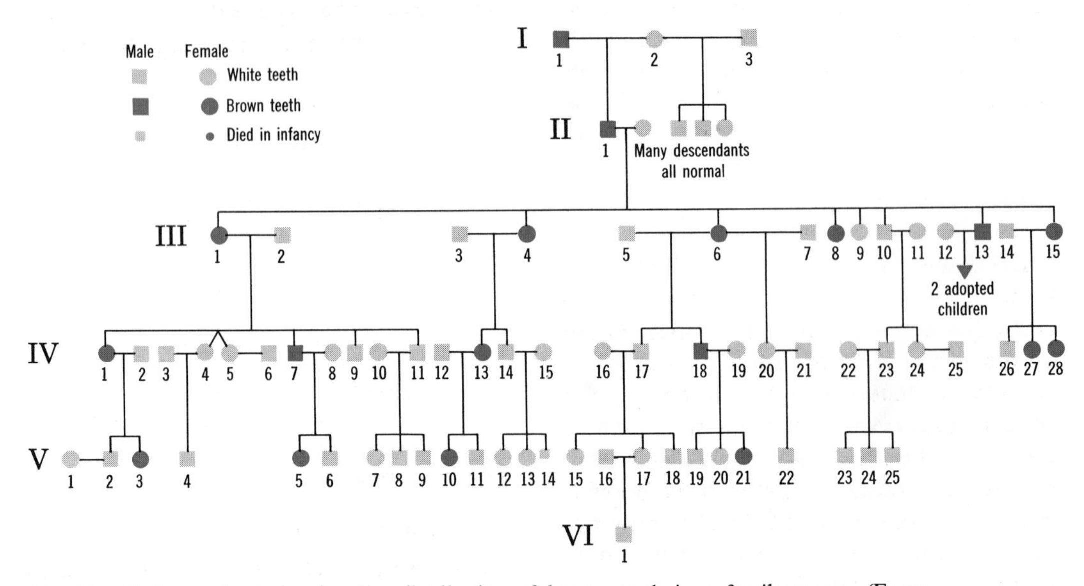


**Fig. 3.1** Pedigree chart showing the distribution of brown teeth in a family group. (From Gardner, *Journal of Heredity*, **42**:289–290, 1951.)

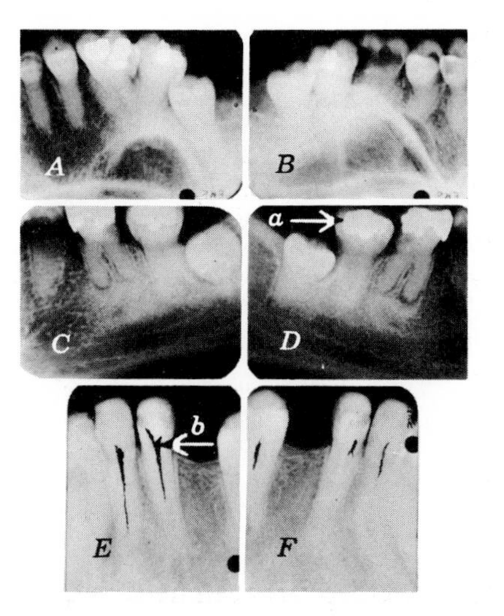


**Fig. 3.2** Roentgenograms of soft, brown teeth lacking enamel, compared with white teeth in which the enamel developed normally. Plates *A* to *D* show all teeth remaining in mouth of a woman 21 years of age. Pulp cavities were closed and fillings were large and numerous. A filling is identified by arrow *a*. Plates *E* and *F* show normal teeth of a brother of the woman. Normal pulp cavity is identified by arrow *b*. (From Gardner, *Journal of Heredity*, **42**:289–290, 1951.)

who have brown teeth (presumably heterozygous) and marry individuals with white teeth might expect about half of their children to have brown teeth. Those individuals who do not express the trait will not transmit it.

## RECESSIVE GENES

Recessive genes represent a different pattern because they are expressed only in homozygous (*aa*) individuals. A population of cross-breeding organisms usually includes more heterozygous (*Aa*) carriers than homozygous (*aa*) individuals who express the trait. All three genotypes (*AA*, *Aa*, and *aa*) are usually available in the population. Although the carriers (*Aa*) may not be detectable phenotypically, they can be identified in experimental material by means of test crosses.

In human family groups, the carriers have a distinctive pattern that can be detected from pedigree studies on the basis of the following criteria: (1) first appearance of the trait in a family group usually is only in sibs but not in parents, offspring, or other relatives; (2) on the average, one-fourth of the sibs are affected; and (3) males and females are equally likely to express the trait unless the recessive gene is sex linked (see Chapter 4). For example, the gene associated with albinism is a relatively rare recessive autosomal gene. Albino people are characterized by a marked deficiency or complete absence of pigment in the skin, hair, and iris of the eye. Homozygous (*cc*) individuals are albino, whereas *CC* and *Cc* are within normal limits of pigmentation. In one Caucasian family of six, two albinos have occurred. Parents are within the normal range of pigment for Caucasian people. Presumably, both parents are carriers (*Cc*) and a chance combination of recessive genes (*cc*) occurred in the two albino sons. The cross is represented diagrammatically in Fig. 3.3. On the average, three normal children to one albino would be expected.

The criteria for detecting autosomal

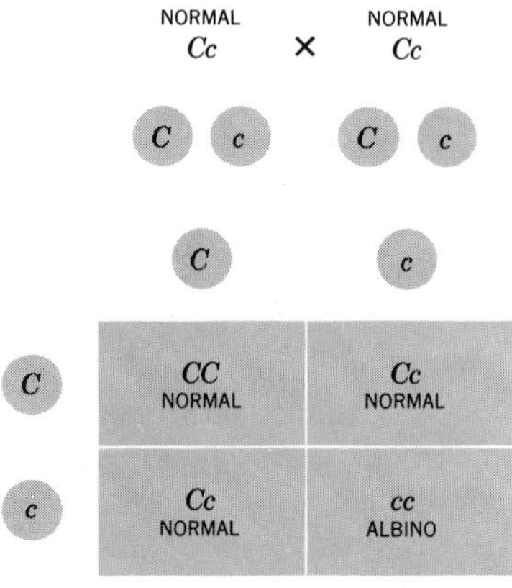


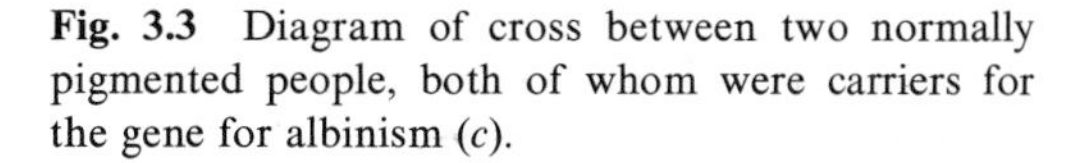


**Fig. 3.3** Diagram of cross between two normally pigmented people, both of whom were carriers for the gene for albinism (*c*).

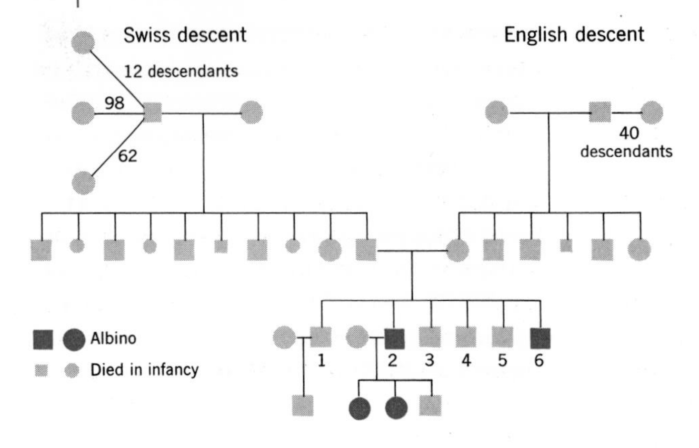


**Fig. 3.4** Pedigree chart of a family group in which albinism has occurred.

recessives are met in this example except for criterion (1), the appearance of the trait in the offspring of an affected person. Son No. 2 on the pedigree chart (Fig. 3.4), an albino, married a normally pigmented woman. The couple has two albino daughters and one normal son. Presumably, the wife is a carrier (*Cc*) of the recessive gene. This occurrence would be rare if the parents are not related and it represents an exception to the first criterion. This cross is the back-cross type and is reconstructed in Fig. 3.5. About half of the children are expected to express the albino trait whereas the other half are expected to be normal phenotypically but carriers (*Cc*) of the gene for albinism.

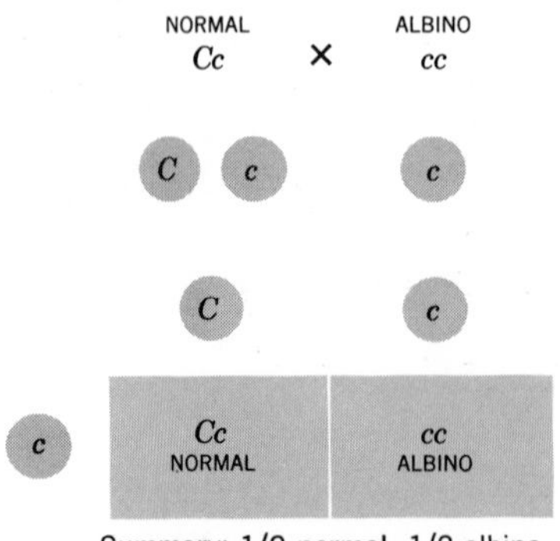


**Fig. 3.5** Diagram of cross between a normally pigmented woman who was a carrier for the gene (*c*) for albinism and an albino man.

## SEGREGATION AND PROBABILITY

Mendel had studied probability in his mathematics courses, and he recognized the 3:1 ratio as a particular mathematical relation which suggested to him a model for the mechanism of segregation. If two members of a pair of determiners with one dominant over the other could separate freely many times in succession, or if several pairs were behaving in this way at one time, the expected summation would be about 3 of the dominant expressions to 1 recessive. The analysis, therefore, was based on a mathematical relation with which Mendel was familiar, but its application and the concept of segregation were Mendel's own contribution.

The laws of probability apply to the genetic mechanism as well as to other processes in which uncertainty exists. The results of Mendelian segregation happen to fit certain laws of probability. In the $F_2$ results of the cross between tall and dwarf garden peas, one-fourth were dwarf, one-fourth homozygous tall, and one-half heterozygous tall. A similar result might be obtained from a simple experiment in tossing coins. A coin that is tossed freely is equally likely to fall heads or tails. If one coin is tossed 100 times, it might be expected to fall heads about 50 times and tails about 50 times. When two coins are tossed together, each behaves independently and falls either heads or tails. From 100 trials, about 25 heads-heads, 50 heads-tails, and 25 tails-tails (1:2:1) might be expected. This result, which parallels Mendelian segregation, is merely the chance occurrence of independent events. The experimenter would not always obtain exactly 25 heads-heads, 50 heads-tails, and 25 tails-tails. It would be surprising if precisely those results were obtained very often. The ratio represents only an average of expected results when independent events occur.

How frequently should the various combinations be expected to occur in succession? The law of probability applied for the solution of this problem is stated as follows: *if two or more events are independent, the chance that they will occur together is the product of their separate probabilities.* When a single coin is tossed, the chance of heads occurring twice in succession would be: $\frac{1}{2} \times \frac{1}{2} = \frac{1}{4}$. The chance of three such occurrences would be $(\frac{1}{2})^3$ or $\frac{1}{8}$, and of four, $(\frac{1}{2})^4$ or $\frac{1}{16}$. When two coins are tossed together the tails-tails combination is expected in one-fourth of the trials ($\frac{1}{2} \times \frac{1}{2} = \frac{1}{4}$). The chance of occurrence of two such tails-tails combinations for two coins in succession would be $(\frac{1}{4})^2$ or $\frac{1}{16}$.

The next question is very important to the geneticist. It concerns the goodness of fit of the numerical result obtained from an actual cross or other experiment as compared with a parameter or hypothetical ratio based on a particular mechanism and a perfect segregation. How much can the experimental result differ from the hypothetical or calculated figure and still be regarded as reasonably close to expectation? In evaluating the results of crosses and determining which modes of inheritance are involved, how much deviation is permissible without casting some doubt as to whether the data agree with a given hypothesis? Too much deviation would surely make the investigator question his hypothesis or discard it entirely. Where shall he draw the line? Unfortunately, there is no precise answer to this question. The best the geneticist can do is to determine the likelihood of the deviation occurring by chance, and use his judgment to decide whether a given result supports a given hypothesis. This is his only means of evaluating goodness of fit of an experimental result as compared with a particular expectation.

## CHI-SQUARE

The chi-square ($X^2$) test, is a valuable tool to aid the investigator in determining goodness of fit. The test takes into account the size of the sample and the deviations from the expected ratio. It can be used for samples of different sizes, and is adapted to ratios with different numbers of classes. Essentially, the chi-square test is a mechanism for reducing deviations from a hypothetical ratio to a single value based on the size of the sample. This allows the investigator to determine the probability that a given sum of deviations will occur by chance. Expected values are obtained from the total size of the sample. If the hypothesis is 1:1, the total is divided into two equal parts. For any other ratio the total is divided into appropriate proportions.

A formula for $X^2$, designed for a sample consisting of two classes (that is, 1:1 or 3:1 ratios) is symbolized as follows:

$$X^2 = \frac{(O_1 - e_1)^2}{e_1} + \frac{(O_2 - e_2)^2}{e_2}$$

where $O_1$ is the observed number for the first class and $e_1$ is the expected number for the same class; $O_2$ is the observed for the second class and $e_2$ the expected. This formula can be simplified by representing as a single figure the difference between each observed and expected value. For example $(O_1 - e_1)$ or $(O_2 - e_2)$, may be represented by a single deviation ($d$). When each of these deviations is squared ($d^2$) and divided by the expected value ($e$) for that class, the resulting fractions can be added ($\Sigma$) to give a single $X^2$ value. The simplified formula can be symbolized as follows:

$$X^2 = \sum \frac{d^2}{e}$$

where $d$ is the deviation between each observed and expected class value, $e$ the expected value in the respective class, and the Greek letter $\Sigma$ is the summation sign. As an example, calculate $X^2$ for the two arbitrary samples, 15:35 and 240:260, (each having the same actual deviation) on the basis of a 1:1 hypothesis. This example will illustrate how the $X^2$ relates the size of the deviation to the size of the sample. For the 15:35 result with a total of 50, the expected ($e$) value for each class is 25. The deviations ($d$) on either side of $e$ are 10; that is, $25 - 15 = 10$ and $25 - 35 = -10$. For the larger sample, 240:260, the expected ($e$) for each class is 250. The deviations ($d$) are $250 - 240 = 10$, and $250 - 260 = -10$.

$$(1)\ X^2 = \sum \frac{d^2}{e} = \frac{(10)^2}{25} + \frac{(-10)^2}{25} = \frac{200}{25} = 8$$

$$(2)\ X^2 = \sum \frac{d^2}{e} = \frac{(10)^2}{250} + \frac{(-10)^2}{250} = \frac{200}{250} = 0.8$$

The $X^2$ value of 8 for the smaller sample is considerably greater than that of 0.8 for the larger sample, even though the actual deviations in the two examples are the same.

When more than two groups are classified from the sample (for example, 1:2:1 or 9:3:3:1 ratios), each class is included in the summation, which is $X^2$. It should be emphasized that the $X^2$ formula is based on actual numerical frequencies and not on percentages. When data are reduced to percentages, the total automatically becomes 100, thus eliminating the important factor of sample size in the evaluation.

The next step is to interpret the $X^2$ value in terms of probability. Here another factor, the number of classes on which the $X^2$ is based, must be considered. The value for a two-class distribution included only two squared deviations, whereas that for a distribution with more classes has more squared deviations. It is therefore necessary to consider the number of classes contributing to a given $X^2$ in evaluating the goodness of fit. The effect of the number of independent classes is included in the mathematical concept as degrees of freedom. For example, a person may have two gloves for his two hands, but in placing the gloves he has only one degree of freedom. If he places a glove on one hand, the other glove must go on the other hand. When the total number of objects or classes is fixed, and all except one have been placed, the one remaining is not free but must fill a particular niche. In general, therefore, the number of degrees of freedom is one less than the number of classes. Ratios of 1:1 or 3:1 for example, have one degree of freedom; 1:2:1 and other 3-class ratios have 2; 9:3:3:1, 3 degrees of freedom, and so on.

When $X^2$ and the degrees of freedom have been determined, Table 3.2 may be consulted for the probability ($P$) value. Locate the figure representing the degrees of freedom at the left, read across horizontally, and find the figures nearest the $X^2$ value in the body of the table: then read the $P$ values directly above on the top line. The $X^2$ of 8, calculated for the first example, is not on the table. The highest

**TABLE 3.2 Table of chi-square**

| Degrees of Freedom | P = 0.99 | 0.95 | 0.80 | 0.50 | 0.20 | 0.05 | 0.01 |
|---|---|---|---|---|---|---|---|
| 1 | 0.000157 | 0.00393 | 0.0642 | 0.455 | 1.642 | 3.841 | 6.635 |
| 2 | 0.020 | 0.103 | 0.446 | 1.386 | 3.219 | 5.991 | 9.210 |
| 3 | 0.115 | 0.352 | 1.005 | 2.366 | 4.642 | 7.815 | 11.345 |
| 4 | 0.297 | 0.711 | 1.649 | 3.357 | 5.989 | 9.488 | 13.277 |
| 5 | 0.554 | 1.145 | 2.343 | 4.351 | 7.289 | 11.070 | 15.086 |
| 6 | 0.872 | 1.635 | 3.070 | 5.348 | 8.558 | 12.592 | 16.812 |
| 7 | 1.239 | 2.167 | 3.822 | 6.346 | 9.803 | 14.067 | 18.475 |
| 8 | 1.646 | 2.733 | 4.594 | 7.344 | 11.030 | 15.507 | 20.090 |
| 9 | 2.088 | 3.325 | 5.380 | 8.343 | 12.242 | 16.919 | 21.666 |
| 10 | 2.558 | 3.940 | 6.179 | 9.342 | 13.442 | 18.307 | 23.209 |
| 15 | 5.229 | 7.261 | 10.307 | 14.339 | 19.311 | 24.996 | 30.578 |
| 20 | 8.260 | 10.851 | 14.578 | 19.337 | 25.038 | 31.410 | 37.566 |
| 25 | 11.524 | 14.611 | 18.940 | 24.337 | 30.675 | 37.652 | 44.314 |
| 30 | 14.953 | 18.493 | 23.364 | 29.336 | 36.250 | 43.773 | 50.892 |

Taken from Table 3 of Fisher: *Statistical Methods for Research Workers,* published by Oliver and Boyd, Ltd., Edinburgh, and by permission of author and publishers.

value on the line for one degree of freedom is 6.635, which has a $P$ of 0.01. This indicates that the probability for obtaining, by chance, deviations as great as or greater than those of $X^2 = 8$ would be considerably less. Therefore, the fit of these results to a 1:1 ratio is not good.

In the second example, $X^2 = 0.8$ falls between 0.455 and 1.642, or between the $P$ values of 0.50 and 0.20. The probability of obtaining a deviation as great as or greater than $X^2 = 0.8$ is between 0.20 and 0.50. This probability value indicates that, if numerous independent repetitions of an ideal experiment involving two independent events were conducted, chance deviations as large as or larger than those observed here ($\pm 10$ corresponding to $X^2 = 0.8$) would be expected to occur in 20 to 50 percent of the trials. Such a deviation could be explained readily by chance. The fit of these results based on a sample of 500 is good.

A hypothesis is never proved or disproved by a $P$ value. The results of an experiment are evaluated by the investigator as acceptable or unacceptable with respect to the hypothesis. The 5 percent point (0.05) on the table is usually chosen as an arbitrary standard for determining the significance or goodness of fit. Probability at this point is one in twenty that a true hypothesis will be rejected. Sometimes the 1 percent point (0.01) is used as a level of significance. At this level there is a smaller probability (0.01) that a true hypothesis will be rejected, but a greater chance that a false hypothesis will be accepted.

It should be emphasized that these are arbitrary points, and judgment is required in making interpretations. In any event, the $P$ value represents the probability of obtaining a deviation as great as or greater than that obtained from the experiment by chance alone. If the $P$ is small, it is concluded that the deviations are not due entirely to chance, and the hypothesis is rejected. If the $P$ is greater than the predetermined level (for example, 0.05), the data conform well enough to the hypothesis and the hypothesis is accepted.

## PEDIGREE ANALYSIS

Practical applications of the Mendelian principles and the laws of probability are made by human geneticists and, in some instances, by animal breeders in analyzing pedigrees. Traits with a simple pattern of inheritance may sometimes be traced accurately enough to justify predictions concerning the likelihood of their expression in future children following marriage of related individuals or in those with a family history for such traits. The first step in such an analysis is to determine whether the gene in question is behaving as a dominant or a recessive. Although most human traits are too complex for this procedure, a few have been associated with the differential action of certain specific genes and have been identified as dominants or recessives in family groups. A confusing feature of this type of analysis is that some phenotypes (for instance, deafness) may behave as dominant in some families and recessive in others. Obviously, there are several gene substitutions that result in deafness.

Recessive genes are difficult to keep track of because they may remain hidden by their dominant alleles generation after generation. It is not known which individuals in the population are carriers until an expression occurs. Traits dependent on recessive genes sometimes appear unexpectedly in families having no previous history of such a trait. Recessives are expressed more frequently in families in which the father and mother are closely related than they are in the general population. The likelihood of similar genes being present is enhanced when the parents have descended from a common ancestor.

In the absence of data to indicate which individuals are carriers, the geneticist may resort to probability as the best available tool for determining the likelihood of expression of a given recessive gene in a certain family. If no expression has occurred in the history of the family, an estimate indicating the frequency of the gene in the general population may be used as a basis of probability. If the trait has appeared in the family, more precise calculations are sometimes possible. Probability is then based on the family history, which may be recorded in a pedigree chart.

The use of probability in human pedigree analysis is illustrated in Fig. 3.6. The trait, adherent ear lobes (Fig. 3.7), dependent on a recessive gene, appeared only once in the known history of the family, as indicated by the single darkened circle. No information other than that shown on the chart is available. Unless there is evidence to the contrary, it may be assumed (to avoid dealing with small probabilities) that those individuals who have married into the family are homozygous for the dominant genes and do not carry the gene in question.

The first step is to identify the genotypes of as many individual family members as possible from the information given. The

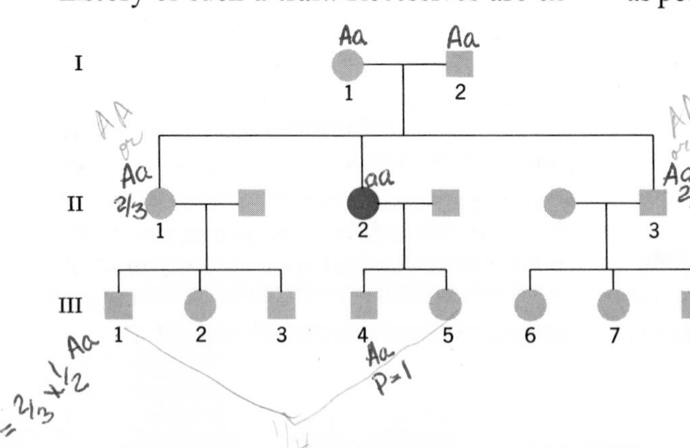


**Fig. 3.6** Pedigree of family group in which a trait (adherent ear lobes), dependent on a recessive gene, has appeared in one individual (identified by the darkened circle).

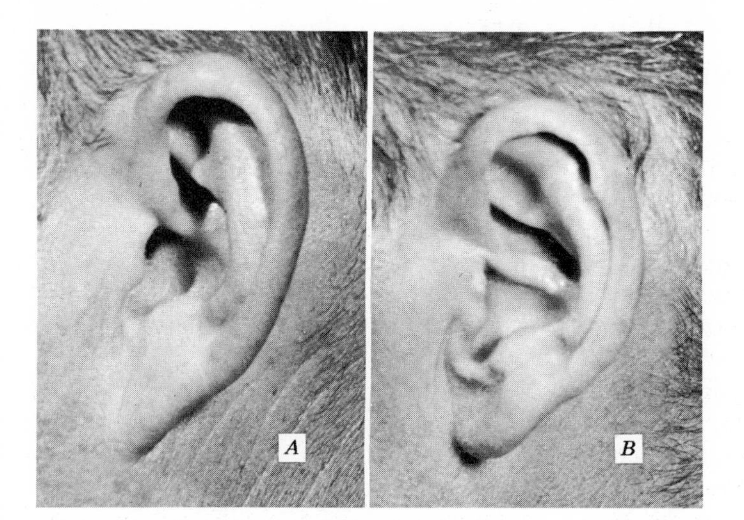


**Fig. 3.7** Adherent ear lobes compared with free ear lobes. *A*, adherent; *B*, free.

woman (II-2) in whom the trait is expressed must be homozygous (*aa*) for the recessive gene. Each of her parents (I-1 and 2) who did not express the trait but contributed an *a* gene to their daughter (II-2) must carry the heterozygous genotype (*Aa*). The sister (II-1) and brother (II-3) must be *AA* or *Aa*. Obviously, they are not *aa* because they do not express the trait. There is no way to determine whether each of these individuals is *AA* or *Aa*. Therefore, the probability that each individual is a carrier (*Aa*) represents the best information available. From the parent cross (*Aa* × *Aa*), the probability of the occurrence of *Aa* in any child with free earlobes is two-thirds and the probability for the occurrence of *AA* is one-third. In the absence of more definite information, II-1 and II-3 may be considered *Aa* with two-third probability. The children of II-1 and II-3 have a one-half chance of being carriers for the gene (*a*) if their parent is a carrier. Therefore, the probability that III-1, III-2, III-3, III-6, III-7, or III-8 is a carrier is $\frac{2}{3} \times \frac{1}{2} = \frac{1}{3}$. The children of II-2 (III-4 and III-5) must be carriers (probability = 1).

*The problem may be carried a step further by calculating the likelihood for an expression (*aa*) of the trait in the first child resulting from a marriage between two of the cousins represented in generation III. The mating III-1 × III-5 will serve for the example. The probability that III-1 is a carrier (*Aa*) is $\frac{2}{3} \times \frac{1}{2}$, and the comparable probability for III-5 is 1. Both could be carriers and yet avoid an expression of the trait in their family. Therefore, another probability must be included, that of parents with genotypes *Aa* having an *aa* child, which is one-fourth. Probability for an expression of the trait in the child of the individuals indicated is:

$$\frac{2}{3} \times \frac{1}{2} \times 1 \times \frac{1}{4} = \frac{1}{12}$$

The chance of each future child expressing the trait is one in twelve.

If the first child should express the trait, the probability that the second child would also express the trait would be one-fourth because evidence would then be available to indicate that the genotypes of III-1 and III-5 were both *Aa*. Two elements of uncertainty or probability would thus be eliminated. At best, probability is a poor substitute for certainty. It is employed in analyses only when definite information is not available.

## INDEPENDENT ASSORTMENT AND PROBABILITY

Probability must be considered in explaining the Mendelian principle of independent assortment as well as that of segregation. It was through Mendel's understanding of the mathematical laws of combinations that he was able to recognize and interpret the dihybrid ratio of 9:3:3:1 as a multiple of the 3:1 monohybrid ratio. If, for example, the 3:1 ratio is changed to an algebraic expression, $3 + 1$, the product of the expected results of two monohybrid crosses is: $(3+1)\times(3+1)=9+3+3+1$. Because the terms represent separate classes, they are not combined, but the product can be converted back to a ratio: 9:3:3:1. This is an example of the expansion of a binomial $(a + b)^n$, in this case $(A + a)^2$, where $A = 3$ and $a = 1$.

Using the $F_2$ results of the cross between peas with round, yellow seeds and those with wrinkled, green seeds (described in Chapter 1) Mendel tested the mathematical relation between the monohybrid and dihybrid cross. He observed that about three-fourths ($^{423}/_{556}$) of the $F_2$ seeds were round and one-fourth ($^{133}/_{556}$) were wrinkled. Likewise, seeds from about three-fourths ($^{416}/_{556}$) were yellow, and those from one-fourth ($^{140}/_{556}$) were green. This observed proportion provided a cross-check for the hypothesis of independence. When the two characters were considered together, the results conformed to the mathematical model expected for two independent events occurring together.

On the basis of the law of probability, Mendel predicted that nine-sixteenths ($\frac{3}{4} \times \frac{3}{4}$) of the $F_2$ would be round, yellow; three-sixteenths ($\frac{3}{4} \times \frac{1}{4}$) round, green; three-sixteenths wrinkled, yellow; and one-sixteenth ($\frac{1}{4} \times \frac{1}{4}$) wrinkled, green. The results that Mendel actually obtained (315:108:101:32) resembled very closely the calculated ratio of 9:3:3:1, based on the hypothesis of complete independence of the genes influencing the shape and color of the seeds. When the $X^2$ test for goodness of fit between the actual and the expected result is applied to these figures, the probability ($P$) of deviations as great as or greater than those obtained by Mendel is between 0.80 and 0.95.

$$X^2 = \sum \frac{d^2}{e} = \frac{(2.25)^2}{312.75} + \frac{(3.75)^2}{104.25} + \frac{(-3.25)^2}{104.25} + \frac{(-2.75)^2}{43.75}$$

$$= 0.016 + 0.135 + 0.101 + 0.218$$

$$= 0.470$$

$$P = 0.80 - 0.95.$$

The actual results fit very closely those expected on the hypothesis of independent combinations. In fact, it is so close that the probability is less than 0.20 that further data would fit the hypothesis this well. Investigators are as concerned about results that are very close to a calculated expectation as about those with large deviations. A very close fit may be obtained occasionally by chance. When the observed data fit "too well" the investigator may have intentionally or unintentionally biased his results. Mendel presented other results that had poor agreement with expectation. In one experiment from which he expected a 3:1 ratio, he obtained 43 round and only 2 wrinkled. From another experiment with the same expectation he obtained 32 yellow and 1 green. He explained these results on the basis of fluctuations due to chance, and in the second case there was also some difficulty in distinguishing between yellow and green seeds.

From his results, Mendel was able to predict the numbers of genotypes to be expected when more than two pairs of alleles were involved in the cross. The expected $F_2$ result from a trihybrid cross involving independent assortment and dominance of one

**TABLE 3.3 Relations among pairs of independent alleles, gametes, $F_2$ genotypes, and $F_2$ phenotypes when dominance is present**[a]

| Number of Heterozygous Pairs | Number of Kinds of Gametes | Number of $F_2$ Genotypes | Number of $F_2$ Phenotypes |
|---|---|---|---|
| 1 | 2 | 3 | 2 |
| 2 | 4 | 9 | 4 |
| 3 | 8 | 27 | 8 |
| 4 | 16 | 81 | 16 |
| 10 | 1024 | 59049 | 1024 |
| $n$ | $2^n$ | $3^n$ | $2^n$ |

[a] Interaction between different alleles will be considered in Chapter 13.

allele in each gene pair is $(A+a)^3$, which expands to 27:9:9:9:3:3:3:1. A cross with four gene pairs under the same conditions would result in $(A + a)^4$, five gene pairs $(A + a)^5$, and so on. Numbers of gametes, genotypes, and phenotypes expected from different numbers of heterozygous pairs of genes are summarized in Table 3.3. It will be observed that the number of kinds of gametes is a multiple of the base 2, that is, $2^n$; the number of $F_2$ genotypes is a multiple of the base 3, that is $3^n$; and the number of phenotypes is $2^n$ when dominance is present. This pattern formed the basis for predictions of results when any number of independent pairs of alleles was present.

This introduction to combinations suggests a third method for working out the expected results from crosses involving independent pairs of alleles. The checkerboard method is cumbersome and time consuming. The forked-line method makes use of probability and provides a system for dividing the complex problem into monohybrid crosses and combining the results. The method now suggested is a mathematical means of arriving at the product of the combinations without drawing them out mechanically. As an example, consider the crosses made by Toyama between two varieties of the silk moth *Bombyx mori*. In one variety the caterpillars were striped and the cocoons were yellow, and in the other variety the caterpillars were not striped and the cocoons were white. From previous crosses, striped was known to be dominant over unstriped and yellow over white. What combinations might be expected in the $F_2$?

If the striped and unstriped alleles are considered separately, three-fourths of the $F_2$ progeny are expected to be striped and one-fourth unstriped. Likewise, three-fourths are expected to be yellow and one-fourth white. The combinations and their products are summarized in Table 3.4. Toyama obtained results from actual crosses which satisfied the predictions.

## EXPANSION OF A BINOMIAL

Many applications can be made of binomial expansion. This method is different from the simple multiplication of separate probabilities because it includes all possible combinations of alternative events. Various combinations in groups of a given size representing a particular ratio can be calculated by expanding the binomial $(p + q)^n$, where $p$ and $q$ represent the prob-

**TABLE 3.4 Expectations and results from crosses between striped, yellow, and unstriped, white moths (data from Toyama)**

| Phenotypes | Combinations | $F_2$ Expectations | Observed |
|---|---|---|---|
| Striped, yellow | $\frac{3}{4} \times \frac{3}{4}$ | $\frac{9}{16}$ 6368.4 | 6385 |
| Striped, white | $\frac{3}{4} \times \frac{1}{4}$ | $\frac{3}{16}$ 2122.8 | 2147 |
| Unstriped, yellow | $\frac{1}{4} \times \frac{3}{4}$ | $\frac{3}{16}$ 2122.8 | 2099 |
| Unstriped, white | $\frac{1}{4} \times \frac{1}{4}$ | $\frac{1}{16}$ 707.6 | 691 |

abilities of occurrence of two alternative events ($p$ = boys, $q$ = girls) and $n$ is the size of the groups involved. If, for example, a 1:1 ratio is assumed for boys and girls in human families, the probability of having a boy is ½ and the probability of having a girl is ½. How many boys and how many girls would be expected in randomly selected families of 2, 3, 4, 5, or more? Combinations for families of a given size may be calculated by expanding the binomial $(p + q)^n$. Thus, for two-child families:

$$(p = q)^2 = p^2 + 2pq + q^2$$
$$p = q = \tfrac{1}{2}$$
$$p^2 = \text{families of boys} = \tfrac{1}{4}$$
$$2pq = \text{families of 1 boy and 1 girl} = \tfrac{1}{2}$$
$$q^2 = \text{families of 2 girls} = \tfrac{1}{4}$$

Among families of 2 children, ¼ would be expected to be composed of all boys, ½ of one boy and one girl, and ¼ of all girls. For three-child families:

$$(p + q)^3 = p^3 + 3p^2q + 3pq^2 + q^3$$
$$p^3 = \text{families of 3 boys} = (\tfrac{1}{2})^3 = \tfrac{1}{8}$$
$$3p^2q = \text{families of 2 boys, 1 girl}$$
$$= 3(\tfrac{1}{2})^2(\tfrac{1}{2}) = \tfrac{3}{8}$$
$$3pq^2 = \text{families of 1 boy, 2 girls}$$
$$= 3(\tfrac{1}{2})(\tfrac{1}{2})^2 = \tfrac{3}{8}$$
$$q^3 = \text{families of 3 girls} = (\tfrac{1}{2})^3 = \tfrac{1}{8}$$

The binomial expansion includes all possible combinations of the two events. In three-child families, for example, there are eight possible combinations:

♂ ♂ ♂ ♀ ♂ ♂
♂ ♂ ♀ ♀ ♂ ♀
♂ ♀ ♂ ♀ ♀ ♂
♂ ♀ ♀ ♀ ♀ ♀

If the chance of a particular birth order is included in the problem, the probability of each sequence is ⅛. If, on the other hand, only the total number of boys and girls is considered, the probability of all boys is ⅛, 2 boys and one girl ⅜, one boy and 2 girls ⅜, and all girls ⅛. The expected distributions of males and females in families of one to five children are summarized in Table 3.5.

When the probability of only a certain combination in a given size group is required, factorials may be employed. These are products of factors derived from function by successively increasing or decreasing by a constant, usually 1. For example, factorial 4 (4!) is the product of 4×3×2×1 (or 4!=4×3×2×1=24). The probability for a particular combination may be calculated from the following formula

$$P = \frac{n!}{x!\,(n - x)!}\,p^x q^{(n-x)}$$

where $n!$ is the product of the integers making up the total size of the group; $x!$, the product of the integers for one class, ($p$); and $(n - x)!$ the product of the integers for one class ($q$). The symbol of $p$ represents the probability for one occurrence (for example, boys) and $q$ is the

**TABLE 3.5 Distribution of boys and girls in families**

| Number of Children in Family | $(p + q)^n$ | Distribution |
|---|---|---|
| 1 | $(\frac{1}{2} + \frac{1}{2})^1$ | ½(1 ♂) + ½(1 ♀) |
| 2 | $(\frac{1}{2} + \frac{1}{2})^2$ | ¼(2 ♂) + ½(1 ♂ :1 ♀) + ¼(2 ♀) |
| 3 | $(\frac{1}{2} + \frac{1}{2})^3$ | ⅛(3 ♂) + ⅜(2 ♂ :1 ♀) + ⅜(1 ♂ :2 ♀) + ⅛(3 ♀) |
| 4 | $(\frac{1}{2} + \frac{1}{2})^4$ | 1/16(4 ♂) + 4/16(3 ♂ :1 ♀) + 6/16(2 ♂ :2 ♀) + 4/16(1 ♂ :3 ♀) + 1/16(4 ♀) |
| 5 | $(\frac{1}{2} + \frac{1}{2})^5$ | 1/32(5 ♂) + 5/32(4 ♂ :1 ♀) + 10/32(3 ♂ :2 ♀) + 10/32(2 ♂ :3 ♀) + 5/32(1 ♂ :4 ♀) + 1/32(5 ♀) |

probability for the other (for example, girls). [Factorial 0 (0!) = 1 and any number to the 0 power = 1]. If, for example, six babies are born in a given hospital on the same day, what is the probability that 2 will be boys and 4 will be girls? For this problem assume that $p = \frac{1}{2}$ and $q = \frac{1}{2}$.

Substituting:

$$P = \frac{n!}{x!\,(n-x)!}\,p^x q(n-x)$$

$$= \frac{6!}{2!\,(4)!}\,(\tfrac{1}{2})^2(\tfrac{1}{2})^4$$

$$= \frac{6 \times 5 \times 4 \times 3 \times 2 \times 1}{2 \times 1(4 \times 3 \times 2 \times 1)}$$

$$(\tfrac{1}{2})^2(\tfrac{1}{2})^4 = 15 \times \tfrac{1}{4} \times \tfrac{1}{16}$$

$$= \tfrac{15}{64}$$

The probability of 2 boys and 4 girls in groups of 6 is $\frac{15}{64}$.

For the example of boys and girls in families of different sizes, the probability values $p$ and $q$ were equal ($p = q = \frac{1}{2}$). The binomial distribution can be applied for other values of $p$ and $q$. If, for example, the trait being considered is albinism in a human family, and the parents are known to be heterozygous (*Cc*), the probability for a normally pigmented child ($p$) would be $\frac{3}{4}$, and the probability for an albino child ($q$) would be $\frac{1}{4}$. In families of 4, what is the probability that 2 will be normally pigmented and 2 will be albino?

Substituting:

$$P = \frac{n!}{x!\,(n-x)!}\,p^x q^{(n-x)}$$

$$= \frac{4!}{2!\,(2)!}\,(\tfrac{3}{4})^2(\tfrac{1}{4})^2$$

$$= \frac{4 \times 3 \times 2 \times 1}{2 \times 1(2 \times 1)}\,(\tfrac{3}{4})^2(\tfrac{1}{4})^2$$

$$= \tfrac{54}{256} = \tfrac{27}{128}$$

The probability of 2 normally pigmented and 2 albino children in families of 4 children from heterozygous (*Cc*) parents would be $\frac{27}{128}$. Other values could be substituted into the binomial expansion for families of given size and the probability for various combinations could be calculated.

## SUMMARY

An element of uncertainty or probability is inherent in Mendelian segregation and independent combinations. This is recognized in accounting for behavior of genes in crosses. Expected results from crosses with two alternative genes (alleles) can be calculated by expanding the binomial $(a + b)^n$, where $a$ and $b$ represent the two classes of monohybrid cross and $n$ represents the number of pairs of genes involved or for classes such as boys and girls, family sizes. The chi-square test is a tool for representing the sum of deviations in an experimental result as compared with a standard or hypothetical value.

## REFERENCES

Fisher, R. A. 1946. *Statistical methods for research workers,* 10th ed. Oliver and Boyd, London. (Statistical methods, including chi-square, with formulas and tables.)

Stern, C. 1960. *Principles of human genetics,* 2nd ed. W. H. Freeman and Co., San Francisco.

# *Problems*

3.1 In garden peas, the gene *D* for tall is dominant over its allele *d* for dwarf. Give the genotypes of the parents in the following crosses: (a) tall × dwarf producing all tall; (b) tall × tall producing 3 tall to 1 dwarf; (c) tall × dwarf producing half tall and half dwarf.

3.2 Diagram completely the following crosses and summarize the expected results: (1) *DD* × *dd;* (2) *Dd* × *Dd;* (3) *Dd* × *DD;* (4) *Dd* × *dd.* What is the chance that a particular plant from each cross will be (a) tall? (b) dwarf?

3.3 A spotted rabbit, when mated with a solid-colored rabbit, produced all spotted offspring. When these $F_1$ rabbits were crossed among themselves, they produced 23 spotted rabbits and 8 solid-colored rabbits. (a) Which of these characters is dependent on a dominant gene? (b) About how many of the 23 spotted rabbits in the $F_2$ generation would be homozygous? (c) How many of the solid-colored $F_2$ rabbits would be homozygous? (d) What ratio would be expected if numerous progeny were produced by rabbits of the same genotype as the $F_1$? (e) Why was this ratio not represented exactly by the results of this cross?

3.4 In the Shorthorn breed of cattle, the gene (*R*) for red coat color is not dominant over its allele for white (*R′*); roan is produced by the heterozygous condition (*R′R*). A breeder of Shorthorn cattle has some white, some red, and some roan cows, and a roan bull. (a) What is the probability that a calf from each of the following matings will be roan? (1) white × roan; (2) red × roan; (3) roan × roan? (b) What is the chance that a calf from cross (3) will be white?

3.5 The inheritance pattern in each of the following pedigrees may be assumed to depend on a single autosomal dominant or a single autosomal recessive gene. (a) Indicate which is the most likely mode of inheritance for each pedigree. (b) Based on your answer to (a) symbolize the probable genotype for each individual in each of the four pedigrees.

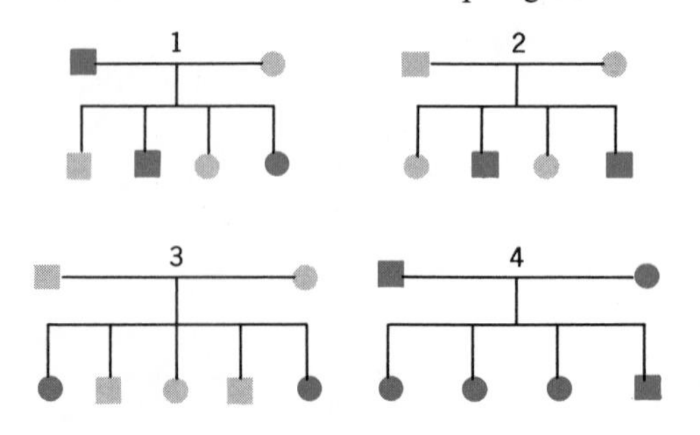


3.6 The trait represented in the following pedigree chart is inherited through a single dominant gene. Calculate the probability of the trait appearing in the offspring if the following cousins should marry: (a) 1 × 3; (b) 2 × 4.

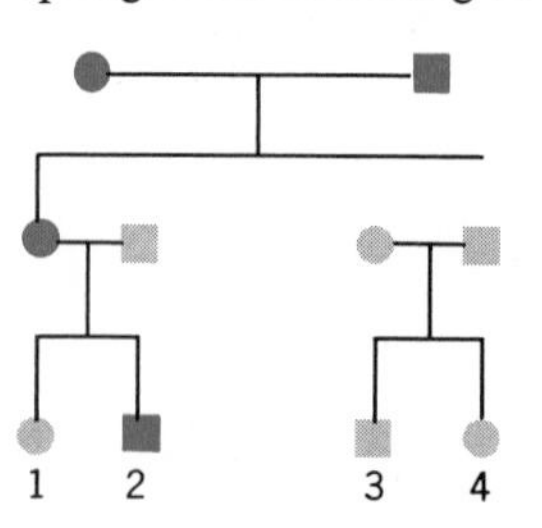

**3.7** In the family pedigree shown in the following chart, an abnormal trait is inherited as a simple recessive. Unless there is evidence to the contrary, assume that the individuals who have married into this family do not carry the recessive gene for the trait. Calculate the probability of the trait appearing in the offspring if the following cousins and second cousins should marry: (a) 1 × 10; (b) 4 × 12; (c) 6 × 11; (d) 16 × 17.

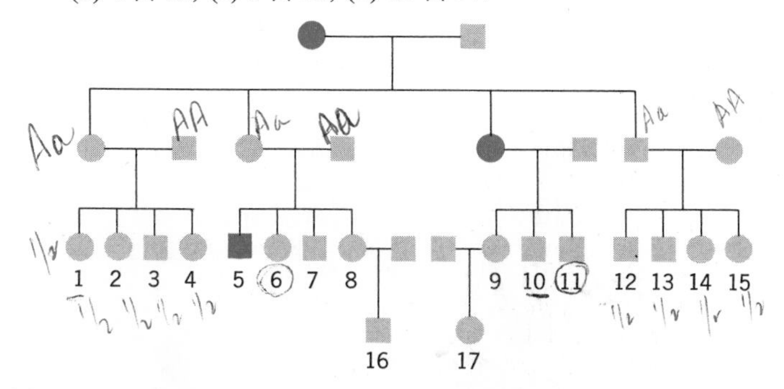


**3.8** In the $F_2$ generation of a certain tomato experiment 3,629 fruits were red and 1,175 were yellow. A 3:1 ratio was expected. (a) Are the discrepancies between the observed and expected ratios significant? (b) In the same experiment 671 plants with green foliage and 569 with yellow were counted. This was a backcross and the hypothetical ratio was 1:1. Test with $X^2$ and explain.

**3.9** The following are some of Mendel's results with the hypotheses to which they were fitted. Test each for goodness of fit and indicate whether each is significantly different from the hypothesis.

| *Cross* | *Results* | *Hypothesis* |
|---|---|---|
| (a) Round × wrinkled seed ($F_2$) | 5474:1850 | 3:1 |
| (b) Violet × white flower ($F_2$) | 705:224 | 3:1 |
| (c) Green × yellow pod ($F_2$) | 428:152 | 3:1 |
| (d) Round yellow ($F_1$) wrinkled green | 31:26:27:26 | 1:1:1:1 |
| (e) Round yellow ($F_1$) × wrinkled green | 24:25:22:27 | 1:1:1:1 |

**3.10** The following $F_2$ results, from pair matings in which the same trait was involved, could represent a 3:1 or 13:3 ratio: (a) 126 red; 48 white; (b) 145:32; (c) 128:46. Test with $X^2$ and indicate whether a decision can be made from these data.

**3.11** When four coins are tossed together in a series, (a) what proportion of the total results will be in the class of 4 heads? (b) 4 tails? (c) 3 heads and 1 tail? (d) 3 tails and 1 head? and (e) 2 heads and 2 tails?

**3.12** The chance that a baby will be a boy is one-half and the chance that a baby will be a girl is also one-half. If four babies are born at a given hospital on the same day: (a) What is the chance that two will be boys and two girls? (b) What is the chance that all four will be girls? (c) What combination of the boys and girls among four babies is most likely to occur? Why? (d) If a certain family has four girls, what is the chance that the fifth child will be a girl?

**3.13** If five babies are born at a particular hospital on the same day, what is the chance of (a) all boys; (b) 4 boys, 1 girl; (c) 3 boys, 2 girls; (d) 2 boys, 3 girls; (e) 1 boy, 4 girls; and (f) all girls?

**3.14** What is the probability in families of 6 of: (a) 1 boy and 5 girls? (b) 3 boys and 3 girls? (c) all 6 girls?

**3.15** Albinism in man is controlled by a recessive gene (*c*). From marriages between normally pigmented people known to be carriers (*Cc*), and albinos (*cc*), (a) what proportion of the children would be expected to be albinos? (b) What is the chance that any pregnancy would result in an albino child? (c) What is the chance in families of 3 that one would be normal and two albino?

**3.16** If both partners were known to be carriers (*Cc*) for albinism, what is the chance of the following combinations in families of 4; (a) all 4 normal? (b) 3 normal and 1 albino? (c) 2 normal and 2 albino? (d) 1 normal and 3 albino?

**3.17** In man, two abnormal conditions, cataracts in the eyes and excessive fragility in the bones, seem to depend on separate dominant genes located in different chromosomes. A man with cataracts and normal bones, whose father had normal eyes, married a woman free from cataracts but with fragile bones. Her father had normal bones. What is the probability that their first child will (a) be free from both abnormalities; (b) have cataracts but not fragile bones; (c) have fragile bones but not cataracts; (d) have both cataracts and fragile bones?

# *Genetic Interactions and Environmental Influences* | 4

Genes may affect viability as well as visible traits of the organism. Appropriate experiments have shown that it is not only through the impaired physical functioning that animals carrying certain mutant genes are at a disadvantage. White-eyed and vestigial-winged Drosophila, for example, have lower viabilities than the wild type. Deep-seated physiological effects are apparently associated with the mutant genes (*w* and *vg*). Some other genes have no effect on the appearance of the fly, but do influence viability in some way. Some mutant genes have such serious effects that the organism is unable to live. These are called "lethal genes." Obviously, if the lethal effect is dominant and immediate, all individuals carrying the gene will die and the gene will be lost. Some lethal genes, however, have a delayed effect so that the organism lives for a time.

Recessive lethals are carried in heterozygous condition and may come to expression when matings between carriers occur. Genes in Drosophila that control such conspicuous phenotypes as curly wings (*Cy*), plum eyes (*Pm*), and stubble bristles (*Sb*), adversely influence the viability of the flies when they are heterozygous. When homozygous, these genes are lethal. They are dominant with respect to the phenotypes for which they were symbolized, but recessive with respect to their lethal action. The reasons for lower viability and lethal action have been determined experimentally in some cases. Apparently, when alone, each of the genes can interfere with vital processes and thus influence viability, but a double dose of the same gene makes it impossible for the organism to live beyond a certain stage in development.

The dominant gene (*C*) in chickens, for example, is responsible for profound developmental changes that result in aberrant forms called "creepers." These birds have short, crooked legs and are of little value except as novelties to be displayed in side shows. When two creepers were mated, a ratio of 2 creepers to 1 normal instead of 3:1 appeared, as illustrated in Fig. 4.1. The missing class was the *CC* class. This was evident because all creepers

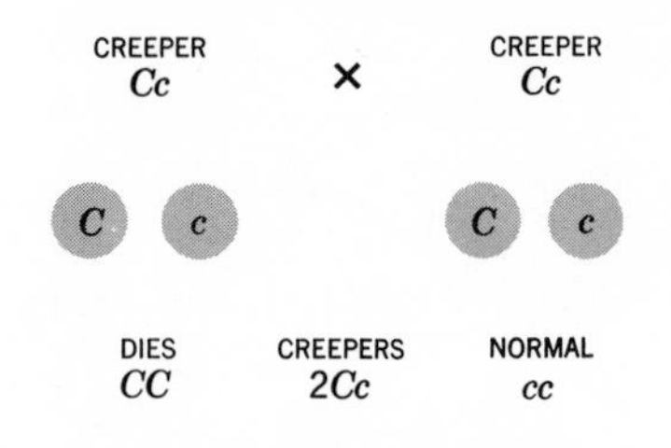


**Fig. 4.1** Diagram of cross between two creeper chickens. The 2:1 ratio replaces the 3:1 because the homozygous (*CC*) embryos die.

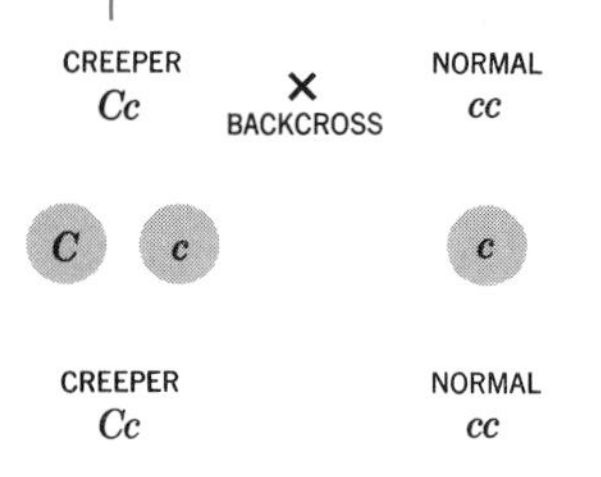


**Fig. 4.2** Diagram of a cross between a creeper and a normal chicken. The expected ratio is 1 creeper: 1 not-creeper (normal).

that lived could be shown by test crosses to be heterozygous (*Cc*). When a creeper was mated with a normal chicken the expected backcross result of 1 creeper to 1 normal was obtained (Fig. 4.2).

Walter Landauer compared the development of creepers with that of normal chickens. He found that the mutant gene causes a general retardation of growth in the early embryo at the time when the limb buds are forming. The effects are widespread in the body. Characteristic abnormalities occur in the head, eyes, and other body structures of heterozygotes (*Cc*) but the leg abnormality is the most conspicuous. Defects in growth can be observed on the second and third days of incubation and the homozygous (*CC*) embryos die on about the fourth day.

At least twenty-seven recessive lethal genes are known to occur in cattle. Some of these have been spread widely through artificial insemination. Thirteen of the twenty-seven abnormalities involve bone formation. In some, or perhaps all of these, the bones are defective and fail to develop properly in the embryo. The same phenotypes have been identified in different breeds, indicating either that different mutations have occurred independently or that the genes have been carried from common ancestors. So-called "bulldog" calves (Fig. 4.3) are best known of all the abnormalities resulting from lethal genes in cattle. They were first described in Germany in 1860. The name came from the abnormal head which resembles that of a bulldog with a short face and short upper jaw. Other conspicuous features are short legs and cleft palate. Usually bulldog calves are aborted at about six to eight months. The Dexter breed in which this trait is prevalent is no longer used to any great extent, mainly because of the serious losses from lethals.

## MODIFIERS

Certain genes alter or modify the visible effects of other genes and thus alter ratios. In a few cases, specific effects of these

**Fig. 4.3** Bulldog calf. This condition is caused by a single recessive gene in homozygous condition, that causes the calves to be aborted at 6 to 8 months from the beginning of development.

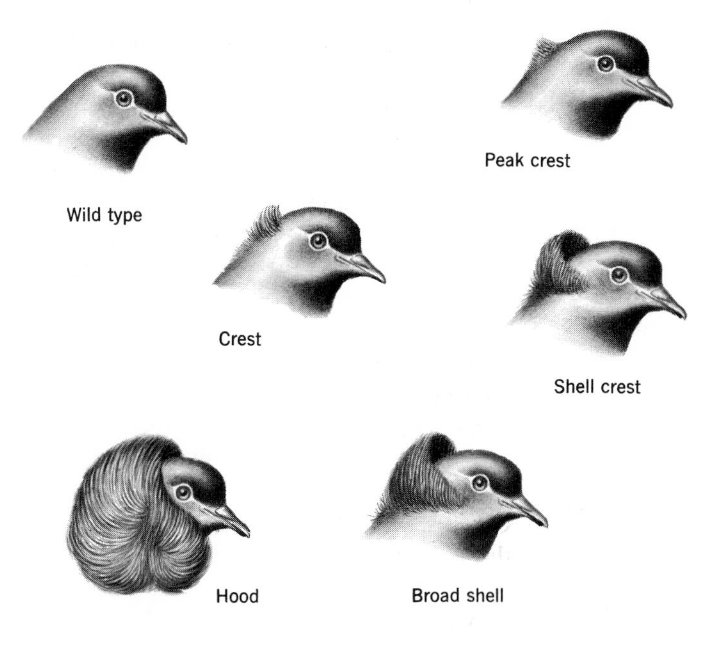


**Fig. 4.4** Pigeon heads illustrating the effect of modifier genes on the appearance of the crest. (Redrawn from National Pigeon Association Booklet.)

individual modifiers have been identified. The distinction between the effects of genetic modifiers and environmental influences is usually difficult to establish. Whether all modifiers represent discrete genes in the usual sense is not known. On the basis of phenotypic effects, some modifiers have been described with great precision.

The wild-type pigeon, for example, has a smooth head with no crest. When the recessive gene (*cr*) is present in homozygous condition, the head bears a crest. Additional genes acting as modifiers determine the size and appearance of the crest. Several crest patterns associated with the basic gene and different modifiers are illustrated in Fig. 4.4. Many modifiers do not have such striking effects, and their presence can only be detected by quantitative measurement.

Modifiers may suppress or enhance other genes. In *Drosophila melanogaster,* a modifier symbolized *su-Hw* suppresses the condition known as hairy wing, which is dependent on a single gene (*Hw*) substitution. This same modifier also has a suppressing effect on the action of several other genes. Most of the phenotypes suppressed are wing abnormalities, but one trait as diverse as yellow body color is influenced. In *Neurospora crassa,* a suppressor, *su-pyr,* inhibits the effects of at least three nonallelic genes that independently interfere with the growth of the mold on a minimal medium. In the presence of any one of these genes, pyrimidine or proline must be added to the minimal medium to make growth possible. When both the suppressor and defective genes are present, the mold grows normally on a minimal medium. The suppressor thus offsets the effects of different nonallelic genes.

Some modifiers intensify the effect of other genes. In *D. melanogaster,* a gene *E-S* enhances the effect of the dominant gene (*S*), for star eye. In the presence of the enhancer and *S* the eyes are smaller than the wild type and very rough. Another dominant gene *M* makes the bristles thin and short. Its effect is intensified by the enhancer symbolized *E-M,* which makes the bristles considerably shorter than they are with *M* alone.

## PHENOTYPES NOT EXPRESSED IN PARENTS BUT IN PROGENY

A classical example of interaction based on the results of crosses between different varieties of chickens was reported in the early part of the present century by William Bateson (1861–1926; Fig. 4.5) and his associate, R. C. Punnett. At Cambridge University, Bateson had become interested in Mendel's work immediately after its discovery in 1900 and he became one of the founders of the science of genetics. In 1894 he published a book entitled *Materials for the Study of Variation.* He then designed and conducted experiments to answer the questions he had raised in his book. These experiments were in progress at the time Mendel's work was discovered. Immediately thereafter new experiments were designed by various investigators to determine whether Mendel's laws held for other plants and, particularly, whether they applied to animals as well. Bateson had been breeding poultry and he, along with C. C. Hurst, undertook experiments to determine whether the Mendelian principles applied in poultry.

**Fig. 4.5** William Bateson, English experimental biologist who demonstrated gene interaction.

Domestic breeds of chickens have different comb shapes (Fig. 4.6). Wyandottes have a characteristic type of comb called "rose" whereas Brahmas have a "pea" comb. Leghorns have "single" combs. The investigators crossed Wyandottes and Brahmas, and all the $F_1$ chickens had walnut combs, a phenotype not expressed in either parent. When the $F_1$ chickens were mated among themselves and large $F_2$ populations were produced, a familiar dihybrid ratio, 9:3:3:1, was recognized, but the phenotypes representing two of the four classes were different from those expressed in the parents. About nine-sixteenths of the $F_2$ birds were walnut, three-sixteenths rose, three-sixteenths pea, and one-sixteenth had single combs. Single comb as well as walnut was not expressed in either original parental line. These two phenotypes were explained as the result of interaction. The results, based on a total of 16, indicated that two different allelic pairs were involved; one pair was introduced by the rose-comb parent and one by the pea-comb parent. A gene for rose and a gene for pea would interact and produce walnut, as in the $F_1$.

Analysis of the $F_2$ results and appropriate test crosses indicated that the $9/16$ class, with the two dominant genes (*R-P-*), were walnut, like the $F_1$ chickens. The $1/16$ class representing the full recessive combination (*rrpp*) was characterized by single combs. The two $3/16$ (rose and pea) classes were *R-pp* and *rrP-*. It was then determined that the homozygous genotype of the rose-comb parent (Wyandotte) was *RRpp* and of the pea-comb parent (Brahma), *rrPP*. The cross is reconstructed diagrammatically in Fig. 4.7. Although the usual 9:3:3:1 ratio was obtained, the result from this cross was unusual in two important respects: (1) the $F_1$ progeny

1. Rose comb

2. Pea comb

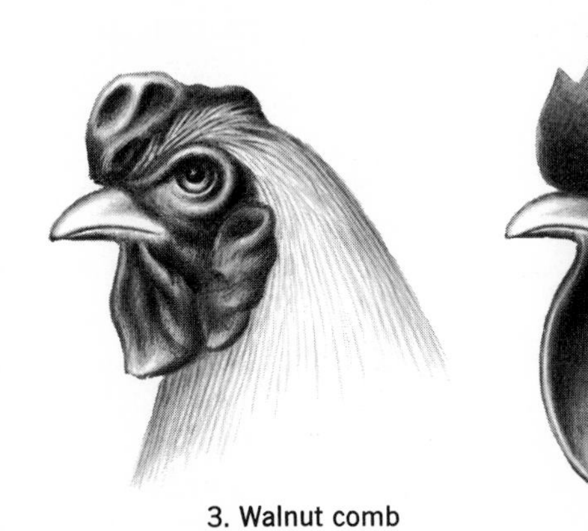

3. Walnut comb

4. Single comb

**Fig. 4.6** Comb types characteristic of different breeds of chickens: (1) rose, Wyandottes; (2) pea, Brahmas; (3) walnut, hybrid from cross between chickens with rose and pea combs; and (4) single, Leghorns.

were different from those of either parent, that is, none were rose or pea, but all were walnut; and (2) two phenotypes (walnut and single), not expressed in the original parents, appeared in the $F_2$.

Another early classical study, also conducted by Bateson and Punnett, demonstrated gene interaction in plant material resulting in a 9:7 ratio. When two white-flowered varieties of sweet peas, *Lathyrus odoratus,* were crossed, the $F_1$ progeny all had colored flowers. When the $F_2$ were classified, nine-sixteenths were purple and seven-sixteenths were white. The base number of 16 was again recognized as that associated with a dihybrid cross, but there were only two classes instead of the usual four. This suggested a modification of the 9:3:3:1 ratio in which the $3/16$, $3/16$, and $1/16$ classes were indistinguishable and therefore were grouped together when the plants were classified phenotypically. The fact that the proportion was based on a total of 16 rather than 4, 64, or some other number was good evidence that two pairs of genes were segregating.

The hypothesis formulated by the investigators was that two nonallelic gene

| | | ROSE | | PEA | |
|---|---|---|---|---|---|
| P | | *RRpp* | × | *rrPP* | |
| | | *Rp* | | *rP* | |
| | | WALNUT | | WALNUT | |
| $F_1$ | | *RrPp* | × | *RrPp* | |

| $F_2$ | *RP* | *Rp* | *rP* | *rp* |
|---|---|---|---|---|
| *RP* | *RRPP* WALNUT | *RRPp* WALNUT | *RrPP* WALNUT | *RrPp* WALNUT |
| *Rp* | *RRPp* WALNUT | *RRpp* ROSE | *RrPp* WALNUT | *Rrpp* ROSE |
| *rP* | *RrPP* WALNUT | *RrPp* WALNUT | *rrPP* PEA | *rrPp* PEA |
| *rp* | *RrPp* WALNUT | *Rrpp* ROSE | *rrPp* PEA | *rrpp* SINGLE |

Summary: 9/16 walnut, 3/16 rose, 3/16 pea, 1/16 single

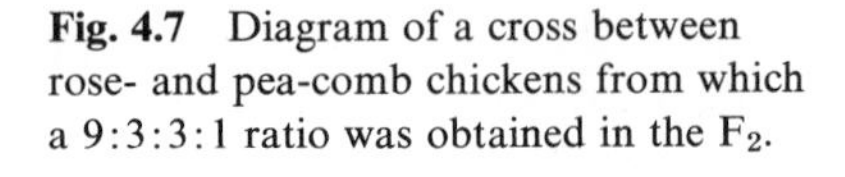

**Fig. 4.7** Diagram of a cross between rose- and pea-comb chickens from which a 9:3:3:1 ratio was obtained in the $F_2$.

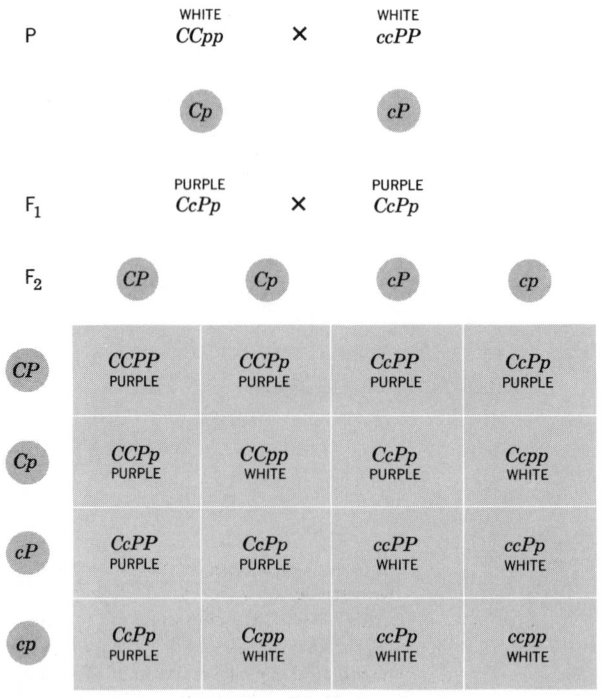


**Fig. 4.8** Diagram of a cross between two white varieties of sweet peas from which an $F_2$ ratio of 9:7 was obtained.

pairs were necessary to produce the purple color. It was thus possible for the flowers of the two original parents to be white for different genetic reasons; that is, in the absence of either one (or both) of two complementary genes. It has since been shown that, in the presence of *C* and *P* genes, anthocyanins are formed in the flowers. In the absence of either of the complementary genes (*CCpp*, *Ccpp*, *ccPP*, *ccPp* or *ccpp*), the flowers are white. Nine of sixteen $F_2$ progeny carried C-P-, but seven-sixteenths lacked one or both. The original white parent varieties were *CCpp* and *ccPP*. The cross is reconstructed diagrammatically in Fig. 4.8. In later experiments, colorless extracts made from the different white varieties were combined in a test tube and produced color. The action of the genes thus was associated with a simple indicator type of chemical reaction.

Historically, the discoveries of different modified $F_2$ ratios, particularly the 9:7, were landmarks in the development of genetics. They required a broader interpretation of Mendelian heredity than was made on the basis of the strict interpretation of Mendel's principles. Now that the principle of interaction is well established, modified ratios have come to be expected. A 9:6:1 ratio occurs when the phenotypes of the two 3/16 classes of the 9:3:3:1 are indistinguishable: 12:3:1, when the 9/16 and 3/16 are alike; 13:3 is associated with a dominant gene that inhibits color (in chickens) in the 9/16 and 3/16 classes, and the 1/16 class lacks a color gene. When the 9/16 and the two 3/16 classes are indistinguishable, a 15:1 ratio is produced.

A classical experiment, which resulted in the 15:1 ratio, was reported by George H. Shull from studies on the plant called shepherd's purse of the genus Capsella (Bursa). Some races have triangular seed capsules and some have top-shaped capsules. When crosses were made between races showing these two characteristics, respectively, an $F_2$ ratio of 15 plants with triangular to 1 with top-shaped capsules was obtained (Fig. 4.9). Two independently

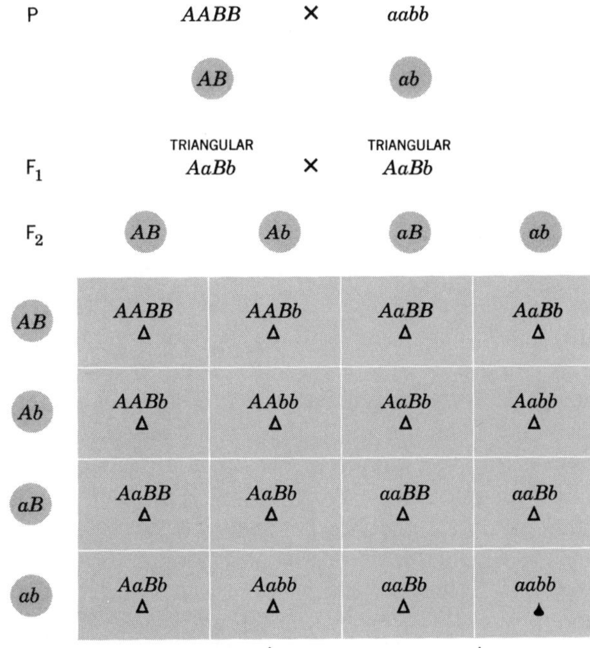


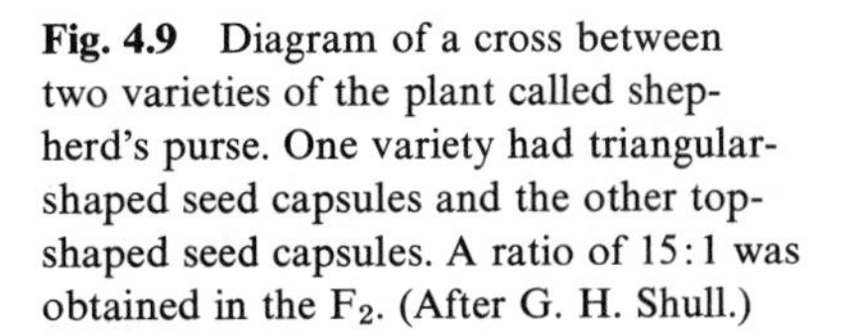

**Fig. 4.9** Diagram of a cross between two varieties of the plant called shepherd's purse. One variety had triangular-shaped seed capsules and the other top-shaped seed capsules. A ratio of 15:1 was obtained in the $F_2$. (After G. H. Shull.)

segregating dominant genes (*A* and *B*) were postulated to influence the shape of the capsule in the same way. All gene combinations with an *A* or *B* would produce plants with triangular-shaped capsules. Only those with the genotype *aabb* would be top shaped. The hypothesis of duplicate dominant genes was shown to be correct when the results of appropriate test crosses were analyzed.

**Fig. 4.10** Albino pigeon. Courtesy of the American King Club.

## EPISTASIS

Epistasis (Greek, standing upon) is a widespread and important type of interaction. Any gene or gene pair that masks the expression of another, *nonallelic* gene is epistatic to that gene. The gene suppressed is said to be hypostatic. This form of suppression should be distinguished from simple dominance, which is associated with pairs of alleles. The most obvious epistatic effects are associated with color patterns. A type of epistasis occurs when a gene necessary to the production of color in a plant or animal is not present. In the absence of such a gene, other genes at other loci (for instance, genes controlling color patterns) are unable to come to expression.

Another kind of epistasis occurs when intense pigmentation obscures delicate gene-controlled markings that might otherwise be expressed. In pigeons, for example, genes producing red color have been shown experimentally to mask a number of patterns that involve lighter and more delicate colors. White (albino) pigeons, Fig. 4.10 on the other hand, do not express some genes that they carry for color patterns. The so-called "spread" type is heavily pigmented and obscures virtually all other patterns for which gene combinations might be present. The genes for red, white, and spread are epistatic to other genes that control several other colors and patterns.

An example of epistasis through the absence of color was illustrated when colored mice (*CCaa*) were crossed with white (albino) mice (*ccAA*) that carried (but did not express) the genes for wild-type or agouti pattern. The agouti pattern is a banding of the individual hairs of the fur which has been favored in natural selection, presumably because it provides concealment for wild animals in their surroundings. Ordinarily, the part of each hair nearest the skin is gray; next comes a yellow band, and then a black or brown tip, depending on the presence of separate color genes, *B* or *bb*, which can express themselves only in the presence of *C*. The cross is reconstructed in Fig. 4.11. (Since both parents were homozygous for the genes *BB* for black pigment, these genes were not included in the diagram.) From the parents, *CCaa* × *ccAA*, the $F_1$ progeny were all *CcAa* and all expressed the agouti pattern. Each gamete from the original colored parent carried a *C* gene, which is basically responsible for color production, and each gamete from the albino mouse carried an *A* gene for the agouti pattern. An interaction between these two genes resulted in the color and pattern expressed by all the $F_1$ mice.

When these $F_1$ mice were mated, their

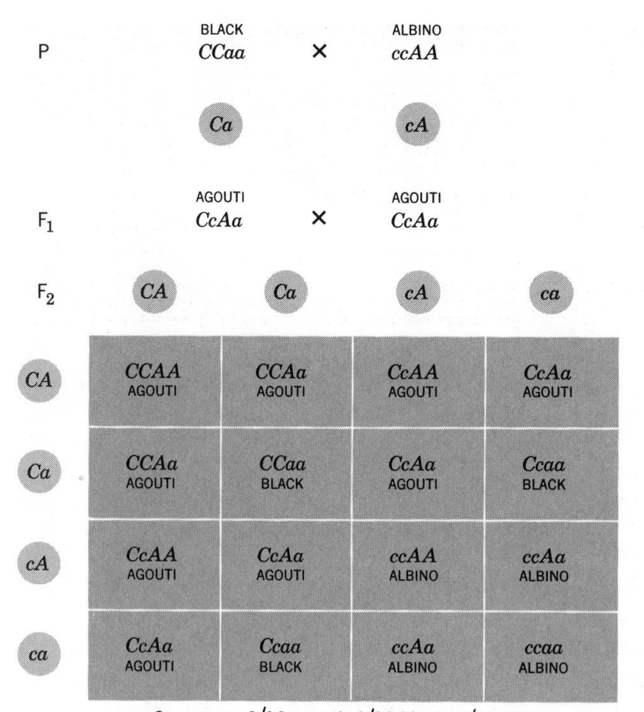


**Fig. 4.11** Diagram of a cross between black and albino mice. A ratio of 9:3:4 was obtained in the $F_2$.

$F_2$ progeny were classified as 9 agouti, 3 colored, and 4 albino. This suggested a modification of the 9:3:3:1 ratio, which was explained on the basis of independent combinations and interaction of two separate pairs of alleles. The 9/16 class, which was agouti, carried the genes *C* and *A;* the 3/16, which were colored, were of the genotype *C-aa;* and the 4/16 albino were *cc* (epistatic to *A* in the *ccA-* class). The modified ratio occurred because the 3/16 and 1/16 classes were indistinguishable; that is, both were albino and all patterns dependent on color were lacking.

## ATAVISM

Through epistatic effects and other gene interactions, traits may remain hidden generation after generation. Occasionally a "throwback" occurs in a strain of domestic animals or plants; that is, an ancestral trait is expressed unexpectedly. This situation was first discussed scientifically by Charles Darwin and was called atavism. It is now explained by the chance combination of genes that allows a long-suppressed or hidden characteristic to finally come to expression. The agouti pattern, for example, which is suppressed by the homozygous *c* gene in albino rodents, may appear in outcrosses in which the *c* gene is replaced by its allele *C*.

One of the best indications of the ancestry of the domesticated pigeon occasionally occurs in progeny of intermated, highly selected strains of show birds. These matings sometimes produce a kind of "wild type" resembling the rock pigeon, *Columba livia.* In these cases, a chance combination of genes apparently removes the effect of epistatic genes that, for generations, have suppressed the expression of certain ancestral traits in the show birds. Examples of powdered silver fantail and

**Fig. 4.12** Pigeons illustrating atavism. *A*, Indian fantail pigeon (photo by H. P. Macklin, courtesy of Wendell Levi); *B*, wild rock pigeon; *C*, bluette pigeon. Intermatings between highly selected varieties, such as the fantail and bluette, sometimes produce progeny resembling the wild rock pigeon.

bluette breeds that sometimes produce throwbacks are illustrated in Fig. 4.12. Without constant attention from the breeders, different types of pigeons would mate indiscriminately, and their progeny would tend to revert to wild (or so-called "mongrel") birds.

The great number of variations possible in any species is explained on the basis of numerous genes segregating in the population and interactions among the products of genes and the environment. Expressions of genes may be suppressed, enhanced, or altered by new gene interactions. Since the phenotype rather than the genotype is directly affected by the environment, gene interactions producing unique results may be of importance in evolution as well as in man's selection of domesticated strains of animals and plants.

## GENE SYMBOLS

With the rapid advance of genetics, the 26 letters in the alphabet were soon associated with particular genes. Drosophila geneticists met this limitation by adding a second letter and a third and fourth, when necessary, taken from the name of the mutant phenotype. Another technical advance from Drosophila geneticists came in the use of + to symbolize wild-type genes either known or assumed to be alleles of mutants. For example, *B* symbolized the bar gene and + the wild-type allele. The lower case *b* could then be assigned to the gene for black body color and + for wild-type gray body. Whenever doubt could exist as to the meaning of a given +, the letter symbol of the mutant was added and either the letter symbol or the + was used as a superscript. Thus, $w^+$ or $+^w$ instead of *W* became the symbol for the wild-type allele of *w*. Another useful device initiated by Drosophila geneticists was the separation of alleles by a cross bar. A pair of alleles at the *w* locus, for example, was symbolized $w^+/w$.

## SEX DETERMINATION

The first investigations relating chromosomes to sex determination were carried out late in the nineteenth century. H. Henking, a German biologist, discovered in 1891 that a particular nuclear structure could be traced in the spermatogenesis of certain insects. Half the sperm received this structure and half did not. Henking did not speculate on the significance of this body but merely identified it as the "X" body and showed that some sperm were different from others because of its presence or absence. In 1902 these observations were verified and extended by C. E. McClung, who made cytological observations on many different species of grasshoppers and demonstrated that the somatic cells in the female grasshopper carry a different chromosome number than do corresponding cells in the male. He followed the X body in spermatogenesis but did not succeed in tracing the oögenesis of the female grasshopper, which is more difficult to study. McClung associated the X body with sex determination, but erroneously considered it to be peculiar to males. Had he been able to follow oögenesis, his interpretation would undoubtedly have been different.

### *The XO and XY Mechanism*

Valuable contributions to basic knowledge about sex determination were made in the early part of the present century by the distinguished American cytologist E. B. Wilson (1856–1939; Fig. 4.13). Wilson and Miss N. M. Stevens, beginning in 1905, reported extensive cytological investigations on several different insects, notably the genus Protenor (Fig. 4.14), an uncommon group of insects closely related to the boxelder bug. In these insects, different numbers of chromosomes were observed in the germ cells of the two sexes. Wilson and Stevens succeeded in following oögenesis as well as spermatogenesis. The unreduced cells of the male carried 13 chromosomes, and those of the female carried 14. By microscopic observations during the later stages of spermatogenesis, some male gametes (that is, sperm) were found to carry 6 chromosomes whereas others from the same individual carried 7. The female gametes (eggs) all had 7. Eggs fertilized with 6-chromosome sperm produced males and those fertilized with 7-chromosome sperm produced females.

The "X" body of Henking thus was

**Fig. 4.13** E. B. Wilson, American cytologist, who studied the mechanics of sex determination.

found to be a chromosome that influenced sex determination. It was identified in several insects and became known as the sex or X chromosome. All the eggs of these insects carried the X chromosome, but it was included in only half of the sperm. All sperm, however, had the usual complement of other chromosomes (autosomes). Eggs fertilized by sperm containing the X chromosome produced zygotes with two X chromosomes, which became females. Eggs receiving sperm without an X chromosome produced zygotes with one X, which became males. This mechanism was called the XO method of sex determination.

The XO pattern was further illustrated by the same authors from detailed microscopic studies of testis sections of the squash bug *Anasa tristis* (Fig. 4.15). In this material, the somatic cells and unreduced germ cells of the female had 22 chromo-

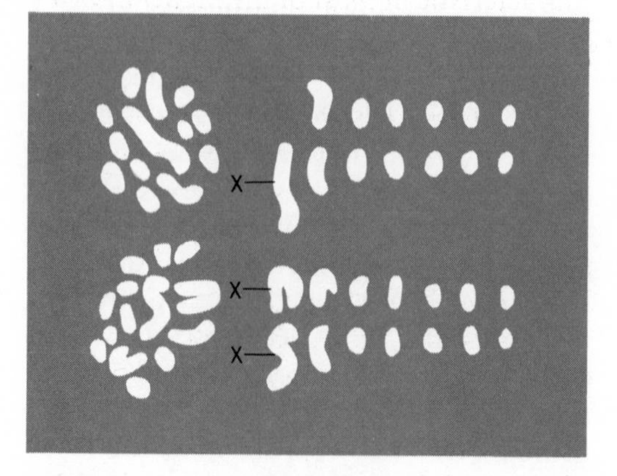


**Fig. 4.14** Chromosomes of Protenor. (Upper) Male chromosomes; (lower) female chromosomes. Chromosomes at left are arranged as they appear in the metaphase of a somatic division, that is, karyotypes. At right they are lined up according to size. This insect illustrates the XO method of sex determination. (From E. B. Wilson, *The Cell,* Copyright 1925. The Macmillan Co.)

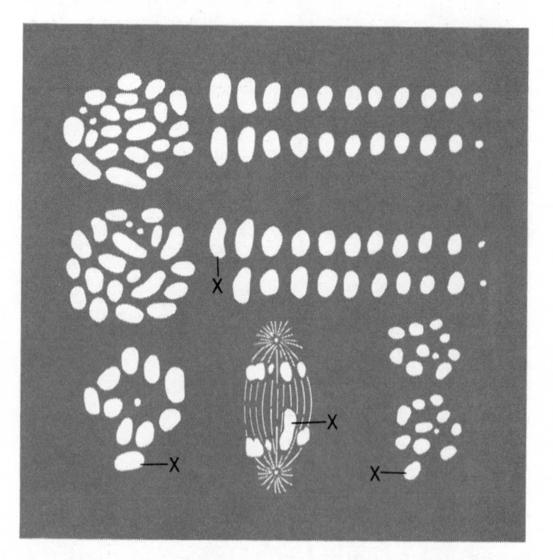


**Fig. 4.15** Chromosomes of the squash bug, *Anasa tristis*. (Top) Chromosomes ($2n$) of a female cell; (center) chromosomes ($2n$) of a male cell. Metaphase karyotypes are presented at left and chromosomes are represented according to size at right; Metaphase configurations of first and second phase of the meiotic sequence are shown at bottom of figure. The squash bug illustrates the XO method of sex determination. (From E. B. Wilson, *The Cell,* Copyright 1925. The Macmillan Co.)

somes (20 autosomes and 2 X chromosomes) and those of the male had 21 (20 autosomes and 1 X). Half of the sperm, however, carried 11, and half carried 10 chromosomes. Thus, as in Protenor, half the sperm had an X chromosome and half had the usual haploid set of autosomes but no X. Eggs fertilized by 11-chromosome sperm became females, and those fertilized by 10-chromosome sperm developed into males.

In the squash bug, the X chromosome could be followed through the entire process of spermatogenesis, as shown in Fig. 4.15. It was the largest chromosome and took its place outside the ring of autosomes during metaphase I. Not only was it larger than the other chromosomes, but throughout the entire meiotic prophase it evidenced greater stability and staining capacity. These properties made it possible to recognize the X chromosome during stages of the meiotic prophase when other chromosomes were indistinguishable.

Although only a few insects had been investigated, the XO mechanism was widely acclaimed in the early 1900's as the common method for sex determination. Insects that were readily available and whose chromosomes were easily studied happened to be the first materials to be studied, and some followed the XO pattern. When more observations were made on a wider variety of animals, other patterns were discovered.

During the same year (1905) that Wilson and Stevens reported on XO sex determination in the squash bug, they observed another chromosome arrangement (Fig. 4.16) in the milkweed bug, *Lygaeus turcicus*. In this insect, the same number of chromosomes was present in the cells of both sexes. The one identified as the mate to the X, however, was distinctly smaller and was called the Y chromosome. Sex determination based on equal chromosome numbers in the two sexes but with

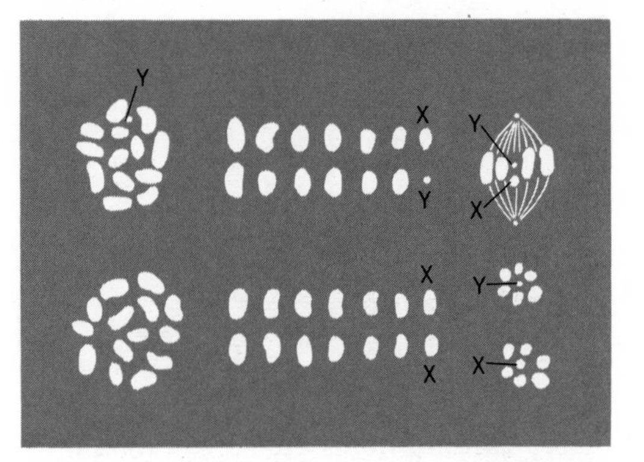


**Fig. 4.16** Chromosomes of the milkweed bug, *Lygaeus turcicus*. (Upper) Chromosomes ($2n$) of a male cell; (lower) chromosomes ($2n$) of a female cell. Metaphase karyotypes are presented at left, chromosomes arranged according to size are shown in center, and diagrams of reduction division in the male are given at right. This illustrates the XY type of sex determination. (From E. B. Wilson, *The Cell,* Copyright 1925. The Macmillan Co.)

different kinds of chromosomes making up one pair was called the XY type. As evidence was accumulated from a wider variety of animals, the XY mechanism was found to be more prevalent than the XO. The XY type is now considered characteristic in most of the higher animals and occurs in at least some plants (for example, *Melandrium album;* see below).

The fruit fly *Drosophila melanogaster* has the XY type of sex determination. Metaphase chromosomes of the male and female are illustrated in Fig. 4.17. The Y chromosome is longer than the X and the spindle fiber attachment is not centered; therefore, it has a short arm and a long arm at anaphase. Male and female gametes each have 4 chromosomes, 3 of which are autosomes. The female gametes carry an X chromosome; half of the male gametes have an X and half a Y.

Man also follows the XY pattern but the mechanism of sex determination is profoundly different from that of Drosophila. The human X chromosome is considerably longer than the Y, as shown in Fig. 4.18.

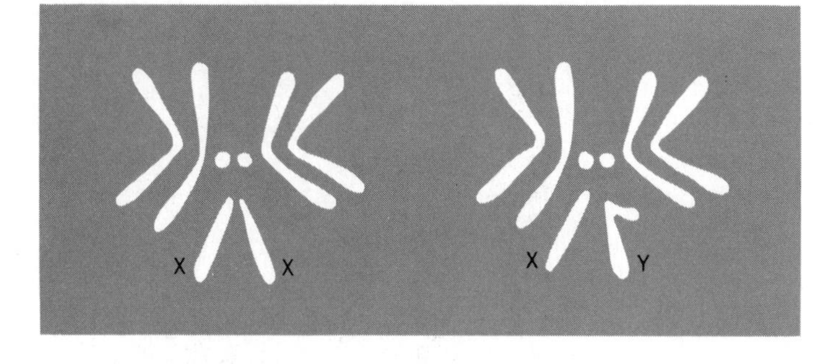


**Fig. 4.17** Chromosomes of the fruit fly, *Drosophila melanogaster*. (Left) Chromosomes ($2n$) of a female cell; (right) male cell. These are metaphase karyotypes.

These chromosomes are shown in end-to-end synapsis as they appear in the meiotic sequence. The total complement of chromosomes includes 44 autosomes, XX in the female, and XY in the male (as shown in Fig. 4.19). Eggs produced by the female in oögenesis have the usual complement of autosomes (22) plus an X chromosome. Sperm from the male have the same autosomal number and either an X or a Y. Eggs fertilized with Y chromosome sperm result in zygotes that develop into males; those fertilized with X chromosome sperm develop into females. Segregation of the XY pair and random fertilization thus explain, at least superficially, why some individuals develop into females and some into males, and why about half of the members of each population of higher animals are males and half are females.

The association of the most conspicuous phenotype (that is, sex) with a particular chromosome greatly strengthened the hypothesis that genes are in chromosomes. This idea originally had been postulated largely because of the parallel observed between the separation of chromosomes in the meiotic process and genetic segregation. Research-substantiated evidence that sex determination was controlled by a particular chromosome provided tangible support for a fundamental hypothesis that genes are in chromosomes.

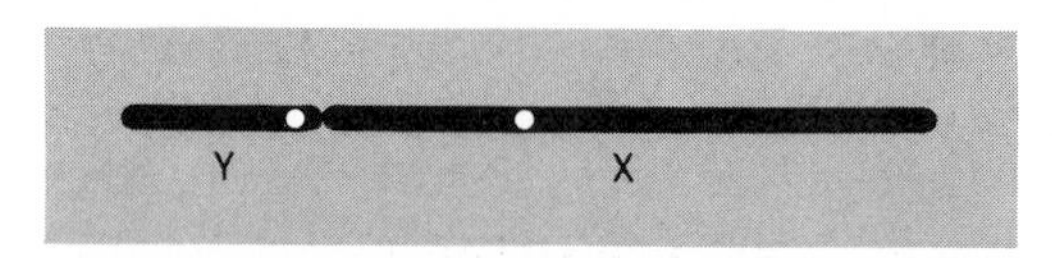


**Fig. 4.18** Diagrammatic representation of the X and Y chromosomes in man exhibiting "end-to-end" pairing at meiosis.

Most of the knowledge presently available on the mechanism of sex determination has come from the brilliant experimental work of C. B. Bridges (Fig. 5.5), R. B. Goldschmidt (1878–1958; Fig. 4.20), and P. W. Whiting. These investigators worked with flies, moths, and wasps, respectively, which lend themselves to experimental investigations better than higher organisms. Experiments with insects formed a basis for speculation and experimentation concerning the sex-determining mechanism in higher forms. Because invertebrate hormones are not functionally comparable with the steroid hormones in birds and mammals, however, such animals as chickens and mice were mainly employed for the experimental work on secondary sex characteristics (those characteristics that distinguish the two sexes but that have no direct role in reproduction) and hormonal influences on phenotypes.

### *Balance Concept of Sex Determination*

Soon after sex chromosomes were identified it became obvious that sex determination was more complicated than preliminary observations had indicated. A more intricate mechanism than the segregation of a single pair of chromosomes was in evidence. The most fundamental

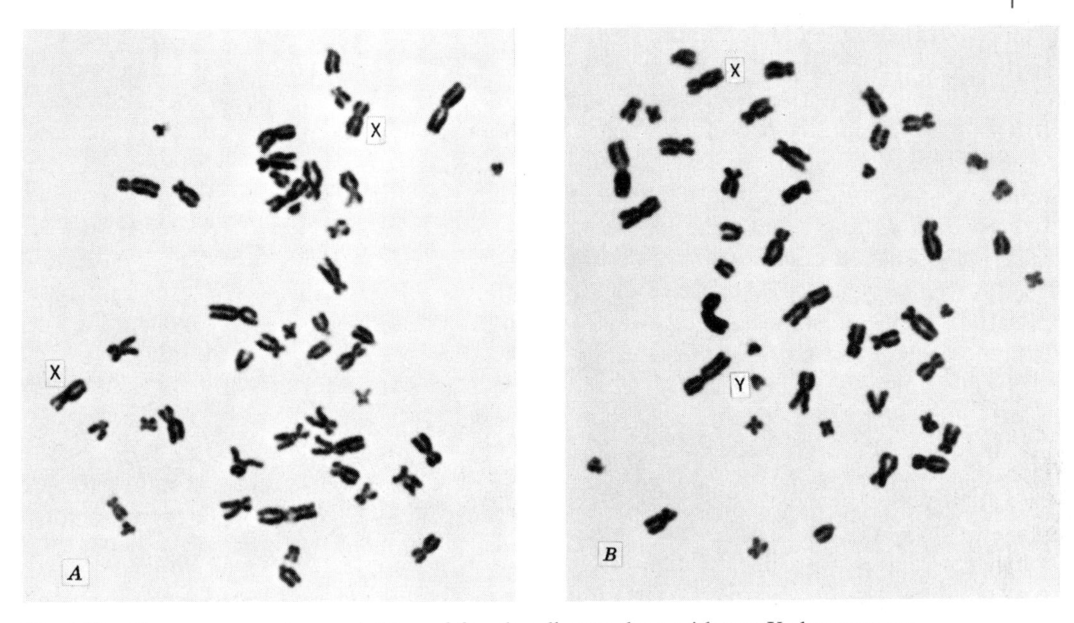


**Fig. 4.19** Chromosomes of man. *A*. Normal female cell metaphase with two X chromosomes and 44 autosomes. *B*. Normal male cell metaphase with one X, a smaller Y chromosome, and 44 autosomes. Sex-linked genes are carried in the X chromosomes. (Courtesy of J. H. Tjio and T. T. Puck, Department of Biophysics, University of Colorado Medical Center, Denver.)

**Fig. 4.20** Richard B. Goldschmidt, pioneer in the field of sex determination and physiological genetics. His early work was done in Germany and later work in the United States.

contributions to the definition of this mechanism came from Bridges' investigations on Drosophila, which showed that female determiners were located in the X chromosome and male determiners were in the autosomes. More than one gene, perhaps a great many (in the X chromosome), were found to influence femaleness. Bridges also demonstrated that genes for maleness were not located in the Y chromosome of Drosophila, but were distributed widely among the autosomes. No specific loci have been identified, and the present evidence suggests that many chromosome areas are involved. Thus, it was shown that sex-determining genes are carried in certain chromosomes in Drosophila, and that all individuals carry genes for both sexes. The genic balance theory of sex determination was devised as a more detailed explanation of the mechanics of sex determination.

The XO or XY chromosome segregation was interpreted as a means of tipping the balance between maleness and femaleness, whereas more deep-seated processes were involved in the actual determination. Bridges experimentally produced various combinations of X chromosomes and autosomes in Drosophila. The first irregular chromosome arrangement resulted from nondisjunction, the failure of paired chromosomes to separate in anaphase of the reduction. X chromosomes, which ordinarily came together in pairs in meiotic prophase of oögenesis and separated to the poles in anaphase of the reduction division, remained together and went to the same pole. As a result, some female gametes received two X chromosomes and some received no X chromosomes (Fig. 4.21).

Following fertilization by sperm from wild-type males, all zygotes had $2n$ autosomes. Some received two X chromosomes from the mother and a Y from the father. These XXY flies, which in appearance were normal females, were mated with wild-type (XY) males. All progeny had two sets of autosomes, whereas some received XXX, others XXY, XY, or YY sex chromosomes. XXX flies, now called metafemales, were sterile and highly inviable. The XXY combination resulted in females that were normal in appearance and reproductive function, XY equated with normal males, and YY zygotes did not survive. Experimentally produced XO males were similar in sex manifestations to XY males, but the XO males were sterile. XXY females were similar to XX females. These results indicated that, in Drosophila, the Y chromosome is not involved in sex determination but that it does control male fertility.

Flies produced experimentally with three whole sets of chromosomes (3 genomes or $3n$ triploids) were then included in the studies and, later, some with four genomes (tetraploids) were added. On the basis of many experimental combinations of autosomes and X chromosomes, Bridges established a standard by which various sets of autosomes and X chromosomes were compared with reference to the relative potency of male- and female-determining capacity. Two sets of autosomes (AA) were found to have enough male-determining potency to overbalance the female-

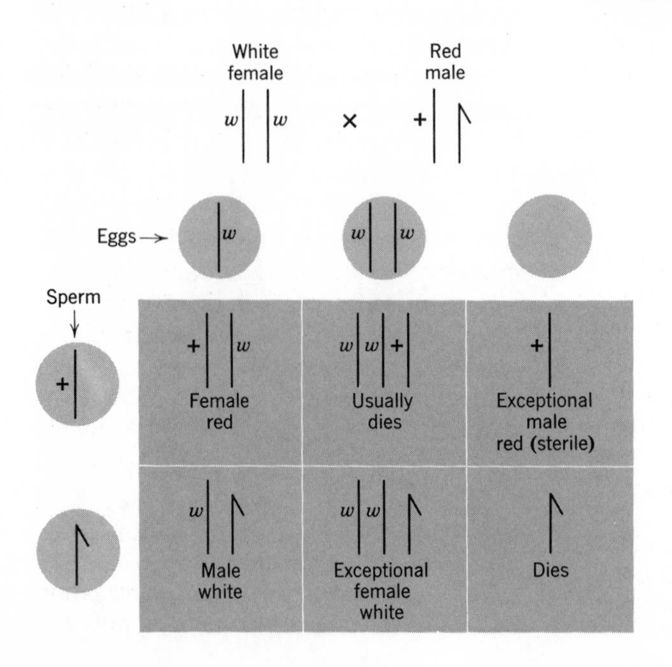


**Fig. 4.21** Diagram of Bridges' cross between white-eyed females and red-eyed males, illustrating the nondisjunction hypothesis formulated to explain exceptional white-eyed females and red-eyed males. The hypothesis was later proved by observations of the chromosomes as illustrated in diagram.

**TABLE 4.1 Different combinations of X chromosomes and autosomes and corresponding sex expressions in Drosophila (after Bridges)**

| X Chromosomes | Sets of Autosomes | Sex |
|---|---|---|
| 1 | 2 | Male |
| 2 | 2 | Female |
| 3 | 2 | Metafemale |
| 4 | 3 | Metafemale |
| 4 | 4 | Tetraploid female |
| 3 | 3 | Triploid female |
| 1 | 1 | Haploid female[a] |
| 3 | 4 | Intersex |
| 2 | 3 | Intersex |
| 2 | 4 | Male |
| 1 | 3 | Metamale |

[a] Determination based on patches of tissue in individual flies which show female traits.

determining capacity of one X chromosome. The chromosome combination AAX(Y) thus gave rise to a normal male. In the presence of two X chromosomes and two sets of autosomes (AAXX), a normal female was produced. Bridges showed that equal numbers of X chromosomes and sets of male-determining autosomes occurred only in females. When the number of sets of autosomes was greater, maleness was expressed. A large overbalance of X chromosomes resulted in metafemales. An overbalance of autosomes was associated with metamales. When the difference in proportion was not great, intersexes with characteristics of both males and females were produced. The various demonstrated chromosome combinations and sex expressions are summarized in Table 4.1.

No other animals or plants have been investigated with equal thoroughness, but indirect evidence suggests that, in many organisms, some such balance is involved. Intersexes can be produced experimentally in some animals by upsetting this balance during the developmental stages. In nature, a margin of safety exists which makes intermediates between the two sexes uncommon.

### *Y Chromosomes in Sex Determination*

The Y chromosome was shown by Bridges to have no influence on sex determination in Drosophila. This seems to be true in some other organisms now investigated, but several examples have been cited; for instance, the plant genus Melandrium, a part of the pink family, and the amphibian genus Axolotl, in which sex determination depends on the Y chromosome. The Y chromosome also has been found to determine maleness in mice and in man (Chapter 10).

In *Melandrium album,* which follows the XY mode of sex determination, H. E. Warmke, M. Westergaard and others have shown that sex is determined by a balance between male-determining genes in the Y and female-determining genes in the X and in the autosomes. In this plant, which is normally dioecious, XY individuals are staminate (that is, pollen bearing), and XX plants are pistillate (egg bearing). The Y chromosome is the largest and most conspicuous member of the complement (Fig. 4.22).

Experimental investigations by means of spontaneous fragmentations have resulted in the mapping of major sections of

**Fig. 4.22** Photomicrograph of chromosomes at first meiotic metaphase in diploid male of Melandrium showing 11 autosomal bivalents and heteromorphic XY pair, ×1400. (After Warmke, *American Journal of Botany,* **33**:648–660, 1946.)

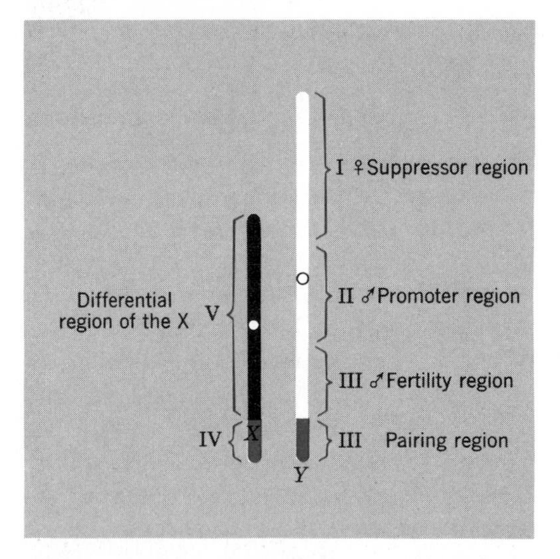


**Fig. 4.23** Diagram of the sex chromosomes in Melandrium. Regions I, II, and III of the Y chromosome do not have homologous segments in the X, and thus they make up the *differential* portion of the Y. Regions IV are homologous in the X and Y, and are pairing regions at meiosis. V is the differential portion of the X chromosome. When I is lost from a Y chromosome, a bisexual plant is produced. When II is lost, a female plant is produced. If III is absent, male-sterile plants with abortive anthers appear. (After Westergaard, *Hereditas*, **34**:257–279, 1948.)

the Y chromosome (Fig. 4.23). Three distinct regions influencing sex determinations and male fertility have been localized on the differential part of the Y chromosome. Region I suppresses femaleness and thus allows maleness to be expressed in a plant carrying a Y chromosome. In the absence of this region, plants are bisexual; that is, they express both male and female characteristics. Region II promotes male development. When this region is missing, a female plant is produced. Region III carries male fertility genes; loss of this region results in male sterility. A part of the Y chromosome is homologous with a part of the X, but the major part of the X is differential with no counterpart in the Y.

Although most female-determining genetic material is in the X, Westergaard found that the autosomes were also involved in female determination. Female plants of this species, like those of many other species of plants and animals have a potentiality for maleness. Pistillate plants infected with a parasitic fungus (for instance, smut) sometimes undergo sex reversal and develop anthers.

### *Balance Between Factors in X Chromosome and Cytoplasm*

Another example of balance mechanism in sex determination, apparently involving the X chromosomes and the cytoplasm, was described by R. B. Goldschmidt and his associates in the gypsy moth *Lymantria dispar*. This species is widespread across the entire Eurasian continent from England to Japan and has now been introduced by man to America. The species is divided into a considerable number of distinctly marked geographical races. Moreover, within geographical races, the two sexes are readily distinguished from each other in secondary sexual characters (color markings) (Fig. 4.24). These differences have made the moth especially useful for studies of geographical distribution and for experimental investigations of genetics and sex determination. Crosses within any

**Fig. 4.24** Above ♀, below ♂ of *Lymantria dispar* L. (German race). (After Goldschmidt.)

**TABLE 4.2 Summary results of reciprocal crosses involving a European and a Japanese geographical race of moths (after Goldschmidt)**

| Cross[a] | | Sons | Daughters |
|---|---|---|---|
| 1. European × Japanese | $F_1$ | Normal | Intersexes |
| | $F_2$ | Normal | ½ normal<br>½ intersexes |
| 2. Japanese × European | $F_1$ | Normal | Normal |
| | $F_2$ | ½ normal<br>½ intersexes | Normal |

[a] In representations of crosses, the female parent is written first.

geographical race of moths were found to result in normal Mendelian patterns and distinct sexes. Males had XX chromosomes and females XY. When, on the other hand, crosses were made between different races, intersexes sometimes occurred. The results of reciprocal crosses involving a European and a Japanese race are summarized in Table 4.2.

An intersex, as defined in this study, is an individual that starts development with its original chromosomal sex but changes sex during development. This change takes place at a certain point, the turning point, and development is finished with more or less of the characteristic pattern of the other sex, although no change in chromosomes has occurred. Intersexes are primarily of two types according to the original sex. Female intersexes have female chromosome complements and begin development as females but change after a turning point and develop male characteristics. Male intersexes begin as males and change to females. These intersexes, unlike intersexes in most other organisms, are fertile. Crosses could be made between representatives of several different geographical races.

The genetic mechanism involved was interpreted by Goldschmidt from the results of reciprocal crosses involving a European and a Japanese race (Table 4.2). When the female parent was from the European race, the $F_1$ males were all normal but the females were all intersexes. Among the $F_2$ progeny from this cross (Cross 1) the males were normal and half the females were normal, but half were intersexes. From the reciprocal cross between Japanese females and European males, all $F_1$ progeny were normal. Half of the $F_2$ males were normal and half were intersexes whereas all $F_2$ females were normal.

Factors for maleness were interpreted by Goldschmidt to segregate in Mendelian fashion and were located in the X chromosomes (which are XX in male moths). The factor for femaleness, which was transmitted without segregation to all offspring, was located in the cytoplasm. To explain why interracial crosses resulted in intersexuality, Goldschmidt ascribed different relative strengths of sex-determining factors to different races. Within any single race, the factors were so well balanced that each individual developed into a normal male or a normal female.

When, on the other hand, factors of different strength were brought together by means of interracial crosses, an imbalance occurred and resulted in intersexuality. If the European race is weak in sex determination and the Japanese race is strong, any zygote carrying a weak female ($F_w$) cytoplasmic factor and a strong male ($M_{st}$) X-chromosome factor will be a

**TABLE 4.3 Interpretation of results of reciprocal crosses involving a European (E) (weak) and a Japanese (J) (strong) race of moths (after Goldschmidt and Dodson)**

| Cross[a] | | Sons | Daughters |
|---|---|---|---|
| 1. E $F_wM_w$ × J $F_{st}M_{st}M_{st}$ | $F_1$ | $F_wM_wM_{st}$ Normal | $F_wM_{st}$ Intersex |
| | $F_2$ | $F_wM_wM_{st}$ | $F_wM_w$ |
| | | or | |
| | | $F_wM_{st}M_{st}$ | Normal |
| | | | or |
| | | Normal | $F_wM_{st}$ Intersex |
| 2. J $F_{st}M_{st}$ × E $F_wM_wM_w$ | $F_1$ | $F_{st}M_{st}M_w$ Normal | $F_{st}M_w$ Normal |
| | $F_2$ | $F_{st}M_{st}M_w$ Normal | $F_{st}M_{st}$ Normal |
| | | or | or |
| | | $F_{st}M_wM_w$ Intersex | $F_{st}M_w$ Normal |

[a] In representations of crosses, the female parent is written first.

female intersex. Any zygote with a strong female ($F_{st}$) and a weak male ($M_w$) will be a male intersex. This is apparently true for both homozygous ($M_wM_w$) and heterzygous ($M_{st}M_w$) male determining factors in the X-chromosome. On this basis, the results of reciprocal crosses (Table 4.2) may be interpreted as illustrated in Table 4.3.

In moths resulting from interracial crosses, the degree of intersexuality was thus interpreted to depend on the relative strength of the factors in the races crossed. Where the difference is great, nearly complete sex reversal may occur. If the difference is slight, only a few traits of the new sex may develop.

Both male and female intersexes, therefore, are expected to include subtypes according to the time of the turning point. An early turning point allows more time for traits to assume the characteristics of the new sex and the individual becomes transformed to a large extent in the direction of the other sex, thus becoming a "high-grade intersex". A later turning point will leave little time for differentiation of the new sex traits and the individual will show only a small mixture of characters of the other sex, thus becoming a "low-grade intersex". For purposes of description, Goldschmidt identified the properties of the races for producing intersexes according to their respective strength. As indicated above, the European race was described as "weak" and the Japanese race as "strong." Other examples are Gifu, which was found to be the weakest of all observed strong races; Fiume was weak; Hokkado was very weak; and Kumamoto was neutral.

### *Male Haploidy in Hymenoptera*

More involved mechanisms for sex determination have been described in the insect order, Hymenoptera, which includes ants, bees, wasps, and sawflies. In several species of Hymenoptera, males arise parthenogenetically, that is, without fertilization, and have a haploid chromosome number (16 in the drone honey bee). The queen honey bee and workers, which arise from fertilized eggs, carry the diploid chromosome number (32). Something associated with the haploid-diploid chromosome arrangement is involved in sex determination in bees. Parthenogenesis also occurs in a genus of parasitic wasps, Habrobracon, in which females are diploid with 20 chromosomes, and males are haploid with 10 chromosomes. Females originate from fertilized eggs, but males ordinarily come from unfertilized eggs.

Some Habrobracon males produced experimentally by Whiting came from fertilized eggs and were diploid, whereas others came from unfertilized eggs and were haploid. All females were diploid. Results of experiments showed that the homozygous or heterozygous status of certain chromosome segments controlled sex determination. Males were produced when these segments were homozygous or hemizygous, as in parthenogenetic males. Females were always heterozygous for these segments. Stated more precisely, haploid males had genotypes *Xa, Xb,* or *Xc;* diploid males were *XaXa, XbXb,* or *XcXc.* Females were always heterozygous with combinations such as *XaXb*, *XaXc*, or *XbXc*. The chromosome segments behaved as if they were multiple alleles. Allelism was proved by experiments with linked genes, particularly the mutant gene for "fused" at 10 map units from the sex-determining locus. A complementary action of different alleles was postulated as necessary for the production of femaleness. Any allele, whether present in single or double condition (hemizygous or homozygous), had no complement with which to interact and, therefore, produced maleness.

### *Single Genes and Sex Determination*

Sex determination in some organisms is influenced by the differential action of single genes. Maize, for example, is monoecious, having staminate flowers in the tassel and pistillate flowers in the ear. A substitution of two single gene pairs makes the difference between monoecious (both sexes in the same plant) and dioecious (separate sexes) plants. The gene for barren plant (*ba*), when homozygous, makes the stalk staminate by eliminating the silks and ears. On the other hand, the gene for tassel seed (*ts*), when homozygous, transforms the tassel into a pistillate structure that produces no pollen. A plant of the genotype *babatsts* lacks silks on the stalk but has a transformed tassel and is therefore only pistillate (female). A plant with $babats^+ts^+$ is only staminate (male). These data suggest how monoecious plants could become dioecious and vice versa by the alteration (mutation) of two genes: $ba^+$ to *ba* and $ts^+$ to *ts*.

Recent investigations have shown that the monoecious character in spinach is controlled by a single gene, *m*, on the X chromosome. The gene is recessive to its allele on the Y and incompletely dominant to another allele of the X. XX plants are ordinarily pistillate and XY plants are staminate. True-breeding monoecious plants are $X^mX^m$. Plants of the genotype $X^mY$ are staminate. Those that are $XX^m$ are more highly pistillate than $X^mX^m$ plants.

In Drosophila, a single recessive gene *tra*, described by A. H. Sturtevant, transforms ordinary diploid females into flies that express the phenotypic characteristics of males but are sterile. A cross between a female carrying *tra* and a male homozygous for this gene is illustrated in Fig. 4.25. Progeny carrying XX and homozygous for *tra* are phenotypically transformed into sterile males. A single gene has thus altered the basic sex-determining mechanism.

Another gene, *Ha*, studied by J. W. Gowen and his associates, which is probably an allele of *tra*, is responsible for a hermaphroditic but sterile condition in

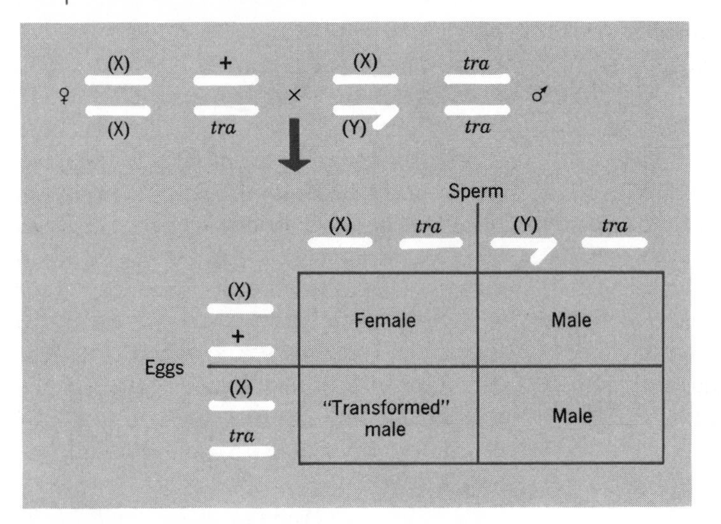


**Fig. 4.25** A cross in Drosophila between a male homozygous for the transformer *tra* gene and a female heterozygous for *tra*. The sex ratio in the progeny is altered from the usual ratio of about one female to one male.

Drosophila. In the presence of this gene, XX flies, which would ordinarily be females, have male as well as female characteristics in the gonads and they are sterile.

## *External Environment and Sex Determination*

In some lower animals, sex determination is nongenetic and depends on the external environment. Males and females have similar genotypes but a stimulus from an environmental source initiates development toward one sex or the other. For example, the male of the marine worm Bonellia is small and degenerate and lives within the reproductive tract of the larger female (Fig. 4.26). The male is conveniently located for fertilization of the eggs, but little else can be said for his situation. All the organs of his body are degenerate except those making up the reproductive system, and thus the male is essentially parasitic. This worm provides an excellent material for the study of an elementary type of sex determination and therefore has been investigated extensively.

F. Baltzer found that any young worm reared from a single isolated egg became a female. If newly hatched worms were released in water containing mature females, however, some of the young worms were attracted to the females and became attached to the female proboscis. These were transformed into the males and eventually migrated to the female reproductive tract where they became parasitic. Genetic determiners for both sexes are apparently present in young worms. Extracts made from the female proboscis will influence young worms toward maleness.

The snail Crepidula also provides an example of sex determination controlled by the environment. As in Bonellia, young isolated organisms invariably develop into females, but if reared in close proximity to adult females some become males. A hormonelike secretion from adults influences the sexual development of the young. As expected, organisms dependent on the environment for sex determination produce disproportionate numbers of the two sexes. They would seem to be at a disadvantage when compared with animals in which sex determination is largely genetic and differentiation occurs at an early stage in development. On the other hand, such animals as Bonellia and Crepidula, even when isolated in small populations, would always have representatives of both sexes.

Some organisms have a built-in mechanism for changing from one sex to the other. A marine segmented worm, Ophryotrocha, for example, starts out as a male and eventually produces sperm. When it becomes older and develops some twenty segments, however, it changes to a female and produces eggs. If it is experimentally reduced in size to less than twenty segments by starvation or mutilation, it becomes a male again. Overall size and number of segments thus control sex determination, which is reversible.

## HORMONES AND SEX DIFFERENTIATION

The hormonal system which regulates the internal or physiological environment of the organism, does not directly influence the fundamental process of sex determination. It is important, however, to the development of the more conspicuous secondary sex characteristics. Sex hormones of higher animals are elaborated by the endocrine glands, particularly the ovaries and testes (gonads), although the

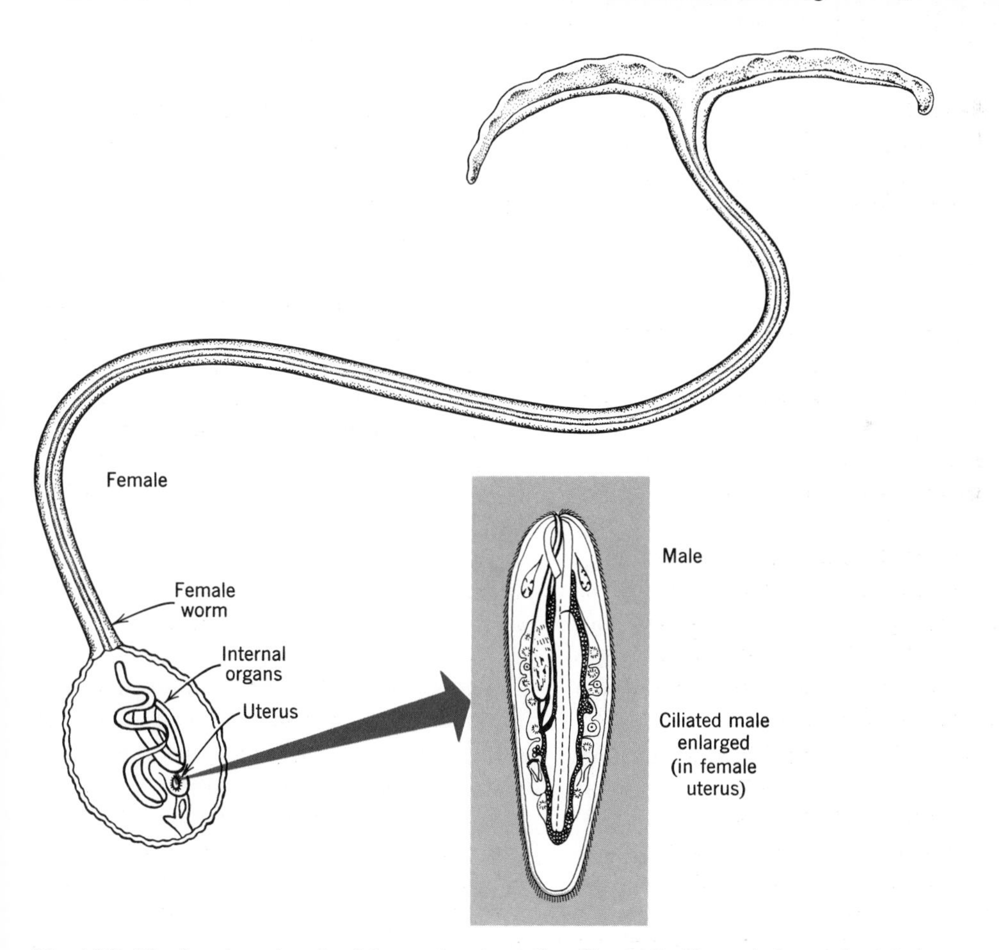


**Fig. 4.26** The female and male of the marine worm *Bonellia viridis.* The male is greatly magnified to show details of internal structure. (Redrawn from Dobzhansky, *Evolution, Genetics and Man,* 1955, John Wiley & Sons, Inc.)

adrenals and pituitary are also involved. Ovaries and testes each have a joint function: they are responsible for the production of the primary sex elements, the eggs and sperm, respectively, as well as of the secondary sex characters, which are controlled by the sex hormones. Certain cells making up the basic structure of the gonad produce mature gametes. Other cells elaborate the hormones that influence the development of secondary sexual characteristics such as physiological differences in the rate of metabolism, blood pressure, heart beat, and respiration. The adrenals produce steroids that are chemically related to those of the gonads and that also influence the secondary sex characteristics.

In higher animals, early differentiation, including that of the sex organs, is influenced by hormones. In salamanders, for example, E. Witschi found that a peculiar type of hormonal balance is involved in the differentiation of the gonads; antagonistic substances are formed by the cortex and medulla of the embryonic gonad. The male hormone is produced by the medulla, whereas the female hormone comes from the cortex. When male and female salamanders were experimentally grafted together, the male substance suppressed the development of the ovary in the female member. When the male graft was considerably smaller than the female, however, the female hormone was dominant and genetically determined males developed ovaries. The quantity of the hormone evidently was a factor in this transition.

Partial sex reversals sometimes occur in adults of higher animal species, indicating that at least the secondary sex characteristics of the opposite sex are potentially present throughout the life of the individual. In fowls, for example, when the ovary of the female is destroyed through injury or disease, male characteristics such as cock feathering, wattles, and crowing ability develop. Primary as well as secondary sex characters of chickens are sometimes involved in the reversal. In one series of experiments, normal hens underwent complete sex reversal when their ovaries were destroyed; the male gonad developed and they fathered chicks. Primary as well as secondary sex structures and functions were thus involved in the reversal. Removal of the gonads of either sex in mammals is followed by the development of secondary sex characteristics of the other sex.

Sexual differentiation in man as well as in other animals is influenced by hormones. When the testes of the male are removed before puberty, female characteristics of body form, voice, and hair pattern develop in the adult. These female tendencies can be counteracted by artificially introducing male hormones. The relationship between secondary sex characteristics and hormones can also be demonstrated experimentally in mammals by injecting sex hormones of the opposite sex into normal males or females. Tumors of the adrenals in women are associated with the development of masculine characteristics, that is, lower pitched voice and increased growth of hair. Development of masculine characteristics such as changes in voice and hair growth in elderly women reflects a natural slowing down of hormone production.

### *Sex-Influenced Traits*

The end product of some gene action is influenced by hormones. For example, autosomal genes responsible for horns in some breeds of sheep behave differently in the presence of the male and female sex hormones. More than a single pair of genes is involved in the production of horns, but assuming all other genes to be homozygous, the example can be treated as if only a single pair were involved. Among Dorset sheep, both sexes are horned, and the gene for the horned condition is homozygous

**TABLE 4.4 Genotypes and corresponding phenotypes in male and female hybrid sheep**

| Genotypes | Males | Females |
|---|---|---|
| $h^+h^+$ | Horned | Horned |
| $h^+h$ | Horned | Hornless |
| $hh$ | Hornless | Hornless |

($h^+h^+$). In Suffolk sheep, neither sex is horned and the genotype is $hh$. Among the $F_1$ progeny from crosses between these two breeds, horned males and hornless females are produced. Because both sexes are genotypically alike ($h^+h$) the gene must behave as a dominant in males and as a recessive in females; that is, only one gene is required for an expression in the male, but the same gene must be homozygous for expression in the female.

When $F_1$ hybrids are mated together, a ratio of 3 horned to 1 hornless is produced among the $F_2$ males, whereas a ratio of 3 hornless to 1 horned is observed among the $F_2$ females. Genotypes and phenotypes of the two sexes are summarized as shown in Table 4.4. The only departure from the usual pattern is concerned with the heterozygous ($h^+h$) genotype. This genotype in the male results in the horned condition, but females with the same genotype are hornless. Dominance of the gene is apparently influenced by the sex hormone.

Some human traits, such as certain type of white forelock, absence of the upper lateral incisor teeth, and a particular type of enlargement of the terminal joints of the fingers, have been reported to follow the sex-influenced mode of inheritance. Other abnormalities such as harelip, cleft palate, and stuttering have hereditary bases and occur more frequently and more severely among males than females. The inheritance mechanism is complex. Environmental as well as genetic factors are involved but autosomal and not sex-linked genes have been associated with the traits. The higher incidence of affected males presumably indicates some sort of sex influence on gene action.

### *Sex-Limited Traits*

Some genes can not express themselves in the presence of certain hormones and therefore are considered to be sex-limited. In most breeds of domestic poultry, plumage of the two sexes is strikingly different, but in some Sebright bantams, for example, both sexes are hen-feathered. In the Hamburgh breed, both hen-feathered and cock-feathered males may be produced, but all females are hen-feathered. Results of appropriate crosses show that hen feathering is due to a dominant gene $h^+$ and cock feathering to its recessive allele $h$. Cock feathering, however, not only requires a particular genotype, but also is limited to the male sex. Even though females carry the proper genotype ($hh$) for cock feathering, they are hen-feathered. Genotypes and corresponding phenotypes that might occur in mixed breeds of chickens are summarized as shown in Table 4.5.

The Hamburgh strain, in which males are cock-feathered and females are hen-feathered, carries the homozygous genotype $hh$. Sebright bantams, in which both sexes are hen-feathered, carry the homozygous genotype $h^+h^+$. In hybrids between the two breeds, the genotype and presence or absence of the male sex hormone determine the feathering pattern. Both alleles are apparently segregating in populations that include hen-feathered and cock-feathered males. In such flocks, all females, regardless of genotype, are hen-feathered,

**TABLE 4.5 Genotypes and corresponding phenotypes in male and female hybrid chickens**

| Genotypes | Males | Females |
|---|---|---|
| $h^+h^+$ | Hen-feathered | Hen-feathered |
| $h^+h$ | Hen-feathered | Hen-feathered |
| $hh$ | Cock-feathered | Hen-feathered |

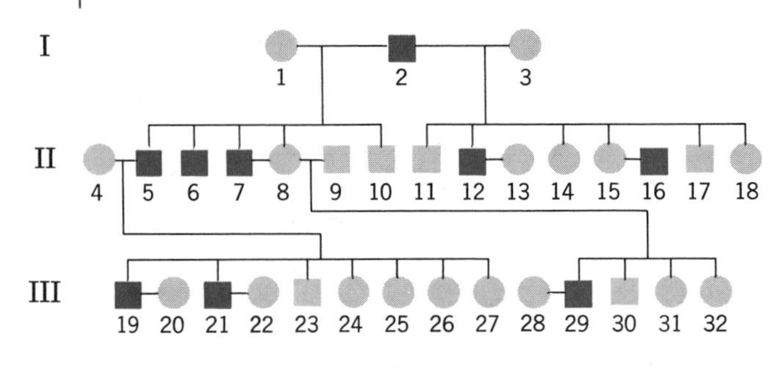


**Fig. 4.27** A pedigree showing incidence of premature baldness in a family group. The men represented by the darkened squares were bald before they reached the age of 35. Those symbolized by light squares were over 35 when the study was made and all had thick hair.

and males carrying the gene $h^+$ are also hen-feathered; only *hh* males are cock-feathered. Experimental gonadectomies have elucidated the relation between genes and hormones. Removal of the ovary in a hen-feathered female (*hh*) results in cock feathering. This indicates that the female sex hormone normally inhibits the *hh* genotype from producing cock-feathering. Furthermore, in castrated males, the $h^+$ gene is inhibited. Thus, the hormones of both sexes limit gene action.

Premature (pattern) baldness in man has also been explained as a sex-limited trait. Other types of baldness are associated with abnormalities in thyroid metabolism and infectious disease. About 26 percent of the men over 30 in the United States are baldheaded. Approximately half of these became bald prematurely, in their twenties or early thirties. Baldness is known to be more common in some families than in others. Several different modes of inheritance have been associated by different investigators with this trait. An explanation for a particular type of premature baldness based on sex-limited inheritance was set forth by J. B. Hamilton and supported by statistical data accumulated by H. Harris. A single dominant gene that expresses itself only in the presence of an adequate level of androgenic hormone was postulated by these investigators to account for the observed facts. The level of hormone necessary for expression of the trait is seldom if ever reached in women, but is attained in all normal men.

A pedigree illustrating a hereditary pattern of baldness in one family group is presented in Fig. 4.27. Affected males, symbolized by darkened squares, became bald before they reached the age of 35. Men symbolized by light squares had thick hair, some even in old age. No women in this family group were baldheaded.

Expressions of some genes are sex-limited for more basic reasons. For example, milk production among cattle and other mammals is limited to the sex that is equipped with developed mammary glands and appropriate hormones. It is true that milk production is affected by environmental factors, but inheritance plays a part, and it is well known that milk-yield genes are carried in the chromosomes of bulls as well as cows. Certain bulls are in great demand among dairy breeders and artificial insemination associations because their mothers and daughters have good milk-production records.

The frequency of twins and other multiple births in human families is hereditary to some extent. Mothers are immediately involved, but evidence indicates that genes from their fathers may influence the tendency toward multiple births. Genes of both parents control directly or indirectly many anatomical and physiological characteristics that express themselves only in one sex. The width of the pelvis, age of onset of menstruation, and distribution of body hair in females depend on genes common to both sexes. Genes that directly or indirectly influence the fertility of one sex or the other are presumably transmitted by both parents.

## GYNANDROMORPHS

In some animals such as insects, upsets in the chromosomal behavior result in sexual mosaics called gynandromorphs. Some parts of the animal express female characteristics while other parts express those of the male. Some gynandromorphs in Drosophila are bilateral intersexes (Fig. 4.28), with male color pattern, body shape, and sex comb on one half and female characteristics on the other half of the body. Both male and female gonads and genitalia are sometimes present.

Bilateral gynandromorphs have been explained on the basis of an irregularity in the chromosome mechanism at the first cleavage of the zygote. Infrequently, a chromosome lags in division and does not arrive at the pole in time to be included in the reconstructed nucleus of the daughter cell. If one of the X chromosomes of an XX (female) zygote should lag in the center of the spindle, one daughter cell would get only one X chromosome and the other would get XX, as illustrated in Fig. 4.29. The basis for a mosaic pattern would thus be established. One cell in the two-cell stage would be XX (female) and one would be XO (male). In Drosophila, the right and left halves of the body are determined at the first cleavage. One cell gives rise to all the cells making up the right half of the adult body and the other gives rise to the left half. If the chromosome loss should occur at a later cell division, a smaller proportion of the adult body would be included in the male segment. The position and size of the mosaic sector would be determined, therefore, by the place and time of the division abnormality.

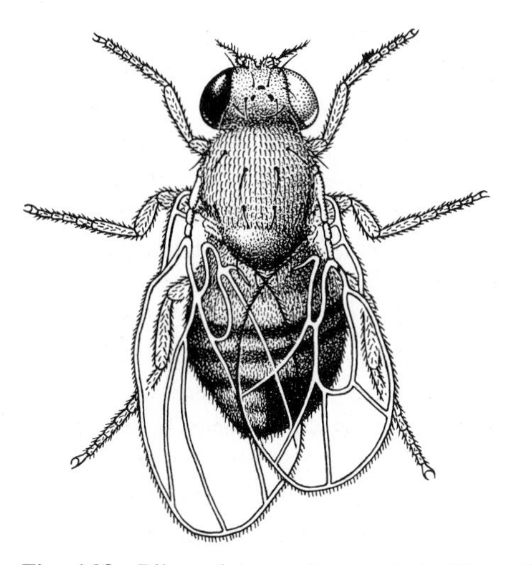

**Fig. 4.28** Bilateral gynandromorph in Drosophila. (After Morgan.)

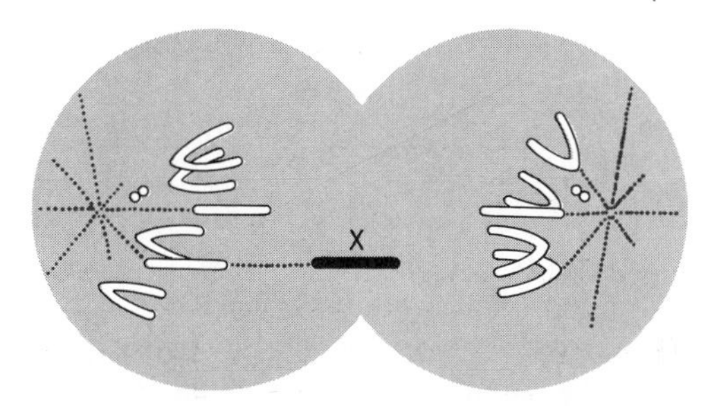


**Fig. 4.29** Diagram of a lagging X chromosome in the first cleavage of Drosophila illustrating the origin of a bilateral gynandromorph. (After Morgan and Bridges.)

Gynandromorphs were described in Drosophila by Sturtevant, Morgan, and Bridges beginning in 1919. Following the original descriptions, a few conspicuous examples were reported in flies, but the condition was considered extremely rare. More extensive observations have since shown that a gynandromorph of some kind is produced in every 2000 to 3000 flies; many of these represent small sections of tissue involving only a few cells. Spencer Brown and Aloha Hannah-Alava devised a technique to increase experimentally the frequency of gynandromorphs by making use of a ring X chromosome first discovered by L. V. Morgan. These chromosomes have undergone structural modification in such a way that the two ends fuse together forming rings. These aberrant chromosomes are frequently eliminated by a natural process from older eggs. When virgin females are not mated until they are 8 to 17 days old, the proportion of gynandromorphs is greatly increased, and when excess yeast is added to the culture, an even greater proportion of the flies is gynanders. Investigators can thus partially control the natural process of chromosome removal and produce gynandromorphs much more frequently than they would ordinarily occur. In treated cultures, as many as 20 percent of the flies are gynanders. Marker genes such as *y* for yellow body color were placed in the X chromosomes and then used to identify male and female tissue. Flies were prepared that began development as heterozygotes, for example, $y/y^+$. When one X chromosome was eliminated from a cell, male tissue was formed in the area arising from the deficient cell. Some patches of male tissue carried the *y* gene and were phenotypically yellow. These methods have proved useful for studies of differentiation of bristles and other body structures.

The bilateral type of gynandromorph typical of Drosophila is not the only type observed in insects. In Habrobracon, gynandromorphs may occur in the anterior-posterior plane, giving rise to such peculiar arrangements as male heads with female abdomens and female heads with male abdomens.

## SUMMARY

Interactions of genes result in different modifications of Mendelian ratios. A lethal may change a 3:1 to a 2:1 ratio. The basic 9:3:3:1 dihybrid ratio may be modified to 9:7, 12:3:1, 13:3, 15:1 or other alterations with a total of 16. Other variations in results of crosses may be explained by different kinds of interactions involving genes and environments.

Investigations on the basic mechanism of sex determination have been carried out mostly with insects but also with several other animals and plants. In organisms studied, each sex has a potentiality for characteristics of the other sex. Determination for one sex or the other is usually accomplished by a balance between genetic factors for maleness and those for femaleness. Several different combinations involving chromosomes, genes, cytoplasm or factors from the hormonal or external environment have been associated with this balance, particularly reflected in the secondary sex characteristics of the organisms concerned. Hormones have been found to influence the expressions of some genes. Gynandromorphs in insects are sex mosaics that have resulted from irregularity in an early cell cleavage. One part of the animal has female characteristics and another part has male characteristics.

## REFERENCES

Allen, C. E. 1940. "The genotypic basis of sex-expression in Angiosperms." *Bot. Rev.*, **6,** 227–300.

Allen, E. 1932. *Sex and internal secretions.* The Williams and Wilkins Co., Baltimore.

Bridges, C. B. 1925. "Sex in relation to chromosomes and genes." *Amer. Nat.*, **59,** 127–137.

Dronamraju, K. R. 1965. "The function of the Y-chromosome in man, animals, and plants." *Adv. in Genet.*, **13,** 227–310.

Goldschmidt, R. 1934. "Lymantria." *Bibliographia Genetica,* **11,** 1–186. (Extensive studies on the gypsy moth. Sex determination shown to depend on balance between X chromosome and cytoplasm.)

Harris, H. 1947. "The inheritance of premature baldness in man." *Annals of Eugenics,* **13,** 172–181.

Hungerford, D. A., A. J. Donnelly, P. C. Nowell, and S. Beck. 1959. "The chromosome constitution of a human phenotypic intersex." *Amer. J. Human Genet.*, **11,** 215–236.

Stormont, C. 1959. "On the applications of blood groups in animal breeding." *Proc. X Int. Cong. Genetics,* **1,** 206–224. University of Toronto Press, Toronto.

Warmke, H. E. 1946. "Sex determination and sex balance in Melandrium." *Amer. J. Bot.*, **33**, 648–660.
Westergaard, M. 1948. "The relation between chromosome constitution and sex in the offspring of triploid Melandrium." *Hereditas*, **34**, 257–279.
Whiting, P. W. 1945. "The evolution of male haploidy." *Quart. Rev. Biol.*, **20**, 231–260. (Sex determination in Habrobracon.)
Witschi, E. 1957. "Sex chromatin and sex differentiation in human embryos." *Science*, **126**, 1288–1290.

# *Problems*

**4.1** In Drosophila, a dominant gene (*D*) for a phenotype called "dichaete" alters the bristles and also makes the wings remain extended from the body while the fly is at rest. It is homozygous lethal. (a) Diagram a cross between two dichaete (*Dd*) flies and summarize the expected results. (b) Diagram a cross between dichaete and wild type and summarize the expected results.

**4.2** In poultry, the genes for rose comb (*R*) and pea comb (*P*) together produce walnut comb. The alleles of both in a homozygous condition (that is, *rrpp*) produce single comb. From information concerning interactions of these genes given in the chapter, determine the phenotypes and proportions expected from the following crosses: (a) *RRPp* × *rrPp*; (b) *rrPP* × *RrPp*; (c) *RrPp* × *Rrpp*; (d) *Rrpp* × *rrpp*.

**4.3** Rose-comb chickens mated with walnut-comb chickens produce 15 walnut, 14 rose, 5 pea, and 6 single-comb chicks. Determine the probable genotypes of the parents.

**4.4** The shape and color of radishes are controlled by two independent pairs of alleles that show no dominance; each genotype is distinguishable phenotypically. The color may be red (*RR*), purple (*R′R*), or white (*R′R′*), and the shape may be long (*LL*), oval (*LL′*), or round (*L′L′*). Using the checkerboard method, diagram a cross between red, long (*RRLL*) and white, round (*R′R′L′L′*) radishes and summarize the $F_2$ results under the headings phenotypes, genotypes, genotypic frequency, and phenotypic ratio.

**4.5** In cattle, the gene (*P*) for the polled condition is dominant over that (*p*) for horns. The roan color (*RR′*) is intermediate between red (*RR*) and white (*R′R′*). (a) Using the forked-line method, diagram a cross between a polled, red cow (*PPRR*) and a horned, white (*ppR′R′*) bull and summarize the $F_2$ results. (b) What is the probability that a given calf from this mating will be horned and white?

**4.6** In sweet peas, genes *C* and *P* are necessary for colored flowers. In the absence of either or both (*ccpp*) of these genes, the flowers are white. What will be the flower color of the offspring of the following crosses and in what proportion: (a) *Ccpp* × *ccPp*; (b) *CcPp* × *Ccpp*; (c) *ccpp* × *CcPp*; (d) *CcPp* × *CcPp*?

**4.7** A purple-flowered sweet pea plant crossed with a white-flowered plant produced 14 purple and 16 white. Give the probable genotypes of the parents.

**4.8** White chickens may be the result of two different genetic combinations: the homozygous state of the recessive gene *o* or the homozygous state of the recessive gene *c*. Color requires the action of both *C* and *O*. What progeny might be expected in the $F_2$ of the following cross and in what proportion: *ccOO* × *CCoo*?

4.9 White-fruit color in summer squash is dependent on a dominant gene (*W*), and colored fruit on the recessive allele (*w*). In the presence of *ww* and a dominant gene (*G*), the color is yellow, but when *G* is not present (that is, *gg*), the color is green. Give the $F_2$ phenotypes and proportions expected from crossing a white-fruited (*WWGG*) with a green-fruited (*wwgg*) plant.

4.10 The White Leghorn breed of chickens is known to carry in homozygous conditions a color gene (*C*) and a dominant inhibitor (*I*) which prevents the action of *C*. The White Wyandotte (*iicc*) has neither the inhibitor nor the color gene. Give the $F_2$ phenotypes and proportions expected from crossing a White Leghorn (*IICC*) with a White Wyandotte (*iicc*).

4.11 (a) How did the discovery of sex chromosomes support the chromosome theory of heredity? (b) Why did McClung not succeed in discovering the chromosomal sex-determining mechanism from his extensive cytological investigations on grasshoppers?

4.12 (a) Distinguish between the XO and XY types of sex determination. (b) Which was considered to be the more widespread in the early part of the century? (c) Which is considered now to be more widespread?

4.13 Describe or illustrate diagrammatically gamete formation and sex determination in an organism of XY type. What difference exists between male and female determining sperm?

4.14 What is the significance of the Y chromosome in sex determination of the following genera: (a) Drosophila, (b) Lymantria, (c) Melandrium?

4.15 (a) Describe Bridges' genic balance theory for sex determination. (b) What is the expected sex of each of the following: (1) 4X 4A; (2) 3X 4A; (3) 2X 3A; (4) 1X 3A; (5) 2X 2A; (6) 1X 2A?

4.16 A cross was made between a triploid (3*n*) female fly with two X chromosomes attached and one free, and a normal diploid male. Assuming the cross to be successful and the gametes of the female to carry one or two whole sets of autosomes, list the expected results in terms of sex and intersex combinations.

4.17 In plants of the genus Melandrium, characteristics of which sex would be associated with the following chromosome arrangements (a) XY, (b) XX, (c) XY with region I removed and (d) XY with region II removed?

4.18 (a) What is an intersex as defined by Goldschmidt in the Gypsy moth? (b) How can intersexes in this insect by produced and detected? (c) What determines whether an intersex will be high grade or low grade?

4.19 What would be expected in the backcross progeny from $F_1$ normal males, represented in Table 4.3, Cross 1, and (a) females from the Japanese race, (b) females from the European race?

4.20 What would be expected if normal $F_1$ females from Cross 2 (Table 4.3) were backcrossed (a) with males of the Japanese race (b) males from the European race?

4.21 What would be expected if the $F_1$ females from Cross 1 (if fertile) were backcrossed with (a) Japanese males (b) European males.

4.22 Based on the investigations of Whiting, what would be the sex of individuals of the following genotypes in Habrobracon: (a) *Xb*, (b) *XaXb*, (c) *XcXc*, (d) *XbXc*.

**4.23** How could maize plants, which are ordinarily monoecious, give rise to plants that are dioecious?

**4.24** (a) If newly hatched marine worms of the genus Bonellia were kept isolated from all other worms, what sex would they represent when adults? (b) If they developed in the vicinity of mature females, what would be their sex? (c) Develop an explanation for this type of sex determination.

**4.25** How can sex reversal in chickens be explained?

**4.26** How can sex-influenced and sex-limited traits be explained?

**4.27** In sheep, the gene $h^+$ for horned condition is dominant in males and recessive in females. If a hornless ram were mated to a horned ewe, what is the chance that an (a) $F_2$ male sheep will be horned? (b) $F_2$ female will be horned?

**4.28** In chickens, the gene $h$, which distinguishes hen feathering from cock feathering, is sex-limited. Males may be hen-feathered or cock-feathered, but females are always hen-feathered. If a cock-feathered male ($hh$) were mated to a homozygous ($h^+h^+$) hen-feathered female, what patterns of feathering might be expected among the (a) male $F_2$ and (b) female $F_2$ progeny?

**4.29** The dominant autosomal gene ($B$) for premature baldness in man is considered to be sex-limited. If a man with the genotype $B^+B$, married a woman with the genotype $B^+B$, what proportion of their (a) male and (b) female children might be expected to become bald prematurely?

**4.30** In a particular species of grasshoppers, two pairs of autosomes are heteromorphic; that is, they can be distinguished by microscopic observation. In one pair, one homologue is rod shaped and the other has a small hook at the end. One member of the other pair has a knob on one end, whereas its homologue is rod shaped. List all distinguishable combinations, with reference to these two pairs, that can be found in the sperm.

**4.31** In Drosophila, the recessive gene ($bb$) for bobbed bristles is located in the X chromosome. The Y chromosome of Drosophila carries a homologous section in which $bb$ or its allele $bb^+$ may be located. Give the genotypes and phenotypes of the offspring from the following crosses:

(a) $X^{bb}X^{bb} \times X^{bb}Y^{bb^+}$ (c) $X^{bb^+}X^{bb} \times X^{bb^+}Y^{bb}$

(b) $X^{bb}X^{bb^+} \times X^{bb^+}Y^{bb}$ (d) $X^{bb^+}X^{bb} \times X^{bb}Y^{bb^+}$

# Sex Linkage

# 5

When the parallelism was discovered between the X chromosome cycle and sex determination, it was generally assumed among investigators that genes other than sex determiners were located in the X chromosome. The first sex-linked trait was found in the current moth *Abraxas grossulariata* in 1906 by Doncaster. When reciprocal crosses were made between members of the variety lacticolor (Fig. 5.1) and other moths of the species *A. grossulariata,* the lacticolor characteristics were shown to follow a pattern that could be explained by X chromosome segregation. When crosses were made between lacticolor females and "typical" males, all $F_1$ moths were typical in appearance. In the $F_2$, about one quarter were lacticolor (as expected for the expression of a recessive gene), but all the lacticolor specimens were females. The gene was located in the X chromosome and female moths were heterogametic. When lacticolor females were mated with $F_1$ males, half of the males and half of the females were lacticolor. Lacticolor males mated with $F_1$ females produced all lacticolor females and all typical males (heterozygous).

The first extensive experimental evidence for sex linkage in a species with heterogametic males came in 1910 with the discovery by T. H. Morgan (1866–1945; Fig. 5.2) of the white-eyed mutant (Fig. 5.3) Drosophila. A single white-eyed male appeared in a culture of red-eyed flies. Evidently, a gene had undergone a change or mutation that resulted in the alteration of one or more chemical reactions in the development of the fly and the eyes were white rather than red. The white-eyed male was mated with a red-eyed female. $F_1$ flies were all red-eyed, but the $F_2$ included both red and white in the ratio of about 3 red to 1 white. This familiar ratio suggested that the gene for red eyes was dominant over the newly created allele for white. More detailed observations, however, showed that all white-eyed flies in the $F_2$

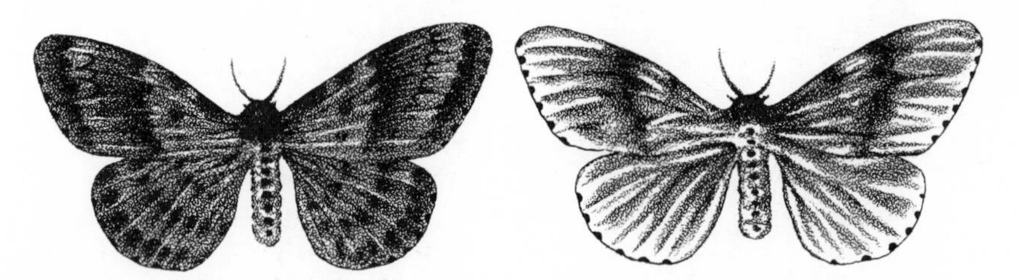

**Fig. 5.1** *Abraxas grossulariata* (left) and its variety, lacticolor (right). (After Doncaster.)

**Fig. 5.2** Thomas Hunt Morgan, American geneticist and embryologist. Nobel Laureate in biology and medicine (1933).

generation were males. About half of the $F_2$ males had white eyes and half had red, but all females had red eyes. The recessive gene apparently expressed itself only in the males. Morgan arrived at an explanation by associating this gene with the X chromosome, as illustrated in Fig. 5.4.

Because the male fly had only one X chromosome and an unlike Y chromosome, it was postulated that a single gene for white eyes was capable of expression when its allele was absent. The word *hemizygous* is used to describe those males that have only one member of an allelomorphic pair of genes. Furthermore, the mutated gene present in the X chromosome of the original white-eyed male was passed on to his daughters (he transmitted a Y chromosome to his sons). All the daughters therefore, were carriers for the gene. The $F_2$ hemizygous males obtained their X chromosomes from their heterozygous mothers. Half received the $w^+$ gene and developed red eyes and half received the $w$ gene and developed white eyes. The equal proportion of red-eyed and white-eyed $F_2$ males was thus explained on the basis of the segregation of the X chromosomes from the $F_1$ mothers to their sons.

Could white-eyed females occur? On the basis of his hypothesis that the gene was

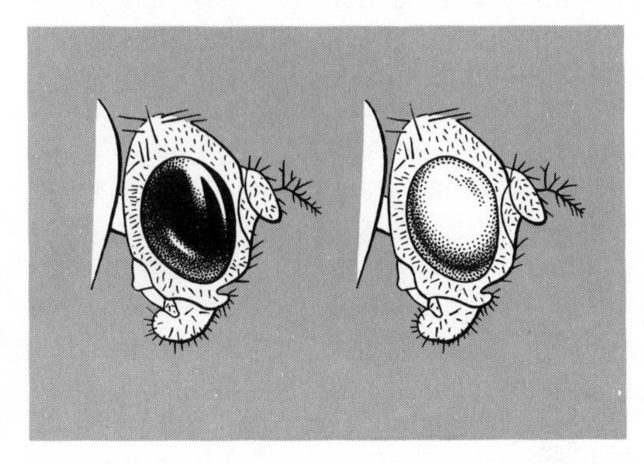

**Fig. 5.3** Illustration of the white-eye mutation in Drosophila. (Left) Red eye of the wild type; (right) white eye of the mutant.

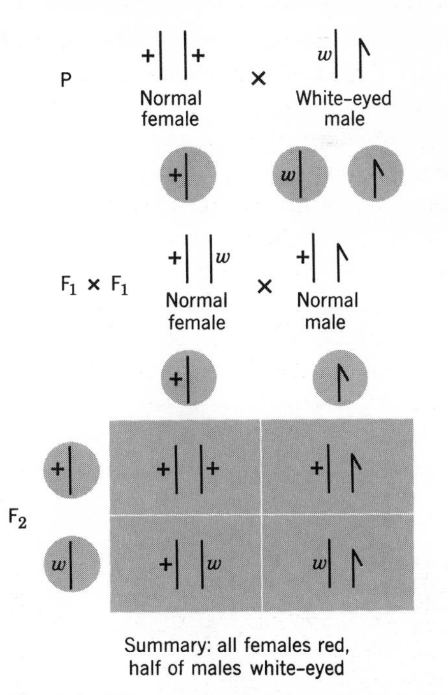


**Fig. 5.4** Diagram on the chromosomes of a cross between a red-eyed female and a white-eyed male. This cross illustrates Morgan's explanation of sex linkage.

carried in the X chromosome, Morgan predicted that a female of the genotype *ww* could be produced and would have white eyes. This was tested experimentally with crosses between males with white eyes and $F_1$ ($ww^+$) females with red eyes. From these crosses, half of the females as well as half of the males had white eyes, as predicted. The white-eyed males and females were then mated and a culture of only white-eyed flies was produced. A stock was thus established and maintained and is now represented in many genetics laboratories. The white-eyed mutation has occurred spontaneously several times since Morgan's original white-eyed fly.

C. B. Bridges (1889–1938; Fig. 5.5) was working as a graduate student in Morgan's laboratory when these exciting experiments on Drosophila were being performed. He made crosses between white-eyed females and wild-type males with red eyes. White-eyed sons and red-eyed daughters were expected, but a few exceptional flies occurred. A small number of the progeny were red-eyed males and white-eyed females. Bridges postulated and later demonstrated that nondisjunction of the X chromosomes had occurred; that is, the two X chromosomes failed to separate from each other in meiosis. This process made it possible for female progeny to receive both of their X chromosomes from their mothers and for the males to receive their X chromosome from their fathers. Attached X chromosomes in flies thus provided a technique for localizing genes in the X chromosomes (Fig. 5.6). The red-eyed males lacked the Y chromosome in which fertility factors are located and were sterile. These experimental results proved beyond question that the gene for white eyes was in the X chromosome. Later studies of a similar nature identified many other genes of the X chromosome. Some are shown on the chromosome map (Fig. 5.7).

**Fig. 5.5** Calvin B. Bridges, American geneticist and cytologist.

The term *sex linkage* was used to describe the association or linkage of a hereditary trait with sex because the gene was in a sex chromosome. Most sex-linked genes were found to be in the X chromosome. Some animals, however, carry genes that have visible effects in the Y chromosome. These Y-linked genes are transmitted directly from father to son. Because Y-chromosome linkage is comparatively rare, sex linkage usually implies X linkage or the presence of the genes in question in the X chromosome. Since all sex-linked genes are on the same chromosome, they are linked with each other as well as with the sex-determining genes. The apparent emptiness of the Y chromosome in Drosophila results in a simplex, or unpaired, condition for the genes in the X chromosome of the male fly. In the absence of dominant alleles, a recessive gene, such as the one (*w*) responsible for white eyes, can express itself. The crisscross pattern of inheritance, which is characteristic of sex-linked genes, means that traits appearing in males are trans-

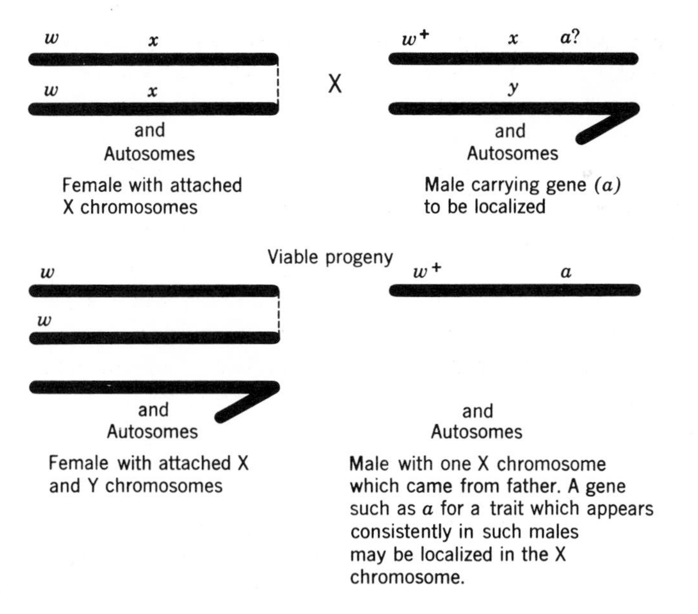


**Fig. 5.6** Diagram of a test for localization of X-linked genes. Progeny with XX and a Y chromosome are normal-appearing females, and progeny with one X and no Y chromosome are sterile males.

mitted (unexpressed) through their daughters to the males in the next generation, where they are expressed.

Cytological studies on the nature and behavior of chromosomes have supported the genetic interpretation of sex linkage. In *Drosophila melanogaster* the X and Y chromosomes can readily be identified by their appearance. The X is rod-shaped with the centromere near one end whereas the Y is hooklike, having a long and a short arm (as illustrated in Fig. 5.6).

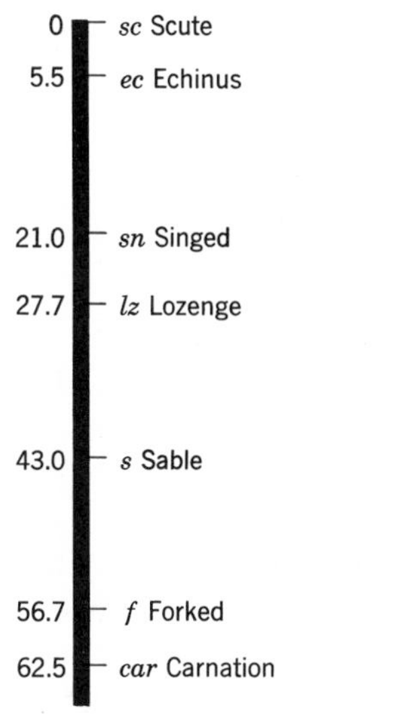


**Fig. 5.7** Map of X chromosome of Drosophila showing 7 sex-linked genes in their relative positions on the chromosome.

Although the Y chromosome is essentially devoid of genes, one small part of the short arm in *D. melanogaster* has a homologous section in the X. This was demonstrated in 1926 by C. Stern following an observation that males known to carry the gene *bb* for bobbed bristles in the X chromosome did not express the trait. The normal allele $bb^+$, which is dominant, was identified in the short arm of the Y chromosome. Genes of this kind, which occur in the X chromosome but have a corresponding gene locus in the Y chromosome, are said to be incompletely sex-linked. Despite the lack of the usual more or less discrete genes, the Y chromosome of Drosophila is not without influence in inheritance. It is composed almost entirely of a different kind of material, heterochromatin, which has special attributes.

The relation of heterochromatin with gene action was elucidated by E. Heitz beginning in 1928. By following chromosomes through the prophase of cell division and later stages of the division cycle, Heitz observed structures in the nucleus which stained densely and therefore could be readily distinguished from other nuclear contents. These bodies did not decondense like other chromosome materials during telophase and in the formation of new nuclei, but they remained visible until near the onset of the next division. At this time, they loosened briefly only to condense again ahead of the other chromosome materials. These bodies could thus be traced during the usual stage of condensation and unraveling, but they appeared like other chromosomes or parts of chromosomes during the most compact stages, that is, late prophase, metaphase and early anaphase. On the basis of these observations, Heitz distinguished two kinds of chromosome material: euchromatin (which underwent a typical cycle of condensation and unraveling) and heterochromatin (which remained compact in the nucleus).

Since the studies of Heitz, heterochromatin has been observed in the cells of many plants and animals. Staining tests show that it contains DNA. It occurs most often at the end of a chromosome, near the centromere, and in the region of the nucleolus organizer—that part of the chromosome which controls the RNA-containing nucleolus observed in nondividing cells. Sex chromosomes (for example Y chromosome in Drosophila) and supernumerary chromosomes in some species of animals and plants (for example, mealy bugs and maize) are composed mostly of heterochromatin. Sometimes the heterochromatin regions of different chromosomes in the same cell coalesce and form an amorphous chromocenter. This occurs in the giant salivary gland chromosomes of *D. melanogaster* as shown in Fig. 5.8. The usual metaphase configuration observed in cells of this species other than the special giant cells is shown in A with heterochromatin parts shaded. Giant chromosomes from a cell of a male larva are shown in B. The heterochromatin near the centromere of each autosome and the X chromosome, along with that making up all of the Y chromosome, is in the chromocenter.

Heterochromatin and euchromatin are now known to be different states of the same material rather than different substances. Heitz considered heterochromatin to be genetically inert and, for the purpose of the present discussion, to establish the basis for sex linkage, this view is quite acceptable. The Y chromosome of *D. melanogaster* has only fertility factors and one active gene locus (*bb*). Likewise, the Y chromosome of many other species has few if any genes. Centric heterochromatin in cells of most species is also essentially devoid of active genes. Studies on gene action and control (Chapter 15), however, indicate that heterochromatin may function by shutting off normal gene action. Furthermore, certain heterochromatin segments may in part be active. For example, an active gene (*nv*) for patterned chlorophyll deficiency in the tomato has been identified in the centric heterochromatin of chromosome 9. Heterochromatin has also been associated with certain position effects (Chapter 9).

## *Sex Linkage in Man*

The inheritance pattern associated with sex linkage is so obvious that it has become a choice example for genetic studies. Sex linkage occurs in man as well as in fruit flies and other animals. This was, in fact, the first pattern of inheritance to be recorded for man. Before the time of Christ, Greek philosophers noticed that some human traits tended to skip a generation. An inherited characteristic was observed to appear in a father but not in

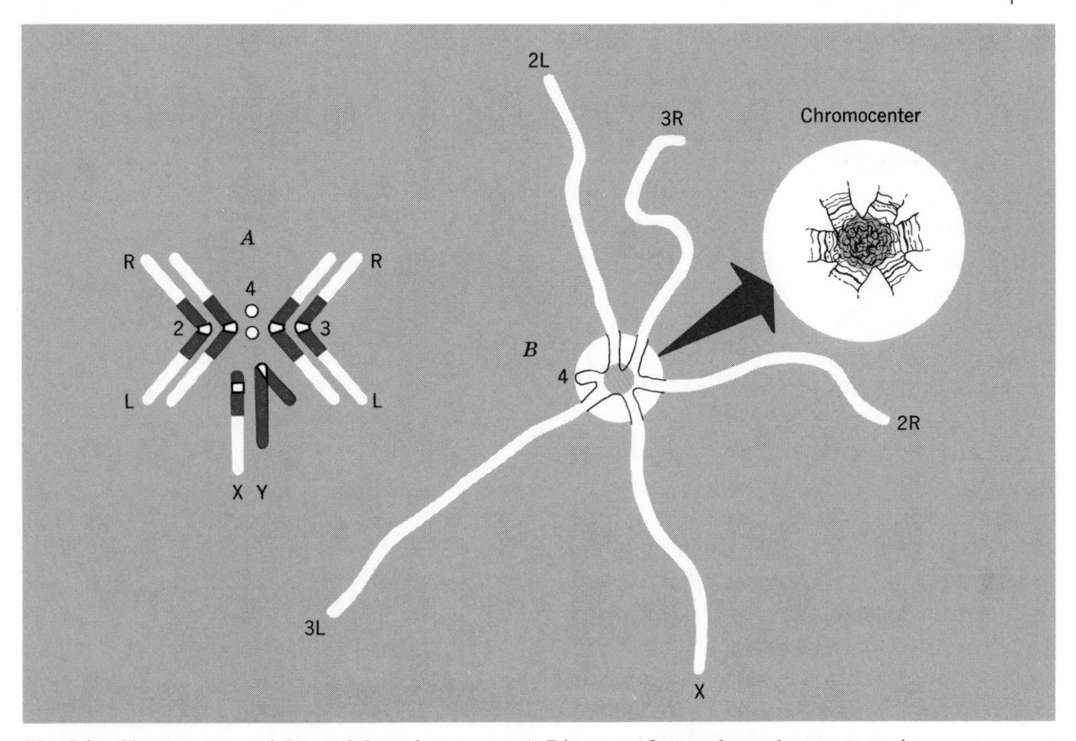


**Fig. 5.8** Chromosomes of *Drosophila melanogaster*. *A*, Diagram of metaphase chromosomes in the body cells of the male; heterochromatic regions are shaded; the centromeres are indicated by clear zones set off by heavy lines; *B*, Diagram of salivary gland chromosomes. The homologous chromosomes are intimately paired along their lengths; the centromeres and centric heterochromatin are combined in the chromocenter; each chromosome arm radiates independently from the chromocenter. (From Spencer Brown, *Science*, **151**:417–425 (1966), Amer. Assoc. Adv. Sci.)

any of his children, either male or female, and then reappear in males of the next generation. This distinctive crisscross pattern, from father through daughter to grandson, replacing the usual pattern for the $F_1$ and $F_2$ generations, now is interpreted as evidence of sex linkage in man. Since man is not subjected to experimental procedures, the characteristic inheritance pattern in family groups, which can be illustrated in pedigree charts, is the best means of detecting sex-linked genes.

A detailed description of the inheritance pattern (now known as sex linkage) of defective color vision (commonly called color blindness) was recorded in 1777 from a study of members of a family who had difficulty in distinguishing red and green (protan defect). In 1793 the same pattern was described for the bleeders disease, hemophilia. One type of night blindness and a form of nystagmus, an involuntary oscillation of the eyeball, were added in the late nineteenth century to the list of human sex-related traits.

Sex linkage has now been indicated for some sixty traits in man including, in addition to those already mentioned, such important and distinctive traits as optic atrophy (degeneration of the optic nerve), juvenile glaucoma (hardening of the eyeball), myopia (nearsightedness), defective iris, juvenile muscular dystrophy (degeneration of certain muscles), epidermal cysts, distichiasis (double eyelashes), white occipital lock of hair, and mitral stenosis (abnormality of mitral valve in the heart). Some of these traits have alternative forms that are dependent on autosomal genes.

Although the pattern now associated with sex linkage was observed in man many years ago, the understanding of the genetic mechanism was a direct consequence of Morgan's work with the white-eye mutant in Drosophila. The explanation given previously for sex-linked inheritance in Drosophila applies equally to traits in man that are associated with sex-linked genes.

Several kinds of defective color vision have now been identified, and the genetic mechanisms are more complex than at first suspected. For the purpose of this example of sex linkage, however, only the protan defect will be considered. It will be treated as a single sex-linked recessive gene without reference to other alternative genes at the same locus. A man defective in red-green color vision would have a single recessive gene (*rg*) in his X chromosome. Since the Y chromosome carries no allele for *rg*, the single gene would be expressed, thus resulting in the color-vision defect. If this man should marry a woman homozygous for the dominant allele ($rg^+$) for normal color vision (Fig. 5.9), all their daughters would receive an X chromosome from the mother carrying $rg^+$ and would be heterozygous carriers. Sons, with only one X chromosome, would have only one gene ($rg^+$) from the mother, and would be free from red-green defective color vision. The Y chromosome, carrying no genes for this trait, would be contributed by the father only to his sons. In the next generation, about half the sons of the carrier females would be normal and half would be color defective. The X chromosome carrying $rg^+$ would segregate to about half of the heterozygous mother's gametes, and the other half would carry *rg*. Half of the daughters of carrier mothers would be carriers.

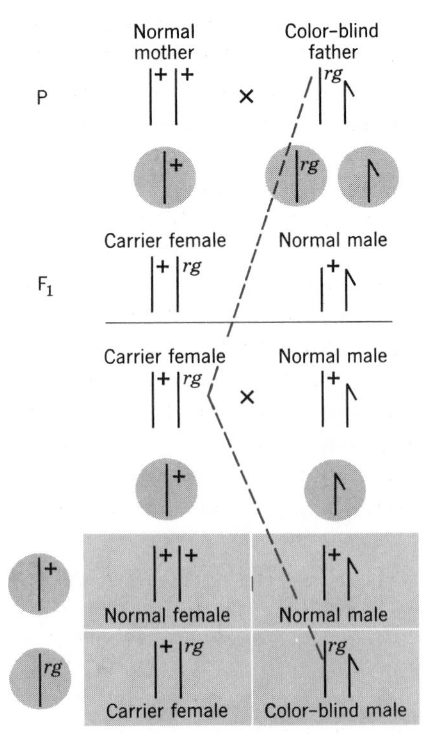


**Fig. 5.9** A diagram with genes on the chromosomes illustrating a cross between a woman with normal vision and a color defective man. The dotted line through the center illustrates the crisscross pattern of inheritance, i.e., from father through daughter to grandson (of original father). The symbol *rg* represents the sex-linked recessive gene for red-green color defective vision.

Segregation of X chromosomes and expression of single recessive genes explains the higher incidence of red-green color defective males than females. About 8 percent of the men in the United States and less than 1 percent of the women are red-green color defective. Color-defective people occur in all human populations. The gene frequency, however, varies among peoples of different ancestral groups. Only about 4 percent of Negro men are reported to be red-green color defective.

Another well-known human trait dependent on a sex-linked gene is the bleeders disease, hemophilia. It is an abnormality of the clot-forming mechanism of the blood. The blood fails to clot normally because of a deficiency in antihemophilia globulin. In the presence of a single gene ($h$) in males, clot formation is slow and abnormal. Only a slight scratch on the skin may result in continuous bleeding and ill health or death of the individual. Hemophilia is uncommon in the general population but has been prevalent in the royal families in Europe where it has received much publicity since the time of Queen Victoria. Some branches of the royal families are illustrated in Fig. 5.10 with the known male hemophiliacs and female carriers of the defective gene identified.

Sex-linked recessive genes are more frequently expressed in males than in females because the expression of such a gene in women would require that both parents carry the rare gene. When a disease such as hemophilia is considered, more involved reasons for the difference in expression between the two sexes may be cited. Only a small percentage of males with the severe type of hemophilia live to a marriageable age. Many of these are in poor health and do not have children. Considering the relatively few affected males who marry and the low frequency of carrier females in the population, the homozygous combination would be expected to occur very infrequently. As expected under these circumstances, only a few cases of true hemophilia (hemophilia A) have been reported in women.

Some 40,000 male hemophiliacs are estimated to be living in the United States. Actual numbers are difficult to obtain because other kinds of "bleeders" are sometimes confused with hemophiliacs. Any one of several different genes may somehow block the clot-forming mechanism. Appropriate clinical tests are required to detect the nature of the abnormality in individual patients. It has been observed that clot-forming time in different women

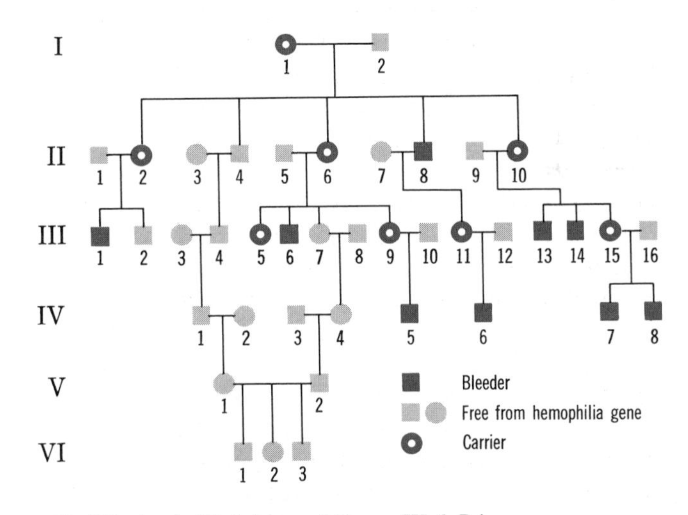


**Fig. 5.10** Hemophilia in the royal families (based on data compiled by J. B. S. Haldane and Hugo Iltis; not all family members are shown; the evidence that II-2 was a carrier and III-1 was a bleeder is circumstantial and not proved). Individuals symbolized on the chart are identified as follows: I-1, Queen Victoria of England; I-2, Prince Albert; II-1, Frederick X, Emperor of Germany; II-2, Victoria, Empress of Germany; II-3, Queen Alexandria; II-4, Edward VII of England; II-5, Ludwig IV of Hesse; II-6, Alice; II-7, Helen of Waldeck; II-8, Leopold of Albany; II-9, Henry, Prince of Battenberg, and II-10, Beatrice; III-1, Boy died in early childhood; III-2, Prince Henry of Prussia; III-3, Queen Mary of England; III-4, George V of England; III-5, Irene of Hesse; III-6, Prince Frederick; III-7, Victoria; III-8, Prince Louis of Battenberg; III-9, Alexandrovna, Czarina of Russia; III-10, Czar Nicholas II of Russia; III-11, Alice; III-12, Alexander of Tech; III-13, and III-14, died young; III-15, Victoria, Queen of Spain; III-16, Alfonzo VIII, King of Spain. IV-1, George VI of England; IV-2, Queen Elizabeth; IV-3, Prince Andrew of Greece; IV-4, Lady Alice Mountbatten; IV-5, Alexi; IV-6, Lord Trematon; IV-7, Alfonzo Pio; IV-8, Gonzalo Manuel; V-1, Queen Elizabeth; V-2, Prince Phillip Mountbatten; VI-1, Prince Charles; VI-2, Princess Anne; VI-3, Prince Andrew.

heterozygous for the hemophilia gene is variable, but, on the average, the clotting time is intermediate between that of normal individuals and hemophiliacs. Carrier women, however, can be detected only by clinical tests, because abnormal bleeding in such individuals is usually not severe enough to impair health.

The criteria for identifying sex-linked recessive genes from pedigree studies may be summarized as follows: (1) expressions occur much more frequently in males than in females; (2) traits are transmitted from an affected man through his daughters to half of their sons; (3) an X-linked gene is never transmitted directly from father to son; and (4) because the gene is transmitted through carrier females, affected males in a kindred may be related to one another through their mothers.

If the X-linked gene should be dominant, such as the *Xg* gene for a rare blood type, males expressing the trait would be expected to transmit it to all their daughters but none of their sons. Heterozygous females would transmit the trait to half of their children of either sex. If a female expressing the trait should be homozygous, all of her children would be expected to inherit the trait. Sex-linked dominant inheritance cannot be distinguished from autosomal inheritance in the progeny of females expressing the trait but only in the progeny of affected males.

### *Incompletely Sex-Linked Genes in Man*

Besides the nonhomologous part of the X chromosome that carries the usual sex-linked genes, the X chromosome of man has a section that is homologous with a part of the Y chromosome. The situation is similar to the case described in Drosophila for the section carrying the gene (*bb*) for bobbed bristles. Several genes have been postulated for this region on the basis of pedigree studies. These include the gene for total color blindness; that for xeroderma pigmentosum, a skin disease characterized by pigment patches and cancerous growths on the body; the gene for retinitis pigmentosa, a progressive degeneration of the retina, accompanied by deposition of pigment in the eye; and that for a type of nephritis, a kidney disease. These are presumably represented in the X and Y chromosomes as allelic pairs and segregate like ordinary autosomal pairs, although they do not segregate independently of sex as do autosomal genes. Even though these genes are located on the X chromosome, the usual crisscross pattern for sex linkage is not expected because of their paired (allelic) arrangement. Questions have been raised concerning the interpretation of genetic or pedigree data for incomplete sex linkage in man, but the cytological evidence is good. Chiasmata have been observed between sex chromosomes. More extensive pedigree studies will undoubtedly provide evidence for this mode of inheritance.

### *Y Chromosome Linkage in Man*

Certain published pedigrees have indicated that the Y chromosome may have a section with genes distinctive to that chromosome. Genes located in a nonhomologous part of the Y chromosome are expected to control "holandric" inheritance because they are transmitted exclusively through the male line. The pedigree evidence for transmission from father to son is the only criterion on which they have been predicted. Published pedigrees interpreted to show this pattern, for the most part, have not been substantiated, and there is reason to suspect that at least some of the most spectacular cases are not accurately reported. One example, that of "hairy pinna" (Fig. 5.11) of the ear reported by Dronamraju in 1960, is well substantiated. Judgment on the extent of Y-linked genes in man must be withheld until more complete evidence is available.

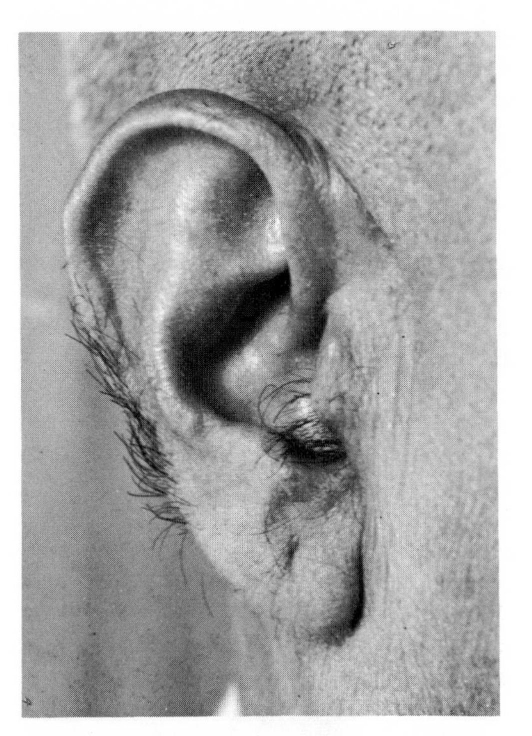

**Fig. 5.11** "Hairy pinna" of the ear. (Courtesy of Dr. K. R. Dronamraju.)

## *Sex-Linked Lethals*

One of the many well-known sex-linked lethals in Drosophila produces the notched-wing effect. Appropriate test crosses and cytological observation have demonstrated that females homozygous for a gene associated with the notch phenotype die before hatching. Numerous other sex-linked lethals have been induced by irradiation in experiments designed to identify mutagenic agents and determine mutation rates under different environmental conditions. Methods of detecting sex-linked lethal mutations are described in Chapter 7.

Induced sex-linked lethal mutations in man have been indicated by differences in the sex ratio following irradiation of parents. W. J. Schull and J. V. Neel have analyzed the sex ratios of children born to parents who were exposed to atomic bombing in Japan during World War II. The data were grouped according to whether the father, mother, or both parents were exposed to irradiation. A trend deviating from the sex ratio in the general population was detected among the children of mothers that were exposed. Male children occurred less frequently than expected. This trend was interpreted to indicate that sex-linked lethals had been induced in the mothers and were being expressed in their sons. Data on sex-linked lethals are thus utilized for determining mutation rates that occur spontaneously and under different environmental conditions.

## *Sex Linkage in Other Animals and Plants*

Despite the great interest in sex linkage and the persistent search for cases in animals, only a few examples are on record. Rats have been studied extensively, but no well-confirmed sex linkage is known. Some 20 sex-linked genes have now been reported in the mouse. Evidence for sex linkage also has been found in some plants, including the date palm and members of the pink family of the genus Melandrium. In birds, it is the male that has two X chromosomes (homogametic) and the female only one (heterogametic). Therefore, the expression of sex-linked genes follows a crisscross pattern from mothers through carrier sons to "granddaughters." This sequence can be demonstrated for such sex-linked genes as the one producing the nonbarred feather pattern in the domestic fowl (Figs. 5.12 and 5.13).

Practical use has been made of the principle of sex linkage in the poultry industry. The problem of how to determine the sex of baby chicks is important to hatchery men. Marker genes for color patterns such as barred feathers have been used to some extent for this type of sexing, called autosexing, but they have some disadvantages. Another gene has been discovered which makes autosexing possible

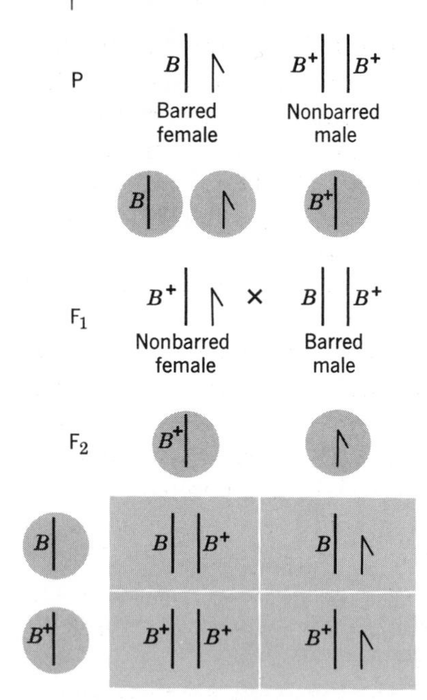


**Fig. 5.12** Diagram on the chromosomes of a cross between a barred female chicken and a nonbarred male. (In chickens the female is heterogametic.)

without introducing differential colors. This gene influences the rate of growth of the feathers. White males homozygous for the slow feather-growth gene (*kk*) are mated with females carrying the normal allele ($k^+$). All females receive the marker gene (*k*) from their fathers and can be distinguished from the heterozygous ($kk^+$) males within a few hours after hatching. The next problem was to convince producers who purchase day-old chicks that slow-feathering birds are normal in other respects, particularly egg-laying ability as they grow older.

## *Sex Chromatin, Sex Differentiation, and Sex Linkage*

Methods for distinguishing the sex of early mammalian embryos have been greatly improved by cytological techniques. As early as 1909, H. de Winiwarter and G. Sainmont described a "basophilic nucleolus," that is, a nuclear body that had an affinity for basic dyes, in the oögonia and oöcytes of the cat. In 1949 M. L. Barr observed chromatin bodies in the nerve cells of female cats. More recently, Barr and others have observed a constant difference between the nuclear contents of human male and female cells in several kinds of tissue including epithelial cells of the buccal mucosa and neutrophils in the blood. With appropriate staining techniques, it was possible to see under the microscope a small chromatin body in the nucleus of cells of the female which was related in some way to the sex chromosomes. No such body could be observed in the cells of the male. The appearance of the nuclei in cells of the two sexes is illustrated in Fig. 5.14. With this technique the sex of human embryos can be distinguished at early stages of development. More recent studies have shown that a sex

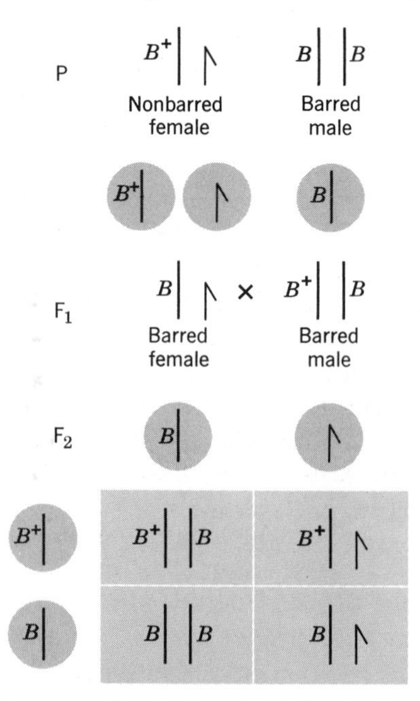


**Fig. 5.13** Reciprocal cross to that illustrated in Fig. 5.12. A cross between a nonbarred female and a barred male.

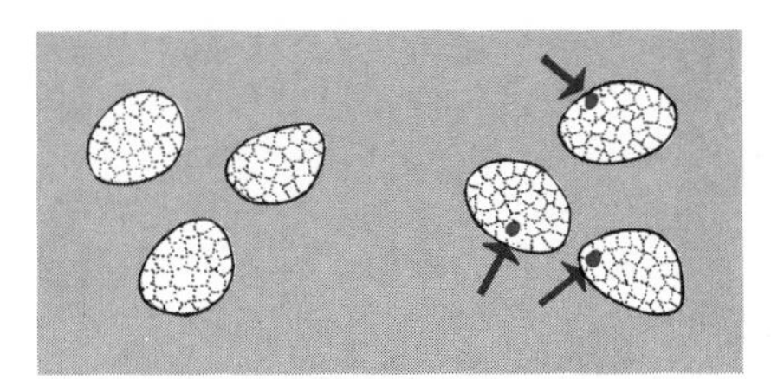


**Fig. 5.14** Cytological method for distinguishing male and female cells of man. Female nuclei have distinct chromatin nucleoli (identified by arrows) in addition to nucleoli common to both sexes. (After M. L. Barr.)

chromatin body is present in most, if not all, somatic cells of female mice. Other female mammals also carry this body. Indeed, this cellular characteristic seems to apply to mammals generally.

Not only can sex chromatin bodies be observed to distinguish normal female from male cells, but these bodies have become useful for diagnosing various kinds of sex chromosome abnormalities. Cytological data have now been associated with several cases of abnormal sexual development in man. In these people, abnormal numbers of chromosomes are related to the number of sex chromatin bodies. For people with two or more X chromosomes, the number of chromatin bodies is one less than the number of X chromosomes present. Cells of abnormal females with only one X chromosome (Turner's syndrome) have no sex chromatin bodies and cells of abnormal males with two X and one Y chromosomes (Klinefelter's syndrome) have one chromatin body. Abnormal females with three X chromosomes have two chromatin bodies in their cell nuclei.

### *Lyon Hypothesis for Gene Action on the X Chromosome*

For many years, geneticists have observed that, in some cases, females homozygous for sex-linked genes do not express a trait more markedly than do hemizygous males. Some sort of dosage compensation has been suggested. Several investigators at about the same time arrived at a hypothesis explaining the sex chromatin body by the inactivation of one X chromosome in the normal female. The hypothesis was named after Mary F. Lyon (1962) who was first to present it in detail. It was based on genetic studies on coat-color genes of the mouse and cytological observations. Hybrid female mice, heterozygous for certain coat-color genes, showed a mottled effect unlike that of either homozygote and not intermediate between the colors expressed in the parents. The fur pattern (Fig. 5.15) was a mosaic made up of randomly arranged patches of the two colors. Normal male mice and abnormal XO mice never showed the mottled phenotype.

The mottled appearance characteristic of some other female mammals (for in-

**Fig. 5.15** Female mouse heterozygous for an X-linked gene for the coat color tortoiseshell. The mosaic phenotype of such females provided one of the first lines of evidence for the Lyon hypothesis. (From Margaret Thompson, *Canad. J. Genet. Cytol.*, **7**:202–213, 1965.)

stance, tortoiseshell or calico cats) heterozygous for sex-linked color genes are also explained on the basis of patches of cells, some from one, and some from the other X chromosome.

The cytological evidence on which the hypothesis was based was the observation that the number of sex chromatin bodies in interphase cells of adult females is one less than the number of X chromosomes observed in metaphase preparations. The chromatin body is therefore a condensed X chromosome. On this premise, it must be assumed that only one X chromosome is required for cellular metabolism in the female cell. Any X in excess of the one required becomes heteropyknotic (that is, stains more densely than other chromosomes) and genetically inactive.

Which X chromosome becomes inactive is a matter of chance, but when an X has become inactivated all cells arising from that cell line will have an inactive X chromosome (a sex chromatin body). In the mouse, the inactivation apparently occurs early in development, but in human embryos no sex chromatin bodies have been observed earlier than the sixteenth day of gestation. Apparently the inactivation occurs later in man. If this is the case, some traits could be influenced early in development by both X chromosomes. Later (after the 16th day), only one X would be functional in a body cell and the female would become mosaic with respect to X-linked genes.

The late occurrence of inactivation in human embryos has been invoked to explain some of the difficulties of the hypothesis as applied to man and other mammals. Individuals with XXY chromosome arrangements, for example, are abnormal males (Chapter 10). They would be expected to have normal XY chromosomes if one X was inactivated. It is postulated that the two X chromosomes may function for a long enough period of time to upset the normal developmental pattern for the male sex and thus give rise to abnormalities associated with Klinefelter's syndrome.

Apparently X chromosome inactivation occurs only when at least two X chromosomes are present. When several X chromosomes are in the same nucleus, all but one will be inactivated. The number of sex chromatin bodies after the period of inactivation is, therefore, one less than the number of X chromosomes.

As examples of the application of the Lyon hypothesis to man, the cases of hemophilia and glucose-6-phosphate dehydrogenase (G6PD) deficiency may be cited. Considerable variation has been observed in laboratory findings and clinical expressions among women known to be heterozygous for the sex-linked gene for hemophilia, as expected if the cell groups are mosaics. In women heterozygous for the X-linked gene that results in a deficiency for G6PD, a red blood cell enzyme, cell mosaics (Fig. 5.16) have been observed. One kind of cell has arisen from a stem line in which the normal gene is active and the other from a stem line in which the abnormal gene is active.

The Lyon hypothesis thus explains certain genetic consequences of sex-linked genes in man or other mammals: (1) dosage compensation for females with two X chromosomes that express traits dependent on sex-linked genes in similar degree to males with only one X chromosome; (2) mosaicism for X-linked gene expressions in heterozygous females; and (3) variability of expression in heterozygous females because of the random inactivation of one or the other X chromosome.

## SUMMARY

Segregation of sex chromosomes explains grossly and superficially the mech-

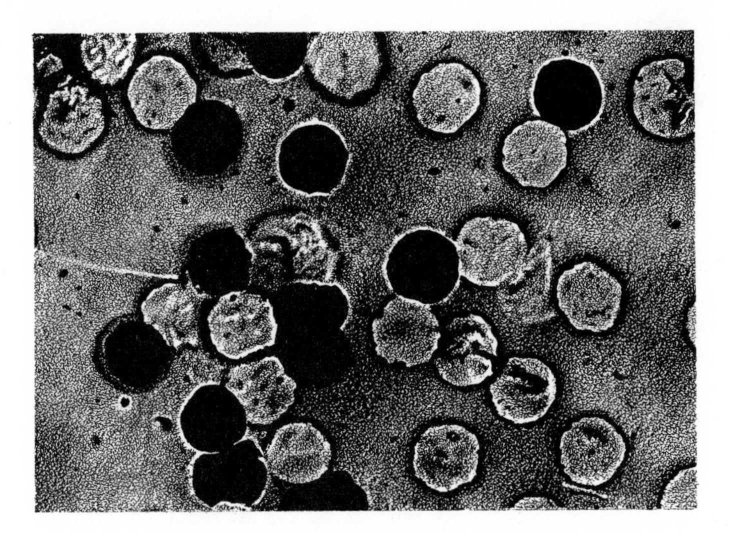

**Fig. 5.16** Red blood cells of patients heterozygous for the G6PD deficiency gene showing a mosaic of normal and abnormal cells. (From Tönz and Rossi, *Nature,* **202:**606–607, 1964.)

anism of sex determination. The XO and XY mechanisms were described from studies of insects early in the present century. Sex linkage and nondisjunction, which were discovered soon after the chromosome mechanism of sex determination, provided further evidence that genes are in chromosomes. A parallelism between the results of hybridization experiments and the behavior of chromosomes in meiosis had already been noted, and further evidence from linkage studies (Chapter 6) and chromosome aberrations (Chapter 9) followed. The discovery of sex chromatin bodies associated with inactivation of one X chromosome in normal female mammals (and all except one in abnormal females with more than two X chromosomes) elucidated the chromosome theory and explained problems of dosage compensation, mosaicism, and phenotypic variability in females heterozygous for sex-linked genes.

## REFERENCES

Bamber, R. C. 1927. "Genetics of domestic cats." *Bibliographia Genetica,* **3,** 1–86.

Barr, M. L. 1960. "Sexual dimorphism in interphase nuclei." *Amer. J. Human Genet.,* **12,** 118–127.

Brown, S. W. 1966. "Heterochromatin." *Science,* **151,** 417–425.

Hutt, F. B. 1964. *Animal genetics.* Roland Press, New York. (Hemophilia demonstrated in female dogs and other examples of sex-linked inheritance in animals.)

Kalmus, H. 1965. *Diagnosis and genetics of defective color vision.* Pergamon Press, New York.

Lyon, M. F. 1962. "Sex chromatin and gene action in mammalian X-chromosomes." *Amer. J. Human Genet.,* **14,** 135–148. (Hypothesis that one X chromosome in normal mammalian females is inactivated and that only one X chromosome is active in abnormal females with more than 2X chromosomes.)

McKusick, V. A. 1964. *On the X chromosome of man.* Amer. Inst. Biol. Sci., Washington, D. C.

McKusick, V. A. 1965. "The Royal hemophilia." *Sci. Amer.,* **213,** 88–95.

Miller, O. J. 1964. "The sex chromosome anomalies." *Amer. J. Obstetrics and Gynec.,* **90,** 1078–1139.

Moore, K. L. 1966. *The sex chromatin.* W. B. Saunders Co., Philadelphia. (Includes contributions of 23 authorities giving background information and clinical applications.)

Morgan, T. H., and C. B. Bridges. 1916. *Sex-linked inheritance in Drosophila.* Carnegie Inst. Wash. Publ. 237.

Schull, W. J., and J. V. Neel. 1958. "Radiation and sex ratio in man." *Science,* **128,** 343–348.

Stern, C. 1960. *Principles of human genetics,* 2nd ed. W. H. Freeman and Co., San Francisco.

Swanson, C. P., T. Merz, and W. J. Young. 1967. *Cytogenetics.* Prentice-Hall, Englewood Cliffs, New Jersey.

## *Problems*

5.1 How was sex linkage first discovered?

5.2 What results would be expected for $F_1$ and $F_2$ males and females from crosses between lacticolor male and typical female moths? Assume that the gene (*l*) for lacticolor is recessive and sex-linked. Female moths are heterogametic.

5.3 If a white-eyed male fruit fly should occur in a culture of red-eyed flies, how could the investigator obtain evidence to answer the following questions? (a) Is a mutant gene or an environmental change responsible for the new phenotype? (b) If a mutation has occurred, is it sex-linked? (c) Can white-eyed females occur?

5.4 The gene (*w*) for white eyes in *D. melanogaster* is recessive and sex-linked; males are heterogametic. (a) Symbolize on the chromosomes the genotype of a white-eyed male, red-eyed male, red-eyed female (2 genotypes) and white-eyed female. (b) Diagram on the chromosomes a cross between a homozygous red-eyed female and a white-eyed male. Carry through the $F_2$ and summarize the expected sex and eye color phenotypes. (c) Diagram on the chromosomes and give the expected phenotypes from a cross between an $F_1$ female and (1) a white-eyed male, and (2) a red-eyed male.

5.5 In fruit flies, the gene (*bb*) for bobbed bristles is recessive and incompletely sex-linked. Diagram on the chromosomes a cross between a homozygous normal female and a bobbed male. Carry through the $F_2$ and summarize expected sex and bristle phenotypes.

5.6 In fruit flies, bar eye is dependent on a dominant sex-linked gene (*B*). Diagram on the chromosome a cross between a wild-type female and a bar-eyed male. Summarize the expected $F_1$ and $F_2$ sex and eye phenotypes.

5.7 How was Bridges led to suspect that the X chromosome in Drosophila sometimes failed to separate in meiosis, that is, underwent nondisjunction? How was the hypothesis proved?

5.8 If a sex-linked recessive and a sex-linked dominant gene with equal effect on viability were present in equal frequency in the same population in which males are heterogametic, would the recessive gene or the dominant gene express itself more frequently in (a) males? (b) females?

5.9 In man, red-green defective color vision is due to the sex-linked recessive gene (*rg*) and normal vision to its allele ($rg^+$). A man (1) and woman (2), both of normal vision, have the following three children, all of whom are married to people with normal vision: a color-defective son (3) who has a daughter of normal vision (6); a daughter of normal vision (4) who has one color defective (7) and two normal sons (8); and a daughter of normal vision (5) who has six normal sons (9). Give the probable genotypes of all the individuals in the family (1 to 9).

5.10 If a mother carried the sex-linked gene for protan defective color vision and the father was normal, would their sons or daughters be defective in color vision?

5.11 Why are there more men defective in red-green color vision than women?

5.12 If a father and son are both defective in red-green color vision, is it likely that the son inherited the trait from his father?

**5.13** Diagram on the chromosomes a cross between a normal woman whose father was defective in red-green color vision and a color-defective man. Summarize the expected results for sex and eye condition.

**5.14** In man, the gene ($h$) for hemophilia is sex-linked and recessive to the gene ($h^+$) for normal clotting. Diagram on the chromosomes the genotypes of the parents of the following crosses and summarize the expected phenotypic ratios resulting from the crosses: (a) hemophiliac woman × normal man; (b) normal (heterozygous) woman × hemophiliac man; (c) normal (homozygous) woman × hemophiliac man.

**5.15** A normal woman, whose father had hemophilia, married a normal man. What is the chance of hemophilia in their children?

**5.16** In the pedigree chart of the royal families (Fig. 5.10), what is the chance that (a) a son or (b) daughter of V-1 × V-2 will be hemophiliac?

**5.17** Gene *Xg* is dominant and X-linked. If a woman heterozygous for this gene (*Xgxg*) marries a man carrying the allele (*xg*), what is the probability that (a) each daughter and (b) each son will receive the *Xg* gene?

**5.18** The gene for hairy pinna of the ear is holandric. (a) What is the chance that each daughter and each son of a man with this trait will inherit the condition? (b) If a man with hairy pinna also has the *Xg* blood factor and is color blind, which of these traits might be expressed in each daughter and each son?

**5.19** In poultry, barring is due to the dominant sex-linked gene ($B$), nonbarring to its recessive allele ($B^+$). Crested head is due to a dominant autosomal gene ($C$), and plain head is due to its recessive allele ($C^+$). Two barred, crested birds were mated and produced two offspring: a nonbarred, plain female and a barred, crested male. (a) Give the genotypes of the parents on the chromosomes. (b) Summarize the expected results for sex, barring, and crest expressions from further matings between these two barred, crested birds.

**5.20** (a) How can the genetic principle of sex linkage be applied to the practical problem of autosexing baby chickens? (b) Could it have similar application in other animals such as dairy cattle?

**5.21** How many sex chromatin bodies are expected to occur in cell nuclei with each of the following chromosome arrangements: (a) XY, (b) XX, (c) XXY, (d) XXX, (e) XXXX?

omit
**5.22** What evidence supports the (Lyon) hypothesis that all but one X chromosome becomes inactivated?

# Linkage, Crossing Over, and Chromosome Maps

# 6

In 1906 W. Bateson and R. C. Punnett analyzed the results of a cross between two varieties of sweet peas and observed a ratio that did not conform to their hypothesis of independent combinations. Sweet peas with purple flowers and long pollen grains had been crossed with a variety that had red flowers and round pollen grains. Purple and long had been shown by previous experiments to be dependent on separate genes that were each dominant over the respective allele for red and round. From this dihybrid cross, Bateson and Punnett expected a 9:3:3:1 ratio in the $F_2$.

Instead, progeny that had either purple flowers and long pollen, or red flowers and round pollen occurred more frequently than expected, whereas the purple and round, and the red and long classes appeared less frequently. Another cross was then made which involved the same traits but in different combinations. Sweet peas with purple flowers and round pollen were crossed with those having red flowers and long pollen. When the $F_1$ plants from this cross were selfed and the $F_2$'s were classified, the parental combinations again were present in exaggerated proportions, and recombinations occurred in lesser proportion than expected on the basis of independent assortment.

Bateson and Punnett developed a theory called "coupling and repulsion" to explain their results. They missed the truth by a narrow margin, largely because they did not relate the mechanism responsible for the genetic results to the chromosomes. In their theory, the condition in which the two dominants tended to enter the gametes together in greater than random porportion was called "partial gametic coupling." The tendency for one dominant and one recessive gene to enter the gametes in the greater proportion was called "repulsion." Although the theory is now obsolete, the terms "coupling" and "repulsion" have been retained and are usefully descriptive. Crosses in which the two dominants enter from the same parents are said to be in the coupling phase. Those that include both dominant and recessive genes from each parent are said to be in the repulsion phase. The purple-long × red-round cross represents coupling, whereas the purple-round × red-long cross illustrates repulsion. Two other terms, *cis* (coupling) and *trans* (repulsion), have also been used to distinguish the two possible arrangements of two pairs of alleles on a single pair of homologous chromosomes. These terms come from organic chemistry, where they are used to designate compounds having the same kind and number of atoms and, therefore, the same molecular formula, but which differ in one or more chemical and physical properties because of differences in arrangement of atoms in the respective molecules (for instance, isomers).

During the first and second decades of the present century, the chromosome theory of inheritance became firmly established. T. H. Morgan and his associates, through their investigation with Drosophila, were largely responsible for supplying experimental evidence that supported the theory established by Boveri and Sutton at the turn of the century. On firm cytological grounds, Morgan replaced the theory of coupling and repulsion with that of linkage and crossing over. His theory associated genes with chromosomes. Linkage was defined as the tendency for genes in the same chromosome or linkage group to enter the gametes in the parental combinations. The alternative, crossing over, was defined as the tendency for genes to enter the gametes in combinations other than those of the parents (recombinations). Four linkage groups were discovered in *Drosophila melanogaster* which corresponded with the four chromosome pairs. It soon became established that the number of linkage groups in species of animals and plants was equivalent to the number of chromosomes.

Soon after linkage and crossing over were established in the fruit fly, other organisms were found to conform to the same pattern. The first clearly recognized linkage in maize was reported in 1911 by G. N. Collins and J. H. Kempton. They found that the gene (*wx*) for waxy endosperm was linked with the gene (*C*) for aleurone color. The principle of linkage was soon firmly established in both plants and animals and was recognized as a widely occurring alternative to independent assortment. Investigations designed to analyze the mechanism of linkage and crossing over represented the next phase in the development of this important principle of genetics.

It would be a simple matter for the geneticist if genes in the same member of a pair of chromosomes would always stay together and thus make linkage complete, but ordinarily they do not do so. Exchange or crossing over between members of chromosome pairs occurs in most plants and animals. The male fruit fly (Drosophila) and the female silk moth (Bombyx) ordinarily have no crossing over; that is, they have complete linkage, although crossing over can be induced in the male fly.

### *Linear Arrangement of Genes in Chromosomes*

The classical investigations that established the linear arrangement of genes in chromosomes and led to the formation of linkage maps were those of Sturtevant beginning in 1913. Morgan had shown (in 1911) that the strength of linkage between sex-linked genes was due to their nearness to each other in the X chromosome. From the results of numerous test crosses, Sturtevant extended this discovery to the autosomes.

He analyzed test-cross data and from accumulated results developed maps of the different chromosomes. These were based on linkage data and they illustrated not only the linear arrangement but also the relative position of genes in a particular chromosome. The following discussion about linkage and linkage maps in Drosophila illustrates the experimental pattern first designed by Sturtevant.

Ordinarily, the parental combinations and recombinations between two loci in the same chromosome pair occur with regular frequency. Furthermore, the percentage of crossing over between two loci is roughly proportional to the distance between these points on the chromosome. Therefore, crossover data can be used to determine the relative position of genes on chromosomes. First the genes must be identified with their respective linkage groups (chromosomes) and the positions of individual genes on the same chromosome must be determined. With this information, the results of crosses involving genes with known linkage relations can be predicted.

### *Detecting Linkage and Crossing Over*

For most experimental organisms, the backcross or test cross is the most convenient method for determining the linkage group to which a gene belongs and the relative position of that gene within the linkage group or chromosome. A properly designed test cross fulfills two different requirements: (1) it provides an opportunity for corresponding parts on a pair of chromosomes to exchange places, and (2) it yields end results that can be used for identifying phenotypically the crossovers that have occurred and the resulting recombinations. The chief advantage of the test cross over the $F_2$ is the simple ratio that it provides for comparison between the experimental result and that based on the hypothesis of independent combinations.

When an $F_1$ plant or animal heterozygous for two pairs of genes on different chromosomes is mated with a fully recessive individual, a ratio of 1:1:1:1 is expected. For example, the gene (*vg*) for vestigial wing in *D. melanogaster* is located in the second chromosome, whereas the gene (*e*) for ebony body color is in the third chromosome (Fig. 6.1). In a basic experiment, a homozygous normal female was crossed with a vestigial, ebony male, and $F_1$ females were mated with fully recessive vestigial, ebony males. The 1:1:1:1 ratio, which is expected in examples representing independent assortment, was obtained, as illustrated in Fig. 6.2. Because the 1:1:1:1 ratio is characteristic of independent assortment, genes of unknown position giving this test-cross result can ordinarily be assumed to be in different chromosomes. It follows that a significant departure from the 1:1:1:1 ratio indicates something other than independent assortment. Linkage is the most likely alternative.

In an attempt to illustrate the operation of an alternative to independent assortment, a homozygous female with straight wings and gray body (both dependent on

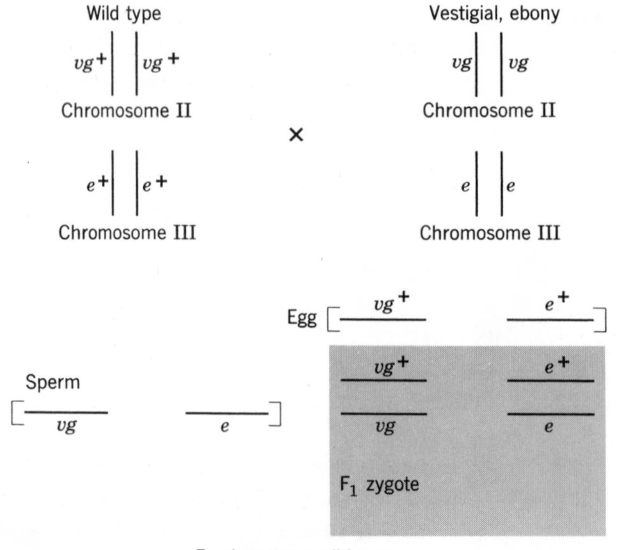


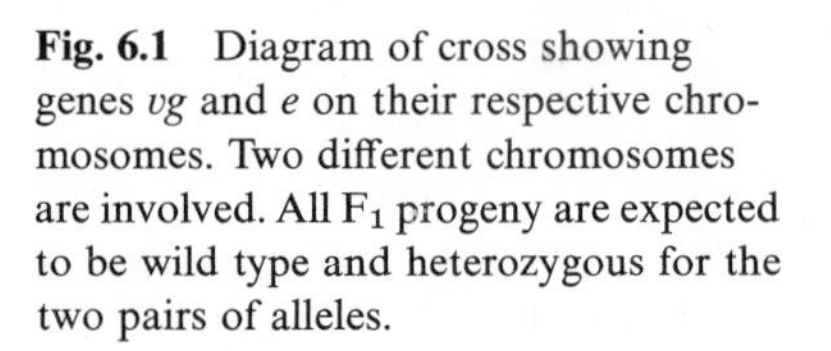

**Fig. 6.1** Diagram of cross showing genes *vg* and *e* on their respective chromosomes. Two different chromosomes are involved. All $F_1$ progeny are expected to be wild type and heterozygous for the two pairs of alleles.

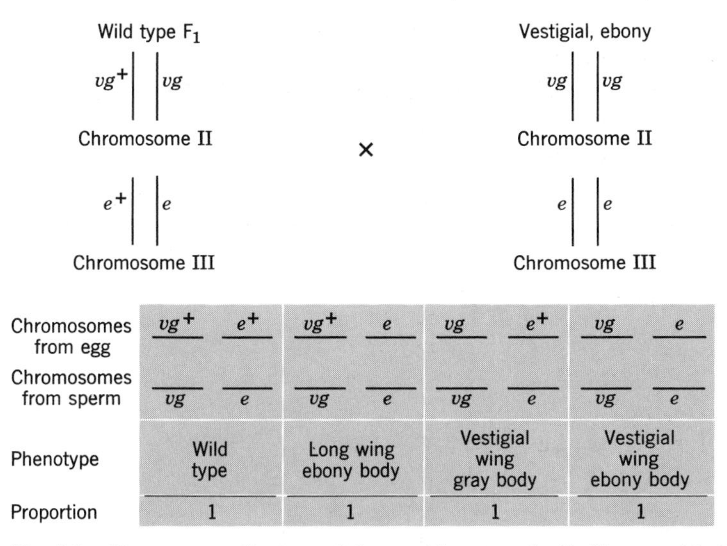


**Fig. 6.2** Chromosome diagram of the cross between the $F_1$ illustrated in Fig. 6.1 and the full recessive vestigial ebony parental type. The assortment of the 2 pairs of chromosomes is illustrated with the resulting 1:1:1:1 ratio.

dominant genes) was mated with a male with curled wings and ebony body (both recessives). When $F_1$ females were mated with fully recessive males, the result was a ratio of about 4 straight, gray; 1 straight, ebony; 1 curled, gray; and 4 curled, ebony. This result indicated that *cu* and *e* were in the same chromosome and in the coupling phase; that is, $\frac{cu^+e^+}{cu^+e^+} \times \frac{cue}{cue}$. When the original cross (P) was between straight, ebony females and curled, gray males, that is, $\frac{cu^+e}{cu^+e} \times \frac{cue^+}{cue^+}$, and $F_1$ females were mated with full recessive males, that is, $\frac{cu^+e}{cue^+} \times \frac{cue}{cue}$, the test-cross results were about 1 straight, gray; 4 straight, ebony; 4 curled, gray; and 1 curled, ebony, as expected when the genes are in the repulsion phase. The three crosses illustrating independent assortment, coupling, and repulsion, respectively, are constructed on the chromosomes in Figs. 6.2, 6.3, and 6.4.

When two genes have been identified in the same chromosome, their relative positions with respect to each other can be estimated by calculating the frequency of crossing over between them. In converting the proportion of crossing over to relative positions on the chromosome, one percent of recombination is equal to one unit on the linkage map. The number of crossover units between two gene loci is the same as the percentage of progeny that result from an exchange between the two loci. If idealized figures (40 straight, gray; 10 straight, ebony; 10 curled, gray; and 40 curled, ebony) are supplied in the foregoing example representing the coupling phase, the parental and recombination groups would be distinguished as follows:

| straight gray | straight ebony |
|---|---|
| 40 | 10 |
| Parental | Recombination |

| curled gray | curled ebony |
|---|---|
| 10 | 40 |
| Recombination | Parental |

The two parental groups combined include 80 percent of the total flies and the two recombination groups, 20 percent. Therefore, the linkage strength between

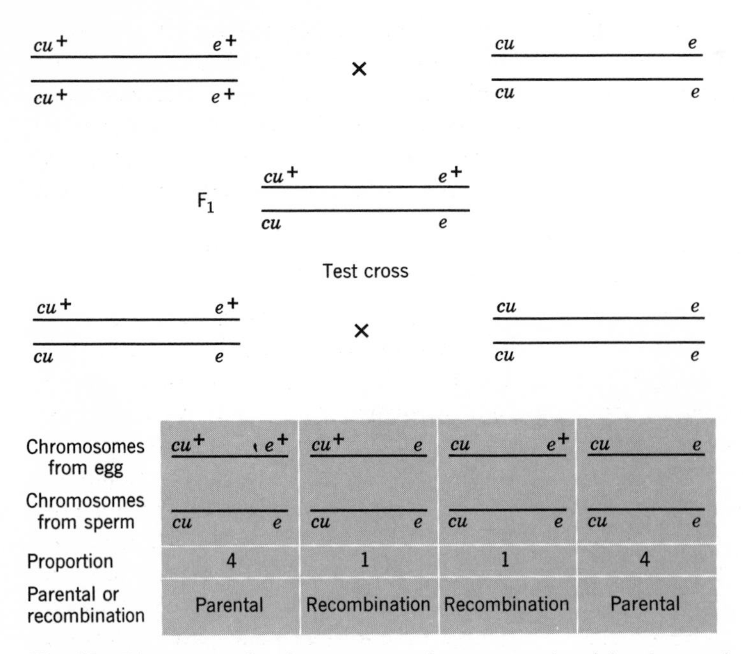


**Fig. 6.3** Diagram on the chromosomes of a test cross involving 2 genes in the same chromosome pair. The results show the parental (linkage) and recombination (crossover) groups. This illustrates coupling.

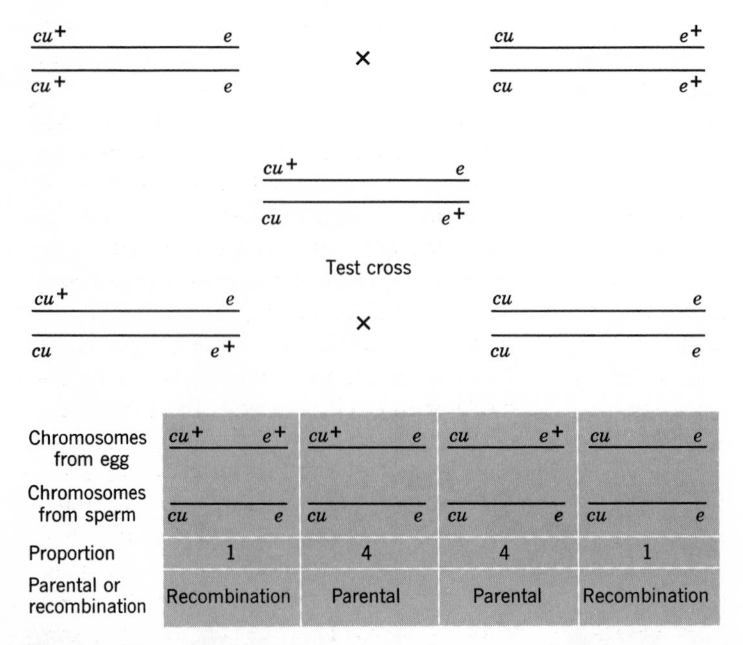


**Fig. 6.4** Diagram on the chromosomes of a test cross involving 2 genes in the same chromosome pair. The results show the recombination (crossover) and parental (linkage) groups. This illustrates repulsion.

these two loci is 80 percent and the recombination is 20 percent. Thus, the loci *cu* and *e* are about 20 units apart. Similar relations are indicated from a repulsion cross when the parental and recombination gametes are properly distinguished. It must be emphasized that idealized figures supplied to illustrate the concept were used in the above example. Data from actual experiments are not as regular as those arbitrarily chosen for the illustration.

The first observation by Bateson and Punnett that suggested a deviation from random assortment was from $F_2$ rather than test-cross results. Such data are as valid as those from test crosses, but they are more cumbersome to handle because of the more complex 9:3:3:1 instead of the 1:1:1:1 ratio with which the results must be compared. However, appropriate comparisons can be made mathematically. $F_2$ data may be more desirable than test-cross data in some cases, especially if the investigator is dealing with self-fertilizing plants such as wheat and barley. In these plants, it is tedious and time consuming to make test crosses by hand emasculation and pollination, whereas it is easy merely to allow the $F_1$ plants to self-fertilize and produce $F_2$ plants. Breeders of cereal crops usually choose the simpler means of making the cross and the more complex methods of analysis and interpretation. Tables have been prepared that provide simple and effective tools for calculating linkage and crossover values from $F_2$ data.

When crossover values are known, predictions can be made as to the proportions of gametes with different gene combinations likely to result from a given cross. From the relative proportions of gametes, the offspring resulting from various crosses can be predicted. J. W. MacArthur, for example, found from appropriate test-cross results with tomatoes that the locus *s* for compound inflorescence is about 20 units from the locus *o* for elongate fruit shape. With this information, it was possible to predict the $F_2$ results, as illustrated in Fig. 6.5. A close fit was obtained when the expected results based on the predicted 20 percent crossing over were compared with the experimental data from actual crosses.

### *Three-Point Crosses*

Two-point test crosses, such as those described above, are made between individuals with two points on one chromosome identified by phenotypically recognizable marker genes. From the results, frequencies of parental and recombination groups of progeny are distinguished. This information is used to determine the chromosome map distance between the two loci. It does not, however, indicate the relative positions of genes with respect to each other on the chromosome. Furthermore, data from two-point crosses tend to underestimate map distances partly because of double crossing over; that is, parts of chromatids cross over and cross back between two points on a chromosome and as a result no crossing over is detected between the two marker genes.

For example, if only the distance between genes *a* and *b* is known, *a* may be either to the right or to the left of *b*. To determine the relative position of genes on a chromosome, it is necessary either to obtain map distances between *a* and *b* and other known genes in the same linkage group or to work with three linked genes at one time and thus determine their relative position with respect to each other. With a three-point cross, it is possible to check two adjacent chromosome areas on one chromosome simultaneously. In addition to the relative position of genes, data obtained from crosses of this kind may identify recombination units between points on a chromosome and thus provide evidence for double crossing over. Therefore, data from three-point crosses correct,

P $\dfrac{o^+ \quad s^+}{o^+ \quad s^+}$ $\dfrac{o \quad s}{o \quad s}$

$F_1$ $\dfrac{o^+ \quad s^+}{o \quad s}$

$F_1 \times F_1$ $\dfrac{o^+ \quad s^+}{o \quad s}$ $\dfrac{o^+ \quad s^+}{o \quad s}$

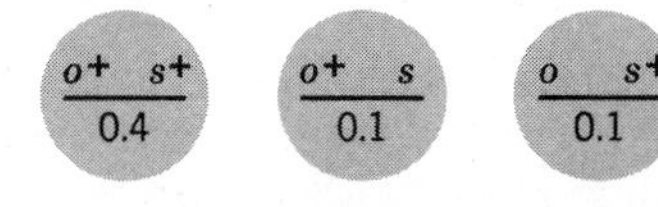


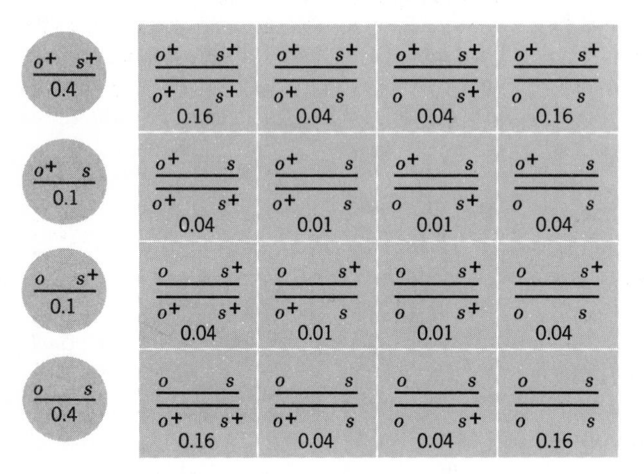


**Fig. 6.5** Diagram of linkage problem in the tomato illustrating the method used to predict the proportions of progeny when linkage values are known. (Data from J. W. MacArthur in *Genetics*.)

**SUMMARY OF EXPECTED RESULTS, PERCENT**

| | Simple Round | Simple Elongate | Compound Round | Compound Elongate |
|---|---|---|---|---|
| Based on 20% crossing over | 0.66 | 0.09 | 0.09 | 0.16 |
| Based on random assortment (9:3:3:1 ratio) | 0.56 | 0.19 | 0.19 | 0.06 |

at least in part, the underestimate of map distances that is inherent with two-point crosses.

A three-point cross may be carried out if three points or loci on a chromosome pair can be identified by marker genes, and test crosses can be conducted successfully with the experimental material under investigation. If, in addition to genes $a$ and $b$ indicated above, a third marker gene $c$ is located in fairly close proximity in the same linkage group, all three markers may be used together in conducting a more precise analysis of the map distance and the relative position of the three points. Matings between individuals carrying $abc$ in homozygous condition and those homozygous for $a^+b^+c^+$ would be expected to result in fully heterozygous $F_1$ progeny. These heterozygotes, when test-crossed with homozygous fully recessive *abc* individuals, would be expected to produce progeny that could be classified into parental and recombination groups. Because all three genes were known to be linked, the results would be expected to deviate from the 1:1:1:1:1:1:1:1 ratio expected from a trihybrid cross under the alternative hypothesis of independent assortment.

Relative positions of the three genes could first be determined by identifying the double crossovers that would obviously be the two smallest classes. It stands to reason that classes requiring two crossovers simultaneously occurring within a given distance would occur less frequently than those requiring only one or no crossovers. If these should be $a^+b^+c$ and $abc^+$ the locus *c* must have been involved in the double crossovers and must be located between loci *a* and *b*. Using single gene symbols to represent phenotypic classes in organisms, the parentals could then be written in proper order: $a^+c^+b^+$ and *acb* and the double crossovers $a^+cb^+$ and $ac^+b$, as illustrated in Fig. 6.6.

Single crossover classes representing exchanges between *a* and *c* would be $a^+cb$ and $ac^+b^+$. Those representing exchanges between *c* and *b* would be $a^+c^+b$ and $acb^+$. Map distance between *a* and *c* could be calculated on the basis of the total proportion of single crossovers between *a* and *c* plus those in the double crossover classes which would each include crossovers between *a* and *c*. Likewise, the distance between *c* and *b* would be based on the percentage of the single crossovers between these two points plus the double crossovers.

A genetics student chose a special project involving a three-point cross to check the relative positions and map distances separating three genes in the Drosophila third chromosome. The project was carried out as follows. The student first mated Drosophila females homozygous for recessive genes *cu* (curled), *sr* (stripe), and *e* (ebony) with wild type, $cu^+$ (straight), $sr^+$ (not striped), and $e^+$ (gray) males. $F_1$ females were mated (test-crossed) with fully recessive curled, stripe, ebony males. The phenotypic results of the test cross were classified as follows:

| | |
|---|---|
| 1. Straight, not striped, gray | 786 |
| 2. Curled, stripe, ebony | 753 |
| 3. Straight, stripe, ebony | 107 |
| 4. Curled, not striped, gray | 97 |
| 5. Straight, not striped, ebony | 86 |
| 6. Curled, stripe, gray | 94 |
| 7. Straight, stripe, gray | 1 |
| 8. Curled, not striped, ebony | 2 |
| | 1926 |

The two largest classes at the top of the list were recognized as being parental types. The next four classes were single crossovers, the first two (Nos. 3 and 4) between *cu* and *sr*, and the next two (Nos. 5 and 6) between *sr* and *e*. Because crossovers in single areas occur more frequently than two simultaneous crossovers in adjacent areas, the two smallest classes (Nos. 7 and 8) must be the double crossovers. These two classes also represent the order

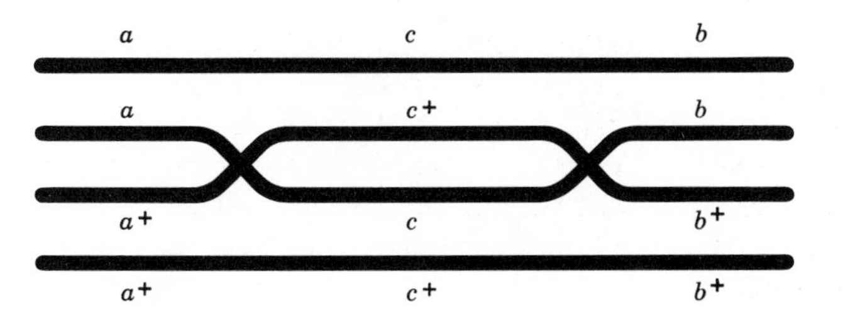


**Fig. 6.6** Diagram illustrating double crossing over as represented on the chromosomes. The two chromatids in the center show double crossing over whereas the chromatids at the top and bottom of the diagram show parental arrangements of genes.

of genes that would be necessary to account for double crossovers with respect to the parental combinations. In this example *sr* must be in the center with *cu* on one side and *e* on the other. A simultaneous exchange in each of the two areas (*cu-sr* and *sr-e*) would be required to produce the phenotypic combinations straight, stripe, gray; and curled, not striped, ebony. Only three individuals in the total of 1926 were recognized. The locus *sr* was exchanged in each double crossover arrangement whereas the *cu* and *e* loci were in parental arrangements. The results indicated that the sequence of the genes on the chromosome must be: *cusre*, and the gene arrangements on the double crossover chromosomes are $cu^+sre^+$ and $cusr^+e$. Parental gene arrangements and crossovers in the $F_1$ females are illustrated diagrammatically in Fig. 6.7. The P cross was represented as follows:

$$\frac{cusre}{cusre} \times \frac{cu^+sr^+e^+}{cu^+sr^+e^+}.$$

The test cross between $F_1$ females and curled, stripe, ebony males was:

$$\frac{cu^+sr^+e^+}{cu\ sr\ e} \times \frac{cusre}{cusre}.$$

The units between the three genes were determined from the data by calculating the percentage of crossing over within the two areas. Between *cu* and *sr*, 207 crossovers (classes 3, 4, 7, and 8) occurred in the total of 1926 flies. Therefore, the proportion of crossovers in areas *cu-sr* was 207/1926 or 10.7 percent. Between *sr* and *e*, 183 crossovers (classes 5 to 8) occurred and the proportion was 183/1926 or 9.5 percent. Therefore, *cu* was 10.7 units from *sr* and *sr* was 9.5 units from *e*. These spacial relations are indicated along with the relative positions of the three genes in Fig. 6.7. The results obtained by the student were compared with those reflected in the Drosophila linkage map (Fig. 6.8). On the linkage map based on extensive data and including the results of cross checks with several different genes in the same vicinity on the chromosome, *cu* is placed at 50, *sr* at 62, and *e* at 70.7 map units from the end of the chromosome. Distances between *cu* and *sr* and *sr* and *e* are, therefore, 12 and 8.7 units, respectively, compared with 10.7 and 9.5 from the results of the student. Linkage relations are based on averages and on the assumption that crossing over occurs at equal frequency in all parts of the chromosome.

When the same test cross was performed with $F_1$ males instead of females, the results were quite different. Only parental phenotypes (curled, stripe, ebony, and wild type) were produced. This result indicated that no crossing over had occurred in male flies.

Some discrepancies in estimates of relative positions of genes on a chromosome can be evaluated and appropriate corrections can be made. The two genes *cu* and *e* in Drosophila, for example, were calculated to be 20 units apart on the basis of single phenotypically detectable crossovers between the locus for *cu* and that for *e*. If the chromatids were involved occasionally

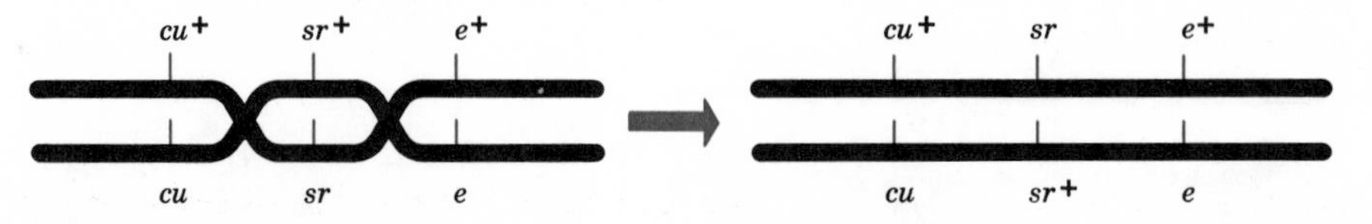


**Fig. 6.7** Diagrammatic representation of the three genes, *cu*, *sr*, and *e*, in their relative positions on a homologous pair of chromosomes in $F_1$ females. Crossovers indicated between *cu* and *sr* and *sr* and *e* are arranged to explain the results of the three-point cross cited in the text. Only two of the four chromatids are shown in this diagram.

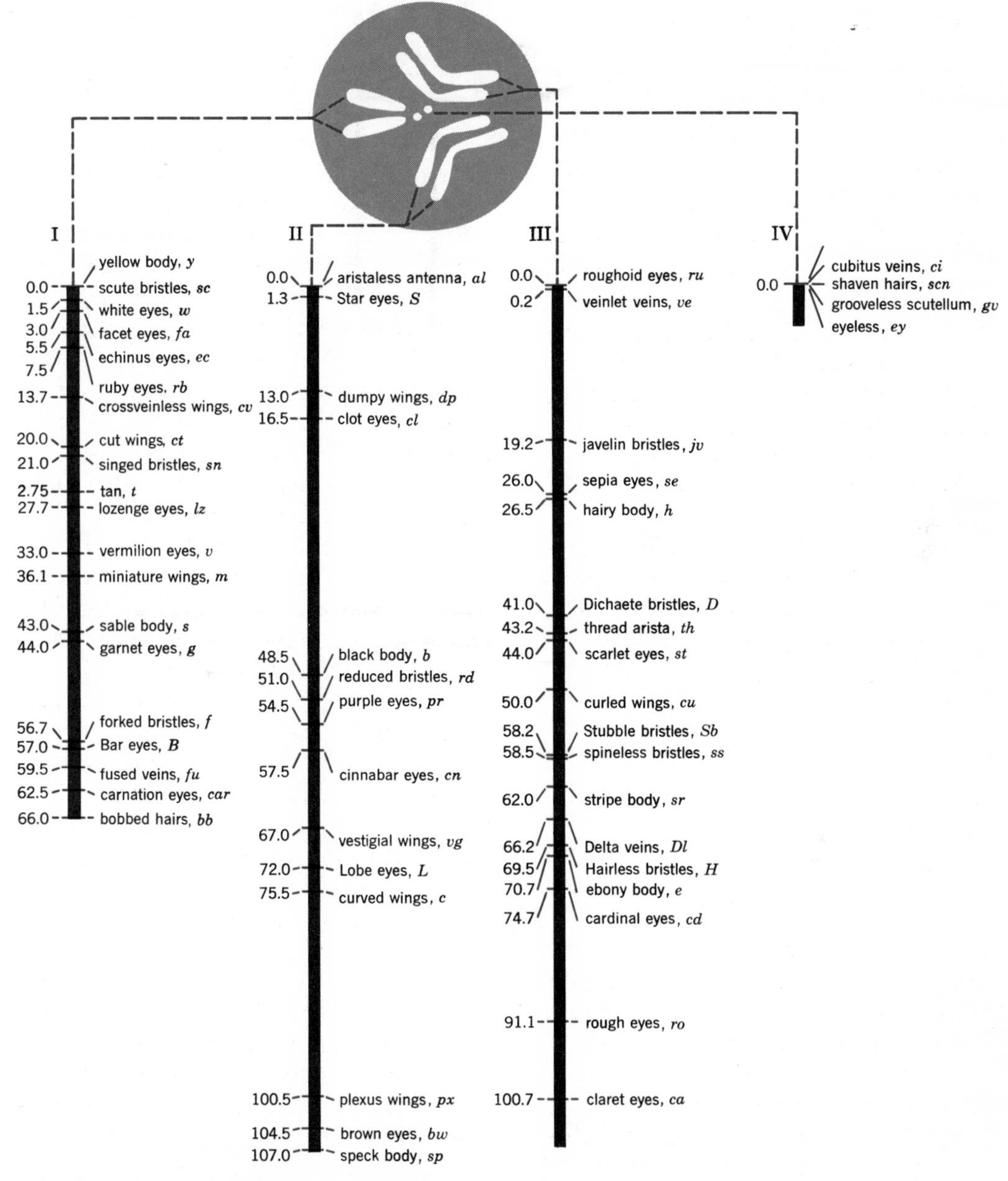


**Fig. 6.8** Linkage map showing the relative position of a few of the better known genes on each of the four chromosomes of *Drosophila melanogaster*. Gene symbols and descriptive phenotypes are given opposite gene locations. (Data from Bridges.)

in two crossovers between *cu* and *e*, a section might cross over and cross back, leaving the end points *cu* and *e* in the parental arrangement. In such cases, no crossing over would be detected in test-cross results. When the third gene *sr* between *cu* and *e* was introduced into the investigation and made possible the identification of double crossovers between *cu* and *e*, the distance $10.7 + 9.5 = 20.2$.

Three-point data correct, at least in part, the error introduced by double crossing over. Correction is necessary for double crossing over only when distances are great enough to permit an appreciable amount of double crossing over to occur. In practice, a distance of 10 or less cross-over (or map) units is considered by Drosophila geneticists to be a safe limit within which an appreciable amount of double crossing over will not occur.

### *Interference and Coincidence*

Some long chromosomes have been reported to undergo as many as 10 crossovers during one cell-division cycle. The distribution of crossovers along chromosomes indicates that the occurrence of a crossover in a given chromosome segment is mostly a chance phenomenon but that the distribution is not completely at random. The chance of two crossovers occurring simultaneously in adjacent regions should, according to the law of probability, be the product of the separate occurrences in the two sections. For example, *w* (for white eyes) at 1.5 and *cv* (for crossveinless) at 13.7 are about 12.2 units apart on the X chromosome of Drosophila, whereas *t* (for tan) at 27.5 is about 13.8 units beyond *cv*. The expected double crossing over between *w* and *t* is the product of the two separate crossover values when converted to decimal fractions, $0.122 \times 0.138 = 0.0168$. Expressed in percent, the value is 1.68, which is an approximation of the expected double crossing over, or the proportion of simultaneous crossovers in the area between *w* and *cv* and that between *cv* and *t*.

H. J. Muller showed in 1916 that the actual double crossing over is less than expected on the basis of purely random distribution. Evidently, a crossover in one place inhibits others in the immediate vicinity. This is called interference. A mathematical model was developed by Muller to express the data obtained from Drosophila and maize. It is the ratio between the observed and expected frequency of double crossing over or:

$$\frac{\text{actual double crossovers}}{\text{expected double crossovers}}$$

This mathematical measure of interference is termed coincidence. Complete interference gives a coincidence of 0; whereas no interference results in a value of 1.

The data cited from the experiment performed by the genetics student can be used to illustrate how to determine the degree of interference. On the basis of probability, $0.107 \times 0.095 = 0.0102$ or slightly more than 1 percent double crossovers should have occurred if the distribution were at random. The actual occurrence was only 3/1926 or 0.0016, and the coincidence was 0.0016/0.0102 or 0.16. Therefore, only 16 percent of the expected double crossovers were recovered, indicating a partial interference of 84 percent. Less interference would be expected if the genes involvea were further apart.

When linkage data were accumulated for mice, the model of coincidence based on Drosophila data was not adequate. A sex difference was detected in studies of linkage group XIII with males exhibiting more intense interference than females, and environmental factors (such as temperature) showing an effect.

## CHROMOSOME MAPPING

The three-point crosses cited above provided data that could be used for the beginning of a genetic map (Fig. 6.7). It was shown that genes *cu* and *sr* were 10.7 units apart and that *e* was 9.5 units beyond *sr* in the same direction. Accumulations of crossover data have led to the construction of elaborate genetic maps of many chromosomes. These are graphic representations of the relative positions and distances of genes in each linkage group. All linkage groups of some organisms have been identified and known genes placed in their relative position in the appropriate group. Distances are expressed in percentages of recombination or crossing over between loci along the chromosome. When short distances (less than 10 units) are considered, simple linear addition may be used in going from one marker point to the next in sequence. Many investigators have participated in the accumulation of recombination data. When variations occur in the results of different investigators, appropriate checks of experimental conditions are made to account for discrepancies in estimating the distances as accurately as possible. The data from many organisms have been condensed into maps of the known genes of those particular organisms.

Drosophila and maize have been especially favorable materials for extensive chromosome mapping. Crossover data obtained from appropriate test crosses and $F_2$ results for these and other experimental organisms have been accumulated, and the relative positions of certain genes have been plotted with respect to positions of other genes in the same linkage group. Numerous genes have now been placed on the maps of these organisms.

The momentum for chromosome mapping was established in the 1920's by Drosophila geneticists, particularly T. H. Morgan, C. B. Bridges, and A. H. Sturtevant. Some of the best-known loci in *D. melanogaster* are listed in Fig. 6.8, along with their relative positions in the four linkage groups corresponding to the four chromosome pairs. It should be noted that three (I, II, and III) of the four groups are large and one (IV) is very small. Linkage is expected to be more common in Drosophila with only three major linkage groups than in organisms with more chromosomes and more chance for independent assortment. Maize (Fig. 6.9), for example, with ten chromosome pairs and ten linkage groups, is expected to have less linkage and more independent assortment than Drosophila. This expectation has been borne out by comparisons of the known genes of these two organisms.

After linkage relations between genes are established for a given organism, an investigator who identifies a new mutant in that experimental material may begin immediately to determine its linkage group and position within the group. Many mutant genes have been mapped in maize, and a good many others have been placed tentatively. Chromosomes of other higher plants, such as tomato (Fig. 6.10), barley, wheat, rice, sorghum, morning glory, and garden pea, are quite well mapped. Tomatoes have twelve chromosome pairs and eleven have been identified with marker genes. Barley has seven chromosome pairs and seven linkage groups are known. Certain investigators and research teams are concentrating on studies of particular linkage groups. Likewise, research teams of the Tomato Genetics Cooperative have chosen particular chromosomes on which to study and report. Meetings are held periodically by barley breeders, tomato breeders, and other groups working on particular organisms at which the various investigators report their progress and exchange ideas for designing new experiments to extend chromosome maps. Progress in chromosome mapping for mammals has been comparatively slow. Mice have twenty chromosome pairs, and twenty linkage groups have been tentatively identified (Fig. 6.11).

Mapping of human chromosomes has been tedious and uncertain, but new statistical methods promise greater progress in the future. Several genes have been identified in the human X chromosome (Fig. 6.12). A number of autosomal

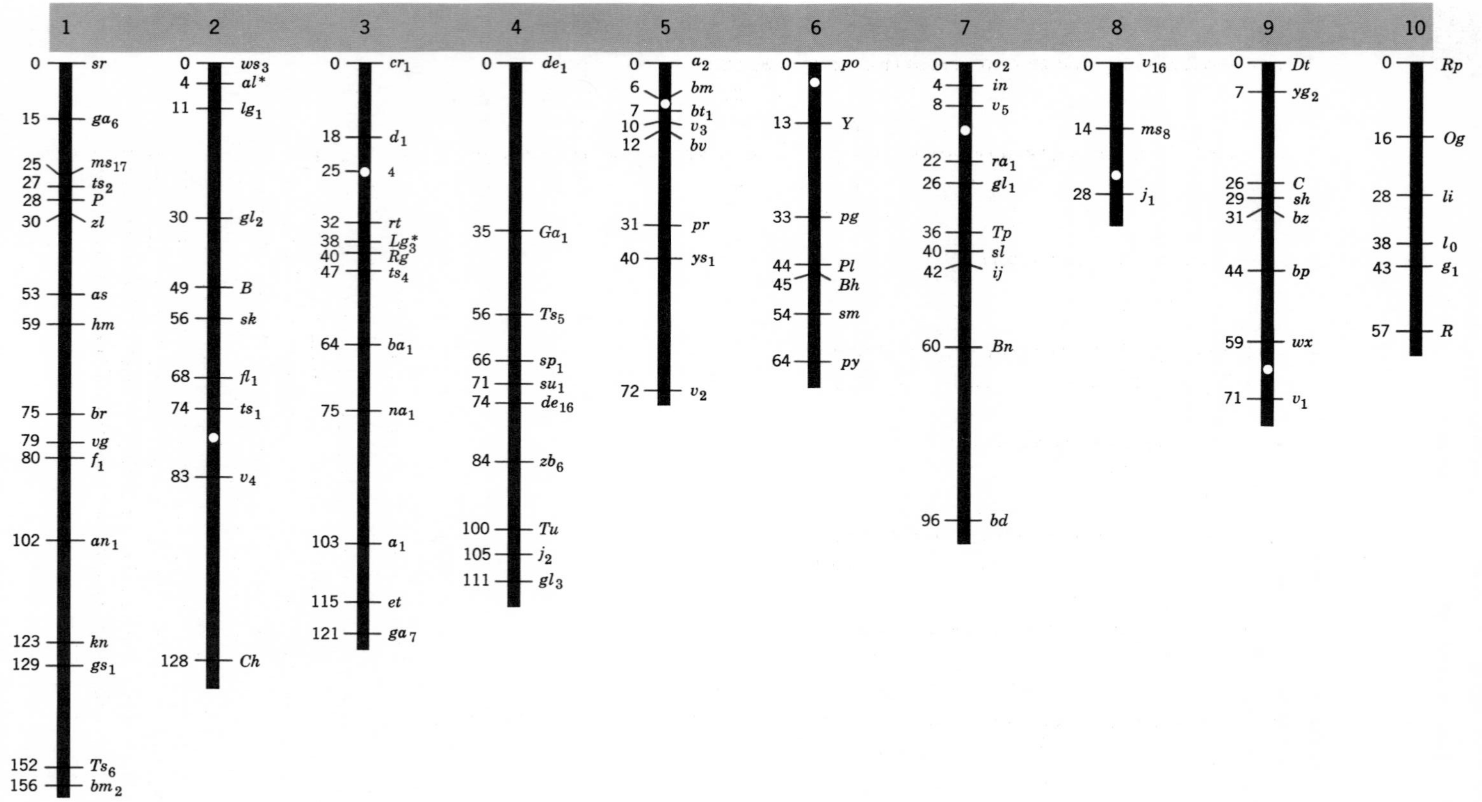

1
0 sr
15 $ga_6$
25 $ms_{17}$
27 $ts_2$
28 P
30 zl
53 as
59 hm
75 br
79 vg
80 $f_1$
102 $an_1$
123 kn
129 $gs_1$
152 $Ts_6$
156 $bm_2$

2
0 $ws_3$
4 al*
11 $lg_1$
30 $gl_2$
49 B
56 sk
68 $fl_1$
74 $ts_1$
83 $v_4$
128 Ch

3
0 $cr_1$
18 $d_1$
25 4
32 rt
38 $Lg_3^*$
40 Rg
47 $ts_4$
64 $ba_1$
75 $na_1$
103 $a_1$
115 et
121 $ga_7$

4
0 $de_1$
35 $Ga_1$
56 $Ts_5$
66 $sp_1$
71 $su_1$
74 $de_{16}$
84 $zb_6$
100 Tu
105 $j_2$
111 $gl_3$

5
0 $a_2$
6 bm
7 $bt_1$
10 $v_3$
12 bv
31 pr
40 $ys_1$
72 $v_2$

6
0 po
13 Y
33 pg
44 Pl
45 Bh
54 sm
64 py

7
0 $o_2$
4 in
8 $v_5$
22 $ra_1$
26 $gl_1$
36 Tp
40 sl
42 ij
60 Bn
96 bd

8
0 $v_{16}$
14 $ms_8$
28 $j_1$

9
0 Dt
7 $yg_2$
26 C
29 sh
31 bz
44 bp
59 wx
71 $v_1$

10
0 Rp
16 Og
28 li
38 $l_0$
43 $g_1$
57 R

**Fig. 6.9** Linkage map of maize (data from Rhoades). Descriptive phenotypes are given below for some of the genes located in each of the 10 chromosomes. *Chromosome 1: sr*, striated; *as*, asynaptic; $an_1$, anther ear-1; $bm_2$, brown midrib-2. *Chromosome 2:* $ws_3$, white sheath-3; $gl_2$, glossy seedling-2; *sk*, silkless; *Ch*, chocolate pericarp. *Chromosome 3:* $cr_1$, crinkly leaf-1; $d_1$, dwarf-1; $ts_4$, tassel seed-4; $ba_1$, barren stalk-1. *Chromosome 4:* $de_1$, defective endosperm; $Ga_1$, gamete differential fertilization; *Tu*, tunicate; $j_2$, japonica-2; $gl_3$, glossy seedling-3. *Chromosome 5:* $a_2$, aleurone color-2; *pr*, red aleurone; $ys_1$, yellow stripe-1; $v_2$, virescent-2. *Chromosome 6: po*, polymitotic; *Y*, yellow endosperm; *Pl*, purple; *sm*, salmon silk; *py*, pigmy. *Chromosome 7:* $o_2$, opaque-2; $gl_1$, glossy-1; *Tp*, teopod; *ij*, iojap striping; *bd*, branched. *Chromosome 8:* $v_{16}$, virescent-16; $ms_8$, male-sterile-8. *Chromosome 9: Dt*, dotted, *C*, aleurone color; *sh*, shrunken endosperm; *wx*, waxy. *Chromosome 10: Rp*, rust resistant; $g_1$, golden-1; *R*, color factor. (○—Approximate position of centromere.)

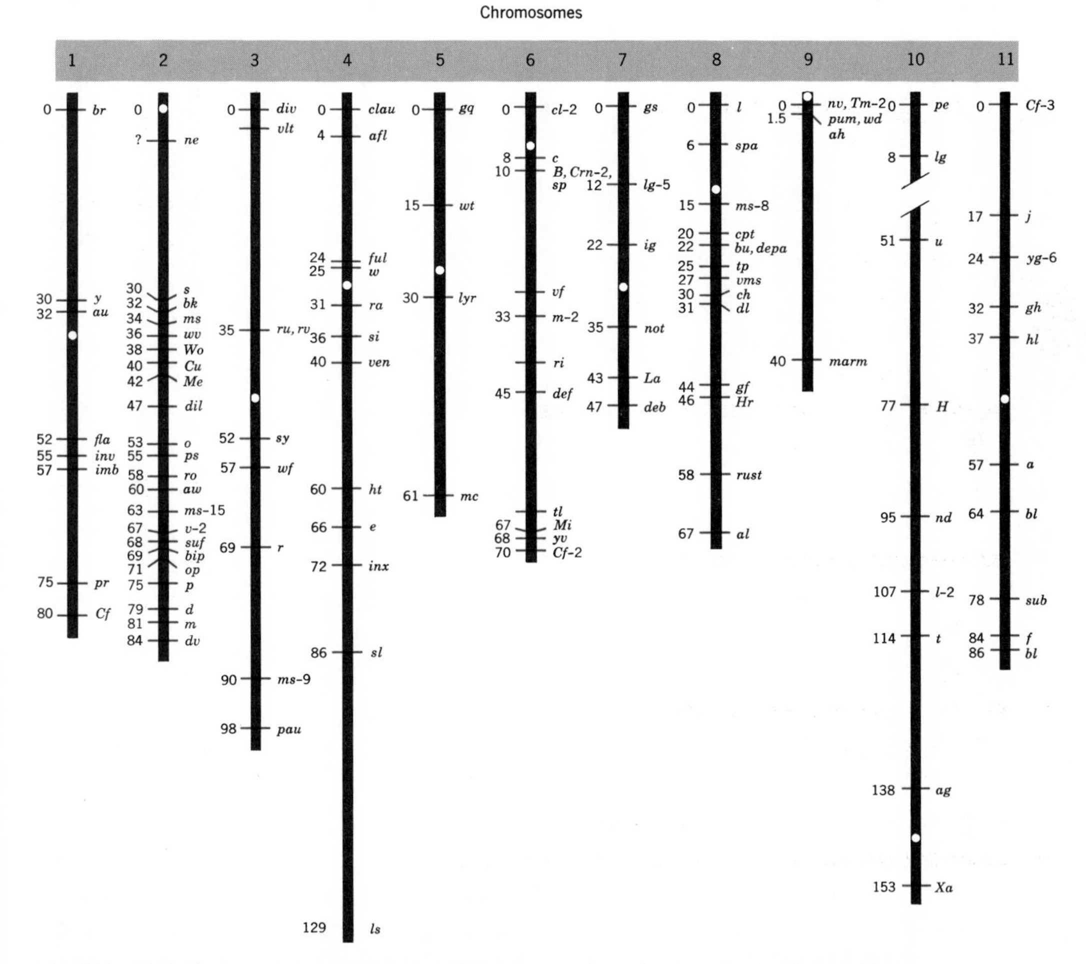


**Fig. 6.10** Linkage map of the tomato. (Data from Tomato Genetics Cooperative Report No. 15.) Phenotypes are given below for some of the genes located in each of the 12 chromosomes. *Chromosome 1: br*, brachytic; *y*, colorless fruit epidermis; *Cf*, *Cladosporium fulvum* resistance. *Chromosome 2: ne*, necrosis; *ms*, male-sterile; *op*, opaca; *d*, dwarf; *m*, mottled. *Chromosome 3: div*, divaricata; *wf*, white flower; *r*, yellow flesh; *pau*, pauper. *Chromosome 4: clau*, clausa; *w*, wiry; *ven*, venosa; *sl*, stamenless; *ls*, lateral suppressor. *Chromosome 5: gq*, grotesque; *wt*, wilty; *lyr*, lyrate; *mc*, macrocalyx. *Chromosome 6: cl-2*, cleistogamous-2; *c*, potato leaf; *sp*, self-pruning; *m*-2, mottled-2, *ri*, ridged; *yv*, yellow virescent. *Chromosome 7: gs*, green stripe; *La*, lanceolate; *deb*, debilis. *Chromosome 8: l*, lutescent; *cpt*, compact; *bu*, bushy; *ch*, chartreuse; *gf*, green flesh; *al*, anthocyanin loser. *Chromosome 9: Tm*-2, tobacco-mosaic virus; *wd*, wilty dwarf; *marm*, marmorata. *Chromosome 10: pe*, sticky peel; *u*, uniform ripening; *t*, tangerine; *Xa*, xanthophyllic. *Chromosome 11: j*, jointless; *hl*, hairless; *a*, anthocyaninless; *bl*, blind. *Chromosome 12:* No genes located. (○—Approximate position of centromere.)

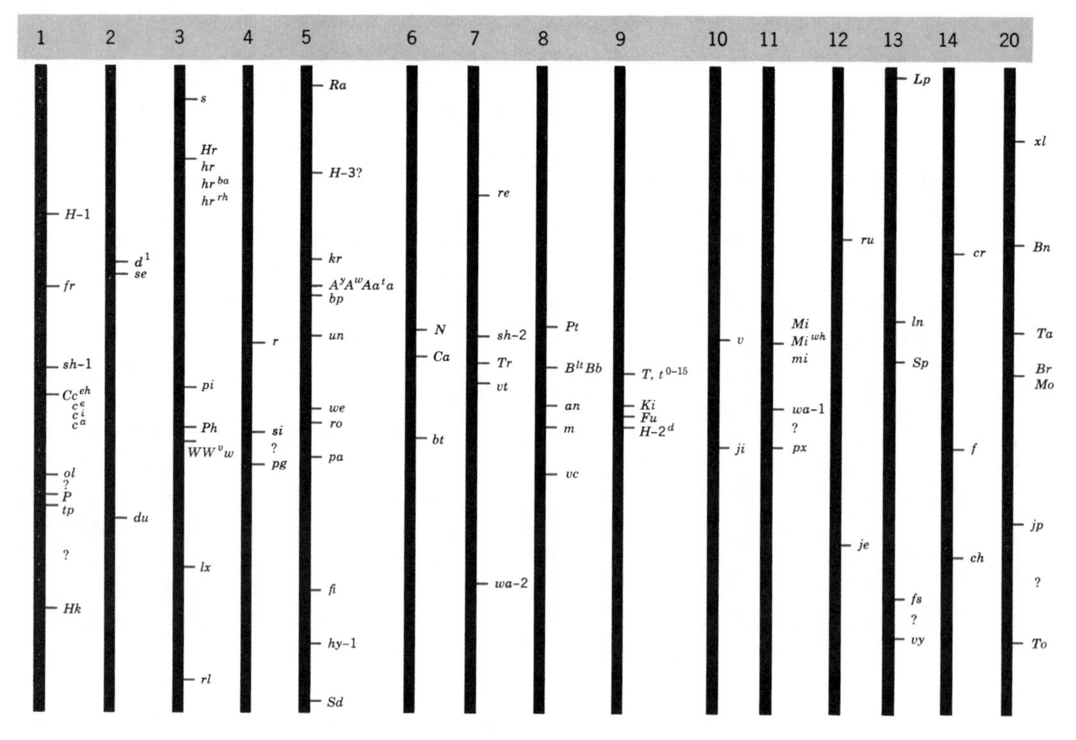


**Fig. 6.11** Linkage map of the mouse. (Data from Margaret M. Dickie and Margaret C. Green.) Phenotypes are given below for some of the genes located in 6 of the 20 chromosomes (15–19 not shown) of the mouse. *Chromosome 1: H-1*, histocompatibility-1; *sh-1*, shaker-1; $C^a$, albino; *P*, pink-eye. *Chromosome 2: d*, dilution; *se*, short ear. *Chromosome 3: s*, piebald; *hr*, hairless; *Ph*, patch; *rl*, reeler. *Chromosome 4: r*, rodless retina; *si*, silver; *pg*, pygmy. *Chromosome 5: Ra*, ragged; *A*, agouti; *ro*, rough; *hy-1*, hydrocephalus-1. *Chromosome 6: N*, naked; *ca*, caracul; *bt*, belted.

linkages in man have now been indicated. For example, the loci for ABO blood group and the nail-patella syndrome have been shown by pedigree studies to be in the same linkage group. The nail-patella syndrome, which is controlled by a single gene, includes abnormalities of the finger-nails and kneecaps. Three other linkages have been well established in man. The locus for the Rhesus (Rh) blood system is in the same linkage group with that controlling the shape of the red corpuscles, called elliptocytosis. Likewise, the genes for two other blood-group systems, Lutheran and secretor, are linked. Finally, the Duffy blood-group locus is in the

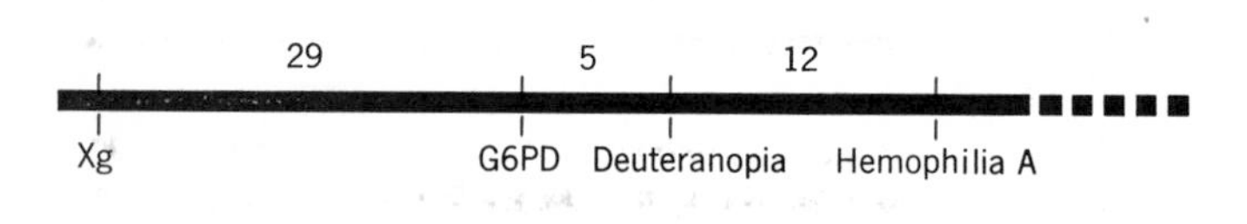


**Fig. 6.12** Linkage map of part of the human X chromosome. Numbers above the line representing the chromosome indicate the map distance between genes. The Xg locus is believed to be at the extreme end of the short arm of the X chromosome.

same chromosome with that of an eye defect, zonular or lamellar cataract in the lens.

Although the relative positions of the genes can be determined from crossover data, the distances between genes, determined by this method, must be considered somewhat debatable. Factors such as temperature, nutrition, sex, and age (particularly maternal age) may influence crossing over. It follows that experimental conditions must be carefully controlled to minimize environmental affects. Some regions of chromosomes apparently cross over more readily than others. When these factors are considered, however, crossover data furnish a valid index of the relative distances between genes in the same linkage group.

Linkage maps are available for some molds and yeasts. Recombination is well established in bacteria and viruses, but mechanisms other than those associated with higher organisms may be involved. Favorable techniques for investigating bacteriophages have made these viruses the most thoroughly mapped of any organism.

## CYTOLOGICAL BASIS OF CROSSING OVER

Genetic evidence for linkage and crossing over became well established around 1914 through the investigations of Morgan and his associates. Linked genes were postulated to occur in linear order in their respective chromosomes. Genetic crossing over was considered a consequence of the exchange of parts between homologous chromosomes. This theory could not be demonstrated cytologically, however, because homologous chromosomes appeared, on microscopic examination, to be exactly alike. It was impossible to observe whether chromosome blocks had changed places until visible markers of some kind could be incorporated on the chromosomes. The long-awaited demonstration was finally accomplished in 1931, through experiments of C. Stern (working with Drosophila), and H. B. Creighton and B. McClintock (working with maize).

Stern found flies with microscopically distinguishable X chromosomes in one of his cultures. A part of the Y chromosome had become broken off and attached to the X chromosome by a fragmentation process. Stern recognized the value of cytological markers for demonstrating crossing over and continued his search for a second marker in the same chromosome pair. Eventually, he was provided with another distinguishing feature at the other end of the X chromosome. This marker had also arisen by fragmentation and subsequent joining of chromosome parts. A part of the X chromosome had been broken off by X-ray treatment and had become attached to the small chromosome IV. The X chromosome was considerably shorter than unbroken X chromosomes. Chromosome IV was enlarged, but it paired with its homologue in meiosis. Now both X chromosomes could be distinguished by microscopic examination, and a cytological demonstration of crossing over was possible.

Stern's experiment, which is one of the classics in genetics, is illustrated in Fig. 6.13. The genes *car* and *B* for carnation-colored eye and bar-shaped eye, respectively, were made heterozygous in the cytologically distinguishable X chromosomes of the females used in the experiment. Females with red, bar-shaped eyes were mated with males having carnation-colored, normal-shaped eyes. The two X chromosomes from the female with distinct cytological markers and the one from the male with no markers were visibly distinguishable and could be identified in the progeny from the cross by appropriate

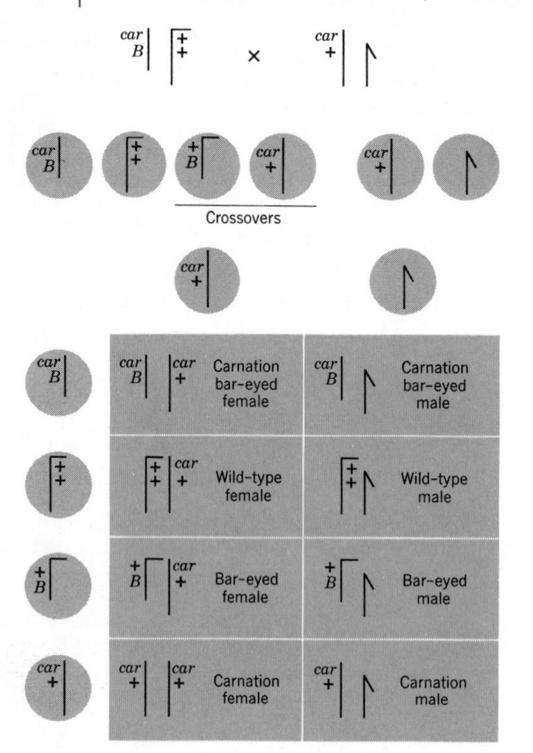


**Fig. 6.13** Diagram representing Stern's classical experiment demonstrating the cytological basis for crossing over.

microscopic examination. Predictions could be made concerning the phenotypes expected as well as of the chromosome arrangement for each phenotypic class, based on the hypothesis of crossing over. The progeny from the cross were classified, and microscopic studies of the chromosomes were made. The genetic (linkage and crossing over) and cytological (chromosome appearance) results were recorded. Flies in which crossing over was indicated phenotypically showed microscopic evidence of exchanges between homologous chromosomes. The physical or cytological basis of crossing over was thus established. Creighton and McClintock, studying maize, made use of a knob on the end of a certain chromosome and a visible irregularity on the homologue as cytological markers. Their results were generally similar to those of Stern.

## STAGE AT WHICH CROSSING OVER OCCURS

The question of when crossing over occurs has been partly answered from experimental results. Since crossing over represents an actual exchange between homologous chromosomes, it must occur while the chromosomes are together in synapsis, that is, in the meiotic prophase. At what stage in the meiotic prophase does it occur? Tetrad analysis in molds and attached X chromosome studies in Drosophila provide direct evidence that it occurs in the four-strand stage of meiosis, but only two of the four strands are involved in a given exchange.

The mold, Neurospora, is especially well suited for experimental attacks on this problem because all four of the products of meiosis are held in the ascus, or reproductive sac, in the order in which they were produced. The order of spores in the ascus is indicative of the pattern of events in meiosis. Evidence concerning the time of crossing over can be obtained by mating individuals carrying two linked genes and analyzing the results of the cross, that is, by making a tetrad analysis. This kind of analysis is not possible in Drosophila and most other organisms used routinely in genetic investigations because the gametes are produced individually from diploid germ cells and released into tubules in the testes where they become mixed with the products of other cells. It is impossible to determine which gametes have come from which cells and the order in which they were produced. The four sperm from a primary spermatocyte, for example, are mixed with sperm from other spermatocytes. In the comparable process in the female, only one of the four products of each meiosis is functional and the other three form polar bodies. More information about meiotic events can be obtained from tetrad analysis than from strand

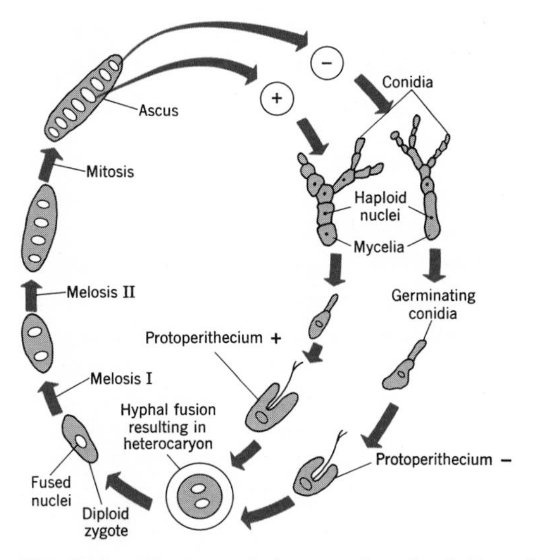


**Fig. 6.14** Diagram of the sexual cycle (left) and asexual cycle (right) in Neurospora. Asexual reproduction is based on mitotic division of haploid nuclei. A heterocaryon may be formed from hyphal fusion of conidia representing opposite mating types.

analysis. The kind of analysis possible in Neurospora is inherent in the biology of the mold (Fig. 6.14).

The life cycle of the mold includes both sexual and asexual reproduction. The asexual process is accomplished by means of spores (called conidia), which are produced on end branches of the mycelium, the interwoven thread-like mass that forms the vegetative portion of the mold. The nuclei of the mycelium are haploid and reproduce themselves by mitotic division. Sometimes a nonsexual fusion occurs between hyphae derived from different genotypes. When this occurs, cells may fuse and thus bring two nuclei into the same cell. The nuclei, however, do not come together but retain their individuality. Such a cell with two nuclei is called a heterocaryon. When the cell divides, each nucleus goes into a new cell. Besides its common asexual vegetative mode of reproduction, Neurospora has a sexual phase that involves the fusion of cells of opposite mating types (+ and −). The union of two mating cells results in a diploid zygote, but the two nuclei do not always fuse immediately. When they do come together, a reduction division similar to that in higher plants and animals follows.

The first two divisions of the zygote are meiotic divisions. Four nuclei, comparable with the four spermatids of animal spermatogenesis, can be seen in the ascus at the end of the second division. A mitotic division follows the meiotic sequence, increasing the number of nuclei to eight. All divisions occur in the plane of the long axis of the ascus, and the nuclei remain in the order in which they were produced. Because the third division is mitotic, each of four that resulted from the meiotic divisions gives rise to an identical nucleus. The eight nuclei are lined up two by two with the identical nuclei next to each other. Each nucleus is eventually surrounded by a spore wall and becomes an ascospore. When an ascus is mature and the proper environment is provided, it ruptures and the ascospores are freed to germinate, with each giving rise to a new mycelium.

Controlled crosses are made by selecting mating types with different gene combinations to produce zygotes. The phenotypic results of the cross can be determined by culturing the ascospores individually and observing or testing by appropriate means. Characteristics of the mycelium arising from a single ascospore reflect the gene combination received by the nucleus in meiosis. If the ascospores are dissected out before the ascus ruptures, they may be raised in separate culture tubes. When the tubes are kept in order, that is, the first ascospore placed in the first tube, the second in the next, and so on, the pattern of segregation of genes from a single zygote can be demonstrated. A single pair of alleles, that is, *aA*, controlling color of the mycelium, may occur in order *aaaaAAAA* (Fig. 6.15) if no exchanges occur between homologous chromosomes. If the alleles should be arranged in the other position,

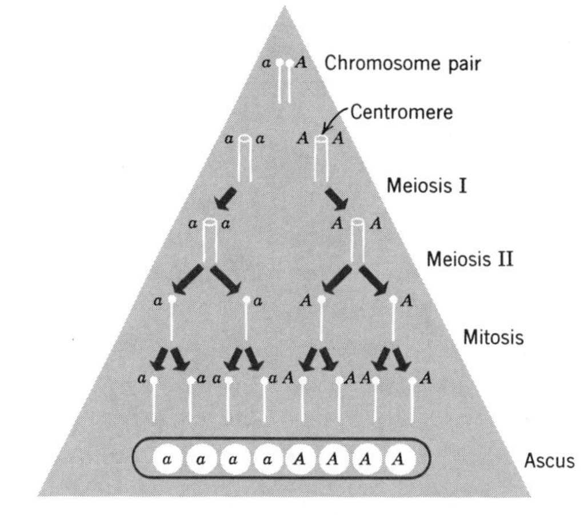


**Fig. 6.15** Diagram illustrating a chromosome pair carrying alleles *aA*, at successive stages during the 2 meiotic divisions and 1 mitotic division in Neurospora. Since no crossing over has occurred, a 4:4 distribution is represented in an ascus.

that is *Aa*, in the first meiotic division the ascospores would occur in the order *AAAAaaaa*. The 4:4 group indicates that the reduction division has occurred in the first meiotic phase. Since the two divisions that follow reduction are of the equational type, two groups of four identical nuclei are expected.

Sometimes the identical nuclei occur in pairs rather than in groups of four; that is, *aaAAaaAA*, *AAaaAAaa*, *AAaaaaAA*, and *aaAAAAaa*. In such cases, the reduction division occurred in the second division rather than in the first at the point on the chromosomes where the marker genes are located. The first division of meiosis is always reductional at the point of the centromere. If crossing over should occur, the area beyond the crossover point would be separating equationally at the time the centromere region separated reductionally, as shown in Fig. 6.16. Thus, by observing the arrangement of the ascospores from a given ascus, it is possible to determine whether the members of a pair of alleles segregated in the first or second division.

If separate pairs of alleles are located at two points some distance apart on the chromosome, it is possible to detect crossing over and to determine whether the process occurs in the two-strand or the four-strand stage. If two strands are present when crossing over occurs, either parental or recombination types might develop in a single ascus. If four strands are present, both parental and recombination types should occur in the same ascus. When two pairs of alleles such as mating types (+ and −) and mycelium colors (*A* and *a*) are followed in the same cross (Fig. 6.17), the results indicate that crossing over occurs in the four-strand stage, but that only two of the four strands are involved in a single crossover. Similar bivalent analyses have been made in other groups of lower plants, yeasts in particular.

Another demonstration of four-strand crossing over was made from a special case in Drosophila, making use of attached-X females. In these females, the X chromosomes are permanently joined and therefore undergo compulsory nondisjunction or failure to separate following synapsis. This material is not as favorable as

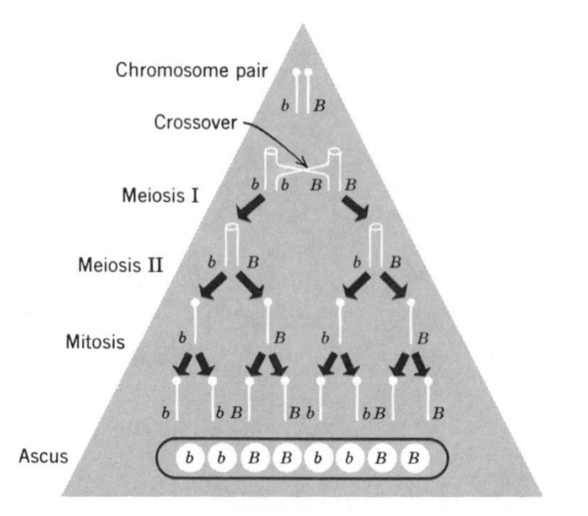


**Fig. 6.16** Diagram illustrating 2:2:2:2 arrangement of ascospores in an ascus. Crossing over has occurred between the centromere and locus for the alleles *bB*, making the second rather than the first meiotic division the reduction division for the locus concerned.

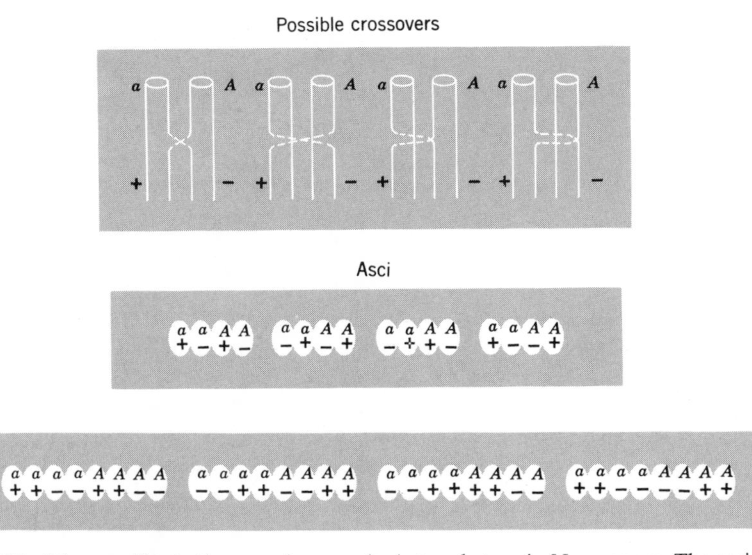


**Fig. 6.17** Diagram illustrating crossing over in 4-strand stage in Neurospora. The asci represent the completion of the meiotic sequence. Meiosis is followed by a mitotic division resulting in eight nuclei per ascus.

Neurospora because only two of the four products of a diploid germ cell can be kept together instead of all four. It does, however, furnish strong support for the hypothesis of four-strand crossing over. If crossing over occurs in the four-strand stage, one crossover strand and one non-crossover strand might be expected to occur in the same attached pair. If, on the other hand, it occurs in the two-strand stage, both should be crossover or non-crossover products.

To test these two possibilities, an experiment was devised that utilized two genes in heterozygous condition on the attached-X chromosomes of Drosophila females. The recessive gene (*y*) for yellow body color was located at the end and *v* for vermilion eye color was near the middle of the chromosomes, as illustrated in Fig. 6.18. These females were mated with wild type males. Some female progeny had yellow bodies and normal red eyes. Exchanges must have occurred in these flies between two of the four strands in the four-strand stage. It could be demonstrated that the X chromosomes remained attached. The phenotype results indicated that crossing over had occurred, since only in this way could the *y* gene be placed on both arms of some attached pairs and presumably on neither arm of other pairs involved. Further, such an exchange would have been possible only when four strands were present. The evidence from these experiments, therefore, constitutes substantial support for the hypothesis that crossing over occurs in the four-strand stage.

The foregoing demonstrations of four-strand crossing over were based on genetic data in which the genes were followed by means of the phenotypes they produced. Supporting evidence can be obtained from cytological observations, and at present the entire sequence of chromosome movements is being demonstrated. The chromatids, single strands of the bivalent, are being followed through the entire mitotic process with autoradiographic techniques and with the electron microscope. Identifying marks can also be observed on some

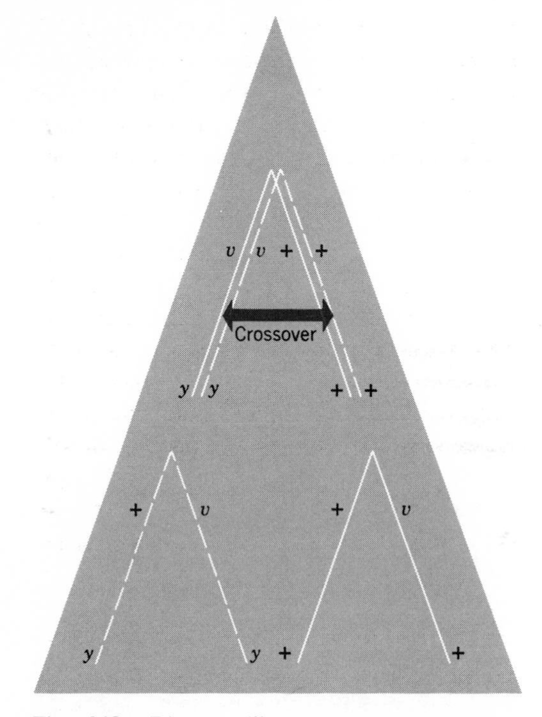


**Fig. 6.18** Diagram illustrating crossing over in attached-X female of Drosophila, which indicates that crossing over occurs in the 4-strand stage, although only 2 of the 4 strands are detectable in a single attached-X female.

chromosomes (for example, those used by Stern and Creighton and McClintock in their cytological demonstrations of crossing over) and thus individual chromatids can be followed part way through the cycle. Observations by cytologists support the genetic data.

In the process of crossing over, exchanges occur between exactly corresponding positions in chromatids. Crossovers that can be detected seem to involve the original maternal and paternal chromatids that came together in synapsis. Presumably, crossovers occur with the same frequency between duplicate chromatids but are not detectable because the genes are identical. Crossing over occurs with exact precision, and apparently without disturbing the surrounding areas.

## MECHANISM OF CROSSING OVER

It has not been possible thus far to elucidate the exact mechanism of crossing over. Visible crosses or chiasmata (Chapter 3) between chromatids can be observed with the microscope during the latter part of the meiotic prophase in many animals and plants. They do not remain in the same position but tend to move toward the ends of the bivalents, that is, they become terminalized. A chiasma is not synonymous with a point of crossing over, but there is a remarkable agreement between the total numbers of chiasmata and crossovers in some organisms that have been investigated. A reciprocal exchange between chromatids is associated with chiasmata formation. Some microorganisms are known to be capable of recombination, and examples have been described in bacteriophage (Chapter 14).

Two different simple explanations and several that are more complex have been proposed to account for crossing over. The best supported of the two is based on a mechanical break and recombination of chromatids during the early part of the meiotic prophase. These breaks must have occurred either before chiasma formation or at the time the chromosome became duplicated. This theory requires that the chromatids have been duplicated prior to synapsis. The unit threads at this stage are thin, tangled, and difficult to observe. It is postulated that they twist around each other and break under stress. Broken ends are further postulated to rejoin, but not necessarily with the same segment from which they were detached. When broken ends of different chromatids become joined, an exchange in genetic material has occurred. Single threads pulling out in the anaphase could thus include parts from different members of the four chromatids, as illustrated in Fig. 6.19. Although this

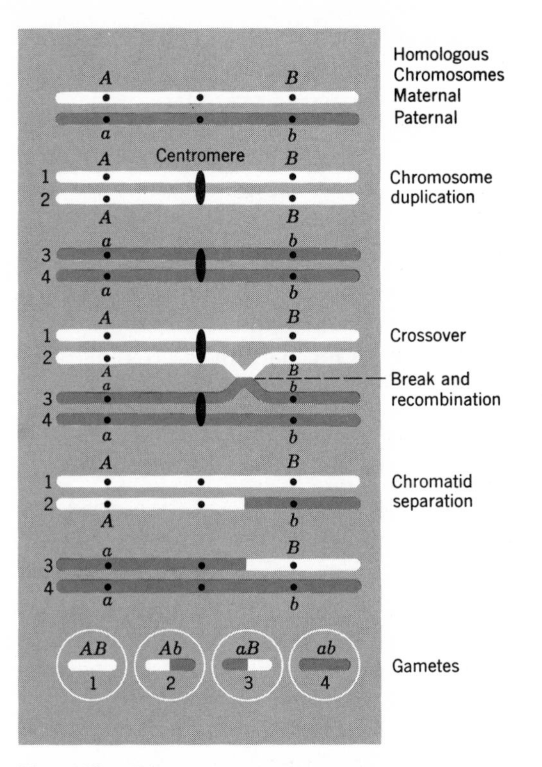


**Fig. 6.19** Diagram representing the steps in the mechanics of crossing over according to the theory of chromosome breakage and rejoining.

simple theory of reciprocal breakage and rejoining will not explain all of the requirements of an explanation for the mechanics of crossing over, it has strong support from data obtained from higher animals and plants and impressive studies (although indirect evidence) from bacteria and viruses. It probably represents the basic mechanism, although other factors may be required to account for some details and variations.

The second simple theory is a new version of a hypothesis proposed by the cytologist Belling in 1932. It fits the "copy-choice" model developed to explain the general duplication process in viruses and has become known as the copy-choice theory. Mainly it has been advanced to explain recombination in bacterial viruses and bacterial transformation. This theory requires that the synthetic activity involved in the duplication process be associated with recombination. According to this theory, recombination results from new arrangements that occur when new strands are formed. Paired chromatids in the early meiotic prophase each are postulated to duplicate their essential genetic units before the connecting links that join them in tandem to form a strand are developed. If the original chromatids, which act as templates, should be twisted around each other when the linear joining occurs, the interconnecting fibers might join parts of different chromatids at some points and adjacent segments of the same chromatid at other points. The four chromatids making up the bivalent could thus develop in such a way that, in effect, nonreciprocal exchanges would have occurred relative to the original chromatids. Very little experimental or observational support has been advanced for this explanation of recombination in higher organisms. A difficulty with the copy-choice hypothesis is that the exchanges of chromosome parts would occur simultaneously with the replication process and the two strands involved would have to be in close proximity. Evidence from studies of virus, bacteria and higher forms now indicates that replication occurs separately on the two strands; that is, it is semiconservative. Copy choice does provide a possible explanation for nonreciprocal crossing over.

## SIGNIFICANCE OF CROSSING OVER

Crossing over is a widespread phenomenon among living organisms. It occurs, with a few exceptions, in all higher plants and animals and has been noted in molds and yeasts. Experimental results suggesting a similar process have been described in bacteria and in viruses. Crossing over is a factor in the sexual process. It increases the likelihood of variation beyond the provision for independent recombination, and variation is vital to evolutionary developments. Crossing over fosters the formation of numerous combinations that can be acted on by natural selection. By experimentally utilizing the crossing over phenomenon, genes have been shown to occur in organized linkage groups and in linear order. These established facts form the foundation for analyzing the genetic mechanism and investigating the nature of the gene.

## SUMMARY

Exceptions to independent assortment were recognized soon after the discovery of Mendel's principles in 1900. As the chromosome theory became established it was shown that genes in the same chromosome pair were not independent with respect to each other and therefore would not be expected to follow Mendel's principle. Morgan and his associates working with Drosophila demonstrated and defined linkage and crossing over, which they associated with chromosomes. Genetic data from test crosses were employed to determine whether two pairs of genes were linked or independent. If they were linked, the frequency of exchanges and thus the map distance between them could be determined. Relative distances and positions of genes in the same linkage group were accumulated and worked into graphic representations of genes or linkage maps. Extensive maps have been constructed for Drosophila, maize, tomatoes, mice, and several other higher animals and plants. Beginnings have been made in linkage maps of human beings. When visible markers were found on chromosomes which could be studied in connection with phenotypic expressions, cytological demonstrations of crossing over were made. Evidence that crossing over occurs in the four-strand stage in meiosis was obtained from Neurospora and Drosophila experiments. The mechanism of crossing over is not known but physical exchanges between chromatids associated with chiasma formation occur in higher forms and could be part of the mechanism of crossing over.

## REFERENCES


Barratt, R. W., D. Newmeyer, D. D. Perkins, and L. Garnjobst. 1954. "Map construction in *Neurospora crassa.*" *Advances in Genetics* (ed. M. Demerec), Vol. 6, Academic Press, New York.

Bridges, C. B., and K. S. Brehme. 1944. The mutants of *Drosophila melanogaster.* Carnegie Inst. Wash. Publ. 552. (An alphabetical listing and description of mutants with chromosome map positions.)

Clayberg, C. D., L. Butler, E. A. Kerr, C. M. Rick, and R. W. Robinson. 1965. "Third list of known genes in the tomato." *J. Hered.,* **57,** 188–196. (Revised linkage map of the tomato, rules of nomenclature adopted by a committee of Tomato Genetics Cooperative, list of mutants and references to earlier publications.)

Creighton, H. B., and B. McClintock. 1931. "A correlation of cytological and genetical crossing over in *Zea mays.*" *Proc. Nat'l Acad. Sci.,* **17,** 492–497.

Immer, F. R., and M. T. Henderson. 1943. "Linkage studies in barley." *Genetics,* **28,** 419–440. (Methods and tables for calculation of linkage intensities from $F_2$ data.)

Morgan, T. H. 1926. *The theory of the gene.* Yale University Press, New Haven.

Morgan, T. H., C. B. Bridges, and A. H. Sturtevant. 1925. "The genetics of Drosophila." The Hague, *Bibliographia Genetica,* **2,** 1–262. (Report of basic investigations including linkage and crossing over in Drosophila.)

Punnett, R. C. 1950. "Early days of genetics." *Heredity,* **4,** 1–10. (A short interesting account of Bateson's work, confirming Mendel and nearly discovering linkage.)

Rhoades, M. M. 1954. "Chromosomes, mutations, and cytoplasm in maize." *Science,* **120,** 115–120.

# Problems

**6.1** Why did (a) Mendel, (b) Boveri, (c) Bateson not discover linkage? (d) How did Morgan succeed in developing a fundamental hypothesis of linkage and crossing over?

**6.2** Suggest experiments to determine genetically (a) whether two genes are located in the same chromosome pair; (b) whether they are in the coupling or repulsion phase.

**6.3** What are the advantages and disadvantages of (a) the test cross method for determining linkage relations? (b) the $F_2$ method?

**6.4** If the linkage strength between two loci is 70 percent, what would be the amount of crossing over between these loci?

**6.5** Genes *a* and *b* are linked with 20 percent crossing over. An $\frac{a^+b^+}{a^+b^+}$ individual was mated with an $\frac{ab}{ab}$ individual. (a) Represent the cross on the chromosomes, illustrate the gametes produced by each parent, and illustrate the $F_1$. (b) What gametes can the $F_1$ produce and in what proportion? (c) If the $F_1$ was crossed with the double recessive, what offspring would be expected and in what proportion? (d) Is this an example of coupling or repulsion?

**6.6** If the original cross in Problem 6.5 was $\frac{a^+b}{a^+b} \times \frac{ab^+}{ab^+}$, (a) represent on the chromosomes the $F_1$; (b) the gametes produced by the $F_1$ and proportions; and (c) expected test cross results. (d) Is this coupling or repulsion?

**6.7** If the crossing over in Problems 6.5 and 6.6 were 40 percent instead of 20 percent, what difference would it make in the proportions of gametes and test cross progeny?

**6.8** If Problems 6.5 (a) and 6.6 (b) with 20 percent crossing over were carried to the $F_2$ ($F_1 \times F_1$), and $a^+$ and $b^+$ were dominant over their alleles, what phenotypic classes would be produced and in what proportions?

**6.9** A fully heterozygous $F_1$ corn plant was red with normal seed. This plant was crossed with a green plant (*b*) with tassel seed (*ts*) and the following results were obtained: red, normal 124; red, tassel 126; green, normal 125; and green, tassel 123. (a) Does this indicate linkage? (b) If so, what is the percentage of crossing over? (c) Diagram the P cross on the chromosomes.

**6.10** A fully heterozygous gray-bodied ($b^+$) normal-winged ($vg^+$) female $F_1$ fruit fly crossed with a black-bodied (*b*) vestigial-winged (*vg*) male gave the following results: gray, normal 126; gray, vestigial 24; black, normal 26; and black, vestigial 124. (a) Does this indicate linkage? (b) If so, what is the percentage of crossing over? (c) Diagram the P cross on the chromosomes.

**6.11** Another fully heterozygous gray-bodied, normal-winged female $F_1$ fruit fly crossed with a black-bodied, vestigial-winged male gave the following results: gray, normal 23; gray, vestigial 127; black, normal 124; and black, vestigial 26. (a) Does this indicate linkage? (b) If so, what is the percentage of crossing over? (c) Diagram the P cross on the chromosomes.

**6.12** In rabbits, color is due to a dominant gene ($c^+$) and albinism to its recessive allele (*c*). Black is the result of a dominant gene ($b^+$), brown to its recessive allele ($b$). Fully homozygous brown rabbits were crossed with albinos carrying the gene for black in the homozygous state. $F_1$ rabbits were crossed to double recessive $\frac{c\ b}{c\ b}$ or $\frac{cb}{cb}$. From many such crosses the results were: black 34; brown 66; and albino 100. (a) Are these genes linked? (b) If so, what is the percentage of crossing over? (c) Diagram the P cross on the chromosomes.

**6.13** In tomatoes, tall vine ($d^+$) is dominant over dwarf ($d$) and spherical fruit shape ($p^+$) over pear ($p$). Vine height and fruit shape are linked, with 20 percent crossing over. A certain tall, spherical-fruited tomato plant (a) crossed with a dwarf, pear-fruited plant produced 81 tall, spherical; 79 dwarf, pear; 22 tall, pear; and 17 dwarf, spherical. Another tall, spherical plant (b) crossed with a dwarf pear produced 21 tall, pear; 18 dwarf, spherical; 5 tall, spherical; and 4 dwarf, pear. Represent on the chromosomes the arrangements of the genes in these two tall, spherical plants. (c) If these two plants were crossed with each other, what phenotypic classes would be expected and in what proportions?

**6.14** Genes $a$ and $b$ are located in chromosome II with a crossover of 20 percent. Genes $c$ and $d$ are located in chromosome III with a crossover of 40 percent. An individual homozygous for $a^+b^+c^+d^+$ was crossed with a fully recessive individual. The $F_1$ was back crossed to the full recessive. (a) Represent the original (P) cross on the chromosomes, (b) the $F_1$, and (c) the gametes that the $F_1$ could produce with their proportions.

**6.15** A student has two dominant traits dependent on single genes, cataract (an eye abnormality), which he inherited from his mother, and polydactyly (an extra finger), which he inherited from his father. His wife has neither trait. If the genes for these two traits are closely linked, would the student's child be more apt to have: (a) either cataract or polydactyly? (b) cataract and polydactyly? or (c) neither trait? Explain.

**6.16** In Drosophila the recessive genes *sr* (stripe) and *e* (ebony body) are located at 62 and 70 map units, respectively, from the left end of the third chromosome. A striped female (homozygous for $e^+$) was mated with a male with ebony body (homozygous for $sr^+$). (a) What kinds of gametes will be produced by the $F_1$ female and in what proportion? (b) If $F_1$ females are mated with stripe, ebony males, what phenotypes would be expected and in what proportion?

**6.17** From a cross between individuals with the genotypes *CcDdEe* × *ccddee*, 1000 offspring were produced. The class appearing *C-D-ee* included 351 individuals. Are the genes, *c*, *d*, and *e* in the same or different chromosome pairs? Explain.

**6.18** If an animal with the genotype *RrSsTt* produced 1020 eggs, of which 127 are *rSt*, 121 *rST*, and 130 *RST*, are the three pairs of alleles in the same chromosome or independent of one another? Explain.

**6.19** In Drosophila, the gene (*vg*) for vestigial wing is recessive and is located at 67.0 units from the left end of the second chromosome. Another gene (*cn*) for cinnabar eye color is also recessive and is located at 57.0 units from the left end of the second chromosome. A fully homozygous female with vestigial wings was crossed with a fully homozygous cinnabar male. (a) How many different kinds of gametes could the $F_1$ female produce and in what proportion? (b) If the females are mated with cinnabar, vestigial males, what phenotypes would be expected and in what proportion?

**6.20** In Drosophila, the recessive genes *st* (scarlet eye), *ss* (spineless bristles), and *e* (ebony body) are located in the same (third) chromosome in the following positions (map distances) from the left end of the chromosomes: *st* 44, *ss* 58, *e* 70. Fully heterozygous females with the genotype $\frac{st\ ss\ e^{+}}{st^{+}ss^{+}e}$ are mated with fully recessive males $\frac{stsse}{stsse}$. If many flies are produced and no interference occurs, what phenotypes will be expected and in what percentages?

**6.21** A cross was made between yellow-bodied (*y*), echinus (*ec*), white-eyed (*w*) female $\frac{yecw}{yecw}$ flies and wild males. $F_1$ females were mated with *yecw* males. The following proportions were obtained when a sample of 1000 flies was counted:

| | |
|---|---|
| wild(+ + +) | 475 |
| *yecw* | 469 |
| *y*+ + | 8 |
| +*ecw* | 7 |
| *y*+*w* | 18 |
| +*ec*+ | 23 |
| + +*w* | 0 |
| *yec*+ | 0 |

Determine the order in which the three loci *y*, *ec*, and *w* occur in the chromosome and prepare a chromosome map.

**6.22** A cross was made between yellow, bar, vermilion female flies and wild males, and the $F_1$ females were crossed with $yB^{+}v$ males. The following results were obtained when 1000 progeny were counted:

| | |
|---|---|
| *yBv* and + + + | 546 |
| *y*+ + and +*Bv* | 244 |
| *y*+*v* and +*B*+ | 160 |
| *yB*+ and + +*v* | 50 |

Determine the order in which the three loci *yBv* occur in the chromosome and prepare a chromosome map.

**6.23** (a) In Neurospora, gene *a* is 10 crossover units from the centromere and *b* is 10 units beyond *a* in the same linkage group. $\frac{a^{+}\ b}{a\ \ b^{+}}$, list the different combinations of genotypes which might be expected in the haploid ascospores resulting from meiosis and the proportions of each. (b) In what proportion would loci *a* and *b* be expected to undergo segregation in the second meiotic division? (Ignore double crossing over.)

**6.24** Present evidence in support of the following propositions (if you do not agree with a proposition state your position and defend it). (a) Genes are in chromosomes. (b) Crossing over results from exchanges between parts of homologous chromosomes. (c) Test crosses are better than $F_2$ crosses for linkage studies. (d) The percentage of crossing over between two genes on the same chromosome is roughly proportional to the distance between them. (e) Crossing over occurs in the four-strand stage in meiosis.

**6.25** In maize genes *Pl*, *sm*, and *py* are on chromosome 6 (Fig. 6.9). From the following cross:

$$\frac{Pl\ sm\ py}{Pl\ sm\ py} \times \frac{Pl^{+}\ sm^{+}\ py^{+}}{Pl^{+}\ sm^{+}\ py^{+}}$$

and the test cross between the $F_1$ and full recessive, what phenotypes would be expected and in what proportions (assuming equal crossing over in all areas along the chromosome, equal viability of all gametes, and progeny, and no interference)?

**6.26** In maize, the genes *Tu*, $j_2$, and $gl_3$ are on chromosome 4 (Fig. 6.9). If plants carrying these three genes in homozygous condition are crossed with plants homozygous for the three dominant alleles and $F_1$ plants are test-crossed to the full recessive, what genotypes would be expected and in what proportion (assuming equal crossing over in all areas of the chromosome, equal viability of all gametes, and progeny, and a coincidence of 0.5)?

**6.27** In tomatoes genes, *cpt ch gf* are on chromosome 8 (Fig. 6.10). If plants carrying these three genes in homozygous condition are crossed with plants homozygous for the dominant alleles and $F_1$ plants are test-crossed to the full recessive, what genotypes would be expected and in what proportion (assuming equal crossing over in all areas of the chromosome, equal viability of all gametes, and progeny, and a coincidence of 1.0)?

# Mutations and Mutagenic Agents

# 7

In the broadest sense, mutations include all changes in the hereditary material. Changes in submicroscopic particles of chromosomes that make up the gene structures, as well as visible structural and numerical changes in chromosomes, are included. Those that can be recognized by observations of organisms must be capable of altering phenotypes. Usually the term "mutation" is employed by geneticists in a restricted sense to specify only gene changes or point mutations, in contrast to visible chromosome changes. In this chapter, mutation is used in this restricted sense. It is not always possible in actual practice, however, to distinguish between point mutations and structural changes. Chromosome deficiencies (deleted segments of chromosomes, for example) grade all the way down in size to the border of visibility with the light microscope and they are known to occur at the molecular level of magnitude in the genetic material.

Through appropriate techniques, such as the use of salivary gland chromosomes in Diptera, it has been possible to find deficiencies not otherwise detectable. A wide range in size exists between the structures that can be seen with the best tools available and the molecular level. The present distinction between chromosome changes and point mutations thus is superficial at best. For convenience in discussion, chromosome structural changes are considered in Chapter 9, and point mutations are discussed in this chapter.

The Dutch botanist Hugo de Vries (1848–1935; Fig. 7.1) is credited with the first modern statement of the mutation theory, the theory that new forms evolve suddenly by large changes rather than by the gradual accumulation of small variations. In the 1880's he observed striking variations in Lamarck's evening primrose, *Oenothera lamarckiana,* a plant that had been introduced from America and had grown wild in Europe. De Vries collected seed from the individual plants that differed from the standard type and raised the plants derived from these seeds in his botanical garden at Hilversum, a few miles southeast of Amsterdam. From careful examination of the seedlings and mature plants, many differences in growth form were observed. The word *mutation* was used to describe the process of phenotypic change. On the basis of limited observation, the occurrence of mutation was presumed to be rare in nature, but when such change occurred it was perpetuated in further generations.

De Vries was a keen observer and an objective scientist. He had already distinguished himself among biologists with his discovery of osmosis in plant cells, and he was one of the three men who discovered

**Fig. 7.1** Hugo de Vries, Dutch botanist who formulated the mutation theory.

Mendel's work in 1900. In 1901 he published his accumulated data in a book entitled *The Mutation Theory*. De Vries was careful to distinguish between hereditary and environmental variation, but his mutations are now known to have included several kinds of changes in the hereditary material. It took nearly half a century to clarify the situation in Oenothera and discover the causes of the variations that he observed. Chromosome changes, both structural and numerical, were eventually found to cause the phenotypic variation that de Vries had grouped under the heading of mutations. One complex alteration is described later on in this chapter in connection with the discussion of permanent heterozygotes. It was de Vries' concept of discontinuous variation rather than his precise observations and examples that became significant. None of his examples would now be classified as gene mutations.

## MUTATIONS AND PHENOTYPIC CHANGE

Because genes are chemical entities that cannot be observed and compared directly, some phenotypic alteration must be associated with the gene change (mutation) or it will go unrecognized. Minor changes presumably occur in genes as a matter of course without producing any phenotypic alterations. Some gene changes are known to be associated with only slight effects on the fertility or viability of the organism. These alterations ordinarily go undetected unless critical comparisons are made. They may, however, influence natural selection and thus represent a factor in evolution.

Mutations also represent the only means by which the presence of particular wild-type genes can be postulated. Normal development of any organism is influenced by numerous genes. An observable characteristic of the adult may be altered by an individual gene substitution, but because the entire organism develops as a unit, the action of individual wild-type genes is not always apparent. The existence of mutant and wild-type genes is substantiated when a gene is changed so that its influence on developmental reactions causes a visible difference from that exerted by the unmutated gene. Mutations thus provide the basis for postulating wild-type genes.

Mutated as well as unmutated genes tend to give rise to other genes exactly like themselves. Once established, a mutated gene is as stable as the original gene from which the mutation occurred. This process of duplication is associated with mitotic cell division and occurs repeatedly as the number of cells increases. Duplication among genes has a crude parallel in the procedure of printing. After type is set and placed on the printing press; similar copies can be made repeatedly. If the type is changed slightly with an altered template replacing the original, the new pattern reproduces itself faithfully. Instead of a physical change, such as the substitution of one piece of metal for another, the gene in the process of mutation undergoes a chemical change. A part of the gene unit is altered by the chemical modification in such a way that it henceforth behaves differently from its unmutated ancestral gene.

Not all mutations are immediately detectable because many, perhaps the great majority, are recessive and must become homozygous before they can express themselves. Because the phenotypic effect is the only readily observable evidence of mutations, however, a sudden phenotypic change that subsequently proves to be heritable is an accepted indication that a mutation has occurred in an organism. In everyday language, the phenotypic change is synonomous with the gene change or actual mutation. This is quite natural because the term "mutation" was coined and used before the present gene concept was established. Historically, therefore, the word has been used to describe the perceptible change rather than the more fundamental gene alteration. It is now known that most mutations that are not detectable by visible phenotypic change influence the viability of the organism in some indirect way.

### *Classifications for Mutations*

Dominance and recessiveness provided convenient, although perhaps superficial, criteria for early classifications of mutations. As we have already observed, mutations also may occur in either the autosomes or the X chromosomes, and thus may be classified as autosomal or sex-linked. Viability mutations have also been classified on the basis of their effect on the organism. Various mutations of this nature in Drosophila have been expressed in the egg, larva, pupa, or adult. When disadvantageous, the mutations are called deleterious; when disastrous to the individual, they are called lethals. Relatively few mutations occur as dominants and even fewer are advantageous in the environments where they occur. The great majority of changes are recessive and detrimental under usual environmental conditions. In a changing environment, a mutation may happen to coincide with new environmental situations and be favorable (Chapter 18).

### *Pleiotropy*

A given mutation may alter the organism severely or have such slight effect that it can be detected only when associated with other genes, through cumulative action. The name and gene symbol associated with a mutation are usually taken from the most conspicuous phenotypic alteration that the mutation produces. Thus, white eye (*w*) is used in contrast to the wild type, red; and ebony (*e*) body designates the deviation of dark from wild type, gray body color. This method of designation perpetuates an overly simplified concept of the effects of mutations. Because they exert their influence on basic chemical reactions in the developmental period, single mutant genes affect more than a single trait and may modify in some way every trait of the organism.

The term *pleiotropy* refers to the situation in which a gene is known to influence more than a single trait. For example, in the presence of the white-eye mutation in *Drosophila melanogaster,* the ocelli, Malpighian tubules, and testicular envelopes are colorless, whereas these structures in wild flies are colored. The balancers and wing muscles are altered and the general viability and fertility of the flies are changed. Sheldon Reed has demonstrated a discrimination against white-eyed flies in mating. Such discrimination indicates that the gene causes some effect on the cuticle that influences the mating stimulus. White eye is thus only one of several effects of the single mutant gene (*w*). Many examples of genes with more than a single effect have been discovered. All genes (mutants and nonmutants) may be pleiotropic, even though their various effects are not recognized at present. Even though a gene may have many end effects, probably it influences only one primary function in the chemistry of the developing individual.

Congenital hydrocephalus in the mouse, cited by Grüneberg, illustrates the manifold effects of a single gene, *ch*, on the developing mouse. The gene occurred as a spontaneous mutation and was found by preliminary studies to influence cartilage formation in early development of the mouse. Mice that carried the gene in homozygous condition were born alive but died immediately after birth because the lungs did not inflate properly. Other conspicuous abnormalities also occurred: the skull, forehead, and face were out of proportion; large protuberances filled with fluid extended out from the cerebral hemispheres because the skull bones were abnormal and only skin covered the forehead; eyelids were always open; sensory hairs of the face were abnormal; and the sternum was abnormal with little or no bone formation. Developmental studies showed that abnormalities occurred as early as the thirteenth day in the embryo. The manifold effects were traced back to a single cause, the abnormal cartilage formation. Various skeletal abnormalities were involved directly; physiological disturbances occurred secondarily. A single primary reaction concerned with cartilage formation was controlled by the mutant gene.

### *Somatic and Germinal Mutations*

Mutations may occur in any cell and at any stage in the cell cycle. The immediate effect of the mutation and its ability to produce phenotypic change is determined by its dominance, the type of cell in which it occurs, and the stage in the cycle of the cell. If the mutation occurs in a somatic cell that can reproduce other cells like itself but not the whole organism, the mutant change would be perpetuated only in somatic cells that descended from the original cell in which the mutation occurred.

The "Delicious" apple and the navel orange have resulted from mutations that occurred in somatic tissues. Changes that gave these two fruits their desirable qualities apparently followed spontaneous mutation in single cells, which constituted only a very small part of the body of the individual apple and orange trees that were involved. In each case, the cell carrying the mutant gene gave rise to more of its own kind, eventually producing an entire branch on its respective tree which had the characteristics of the mutant type. Fortunately, it is possible to propagate desirable types of many plants by vegetative methods such as budding and grafting. Vegetative propagation was feasible for both the Delicious apple and the navel orange, and today numerous progeny from grafts and buds have perpetuated the original mutation. Descendants of the mutant types are now widespread in apple orchards and orange groves. The result of a somatic mutation in a snapdragon flower is shown in Fig. 7.2.

Results of somatic mutations have been detected in animals as well as in plants. In Drosophila, white sectors (Fig. 7.3) are infrequently observed in an otherwise red eye. Sectors in some male flies have been demonstrated to be composed of descendants from a single cell in which a mutation had occurred (at the *w* locus in the X chromosome). If the same change had occurred in a germ cell, a white-eyed male might have been produced.

**Fig. 7.2** Snapdragon flower showing results of somatic mutation. Other flowers of the plant from which this blossom was taken were white and other members of the same strain of *Antirrhinum majus* had all-white flowers. This single blossom appeared with petals colored with red. (Courtesy of Brookhaven National Laboratory.)

If dominant mutant genes occur in germ cells, their effects may be expressed immediately in the progeny. If they are recessive or hypostatic, their effects may be obscured by other genes. Germinal mutations, like somatic mutations, may occur at any stage in the cycle of the organism but they are more common in some stages, particularly during the gene replication process preceding gametogenesis. If the mutation arises in one of the gametes produced by an individual, a single member of the progeny may receive the mutant gene. If, on the other hand, a mutation occurs during an earlier stage of gametogenesis, several gametes may receive the mutant gene and therefore several individuals could perpetuate it. In any case, the dominance of the gene and the stage in the cycle when the mutation occurs are major factors in determining the extent of any expression that follows.

The earliest recorded germinal mutation in domestic animals was that observed by

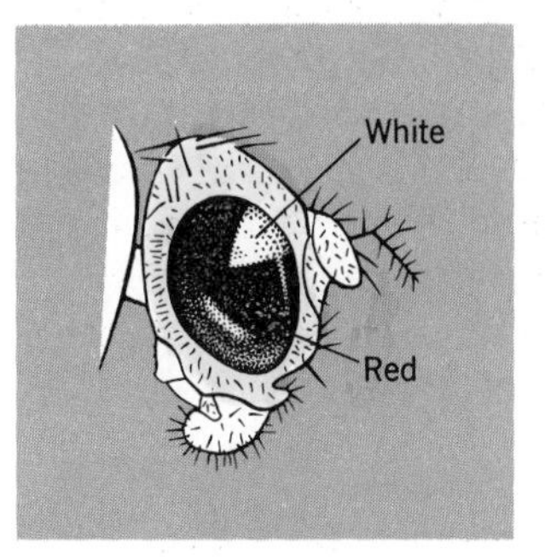


**Fig. 7.3** Schematic view of Drosophila eye showing white sector in otherwise red eye, resulting from somatic mutation.

**Fig. 7.4** Short-legged sheep of the Ancon breed. (Left) short-legged sheep; (right) sheep with normal length legs. (Courtesy of Australian News and Information Bureau.)

Seth Wright in 1791 on his farm by the Charles River at Dover, Massachusetts. Wright noticed a peculiar male lamb with unusually short legs in his flock of sheep (Fig. 7.4). It occurred to him that it would be an advantage to have a whole flock of these short-legged sheep, which could not get over the low stone fences in his New England neighborhood. Wright used the new short-legged ram for breeding his 15 ewes in the next season. Two of the 15 lambs produced were short-legged. Short-legged sheep were then bred together and a line was developed in which the new trait was expressed in all individuals. The mutation that gave rise to the short-legged sheep was obviously of the germinal type because the cell carrying the mutation had the capacity to reproduce the entire organism. Other examples of germinal mutations have since been described in a wide variety of animals and plants.

## FREQUENCY OF SPONTANEOUS MUTATIONS

Although spontaneous mutations are rare, their rates of occurrence are measurable. Populations rather than individuals must be considered in estimates of rates or frequencies. It is not easy to arrive at unbiased estimates. This is particularly true of investigations involving higher animals and man. Tests have been devised for estimating mutation rates for dominant and recessive autosomal genes and sex-linked genes in experimental animals. Mutations with lethal effects are more frequent than those producing visibly changed phenotypes and, therefore, have been studied more effectively. Among the visibles, dominants are more readily detected than recessives. More complicated tests are required for recessives that must become homozygous before they are expressed. Sex-linked mutations present special problems but also certain advantages because usually two X chromosomes are present in the female and only one in the male.

M. Demerec has made extensive investigations on mutability in Drosophila and, more recently, in bacteria. His studies have shown that each gene has its own characteristic mutational behavior. Some genes undergo mutations ten times more frequently than others in the same organism. Those with unusually rapid mutation rates are called unstable, but it must be recognized that a wide range of mutation rates exists among genes that are considered stable. The average mutation rate for bacteria is in the order of one in ten million or $10^{-7}$ per cell generation. For fruit flies, the average for a mutation in a particular locus is in the order of 1 in 100,000 with a range from 1 in 20,000 to 1 in 200,000.

L. J. Stadler studied endosperm characters in large populations of maize and found that mutation frequency varied widely among different genes. Eight loci were studied extensively and all showed different mutation rates. The *R* gene, for color, mutated 492 times per $1 \times 10^6$ gametes, whereas the $wx^+$ gene for normal in contrast to waxy endosperm failed to mutate in $1.5 \times 10^6$ gametes. Between the extremes in this particular investigation, the gene $sh^+$ for full, mutated to *sh*, for shrunken kernel, three times in about $2.5 \times 10^6$ gametes. The spontaneous mutation rates of different alleles at the same locus were also shown to vary widely. It therefore was impossible to designate a locus in maize as stable or unstable. Specific alleles had to be considered.

Since a given individual has a number of chromosomes and many loci on each chromosome, a new mutation may occur rather frequently somewhere in the germ plasm of an individual. Muller has estimated that 1 in 20 fruit flies may, at some stage of life, undergo spontaneous mutation at some locus. This estimate is based on studies of sex-linked lethals. A minimum estimate of the total number of genes in one diploid set of chromosomes in the fly was placed at 5000 and the average frequency of mutation at each locus at $10^{-5}$ cells (zygotes). Therefore, about 1 fly in 20 might be expected to have a spontaneous germinal mutation.

Present estimates for man indicate a somewhat more frequent rate than those cited for stable genes in other organisms. Genes associated with such human traits as intestinal polyposis and muscular dystrophy were estimated to have a mutation rate of $10^{-4}$ to $10^{-5}$. Samples collected thus far have been small, and the methods used were indirect and subject to large errors. A human generation is equal to about 50 to 100 cell generations. The difference in average rates in different organisms may not be so great when the rates are expressed in terms of cell generations.

Special methods are required to evaluate the frequency of mutant genes in particular materials. The Russian geneticist, S. S. Tschetwerikoff, collected 239 wild Drosophila and subjected them to critical mating tests in the laboratory. Thirty-two different recessive mutations were found, all carried in heterozygous condition. One conspicuous common laboratory mutant, aristapedia, characterized by legs growing in place of an antennae, was found in the wild before it was discovered in the laboratory. N. P. Dubinin, a student of Tschetwerikoff, continued the study of mutations in wild populations and found that the number of mutant genes carried by the flies fluctuated from season to season. Such investigations have demonstrated that many wild-appearing flies carry recessive mutations. This is also true of populations of most plants and animals.

Although individual mutations occur at random and cannot be directed by any known force, some internal and external factors may change the overall rate with which mutations occur. An animal that does not maintain a constant body temperature, for example, will ordinarily undergo more mutations at a high temperature than an animal of the same strain raised at a lower temperature. Since mutations represent chemical changes in genes, it would be expected that factors altering the rates at which chemical reactions occur would influence mutation rates. It is to be expected, therefore, that factors (such as oxygen tension) that influence the intimate environment of the genes would have some effect on the tendency of genes to mutate.

Young Drosophila males have a higher proportion of mutations in their sperm cells than do older males. Likewise, male fruit flies as well as males of some other species have a higher proportion of mutations in stored sperm than in fresh sperm. Among human beings, older mothers have a consistently higher rate of chondrodystrophic children than do young mothers. This correlation was shown to be a true age effect independent of the number of preceding births. The age of the father may also influence mutation rates. On the basis of current data, sex-linked mutations in Drosophila occur about three times as often in males as in females. Whether conclusions from these studies can be applied universally for all organisms is not known.

**Fig. 7.5** Flowers from Better Times rose plants. Right, unstable mutant with white and splashed-white sectors in an otherwise pink flower; upper, pink stable mutant; lower, white flower characteristic of this variety. (Courtesy of Brookhaven National Laboratory.)

## MUTABLE AND MUTATOR GENES

Ordinarily genes are relatively stable and mutate infrequently, but a few genes mutate spontaneously so often that individuals carrying them are mosaics of mutated and unmutated genes. Certain genes in maize, for example, were found by R. A. Emerson to undergo alteration much more frequently than others. These "mutable" genes are either more unstable than others or they are influenced by other factors in the genetic environment. Genes in maize have been shown by McClintock to influence the stability of other genes and thus alter the tendency for the latter genes to mutate. These have been called "mutator" genes. Certain chromosome sections in maize have a profound effect on the stability of any region of any chromosome with which they are associated.

Examples of highly mutable genes have been found in both plants and animals, but they seem to be more common in plants. They occur frequently in somatic tissue and occasionally in germ cells. Somatic mutations may show their effects as color variegations in such plant parts as endosperm, leaves, and petals. Many common plants (including the larkspur, snapdragon, sweet pea, four o'clock, and morning glory) have color variegations suggesting unstable or mutable genes. An unstable mutant of the Better Times rose is shown in Fig. 7.5 along with a stable pink mutant and a white flower characteristic of this variety.

Several mutable genes have been identified in *Drosophila virilis*. These include the gene *a*, which influences body color; *m*, which conditions a purplish eye color; and *mt*-3 and *mt*-5, which determine miniature wings. In some *D. virilis* stocks that are homozygous for the recessive gene associated with miniature wing, 5 to 10 percent of the flies are wild type, that is, long-winged. Others in the same stock are mosaics, with patches of miniature and wild-type tissue. Demerec explained the occurrence of wild type in these cultures on the basis of reverse mutations (that is, miniature to wild type) in the germ cells. The mosaics were attributed to similar mutations in somatic cells.

A striking example of the action of a mutator (catalyst-type) gene with a specific effect on a basic color gene in maize was described by M. M. Rhoades. The color in maize leaves and other plant parts is dependent on a complex of three complementary genes, symbolized *A*, *C*, and *R*. All three dominant members of the pairs, that is, *ACR*, are required to produce a color other than green. The color may be purple if gene *P* is also present, or red (*pp*), or some other color depending on what other genes are included. Plants with *aa*, *cc*, or *rr* are green. A mutator gene, *Dt*, in the presence of *aa C-R-* has been shown to control a dotted or variegated color in the corn kernel (Fig. 7.6) and other parts. This gene was found to produce its effect through an influence on the *a* gene of the *Aa* pair of alleles. In its presence the *a* gene is highly mutable. Plants with the genotype *aa C-R-* would be expected to be green, but in the presence of *Dt* they are variegated. Patches of cells scattered throughout the plant carry *A* genes resulting from mutations of *a* to *A*. On the leaves, these patches give the speckled appearance of colored spots on green leaves. The size of the spots depends on the stage of development at which the mutations occur. Green cells contain unmutated genes, that is, *aa*. A factor in the genetic environment was thus shown to influence the mutation rate of a specific gene.

An example of a mutator gene in an animal with a general effect on many loci was described by Demerec in *D. melanogaster.* In a study designed to compare the spontaneous mutation rates of flies collected in different parts of the world, it was observed that sex-linked lethal mutations occurred much more frequently in the Florida stock than in 14 others originating in different localities. Genetic analysis showed that the high mutation rate was determined by a recessive gene in the second chromosome. Further investigation showed that the mutator gene not only increased the rate of sex-linked lethals, but also altered phenotypes, reflecting an increased mutation rate for a number of other genes as well. Several Drosophila strains have now been shown to have relatively high mutation rates in comparison to other strains. The rates were found to be under genetic control.

A genetic locus responsible for generalized high mutability in *E. coli* was described by Zamenhof. The mutable gene was found to be located near the gene that controls the production of the amino acid, leucine. It increased the spontaneous mutation rate to a point where 15 percent of

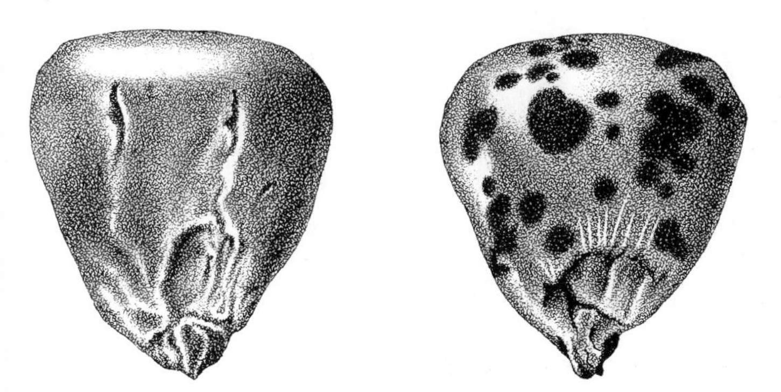

**Fig. 7.6** Colorless and spotted maize kernels. Kernel at left carries genes *aa* and that at right carries *aa* and *Dt* mutator gene.

the cells carrying the mutator gene were mutants. The effect of this mutator was not specific on any one locus but general in nature for a large proportion, perhaps all, genes in the organism. Besides examples in maize, Drosophila and *E. coli,* mutators have been described in yeast, Streptomyces, and Salmonella.

## INDUCED MUTATIONS

H. J. Muller demonstrated in 1927 that the mutation rate of *D. melanogaster* could be markedly increased by treating the flies with X-rays. Expressions of induced mutations (Fig. 7.7) seemed to be the same as those of comparable mutations that occurred spontaneously, but the frequency was increased as much as 150-fold. For the first time in history, a particular agent from the external environment had been shown to increase the frequency of mutations. A year after Muller's demonstration of induced mutations, Muller and E. Altenburg showed that the frequency of structural rearrangements, such as translocations between chromosomes, was also increased by X-ray treatment. It was then suggested that the effect of irradiation was destructive and that at least the induced type of mutation may have resulted from the loss of a minute part of the chromosome.

The extent to which X-ray-induced mu-

**Fig. 7.7** Fruit flies, *Drosophila melanogaster,* sired by males exposed to radiation, showing several different mutant phenotypes. (Courtesy of Brookhaven National Laboratory.)

tations represent the destruction of genes or chromosome segments in other organisms still is not known. Indirect but relevant evidence from Drosophila investigations, however, is based on reverse mutations. Mutations, presumably X-ray induced, were reported by early investigators of mutations in *D. melanogaster* to be reversible. The gene for red eye pigment, for example, mutated in such a way that white or an intermediate color between red and white was produced. Later the mutant gene was reported to have changed in such a way that red or an intermediate color was obtained. For a mutation to be reversible, the chemical structure of the mutant gene must remain intact with no essential part permanently altered or destroyed by the change. New investigations employing improved techniques and involving somatic as well as germ cells failed to produce evidence for X-ray-induced reversible mutations in three alleles at the *w* (white-eye) locus. One allele had arisen spontaneously, one was induced by X-rays, and one was induced by a nitrogen-sulfur chemical mutagen.

When the *f* (forked) locus, also in the X chromosome, was investigated, a few reverse mutations were detected. Investigations by M. M. Green and George Lefevre, Jr., showed no significant difference in the frequency of reversals at the forked locus for spontaneous as compared with X-ray-induced mutations. Apparently the *w* and *f* loci behave differently in their tendency toward reverse mutations. Furthermore, the various alleles of *f* that were tested behaved differently when compared with one another. Alleles were classified as high, medium, and low in their tendency to undergo reversals. Some alleles may have resulted from a destructive process while others resulted from chemical alterations that were reversible.

In the pink bread mold (Neurospora), the situation is quite different from that in maize and Drosophila. In Neurospora, mutations occur readily back and forth from one allele to another. Obviously no irreversible process is associated with these mutations. One mutant, for example, cannot grow on a medium that lacks adenine. When, however, numerous samples of adenine-requiring organisms were introduced on an adenine-free medium, a few organisms grew. These had apparently changed back to adenine-independent forms. The problem then was to determine whether the mutant gene had actually mutated back to wild type or whether some other change had circumvented the requirement. Critical analyses have now shown that some of these reversals involve different loci entirely. Apparently another locus can suppress the mutant gene or otherwise take care of the deficiency. In some cases, however, reverse mutations can be shown to have taken place.

In 1928 Muller and F. B. Hanson and F. M. Heys independently showed that gamma rays would also induce mutations. Neutrons and virtually all ionizing radiations, when administered to the gonads of animals in sufficiently high dosages, were later found to increase the frequency of mutations. Effect of irradiation seemed to be general rather than specific. Mutagenic agents were presumed to cause a disturbance among the molecules, resulting either in destruction of some unit or in chemical reorganization. The mutation rate is generally proportional to the dosage of irradiation, as illustrated in Fig. 7.8. Above 5000*r* (roentgens) viability is low and data are difficult to interpret, but P. T. Ives has extended the curve to 12,500*r* for Drosophila sperm irradiated with cobalt-60 gamma radiation. Some features of the curve at lower dosages also require further investigation and interpretation. The induced mutation rate of doses below 25*r* is difficult to separate from the spontaneous mutation rate. In a laborious experiment,

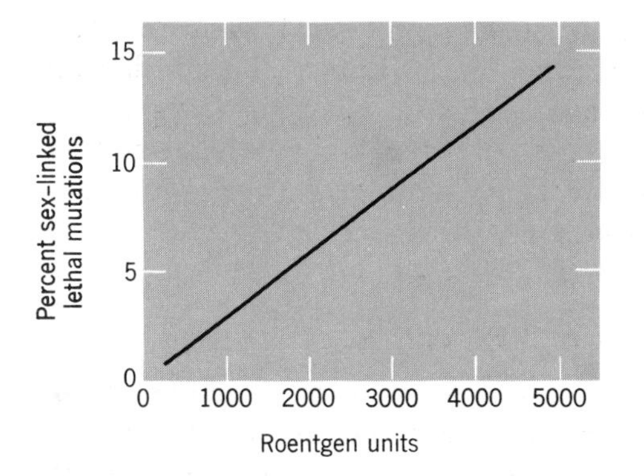


**Fig. 7.8** Graph illustrating the relation between dosage of irradiation and frequency of sex-linked lethal mutations. The frequency of mutations was shown to be proportional to the number of roentgen units to which the living tissues were subjected.

Demerec and Sams worked with dosages as low as 8.5*r*. Their results indicated that the same relation between dosage and mutations exists at the low end of the curve. There was no threshold level. Growing plants being irradiated with cobalt-60 are shown in Fig. 7.9.

In general, the proportionality rule for dosage holds for quantity of damage. Small amounts of irradiation do slight genetic damage and greater dosages do proportionally more extensive damage. This rule does not hold, however, for quality of damage. A single mutation may be of great importance to the individual and his descendants.

**Fig. 7.9** Growing plants arranged in concentric rings around a radioactive cobalt-60 source. The source, with an activity of 7.5 curies, can be raised or lowered by remote control. While the source is up, the plants receive a continuous dosage of gamma radiation, that varies in intensity, depending on the distance from the source. (Courtesy of Brookhaven National Laboratory.)

When Drosophila spermatozoa were used as experimental material in irradiation studies, no intensity effect relative to genetic damage could be noted. It made no difference whether a given amount of irradiation was administered in a large dose or in several small doses, the end results were the same. W. L. Russell showed in studies on the mouse, however, that the effects are related to the stage in the life cycle. When spermatogonial cells were treated, the intensity had a significant effect, suggesting a different mechanism in these cells as compared with sperm. Recent studies on mice have shown that the total mutagenic effect of fractionated doses of irradiation is less than the effect of an equally large single dose. Low-level chronic irradiation on bacteria produces different results than large doses. More data on different organisms and different mutagens will be required to clarify this point.

As pointed out earlier, there are different kinds of mutations and undoubtedly many different kinds of gene changes. An early attempt to explain mutations involved the "target theory," which postulated that a specific gene was hit and changed by a mutagenic agent. The change could be destructive and therefore irreversible, or it could be an alteration of one or more chemical groups. A single alpha particle is capable of creating a mutation. In the wasp, Habrobracon, it has been shown that one hit in the nucleus will bring about inactivation of a gene. The hits occur at random. It has been shown that such factors as oxygen tension and temperature, which are associated with irradiation, may significantly alter the frequency of mutations. Low oxygen tension results in decreased mutations. Oxygen magnifies the effect of radiation, but to be effective the oxygen must be present at the time the irradiation is administered. When ionization is intense, oxygen tension is less effective than under moderate conditions of ionization. Environmental agents that protect germ cells from radiation damage often do so by lowering the oxygen concentration of tissue, and those that enhance the effectiveness of radiation add oxygen. Concentration of oxygen may be altered by chemical processes.

### *Other Mutagenic Agents*

Ultraviolet rays exert a significant but less potent effect than X-rays in inducing mutations. These rays are not as penetrating as X-rays and they are readily absorbed in the tissues. When sperm or spores, which have little or no insulating material, are treated, ultraviolet can be shown to induce mutations. Because ultraviolet irradiation is known to be less destructive to living materials than X-rays, it has been considered to have some of its effect through an influence on the activity of the molecules within the chromosomes rather than by causing chromosome breaks. Ultraviolet rays result in proportionally more reversible gene changes and fewer destructive effects than do X-rays. Different kinds of changes may produce similar phenotypic effects. Stadler distinguished between changes resulting from the loss of a gene and those influencing the action of a gene, or, in his words, "producing a constrained effect on a gene."

Certain chemical agents have also been shown to increase the mutation rate. These include mustard gas and other members of the chemical family of nitrogen sulfur mustards, ethyl urethane, phenol, methylcholanthrene, and dibenzanthracene. Formaldehyde, which is used commonly as a preservative for materials in zoology laboratories, has a slight but significant mutagenic effect. At the time chemical mutagens were first discovered by Charlotte Auerbach and her associates during World War II, the data were classified. When the results of these experiments became available, a few relatively uncommon chemicals, particularly mustard gas, were shown to increase the mutation rate. Since then, numerous chemicals have been studied experimentally and a long list of mutagenic agents has been compiled. A few of these, such as nitrous acid, base analogs, and acridines (Chapter 13), have specific effects. Most chemical mutagens identified thus far, however, seem to have a general effect like irradiating agents. No specific chemical reaction seems to explain the increase in mutation rate. Rather, a general instability of some kind is induced by the foreign agents which results in chemical changes within the genes. This interpretation has been supported by Demerec and others, who have shown that mutagenicity in bacteria is not a specific property of any one group of chemicals but that it occurs among widely separated groups. Furthermore, these investigators have shown that chemical mutagens do not induce gene changes directly. The action occurs somewhere else in the cell, and the gene is induced indirectly to mutate. Requirements for a chemical mutagenic agent are (1) the ability to penetrate the cells, and (2) the ability to alter in some way the chemical structure of the genetic material within the cell. Mechanisms through which mutations may occur will be discussed in later chapters in connection with biochemical aspects of genetics.

In spite of the impressive lists of physical and chemical mutagens which have been accumulated, it should be pointed out that most of the common environmental agents investigated do not induce germinal mutations. The germ plasm is remarkably well protected and stable. Whether environmental agents of some kind are responsible for spontaneous germinal mutations is still unknown. Spontaneous somatic mutations, at least, will probably be associated eventually with some factors in the environment. Certain kinds of cancer that may be related to somatic mutational changes are influenced by environmental factors. Lung cancer has been shown to be more common among cigarette smokers than among nonsmokers. Skin cancer is increased by contact with tar products, and testicular cancer has been reported to be more prevalent among chimney sweeps than in the general populations.

### *Practical Applications of Induced Mutations*

Even though most mutations make the organism less efficient and are disadvantageous to the organism, the possibility of developing new desirable traits through induced mutations has been attractive to many plant breeders. The German plant breeder H. Stubbe, for example, has reported induced mutants in barley, wheat, oats, soybeans, tomatoes, and fruit trees, which show promise of improving presently cultivated strains. Barley mutants, for example, have been obtained for increased yield, resistance to smut (Fig. 7.10), stiff straw, increased protein content, and absence of hull on seed.

Some success has come from inducing mutations for disease resistance in otherwise useful varieties. In studies to develop disease-resistant mutations in grain, seeds from irradiated plants were treated with toxin from a disease organism that was grown in mass culture. The seeds were then germinated on moist filter paper. Disease-susceptible seeds were killed by the toxin and did not germinate, whereas a few seeds in which a mutation for resistance had occurred survived and perpetuated the resistance for a specific disease in their progeny. Results of such an experiment are illustrated in Fig. 7.11.

## DETECTION OF MUTATIONS

We might ask why it took so long to discover that mutations could be induced by X-rays and certain other environmental

**Fig. 7.10** Barley heads which had the same opportunity for infection with covered smut. The two heads at the left are from the resistant Bonneville variety. The five heads at the right are from nonresistant varieties.

agents. Actually, attempts were made many years before 1927 to test this possibility. In 1910, Morgan exposed fruit flies to radium to see if mutations could be induced by this agent. Mutations were observed not only in the experimental cultures, but also in the controls. With the methods then available, it was impossible to distinguish between induced mutations and those occurring spontaneously. In these experiments Morgan discovered the famous white-eye mutation, which occurred in a nontreated culture. Muller spent some ten years working on methods of detecting mutations and finally developed suitable techniques, including the now classical *ClB* method (Fig. 7.12) for detecting sex-linked lethals.

The *ClB* stock carries in heterozygous condition an inversion ("C"); that is, a chromosome rearrangement that acts as a crosssover suppressor, a recessive lethal

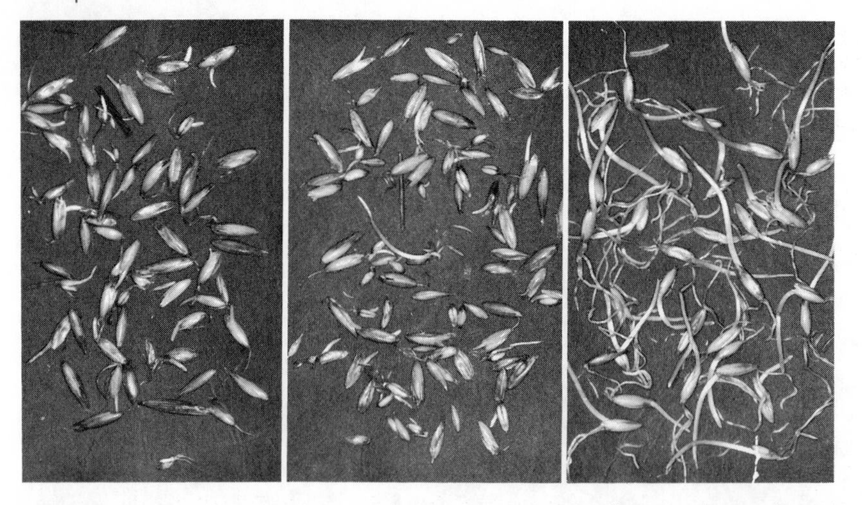

**Fig. 7.11** Results of an experiment to induce a mutation for disease resistance in grain. (Left) Seeds of susceptible variety treated with a disease toxin and killed. (Center) Seeds irradiated with 30,000 r before treatment with disease toxin. One (sprouted in center) survived and perpetuated disease resistance in its progeny. (Right) Untreated control, all seeds germinated. (Courtesy of Brookhaven National Laboratory.)

(*l*), and a dominant gene (*B*) for bar eye. The lethal is associated with the inversion. Half of the gametes produced by *ClB* females carry the inversion and half receive the X chromosome without the inversion.

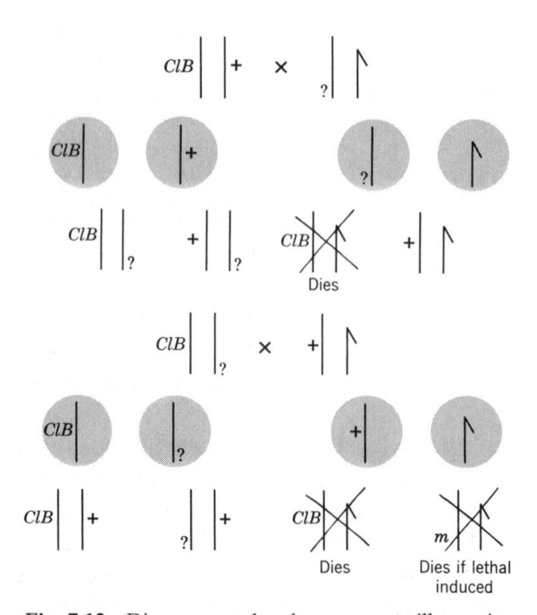


**Fig. 7.12** Diagram on the chromosomes illustrating the *ClB* method for detecting sex-linked lethal mutations in Drosophila.

At fertilization, about half of the zygotes receive an X and about half a Y chromosome from the male. All male-producing zygotes from *ClB* females that receive the *ClB* chromosome die, leaving only half as many male as female progeny. Surviving males do not receive the *ClB* chromosome from their mothers and do not have bar eyes. To carry out the *ClB* test, males that have been treated with X-rays, or that for other reasons are suspected of carrying sex-linked genes that behave in development as lethals, are mated with *ClB* females. The $F_1$ bar-eyed females, carrying the X chromosome from the male being tested, are pair mated with wild-type males. All the male progeny that receive the *ClB* chromosome from the mother die before hatching. If a lethal mutation that is not an allele of the *l* in the *ClB* stock should be present in the homologous X chromosome that comes from the male being tested, no male progeny will appear.

When this method was developed, it represented a landmark and provided an effective test to determine whether a sex-linked lethal mutation had occurred in a given male. It enabled Muller and others to learn much about mutagenic agents and mutation rates. Now it is rarely used, in spite of its elegance, because of certain disadvantages and marked improvements in other tests. The Muller-5 stock, for example, carries a complex inversion system and therefore has better crossover suppression than *ClB*. Muller-5 does not carry a lethal. Two marker genes are present in the Muller-5 stock, one for eye color (*apr*) and one for eye shape (*B*). These markers enable the investigator to distinguish two kinds of males and two kinds of females among $F_2$ progeny. Even though the chromosome carrying the inversion is homozygous lethal, it can be carried to further generations for study by breeding heterozygous females. Mutation rates obtained for the X chromosome of Drosophila have served as an index for other chromosomes and other materials that do not lend themselves so well to study.

Attached-X stocks of Drosophila, in which compulsory nondisjunction occurs, have proved valuable for detecting sex-linked visible mutations. Advantages of the attached-X method can be observed from the accompanying diagram (Fig. 7.13). Females with attached-X chromosomes are crossed with males in which mutations are suspected to have occurred. First-generation males express the phenotypic change produced by a recessive sex-linked mutant gene.

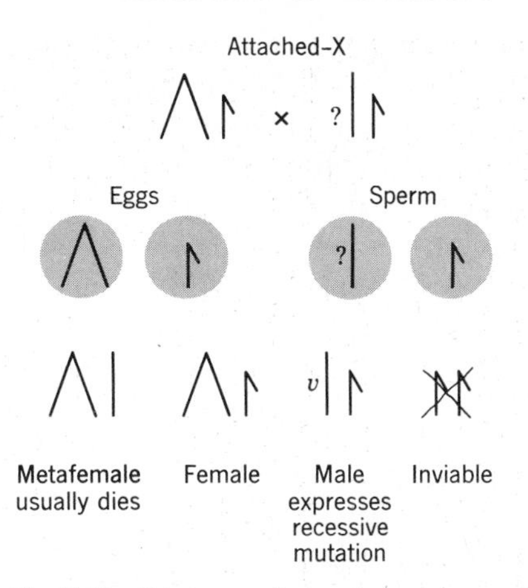


**Fig. 7.13** Diagram of cross between attached-X female and male treated with X-rays. If a recessive sex-linked mutation with visible expression has been induced, it can be detected in $F_1$ males.

Elaborate techniques for the detection of morphological mutations and those resulting in nutritional deficiencies have been devised for Neurospora. The wild-type mold can be raised on a minimal medium with only basic inorganic materials, sugar, and the vitamin biotin. These organisms are capable of producing independently all other vitamins and amino acids required for their nutrition. Nutritional deficiency mutations, such as the adenine-requiring example mentioned earlier, result in a loss by the organism of its ability to produce certain essential nutritional elements. When induced or spontaneous mutations are suspected of having occurred, the molds are established and maintained on a standard medium with all essential elements supplied. They are next transferred vegetatively to a minimal medium. If they do not survive, it is postulated that a nutritional deficiency mutation has occurred. Transfers are then made from the same original culture to a number of other types of media, lacking different single nutritional elements. By determining which nutrient must be supplied, it is possible to classify mutants and sometimes to suggest synthetic processes that have been altered. The stock is then maintained for further investigation on a complete medium or on one containing the material that the organism is unable to synthesize.

The detection of mutations is at best a time-consuming task, and any technical improvements in method have immediate value. The standard method used in detecting Neurospora mutants has been that of transferring to different types of selective media great numbers of irradiated conidia, that is, asexual spores that are produced in chainlike arrangement on the ends of the hyphae. Morphological or visible mutations were detected by gross observation of colony formation and microscopic examination of individual organisms, and nutritional mutations were detected by their inability to live on certain types of media. Because of the low frequency of mutations, the process is tedious and time consuming. It is now possible to germinate and filter out the unmutated spores, leaving only those with certain types of mutations for further sorting by plating techniques.

Ingenious methods have been devised to facilitate the detection of mutations that make bacteria resistant to certain chemicals that can be added to the medium. Modern techniques are dependent on the direct transfer of bacteria from a culture on a standard plate containing a complete medium, to successive plates containing selective media. Bacteria are ordinarily grown on solid media in petri plates and transferred with a needle from one culture to another. Mutants occurring in the order of one per ten million cells were difficult to find by older methods. J. and E. M. Lederberg developed a method for direct transfer of all colonies on a plate to one or more plates, which is now called the replicate plate method, Fig. 7.14. A velvet-like cloth with thick pile is pressed on the surface of the agar plate. Colonies adhere to the pile, which is then used to inoculate other plates in succession. In this way, replicas of the original pattern are produced on different plates containing selective media. The selective media are created by introducing a different selective agent into each of several culture plates. Because most bacteria have no resistance to certain poisons and do not survive in their presence, the transferring of all colonies directly from a standard plate to each of the different selective plates makes it possible to distinguish particular mutants that can survive on particular types of media. The parent colony, which is in a similar position on the standard plate, can then be located. Once detected and isolated, these mutants can be raised on appropriate media for further study.

The same methods that greatly facilitated the detection of mutations in bacteria simultaneously provided excellent tools for demonstrating that acquired characteristics are not inherited. In one of the experiments performed by the Lederbergs, for example, bacteria initially were grown on the usual standard solid medium. When the organisms had established themselves and covered the plate, direct transfers were made to several plates to which streptomycin had been added. Only a very few of the vast numbers of organisms on the original culture survived on the selective medium. These few multiplied and produced colonies. The same pattern was found on all of the experimental plates, showing that the organisms in one colony were resistant to the streptomycin. When the colony that had given rise to the resistant colonies on the replicated plates was identified on the original plate that had not been treated with streptomycin, the members of this colony were found to be resistant. The mutation for resistance had occurred before the organisms were introduced to the poison. Mutants resistant to streptomycin were merely selected by the medium on the plates to which the same culture was transferred.

## BALANCED LETHAL MUTATIONS

Sometimes through the process of mutation two recessive lethals occur at different loci but on each member of the same pair of homologous chromosomes. If the loci involved are near each other, or if chromosomal aberrations are present to "sup-

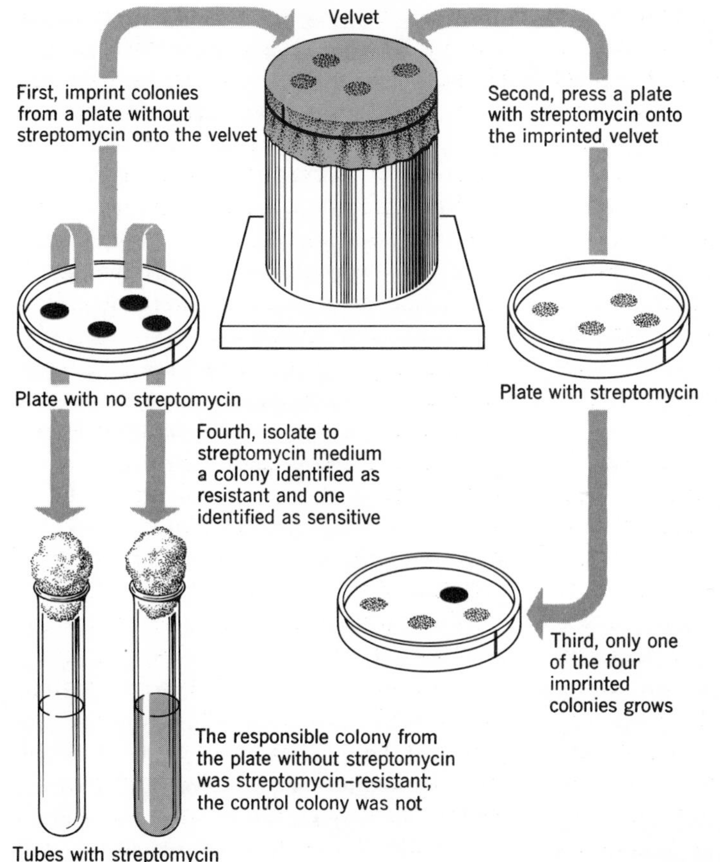


**Fig. 7.14** The replica-plating technique which demonstrates the preadaptive nature of mutation. For diagrammatic reasons, too few colonies are indicated on the plates. (From Sager and Ryan, *Cell Heredity* John Wiley and Sons, Inc.)

press" crossing over between them, an enforced heterozygous condition may be established. This occurs because individuals homozygous for each lethal die, and only those heterozygous for both lethals survive. The first documented case of a balanced lethal was that described by Muller in Drosophila. He had been maintaining in his laboratory the *Bd* (beaded) stock producing flies with scalloped wings (Fig. 7.15). Since the beaded phenotype was controlled by a dominant homozygous lethal gene (*Bd*), the progeny from the crosses between beaded flies were two-thirds beaded and one-third normal, as

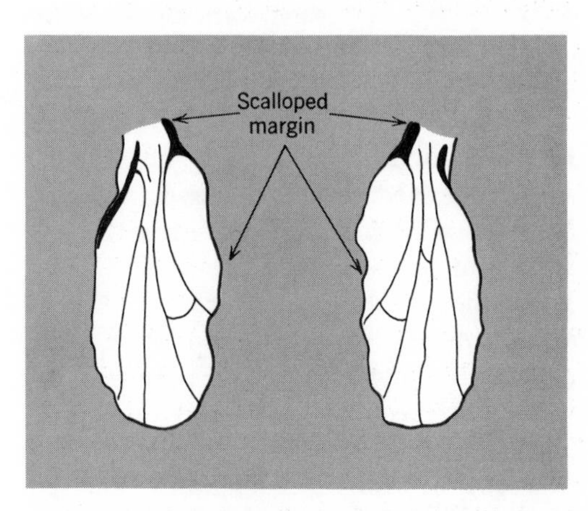


**Fig. 7.15** Pair of scalloped wings from Drosophila beaded (*Bd*) stock.

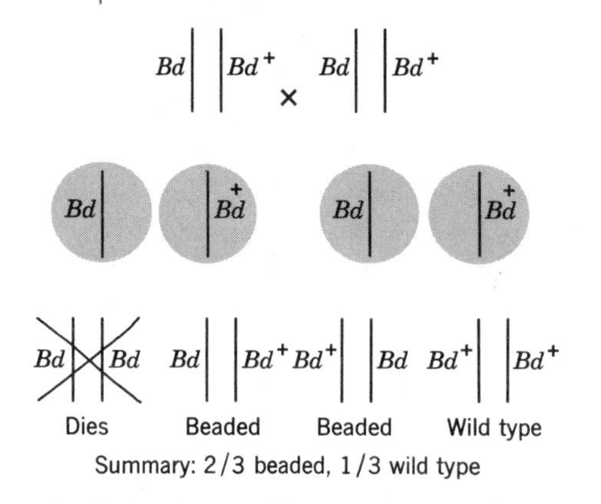


**Fig. 7.16** Diagram illustrating a cross between two *Bd* flies. Since the gene *Bd* is homozygous lethal, all surviving beaded flies are heterozygous and ¼ of the progeny from beaded parents die before hatching. One-fourth of the total and ⅓ of the flies which survive are wild type (not beaded).

illustrated in Fig. 7.16. All those homozygous for beaded were dead, and thus the 2:1 ratio replaced the 3:1 ratio, which would otherwise have been expected. This pattern was similar to that described in Chapter 4 for creeper chickens.

Abruptly, with no visible change in the beaded phenotype, all of the flies in the cultures began to appear beaded. In an attempt to explain the change that had occurred, Muller postulated that a new lethal (*l*) had been created by mutation in the homologous chromosome opposite *Bd*. An inversion associated with the gene for beaded "suppressed" crossing over, and only two kinds of gametes were produced by the beaded flies, one carrying the gene (*Bd*) for beaded, the other carrying the new lethal (*l*). The cross representing the new arrangement is illustrated in Fig. 7.17. When these chromosomes were segregated and fertilization was accomplished, some zygotes became homozygous for *Bd* and were therefore lethal; others became homozygous for *l* and also died. Only those heterozygous for both *Bd* and *l* survived. Therefore, the heterozygous condition was enforced. This explanation was substantiated and the term "balanced lethal" was used to designate such an arrangement involving two lethals in the same chromosome pair in which crossing over is infrequent or "suppressed" entirely.

Practical applications have been associated with balanced lethals, particularly in maintaining Drosophila stocks in the laboratory. Stocks with dominant phenotypes and homozygous lethal genes (such as *Bd*) can be maintained with 100 percent expression when another homozygous lethal becomes established on the homologous chromosome and crossing over between them is negligible in effect. Genes with recessive phenotypes can also be carried in balanced stocks, but they are always heterozygous and do not come to expression.

Balanced lethals have also been identified in barley. Two recessive genes, $a_n$ and $x_c$, are located on homologous chromosomes. Both are lethal when homozygous but both lethals are distinguishable in the seedling stage. The genotype $a_n a_n$ produces white (albino) seedlings. They are white because of the absence of chlorophyll, which also makes them incapable of carry-

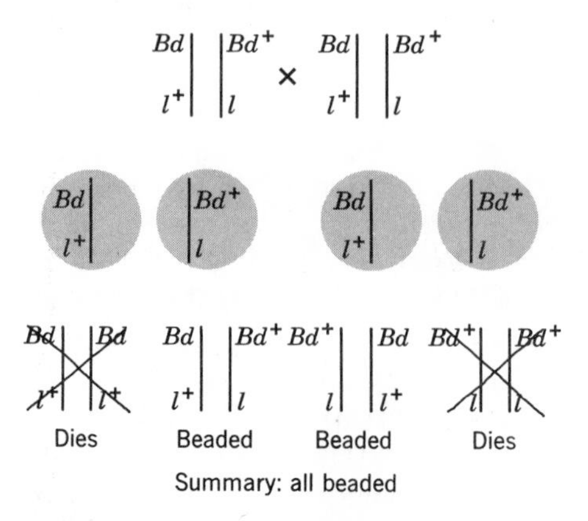


**Fig. 7.17** Diagram representing a cross between two beaded flies after a new lethal mutation (*l*) had occurred on the same chromosome with *Bd*. All progeny homozygous for *Bd* and those homozygous for *l* died. All of the survivors expressed the beaded phenotype.

ing on photosynthesis. As soon as the food stored in the seed is exhausted, two or three weeks after the seed germinates, the seedlings wither and die. The genotype $x_c x_c$ produces yellow seedlings. These are also unable to manufacture their own food and die when the stored food in the seed is depleted. Since both of these lethals are recessive, they can be carried in heterozygous, that is,

$$\frac{a_n^+ \ x_c}{a_n \ \ x_c^+}.$$

When plants of this genotype are self-fertilized and the seeds are germinated, white, yellow, and green seedlings are produced in expected proportion (Fig. 7.18).

This enforced heterozygote or balanced lethal situation is not complete, however, as it is in the case of *Bd* in Drosophila, because a crossover suppressor is not present in the barley chromosome concerned, and the genes $a_n$ and $x_c$ are far enough apart to allow about 10 percent of crossing over. As the result of crossing over, wild-type alleles occasionally may come together in the same chromosome and thus eliminate the $a_n$ and $x_c$ genes. Therefore, the heterozygous condition is enforced only to the extent to which crossing over fails to occur. In this case, heterozygosis is maintained in about 90 percent, which is the linkage strength between the $a_n$ and $x_c$ loci.

**Fig. 7.18** Seedlings from barley with balanced lethal arrangement in chromosomes. White, green, and yellow seedlings occur in the proportion of about 1:2:1.

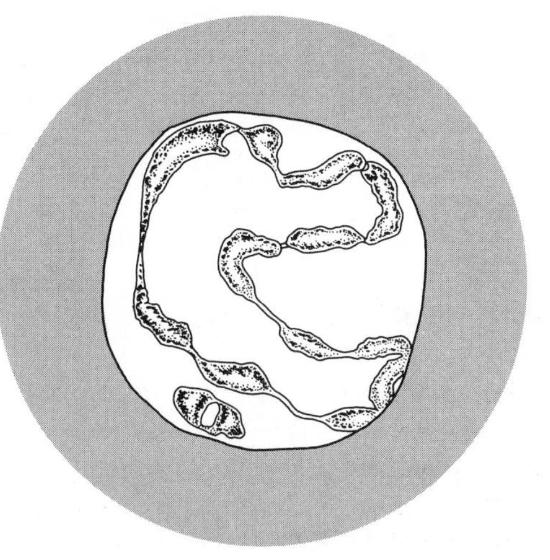

**Fig. 7.19** Chromosome complex in *Oenothera lamarckiana* in late meiotic prophase showing a ring of 12 and 1 pair. (After Cleland.)

"Permanent heterozygotes" described in *Oenothera lamarckiana* are also maintained in a balanced lethal system. This plant is characterized by gene complexes made up of several chromosomes joined through translocations (Fig. 7.19). The ordinary segregation of independent chromosomes does not occur. Different complexes, however, have different gene combinations, and when gametes are formed the complexes separate as units. Two kinds of hybrids, that is, twin hybrids, are produced when plants carrying such complexes are outcrossed. Appropriate names have been associated with the different gene complexes. Lamarckiana is composed of the complex called *gaudens* and *velans*. The *gaudens* complex has genes for green bud, nonpunctate stem, broad leaf, and red flecks on the leaves. The *velans* complex carries genes for red-striped bud, punctate stem, narrow leaf, and no red flecks on the leaves. Half the gametes carry the *gaudens* gene combination and half the *velans*. If the complexes were capable of independent segregation with respect to each other, crosses between individual plants would be expected to produce three combinations in the following proportions: ¼ *gaudens gaudens,* ¼ *velans velans,* and ½ *gaudens velans.* Actually, only *gaudens velans* survive. This leads to the conclusion that each of the complexes in homozygous condition is lethal. Only the heterozygotes survive and maintain themselves as balanced lethals.

## PRACTICAL APPLICATION OF MUTATIONS

As pointed out earlier in this chapter, most mutations are detrimental to an organism under conditions of its usual natural environment. The chance of immediately improving the well-adapted and highly organized animal or plant in its environment by random changes is remote. Random changes might sometimes be coordinated with environmental situations controlled by man and result in improvements in domesticated animals. Short-legged sheep, for example, are more desirable for man under certain conditions than those with longer legs. "Delicious" apples, navel oranges, and seedless grapes are all the results of mutational changes that have improved the fruit for man's use compared with the original varieties in which the mutations occurred. Mutations in mink and other fur-bearing animals have provided variety and satisfied the desires of those who wear fur coats, and thus have proved valuable to fur breeders.

Since the original source of gene variation is mutation, the extent to which selection can act in a population depends on mutations somewhere in the ancestral history of the organism. Possibilities exist for further improvement in domesticated plants and animals by selection of variations already represented among the genes and perhaps also by new mutations, either induced or spontaneous. The possibility of improving higher animals and plants by induced mutations is doubtful, however. Because mutations occur at random, the chance of obtaining a desirable change without undesirable mutations is small, indeed. Perhaps greater hope lies in the possibility of eventually learning how to direct mutations. This would be much more satisfactory than the present method of waiting for desirable changes to occur at random. At present, however, there is no way of inducing a particular mutation. In lower organisms such as molds and bacteria, large numbers of individuals can be raised and treated with mutagens. Asexual reproduction, small size, and limited number of genes make the chance of obtaining and perpetuating a desirable change more favorable.

One application of induced mutations came from concentrated effort to improve the yield of penicillin by the mold Penicillium. When penicillin was first discovered, the yield was low and the production of the valuable antibiotic was seriously limited. Millions of spores were irradiated and a few colonies were selected which produced considerably more penicillin than the average. Improvement was possible because large numbers could be produced and selection could be made efficiently.

A late-ripening peach (Fig. 7.20) has been developed at Brookhaven National Laboratory from gamma radiation. It would be almost impossible to carry out large-scale experiments using higher animals similar to those using plants. Plants are cheaper and easier than animals to raise in large numbers. In Sweden, Germany, and also in the United States, some progress has been made in improving plants for man's purposes by induced mutations.

## MUTATIONS AND MAN

The problem of mutations in man has a negative significance. Purposeful artificial selection is not practiced and, therefore,

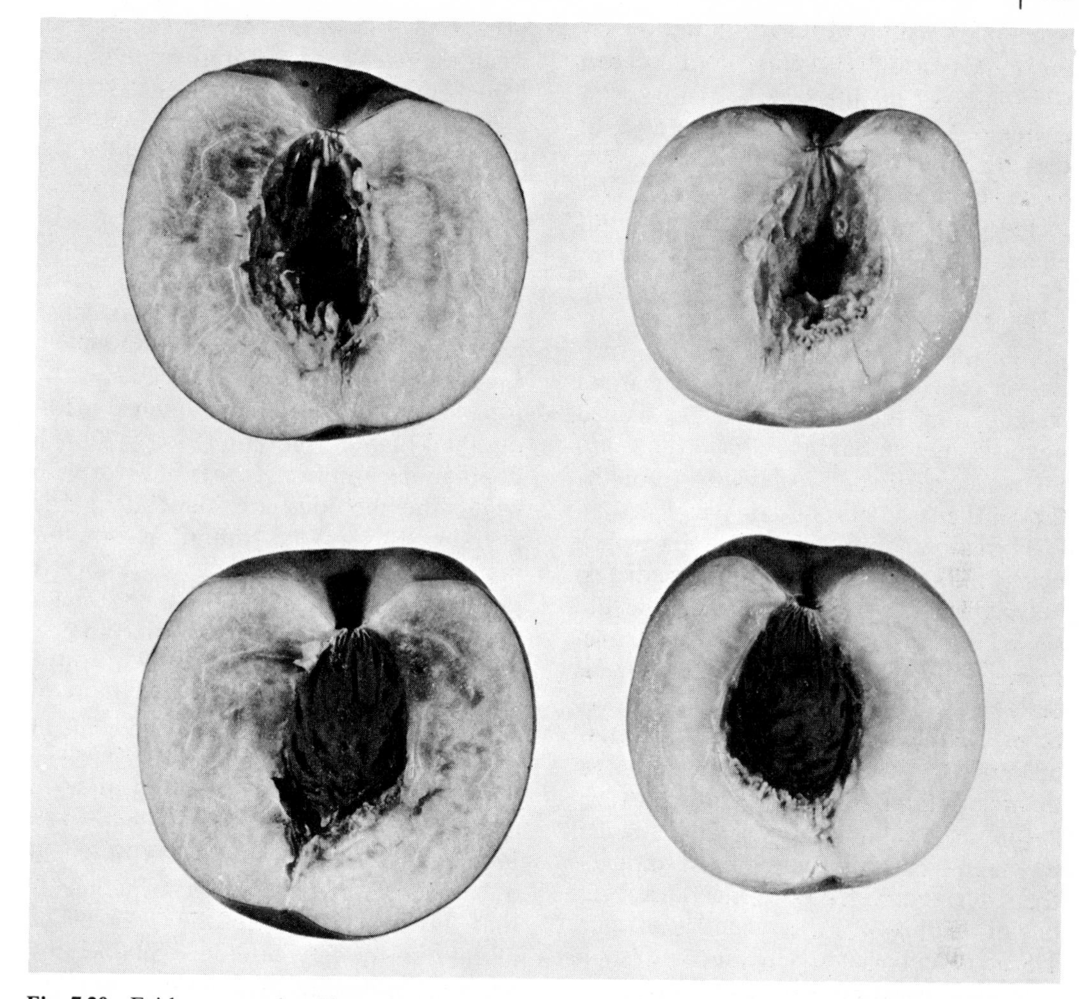

**Fig. 7.20** Fairhaven peaches illustrating the effects of a radiation-induced mutation for late ripening. The smaller clear-fleshed fruit at right is normal for this variety. The larger fruit at the left, with darker areas in the flesh, is the late-ripening mutant which appeared on a tree grown in the Brookhaven gamma radiation field. Dark pigment in the flesh is the result of extra anthocyanin pigment which diffuses through the flesh of the late ripening type. (Courtesy of Brookhaven National Laboratory.)

the possible advantages cited for domestic animals and plants would not carry over to mankind. Variations do exist in populations, however, and presumably they originated through mutation somewhere in the ancestral history. Since most new mutations are detrimental in the usual environment, it would seem advantageous from the standpoint of short-term effects for man to avoid excessive exposure to mutagenic agents. The danger level from irradiation has been estimated differently by those concerned with different aspects of the problem. Two types of danger should be considered: (1) the immediate damage to the exposed person, and (2) the more insidious damage to the genes in the reproductive cells of people now living, which would affect future generations. The first type is indicated by burns and other direct or secondary effects on the body tissue. Damage of this kind is apparently negligible under low dosage, but the effects on induction of leukemia and general shortening of the life span are difficult to evaluate at this time. When doses are in the order of 50 mr (milliroentgens) or lower, no immediate damage can be detected, although some unseen harmful effects may occur. If the exposure does not exceed the "permissible" dose, it is considered "safe." Larger doses prescribed by physicians as therapeutic measures, such as for cancer treatment, require careful weighing of the benefits to be gained against possible damage. Partial or complete recovery is possible only from the first of the two types of damage.

The second type of damage, that which occurs in the germ cells, is not immediately detectable. The effects will only be observed in future generations. There is reason to believe, however, that exposure to high-energy irradiations of any kind, and at any dosage level, is potentially harmful. Mutations are generally proportional to the dosage and the effect is cumulative.

Proportionality cannot be investigated in man at present because of the complexity of the subject and the special difficulties of dealing with the genetics of man. The problems have been recognized in investigations concerning the survivors of the Hiroshima and Nagasaki bombings. The Atomic Bomb Casualty Commission is investigating the effect on the people exposed to atomic bomb irradiation and their descendants. Preliminary reports, including data on children born to parents who survived the bombing, have revealed no startling effects. A significant increase in the incidence of leukemia has been reported among those exposed to irradiation. The normal sex ratio has been altered, and the changes have been interpreted as resulting from induced sex-linked lethals. Considering the nature and complexity of man and mutation data from other organisms, no spectacular results would be expected. Most of the data available on mutation rates and the nature of mutations have come from other organisms and it is only by inference that they are applied to man. The general effects of irradiation, however, seem to apply to all organisms, including mankind. In the absence of specific data, the facts learned from other organisms should be considered seriously.

The origin of so-called "spontaneous" mutations, which proceed from unknown causes, also has great significance. J. V. Neel and W. J. Schull have outlined methods for estimating mutation rates in human populations and the sources of error with which the methods are associated. The average spontaneous mutation rate for man at a particular locus is about 1 per 100,000 eggs or sperm. When mutations were induced in experimental animals and plants, the question arose concerning the source of spontaneous mutations in man. Cosmic rays were known to come in from outer space and strike man as well as other objects. Ultraviolet light and radioactive chemicals were also known to be present in man's environment. Muller and others calculated from fruit fly experiments that only about 1/2000 of the spontaneous mutations in flies can be explained by these factors. Chemical mutagens could account for some of these.

The situation for man may be quite different from that of the fruit fly. He is larger than the fly and his life span is considerably longer. If these factors are taken into account, it might be expected that some 30 percent of man's spontaneous mutations would be produced by the natural background. This figure is based on the assumption that he has the same sensitivity to mutations as the fly. If he is more sensitive, as suggested by extrapolation from mouse studies, a higher proportion of his spontaneous mutations could be accounted for in this way. The effect of fallout and other present or potential sources of irradiation on human populations depends on man's sensitivity, which at present is an unknown quality. It is expected that increased exposure to irradiation will be detrimental to future generations.

Two suggestions regarding the origin of spontaneous mutations can be made: (1) chemicals in cells occasionally could behave atypically and produce new configurations, or (2) chance energy changes could alter genes. These are highly theoretical postulates and difficult to prove. No satisfactory explanation for spontaneous mutations exists at present, but it is not unlikely that an environmental factor causes most or all mutations.

## SUMMARY

In this chapter, only point mutations are considered. Although a mutation itself is a particular and restricted change in a gene, the end result or expression may be associated with one or several traits of the individual organism. Mutated genes are usually expressed as recessives but a few have dominant expressions when they first occur. Mutations may be autosomal or sex-linked; somatic or germinal, depending on the chromosomes and cells in which they occur. Frequencies of spontaneous mutations are in the order of $10^{-5}$ to $10^{-6}$ per cell generation. Some mutable genes are less stable than the usual genes and others (mutators) increase the mutation rate in other genes. Mutation rates may be increased by mutagenic agents such as X-rays, ultraviolet rays, and chemical mutagens. Special techniques are required to detect mutations and to determine mutation rates in Drosophila, bacteria and other organisms. Applications include the use of balanced lethals for maintaining certain Drosophila stocks; propagation of desirable mutant forms of apples, oranges, mink, Penicillium, and other organisms; and, in a negative way, avoiding mutagenic agents in the human population.

## REFERENCES


Auerbach, C. 1962. *Mutation, an introduction to research on mutagenesis.* Oliver and Boyd, Edinburgh.

Beadle, G. W., and E. L. Tatum. 1945. "Neurospora II, methods of producing and detecting mutations concerned with nutritional requirements." *Amer. J. Bot.,* **32,** 678–686.

D'Amato, F. 1956. "Metabolism and spontaneous mutations in plants." *Advances in Genetics.* M. Demerec (ed.), Vol. 8. Academic Press, New York.

Demerec, M. 1954. "Genetic action of mutagens." *Proc. IX Int. Cong. of Genet.,* Part I, 201–217.

Hearings Before the Special Subcommittee on Radiation of the 85th Congress. 1958. The nature of radioactive fallout and its effects on man. U. S. Govt. Printing Office, Washington, D. C.

Lederberg, J., and E. M. Lederberg. 1952. "Replica plating and indirect selection of bacterial mutants." *J. Bact.,* **63,** 399–406.

McElroy, W. D., and B. Glass (eds.), 1957. *A symposium on the chemical basis of heredity.* John Hopkins Press, Baltimore.

Muller, H. J. 1954. "Damage to posterity caused by irradiation of the gonads." *Amer. J. Obstetrics and Gynecol.,* **67,** 467–483.

Neel, J. V., and W. J. Schull. 1954. *Human heredity.* University of Chicago Press, Chicago. (Chapter II is a discussion of mutation rates.)

Rhoades, M. M. 1954. "Chromosomes, mutations, and cytoplasm in maize." *Science,* **120,** 115–120.

Stern, C. 1960. *Principles of human genetics,* 2nd ed. W. H. Freeman Co., San Francisco.

"Symposium on mutation and mutagenesis." 1959. *Proc. X Int. Congress Genet.,* **1,** 245–317. Participants: H. Stubbe, N. H. Giles, E. M. Wilkin, C. P. Swanson, and H. J. Muller.

United Nations Report of the Scientific Committee on Effects of Atomic Radiation. 1962. General Assembly Official Records, 17th Session. Supplement No. 16(A5216).

Wagner, R. P., and H. K. Mitchell. 1964. 2nd ed. *Genetics and metabolism.* John Wiley and Sons, New York.

Zamenhof, P. J. 1966. "A genetic locus responsible for generalized high mutability in *Escherichia coli.*" *Proc. Nat'l. Acad. Sci.,* **56,** 845–852.

# *Problems*

**7.1** Distinguish between (a) point mutation and chromosome deficiency; (b) germinal and somatic mutation; (c) sex-linked and autosomal mutations; (d) spontaneous and induced mutations; (e) stable and unstable genes; and (f) mutable and mutator genes.

**7.2** Viewed now in perspective, what is the most significant contribution from de Vries' mutation theory?

**7.3** A precancerous condition in man (intestinal polyposis) in a particular family group seems to be determined by a single dominant gene. Among the descendants of one woman who died with cancer of the colon, eight people have died with the same type of cancer and six now have intestinal polyposis. All other branches of the large kindred have been carefully examined and no cases have been found. Suggest an explanation for the origin of the defective gene.

**7.4** Juvenile muscular dystrophy in man is dependent on a sex-linked recessive gene. In an intensive study, 33 cases were found in a population of some 800,000 people. The investigators were confident that they had found all cases that were well enough advanced to be detected at the time the study was made. The symptoms of the disease were expressed only in males. Most of those who had it died at an early age and none lived beyond 21 years of age. Usually only one case was detected in a family, but sometimes two or three cases occurred in the same family. Suggest an explanation for the sporadic occurrence of the disease and the tendency for the gene to persist in the population.

**7.5** If a single short-legged sheep should occur in a flock, suggest experiments to determine (a) whether it is the result of a mutation or an environmental modification, and (b) if it is a mutation, is it dominant or recessive?

**7.6** Products of somatic mutation such as the navel orange and the Delicious apple have become widespread in citrus groves and orchards but they are uncommon in animals. Why?

**7.7** Compare the average spontaneous mutation rates for bacteria, fruit flies, and man on the basis of data now available.

**7.8** What factors may change the rate of spontaneous mutations? Suggest a mechanism through which these factors might influence mutations.

**7.9** Why were induced mutations not discovered before 1927?

**7.10** How can mutations be detected in (a) fruit flies? (b) bread mold? (c) bacteria?

**7.11** Compare the attached-X and *ClB* methods for detecting mutations in fruit flies with respect to (a) the time required for test, and (b) the type of mutations for which each is most efficient.

**7.12** (a) What practical advantages could induced mutations have in plant and animal breedings? (b) Evaluate the likelihood of effective practical applications of induced mutations in the future.

**7.13** Why has irradiation not been used to a greater extent in creating mutations designed for plant crop improvement?

**7.14** Evaluate the effects, immediate and potential, that might come from intense, mass irradiation of people.

**7.15** In a strain of bacteria, all organisms are usually killed when a given amount of streptomycin is introduced into the medium. Mutations sometimes occur which make the bacteria resistant to streptomycin. Resistant mutants are of two types: some can live with or without streptomycin, others cannot live unless this drug is present in the medium. Given a nonresistant strain, outline an experimental procedure by which resistant strains of the two types might be established.

**7.16** In *D. melanogaster,* the gene *Bd* is dominant with respect to a wing abnormality but is homozygous lethal. Another homozygous lethal gene (*l*) is located on the homologous chromosome and a crossover suppressor prevents crossing over between *Bd* and *l*. What results would be expected from a cross between two flies with the genotype $Bdl^+/Bd^+l$?

**7.17** How could a balanced lethal be established?

**7.18** What advantage could balanced lethals have in a Drosophila laboratory?

**7.19** In barley, $a_n$ for white seedlings and $x_c$ for yellow seedlings are on the same chromosomes with a crossover value of 10 percent. Homozygous $a_n$ and $x_c$ plants die in the seedling stage. A plant with the genotype $a_n x_c^+/a_n^+ x_c$ was selfed. Give the expected results.

# Multiple Alleles; Blood-Group and Serum-Protein Genetics

8

Although much has been learned about the chemistry of genetic material and the mechanism of gene action in microorganisms and in higher forms, the basic principle of allelism discovered by Mendel but explained and named by Bateson remains substantial and valid. For this discussion, alleles will be considered in the traditional sense as alternative genes at the same locus in a chromosome. Examples will be cited from several animals and plants. Human blood-group and serum-protein genes that illustrate various combinations of alleles and nonalleles will then be described.

A few definitions will first be reviewed in their historical setting. The word "gene" as used by Johannsen in 1903 was a convenient invention to cover such terms as *unit factor, genetic element,* or *allele* as represented in the gamete. Johannsen also coined the words "genotype" to identify the genes of a particular individual and "phenotype" to denote the trait or expression of the genes. Mendel had suggested a physical element and Boveri and Sutton had observed a parallel between the behavior of such units and that of chromosomes, but the physical nature of genes was not yet appreciated. Proof of their physical existence was established when Morgan, Sturtevant, Bridges, and others demonstrated that genes were spatial entities arranged in linear order in chromosomes. The term "gene" was then extended to mean a locus, that is, a discrete unit or location in a chromosome; and alleles, which had previously been considered by Bateson only as hypothetical partners involved in Mendelian segregation, were defined as alternative genes at the same locus. The ultimate source of new alleles was recognized as gene change or mutation in an individual organism or somewhere in the ancestry of that organism.

Since alleles are located in corresponding parts of homologous chromosomes, only one member of a pair can be present in a given chromosome and only two are ordinarily present in a cell of a diploid organism. The traditional criteria for identifying mutant genes as members of allelic pairs are summarized as follows: (1) alleles must segregate into separate gametes, and (2) the heterozygote usually expresses the phenotype of the parent or an intermediate between those of the two parents. The first criterion is indicated by the simple monohybrid ratios (1:2:1 or 3:1) that can be expected from crosses between diploid individuals heterozygous for the alternative genes. In haploid organisms such as Neurospora, where each strain carries a single allele, the expected ratio from a cross between strains with different alleles is 1:1.

Examples given thus far in this book have involved only single pairs of alleles, usually with one member wild-type and the other a mutant type.

## MULTIPLE ALLELES

Many examples have been found in which more than two alternative alleles or multiple alleles are present in a population. In such cases, two or more different mutations must have occurred at the same locus but in different individuals or at different times. Multiple alleles are thus alternative states at the same locus. The different members of a series are conventionally represented by the same basic symbol. Superscripts and subscripts are used to identify different members of a series of alleles.

Most alleles produce variations or gradations of the same character, but some produce very different phenotypes. In *Drosophila melanogaster,* for example, the gene *ss* makes the bristles small in contrast to the effect of the wild-type gene $ss^+$. No effect has been observed on the legs or antennae. Another allele in the series, $ss^a$ (aristapedia), reduces the bristles slightly, but the flies also undergo a more conspicuous phenotypic alteration: legs develop on the head in place of antennae (Fig. 8.1).

A classical example of multiple alleles was discovered many years ago in rabbits. Albino (white) rabbits were known to occur occasionally in wild (variously colored) populations. It was shown by the monohybrid results (for example, 3:1 ratio in $F_2$) from crosses between colored and white rabbits that members of a pair of alternative genes, $c^+$ or $c$, were responsible for the production of either colored or albino rabbits, respectively. When crosses were made between homozygous colored ($c^+c^+$) (Fig. 8.2*A*) and albino ($cc$) (Fig. 8.2*D*) rabbits, all the $F_1$ progeny were colored and the $F_2$ were about 3 colored to 1 albino. This ratio indicated that only one single pair of alleles was involved (one wild type, $c^+$ and one mutant allele, $c$) and $c^+$ was dominant over $c$.

Other rabbits, called chinchilla, (Fig. 8.2*B*) had a gray appearance because of mixed black and white pattern. When crosses were made between fully colored and chinchilla rabbits, all of the $F_1$ progeny were colored, whereas the $F_2$ were about 3 colored to 1 chinchilla. This ratio indicated that these genes were also alleles and that $c^+$ was dominant over the chinchilla gene $c^{ch}$.

Another fur pattern (himalayan) was characterized by a white coat and black tips on the ears, nose, and feet (Fig. 8.2*C*). When crosses were made between himalayan and fully colored rabbits, all the $F_1$

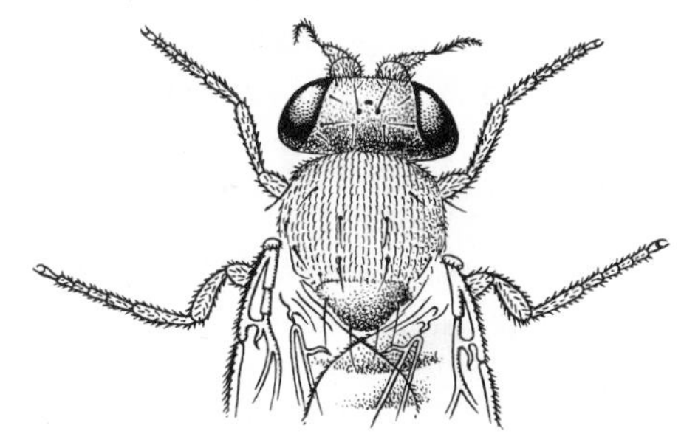

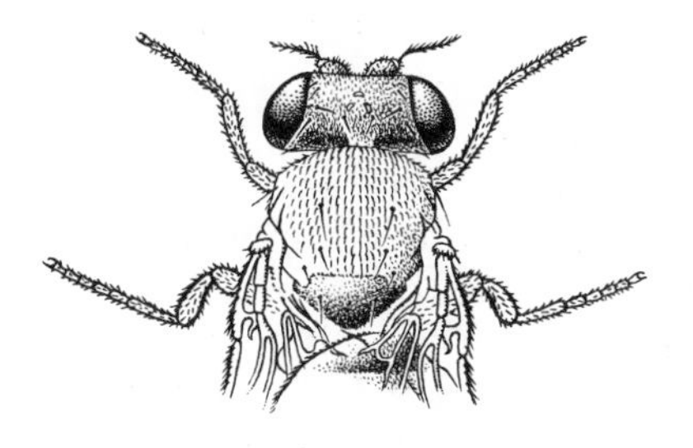

**Fig. 8.1** Different phenotypes of Drosophila antennae produced by different alleles. Left, spineless-aristapedia ($ss^a$); dorsal view of head and thorax. Right, spineless ($ss$); dorsal view of head and thorax.

**Fig. 8.2** Coat colors in rabbits dependent on members of a series of multiple alleles. *A*, full color, *B*, chinchilla, *C*, himalayan, and *D*, albino. (From L. H. Snyder and P. R. David, *The Principles of Heredity*, © 1957 by D. C. Heath and Co. Reproduced by permission.)

progeny were colored. In the $F_2$, the proportion of about 3 colored to 1 himalayan was recognized. Crosses between chinchilla and himalayan resulted in all chinchilla in the $F_1$ and about 3 chinchilla to 1 himalayan in the $F_2$. This result indicated that $c^{ch}$ and $c^h$ were also alleles and that $c^{ch}$ was dominant over $c^h$. Finally, crosses between himalayan and albino produced only himalayan in the $F_1$ and about 3 himalayan to 1 albino in the $F_2$. The consistent monohybrid ratios indicated that all four genes were members of the same series of alleles. Gradation in dominance was recognized in the following order: $c^+$, $c^{ch}$, $c^h$ and $c$. Presumably, $c^{ch}$, $c^h$, and $c$ originated

**TABLE 8.1 Phenotypes and corresponding genotypes for alleles of *c* locus in rabbits**

| Phenotypes | Genotypes |
|---|---|
| Full color (agouti) | $c^+c^+$, $c^+c^{ch}$, $c^+c^h$, $c^+c$ |
| Chinchilla | $c^{ch}c^{ch}$, $c^{ch}c^h$, $c^{ch}c$ |
| Himalayan | $c^hc^h$, $c^hc$ |
| Albino | $cc$ |

somewhere in the ancestry as mutations from the wild-type gene ($c^+$). The phenotypes and corresponding genotypes are summarized in Table 8.1.

In another example from rodents, color pattern as well as viability could be shown to depend on different members of a series of multiple alleles. The gene *A* controlling the agouti pattern in mice (and other mammals) has several alleles. Among the members of the series a gradation exists in dominance, similar to that of the *c* series in rabbits, but in this example two members, $A^y$ and $A^L$, are dominant over the wild-type gene $A^+$. The alleles are listed according to dominance in Table 8.2 and the phenotypic patterns are illustrated in Fig. 8.3. Studies on yellow mice carried out in the early 1900's showed that it was impossible to obtain a pure yellow strain. Yellow mice mated with nonyellows produced half yellow and half nonyellow, whereas yellows mated to yellows produced 2 yellows to 1 nonyellow. The gene $A^y$ for yellow mice thus behaved like the gene *C* for creeper chickens (Chapter 4), as a homozygous lethal. In heterozygous

**TABLE 8.2 Agouti (A) series of alleles in mice, listed in order of dominance**

| Phenotype | Allele |
|---|---|
| Yellow | $A^y$ |
| Agouti light belly | $A^L$ |
| Agouti | $A^+$ |
| Black and tan | $a^t$ |
| Nonagouti (black) | $a$ |

condition, the gene $A^y$ removes nearly all the black pigment from the fur but does not affect the color of the eyes.

A series of multiple alleles was discovered to account for an interesting group of wing characteristics of *D. melanogaster*. In this example, a progressive series of wing abnormalities was recognized, ranging in size from no wing at all to a normal wing. Graduations in the amount of wing present were associated with certain gene combinations. Normal wings (shown in Fig. 8.4*A*) are dependent on the $vg^+$ allele. The extreme expression with no wings is the result of one allele $vg^{nw}$ in homozygous condition. A small stump (Fig. 8.4*E*) is produced by another member, *vg*, of the series. A narrow straplike wing (Fig. 8.4*D*) is associated with the allele $vg^{st}$, notched (Fig. 8.4*C*) with $vg^{no}$, and nicked (Fig. 8.4*B*) with $vg^{ni}$. Each of these phenotypes results from the homozygous arrangement of a particular allele. Heterozygous combinations usually produce intermediate phenotypes, but the wild-type allele ($vg^+$) is dominant over the other members of the series, except in the presence of certain modifiers.

Multiple alleles have been associated with self-incompatibility in several groups of plants. As early as 1764 Kölreuter described self-sterility in tobacco, Nicotiana. The reason for the incompatibility was discovered in 1925, when it was shown that pollen grains produced by certain plants failed to germinate, or that the pollen tubes grew too slowly to be effective in fertilization when placed on the stigmas of the same plant or those of certain other plants. Results of appropriate crosses showed that the genes associated with the pollen tube inefficiency were members of a series of multiple alleles, and the letter *S* was used as the base symbol for their identification. Subscripts were used to identify the different alleles. Thus, one plant was found to have $S_1S_2$ and another

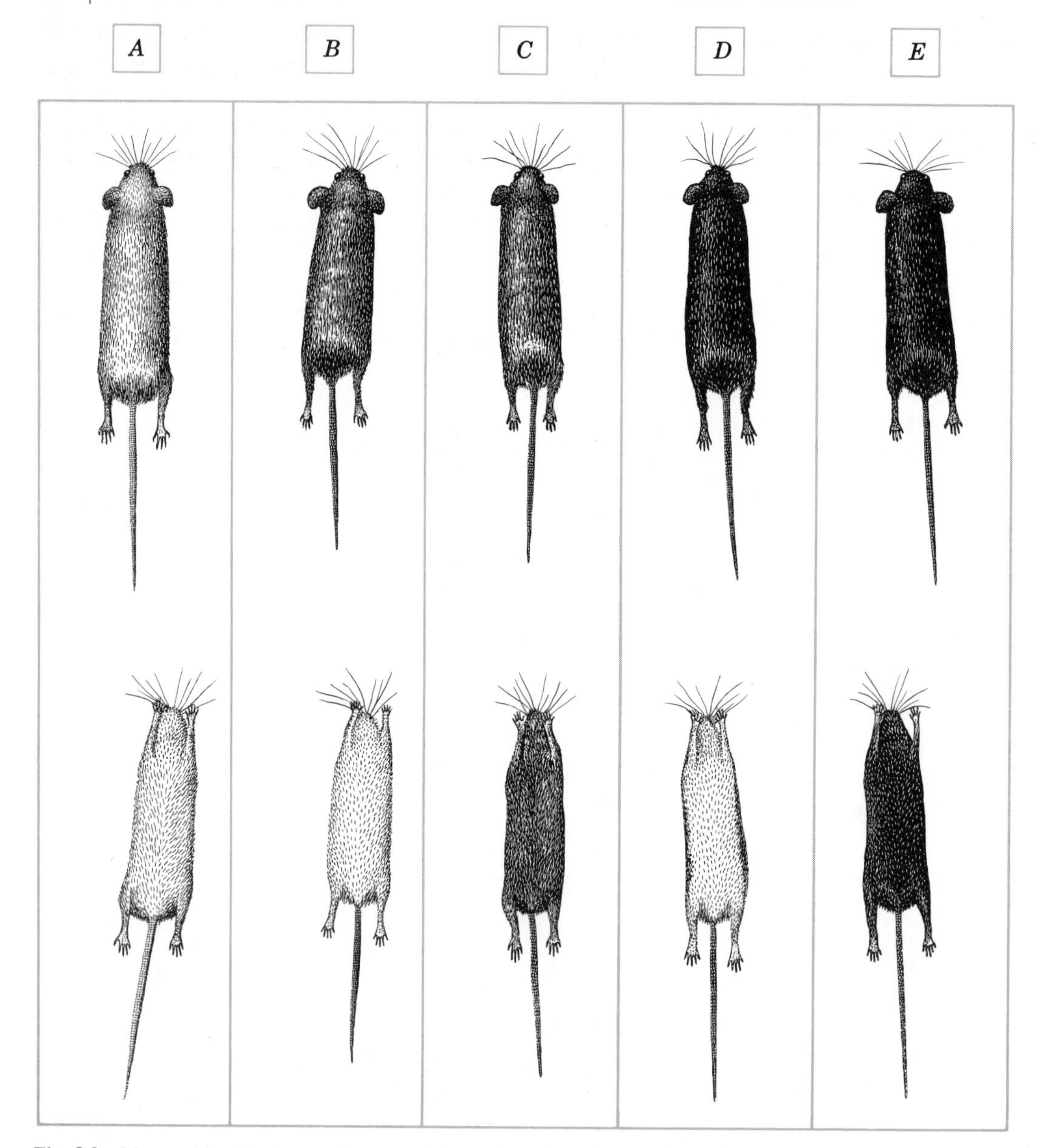


**Fig. 8.3** Mouse skins illustrating the expressions of a series of multiple alleles at the *A* locus. (Upper) Dorsal surface; (lower) ventral surface of the same specimens. *A*, yellow, *B*, agouti light belly, *C*, agouti, *D*, black and tan, *E*, black.

$S_3S_4$. None of the cross-fertilizing tobacco plants was homozygous, for example, $S_1S_1$ or $S_2S_2$. When crosses were attempted between different $S_1S_2$ plants, it was observed that the pollen tubes did not develop normally, but pollen from $S_1S_2$ plants was effective on stigmas of plants with other alleles, for example, $S_3S_4$.

When crosses were made between seed parents with $S_1S_2$ and pollen parents with $S_2S_3$, two kinds of pollen tubes were distinguished. Pollen grains carrying $S_2$ were not effective, but the pollen grains carrying $S_3$ were capable of fertilization. Thus, from the cross $S_1S_2 \times S_2S_3$, two kinds of progeny, $S_1S_3$ and $S_2S_3$, were produced. From a cross $S_1S_2 \times S_3S_4$, all the pollen was effective and four kinds of progeny resulted: $S_1S_3$, $S_1S_4$, $S_2S_3$, and $S_2S_4$. Some combinations are summarized in Table 8.3. Several other $S$ alleles were found, and many combinations occurred in different populations of tobacco plants.

In a rare species of the evening primrose, Oenothera, 37 members of an allelic series of incompatibility genes were detected among 500 plants collected at random. A similar series of incompatibility alleles was found in red clover. In one particular study, 41 were distinguished and symbolized $S_1$ to $S_{41}$. Exhaustive investigations would undoubtedly uncover even larger series of multiple alleles affecting the fertility of plants.

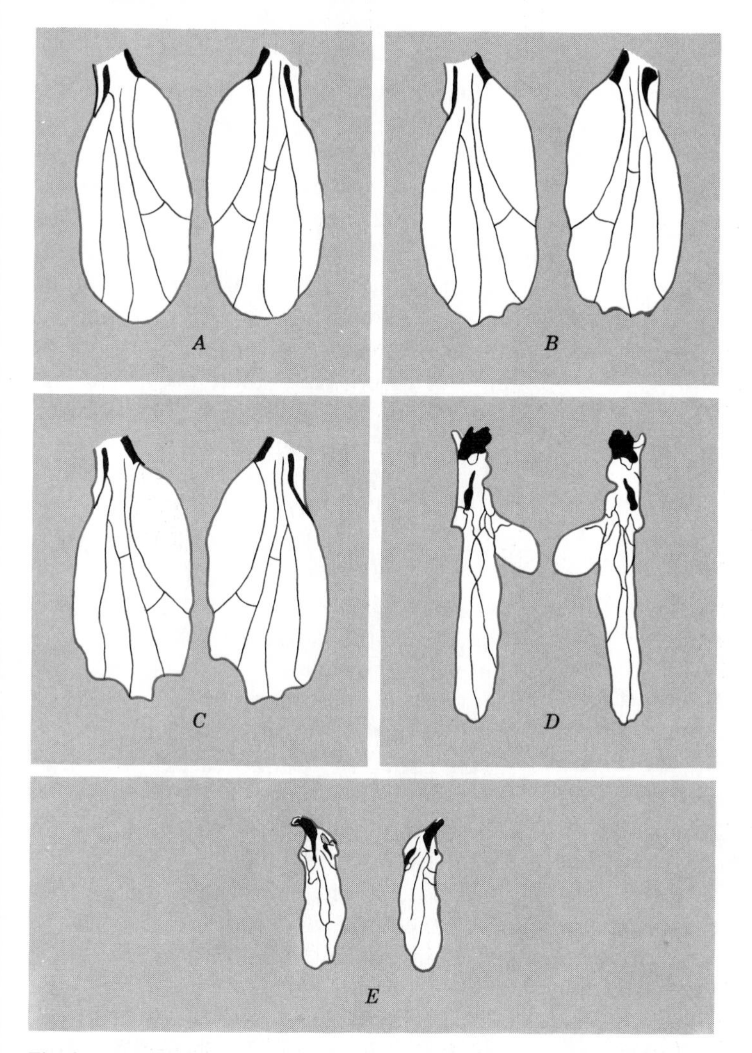


**Fig. 8.4** Wings of the fruit fly, illustrating expressions of different members of a series of multiple alleles at the *vg* locus. *A*, normal wings ($vg^+$); *B*, nicked ($vg^{ni}$); *C*, notched ($vg^{no}$); *D*, strap ($vg^{st}$); *E*, vestigial ($vg$).

**TABLE 8.3 Combinations of compatibility factors in Nicotiana**

| Seed Parents | Pollen Parents | | | |
|---|---|---|---|---|
| | $S_1S_2$ | $S_2S_3$ | $S_3S_4$ | $S_4S_5$ |
| $S_1S_2$ | | $S_3S_2$<br>$S_3S_1$ | $S_3S_1$<br>$S_3S_2$<br>$S_4S_1$<br>$S_4S_2$ | $S_4S_1$<br>$S_4S_2$<br>$S_5S_1$<br>$S_5S_2$ |
| $S_2S_3$ | $S_1S_2$<br>$S_1S_3$ | | $S_4S_2$<br>$S_4S_3$ | $S_4S_2$<br>$S_4S_3$<br>$S_5S_2$<br>$S_5S_3$ |
| $S_3S_4$ | $S_1S_3$<br>$S_1S_4$<br>$S_2S_3$<br>$S_2S_4$ | $S_2S_3$<br>$S_2S_4$ | | $S_5S_3$<br>$S_5S_4$ |
| $S_4S_5$ | $S_1S_4$<br>$S_1S_5$<br>$S_2S_4$<br>$S_2S_5$ | $S_2S_4$<br>$S_2S_5$<br>$S_3S_4$<br>$S_3S_5$ | $S_3S_4$<br>$S_3S_5$ | |

## BLOOD GROUP ALLELES IN MAN

### *ABO System*

The best-established series of multiple alleles in man is associated with the different blood types, A, B, AB, and O. At the beginning of the present century (1900 and 1901) it was observed by K. Landsteiner that agglutination, or clumping, sometimes occurred when the red corpuscles of one person were mixed with the blood serum of another. Landsteiner took samples of blood from six of his colleagues, separated the serum from the formed bodies and prepared saline suspensions of the red corpuscles (erythrocytes). Each serum was mixed with each cell suspension. In some mixtures the cells were agglutinated, in others they were not. On the basis of the reactions, Landsteiner divided mankind into three groups, A, B, and O. The fourth and most rare, the AB blood group, was discovered in 1902 by two of Landsteiner's students, von Decastello and Sturli.

Antigens or agglutinogens carried by the red corpuscles of certain individuals were found to react with antibodies or agglutinins, carried in the serum or plasma of others. Two antigens, A and B, and corresponding antibodies were distinguished. Some people were found to have A antigens, some had B, some had both A and B, and some had neither A nor B antigens. Those with A-type blood did not carry the corresponding anti-A antibody, but they did carry anti-B in their serum or plasma. B-type people carried anti-A but no anti-B. For this reason, clumping of corpuscles and resulting ill effects would be expected to occur when A-type blood is transfused into a B-type person or B-type into an A person. The same clumping reaction occurs when A and B types of blood are mixed with their respective antisera in a test tube or on a microscope slide. It is possible, therefore, to cross-match blood and determine compatibility before transfusions are made.

Persons with AB-type blood have both A and B agglutinogens associated with the red corpuscles but no antagonistic agglutinins in their serum or plasma. O-type individuals lack both A and B agglutinogens, but carry both anti-A and anti-B agglutinins in the serum or plasma. They can give blood to members of any group if the blood is diluted and introduced slowly enough to permit rapid dilution of anti-A and anti-B in the donor's plasma by the blood of the patient. With the proper technique, the transfer can be made slowly enough to avoid serious interaction between the antibodies introduced from the donor and the antigens on the corpuscles of the recipient. Reactions following the mixing of different types of corpuscles and serum are illustrated in Fig. 8.5. Inadequate or improper typing undoubtedly was responsible for many of the unfortunate

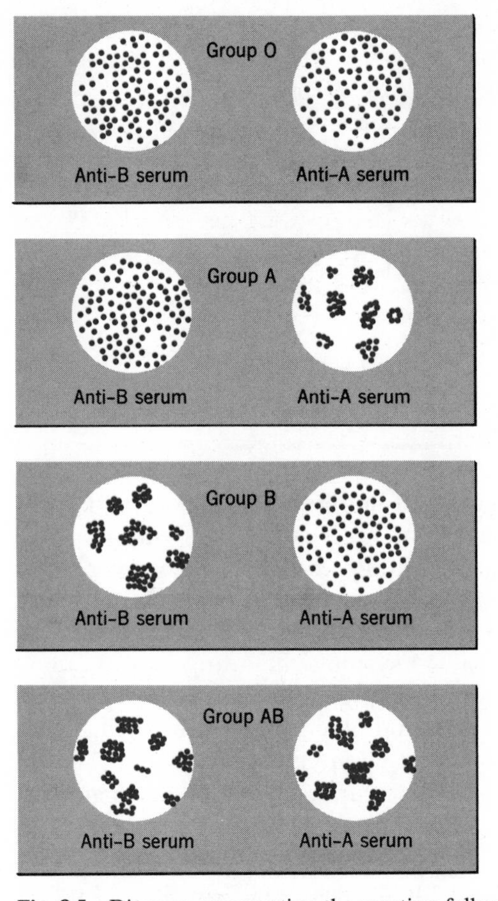


**Fig. 8.5** Diagram representing the reaction following the mixing of different types of corpuscles and blood serum. The type of antiserum is indicated at the left and right, blood group in the center. A clumped pattern within a circle illustrates agglutination of the red corpuscles.

results associated with transfusions in the early part of the present century before cross-matching was introduced as a necessary technique in testing blood for transfusions. Other blood antigens unknown at that time, including the Rh factor to be discussed later in this chapter, were also associated with ill effects.

Thousands of transfusions are now given each year and comparatively few difficulties occur. Blood banks have greatly facilitated the procedure for making available the right kind of blood for all patients requiring transfusions. Blood plasma is prepared by removing the corpuscles with their antigens and partially neutralizing the antibodies. Normal human plasma can therefore be given to anyone without cross-matching and thus is introduced into a patient for immediate treatment of shock on the battle field or at the scene of an accident.

The student of genetics is concerned with the relation among antigens, antibodies, and genes. Specific genes exert a direct control over the antigens. Blood groups are remarkably stable and free from obscuring effects of age, disease, and the influence of other genes in the body and, until recently, they were thought to be completely independent of the environment. It is now evident that they may, on rare occasions, be modified by disease. Several cases are now on record in which patients with leukemia have shown a modified response to anti-A serum. People who previously had given a strong response to anti-A serum were found to have a weak or entirely absent antigenic reaction after the onset of leukemia. In some cases a weak anti-B response was shown by patients who should test for anti-A. These cases have given proof that on rare occasions an antigenic change, ordinarily inherited, can be acquired. Nevertheless, blood serological traits are essentially constant and true expressions of the controlling genes. They are used effectively to identify individuals and populations. The blood group genes are the best markers found thus far for human linkage studies. Single alleles in the ABO system control the antibodies in the serum as well as the antigenic properties of the erythrocytes.

An explanation of the genetic behavior of the ABO blood-type genes, based on a series of three alleles, was described by Bernstein in 1924 from a statistical analysis of human data then available. The symbols A, B, AB, and O were used to represent phenotypes. All three members of the allelic series may be symbolized with the letter A. (The letter I for "*isoagglutinogens*" was previously used as the basic symbol but now this letter is used for another blood group system, as shown in Table 8.5.) The gene responsible for A-type blood is symbolized $A$. Because this gene is dominant over the allele ($a$) for O, an A-type individual may be homozygous $AA$ or heterozygous $Aa$. B-type is dependent on the gene $A^B$ which is also dominant over the allele $a$. AB-type has only one genotype $AA^B$ because $A$ and $A^B$ are codominant, that is, both express themselves when the two alleles are present in the same person. O-type is represented by the homozygous recessive genotype, $aa$.

Subgroups have been discovered within group A. The best established is $A_1$, which can be distinguished serologically from $A_2$. Groups A and AB are thus divided into $A_1$ and $A_2$, and $A_1B$ and $A_2B$. $A_1$ people have two antigens A and $A_1$, whereas $A_2$ people have only one, A. Anti-A sera contain two antibodies, anti-A and anti-$A_1$.

Evidence now indicates that $A_1$ may be dependent on another allele of the series, differing in its phenotypic effect from that of A by a smaller margin than that by which the $A$ differs from its $A^B$ allele. This extends the series of Bernstein from three to four alleles. When the convention of using the same basic symbol for all members of a series of multiple alleles is applied to $A_1$, this allele is symbolized $A_1$. Subgroups of A increase the numbers of groups in the ABO series from four to six: $A_1$, $A_2$, B, $A_1B$, $A_2B$, and O. Genotypes and corresponding phenotypes are summarized in Table 8.4. Other rare types, such as $A_3$, $A_x$, $A_m$, and $B_3$, may also be controlled by alleles in the ABO series.

At the time of World War II and since, rapid expansion has occurred in blood transfusion services bringing new technical improvements and increased numbers of blood samples for examination. With the increased momentum in sampling and cross-matching, new alleles and new relations among existing alleles were discovered. In addition, several entirely new blood group systems were detected. Now some 14 systems including more than 60 blood group genes (Table 8.5) are known in man and others more or less related are known in nonhuman organisms.

**TABLE 8.4 A, $A_2$, B, O blood groups as defined by anti-A, anti-$A_1$ and anti-B with corresponding genotypes**

| Genotypes | Phenotypes |
|---|---|
| $A_1A_1$ | $A_1$ |
| $A_1A_2$ | |
| $A_1a$ | |
| $A_2A_2$ | $A_2$ |
| $A_2a$ | |
| $A^BA^B$ | B |
| $A^Ba$ | |
| $A_1A^B$ | $A_1B$ |
| $A_2A^B$ | $A_2B$ |
| $aa$ | O |

Blood groups are defined by their serological properties. Antigens are identified by antibodies that may be derived from the same species in which the antigen is demonstrated or from different species. Genes controlling antigenic specificity of blood do not specify the synthesis of entire chemical units but provide information for only certain characteristics of the sugar surface coating that is supplied to the already formed glycoprotein on the red blood corpuscle. Glycoprotein is the common precursor of blood-group substances which is acted upon by the different blood-group genes. The addition of a sugar residue to a preformed carbohydrate chain produces a particular serological specificity.

Three gene systems, secretor, H, and Lewis are closely interrelated with the ABO system but they are inherited independently. About 20 percent of the people with A or B antigens on their red corpuscles fail to secrete the corresponding substances in body fluids such as saliva and

**TABLE 8.5 Blood-group systems in man**

| System | Some Detectable Antigens | Basic Genes |
|---|---|---|
| ABO | A, B, H | *A*, $A_2$, $A^B$, *a* |
| Lewis | $Le^a$, $Le^b$ | *Le*, *le* |
| MNSs | M, $M^g$, $M_1$, N, $N_2$, S, s, U, $Mi^a$, Vw, Mu, Hu, He, Vr, $Mt^a$, $Ri^a$, $St^a$ | $L^M$, $L^{Mg}$, $L^{M_1}$, $L^N$, $L^{N_2}$, *S*, *s*, $S^u$, $Mi^a$, *Vw*, *Mu*, *Hu*, *He*, *Vr*, $Mt^a$, $Ri^a$, $St^a$ |
| P | $P_1$, $P_2$, $P^k$ | $P_1$, $P_2$, *p* |
| Rh | C, $C^w$, c, D, E, e | See Table 8.6 |
| Lutheran | $Lu^a$, $Lu^b$ | $Lu^a$, $Lu^b$ |
| Kell | K, k, $Kp^a$, $Kp^b$, $Js^a$, $Js^b$, $K^o$ | *K*, *k*, $Kp^a$, $Kp^b$, $Js^a$, $Js^b$, $K^o$ |
| Duffy | $Fy^a$, $Fy^b$, $Fy^x$ | $Fy^a$, $Fy^b$, $Fy^x$, *Fy* |
| Kidd | $Jk^a$, $Jk^b$ | $Jk^a$, $Jk^b$, *Jk* |
| Diego | $Di^a$, $Di^b$ | $Di^a$, $Di^b$ |
| Auberger | $Au^a$ | $Au^a$, *Au* |
| I | I | *I*, *i* |
| Xg | $Xg^a$ | $Xg^a$, *Xg* |
| Dombrock | $Do^a$ | $Do^a$, *Do* |

gastric juice. Secretor ability is controlled by a pair of alleles, *Se* and *se*, inherited independently with respect to the ABO alleles. *SeSe* or *Sese* individuals are secretors while *sese* people are nonsecretors.

The active substances A, B, H, and $Le^a$ (Lewis antigen) are identical qualitatively. Each contains five sugars: D-galactose, L-fucose, N-acetyl-D-glucosamine, N-acetyl-D-galactosamine, and N-acetylneuraminic acid (sialic acid). Structural formulas of these sugars are shown in Fig. 8.6. Specificity is obviously not due to qualitative differences in the sugars or in the amino acids present in the basic substances. Careful quantitative comparisons have shown the A substance to have a higher N-acetylgalactosamine and lower L-fucose content than other active substances.

This observation supports the results of enzyme inhibition studies which indicate that the carbohydrate chains in the A substance have a terminal nonreducing N-acetyl-D-galactosamine residue (Fig. 8.6*A*). The B substance specificity was likewise associated with a terminal D-galactose residue (Fig. 8.6*B*). The only difference between these sugar molecules is a replacement at the position of carbon No. 2. A hydroxyl group at this position in D-galactose is replaced by an N-acetylamino group in N-acetyl-D-galactosamine. The difference in A and B specificity is thus identified more narrowly as a substitution at the position of carbon atom No. 2 in the

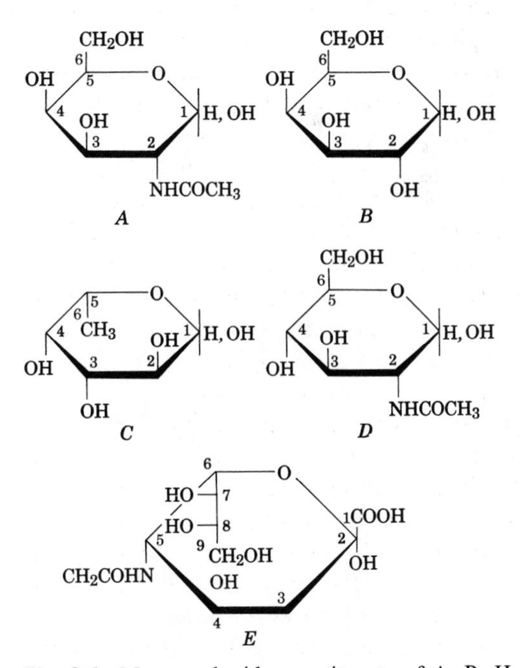


**Fig. 8.6** Monosaccharide constituents of A, B, H, and $Le^a$ substances. *A*, *N*-acetyl-D-galactosamine; *B*, D-galactose; *C*, L-fucose; *D*, *N*-acetyl-D-glucosamine; *E*, *N*-acetylneuraminic acid. (From W. M. Watkins, *Science* **152:**172–181, 1966 © *Amer. Assoc. Adv. Sci.*)

sugar molecule. This difference and the linkage of sugar molecules made possible by the arrangement of the atoms apparently provides the basis for antigenic specificity. The genetic mechanism is based on particular transferase enzymes specified by genes.

The H substance first described in O individuals is controlled by a pair of alleles, *H* and *h*. *HH* and *Hh* genotypes in individuals give rise to the H substance. Rare *hh* individuals lack the H substance. O-type people have large quantities of H substance, but those with A or B and also carrying the gene *H* have a lesser amount. It is postulated that the H substance is the precursor for A and B substances and that, under the influence of *A* or $A^B$ genes, the H substance is converted into A or B active substances (Fig.8.7). In the presence of the *hh* genotype, the production of H and, thus, that of A and B substances, is suppressed.

Individuals lacking A, B, and H reactivity (that is, the erythrocytes are not agglutinated by anti-A, anti-B, or anti-H and the serum contains anti-A, anti-B, and anti-H) express the Bombay phenotype. Some 35 to 40 individuals with this combination have been identified in India. They may carry *Se-* or *sese*.

The Lewis system is defined by a pair of allelic genes, *Le* and *le*, which are inherited independently of the ABO, H, and secretor systems. *LeLe* and *Lele* genotypes result in $Le^a$ specific substance and *lele* results in the absence of such a material. The expression of *Le* is not influenced by the *Sese* gene system. When *Le* and *H* genes are present together, the $Le^b$ phenotype is produced.

Inhibition tests have indicated that the alpha-L-fucosyl residue (Fig. 8.6*C*) is associated with H substance specification. This sugar is identical with the D-galactosyl residue except for a substitution at the carbon No. 5 position. Further studies involving the $Le^a$ substance indicated that the terminal nonreducing sugar alone could not specify the active substance. The linkage of one sugar to the next in a chain or the nature of the second sugar is important in determining specificity.

The simplest hypothesis for the action of genes *A*, $A^B$, *H*, and *Le* is that they control the formation or activity of specific glycosyl transferase enzymes that add sugar units from a donor substrate to the

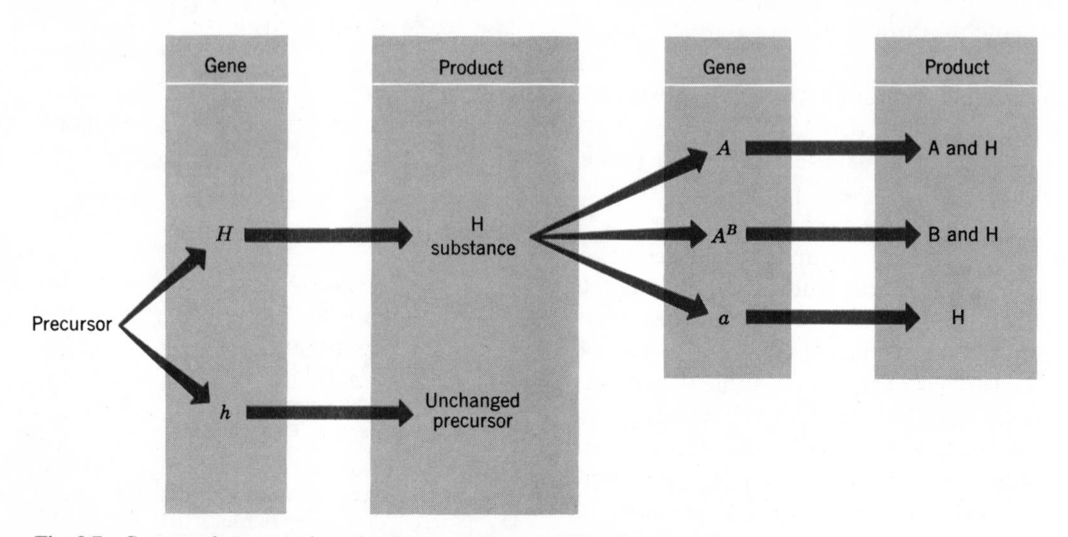


**Fig. 8.7** Genes and gene products leading to A, B, and H blood-group substances.

carbohydrate chains on a preformed glycoprotein molecule. Alleles of *A*, $A^B$, *H* and *Le* (that is, *a*, *h* and *le*) have not been found to produce changes in the glycoproteins. They are therefore, inactive genes called amorphs.

### *MNSs and P Blood Groups*

In 1927, when only the ABO blood group system was known in man, Landsteiner and P. Levine injected rabbits with red cells of different people. Antibodies were formed in the rabbits which distinguish the blood of certain people. On the basis of tests in 64 families with a total of 286 children, Landsteiner and Levine recognized two new blood types, which were called M and N. They postulated a pair of alleles to distinguish the M and N blood types. This two-gene theory was soon confirmed by other investigators. The basic symbol L for Landsteiner will be applied to the MN alleles.

The MN system has little importance in blood transfusions because the M and N proteins are not antigenic for man. When specific antibodies are produced in rabbits and introduced into man, the M and N factors are useful as identifying markers in human populations. In medico-legal genetics, M and N are used along with other blood-group systems for negative evidence; for instance, for ruling out certain individuals in cases of questioned paternity and for negative evidence in accusations of exchanged babies in a hospital.

Some 20 years after M and N types were identified, the Ss groups were discovered and were found to belong to the MN system. Genes for S and s were not alleles of the MN genes, however, but were postulated to be closely linked and interrelated with the M and N genes. Now more than a dozen antigens have been detected by antibodies related to this system. The same type of explanation presented for the specificity of A, B, and H antigens accounts for that of the M and N substances. Results of studies on human and rabbit antisera indicate that terminal nonreducing N-acetylneuraminic acid residues (Fig. 8.6*E*) are involved in serological specificity. These investigations have suggested sequential, gene controlled changes on a common precursor substance which may also form a pattern for the synthesis of the numerous other antigens ($Mi^a$, Vw, Mu, Hu, He, $M^g$, Vr, $M_1$, $Mt^a$, $Ri^a$, $St^a$, and U) associated with the MN system.

Another discovery made in the 1927 immunization experiments of Landsteiner and Levine was the P blood-group system. This system includes three phenotypes $P_1$, $P_2$, and anti-$P_1$ controlled by a series of three alleles $P_1$, $P_2$, and $P$ with $P_1$ and $P_2$ acting as codominants. Another very rare type, $P_k$, has more recently been discovered. This does not behave as if it were controlled by an allele of the *P* genes, but may be the result of genes acting on a precursor of the P substance in the same way as the Bombay factor is related to the A, B, and H substances in the ABO system. The $P_1$ antigen of the P system has not yet been isolated from human red corpuscles. A substance with similar specificity, obtained from sheep, however, has a carbohydrate chain with D-galactose (Fig. 8.6*B*) in the position for linkage between sugars.

### *Rh System*

The Rh factor was discovered in 1940 by Landsteiner and A. S. Wiener from rabbits immunized with the blood of a monkey *Macacus rhesus.* The resulting antibodies agglutinated not only the red corpuscles of the monkey but those of a high percentage of the Caucasian people of New York. The symbol "Rh" came from the first two letters of the species name of the

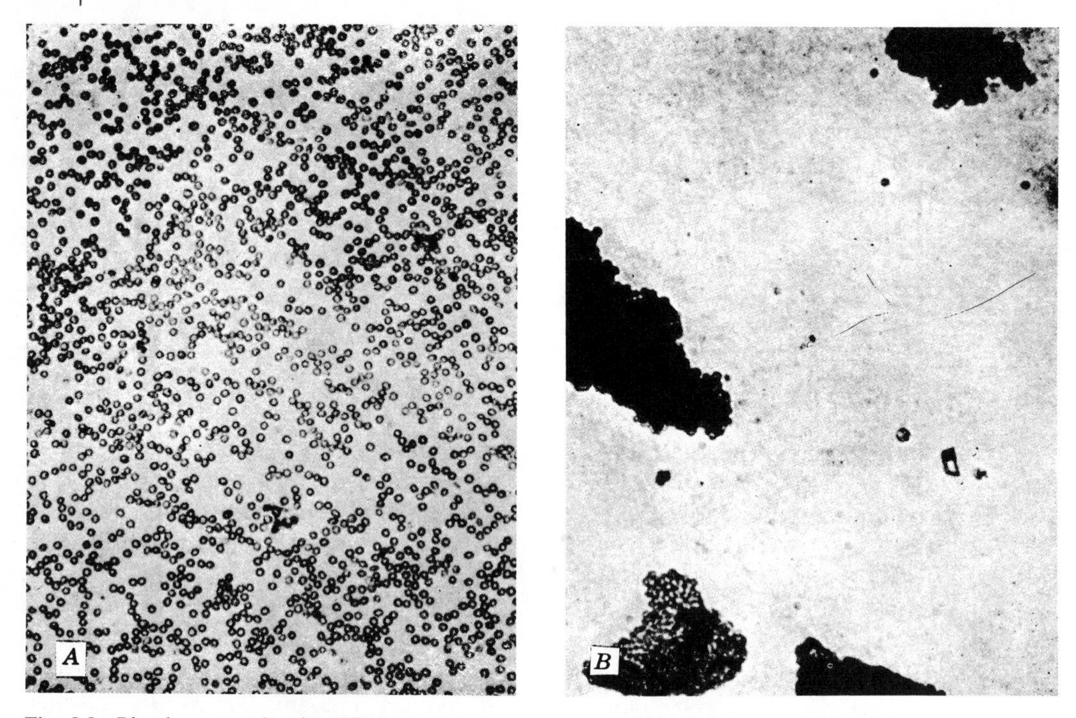


**Fig. 8.8** Blood smears showing Rh incompatability reaction. *A*, erythrocytes are distributed evenly on slide, indicating no reaction. *B*, erythrocytes are agglutinated, indicating incompatability. (Courtesy of A. S. Wiener.)

monkey. The appearance of the slides used to test Rh compatability is illustrated in Fig. 8.8.

The original agglutinogen, now symbolized $Rh_0$, is highly antigenic to man. One source of introduction of the wrong kind of blood is through transfusion. Cross-matching of the Rh factor, as well as of the A, B, and O types, is now used to avoid such an error. Rh-negative individuals must always be transfused with Rh-negative blood to avoid immunization and subsequent reactions. Another means of transferring blood from one person to another occurs between mother and child during pregnancy or during the birth process. An Rh-negative mother may be immunized by an Rh-positive fetus that she carries. Usually no ill effects are associated with the original introduction of Rh-positive antigen, but subsequent Rh-positive children carried by the same mother may be affected and develop symptoms of hemolytic jaundice and anemia. The symptoms may be mild or severe, sometimes resulting in the death of the fetus or newly born infant.

At first, the genetic mechanism of the Rh system seemed simple. A single pair of genes, *R* and *r*, was postulated to account for the difference between Rh-positive and Rh-negative individuals. New antibodies were soon discovered, however, and additional genes had to be postulated to explain the more complicated situation. Wiener developed an hypothesis based on a series of multiple alleles (Table 8.6). Eight alleles were included in the series and more have since been added. Much evidence has been presented in support of this hypothesis. On the other hand, R. R. Race, R. A. Fisher, and other British and

American investigators explained the same data on the basis of three pairs of closely linked genes (*C*, *D*, and *E*) located near each other on the same chromosome. Very closely linked genes might be expected to act like true alleles.

In general, the Rh-positive gene *R* is dominant over the Rh-negative *r*. These alleles control the antigen or agglutinogen characteristic of the red corpuscles. There are no natural corresponding antibodies similar to those associated with the A and B alleles of the ABO system, but under certain conditions, the agglutinogens induce the production of antibodies against themselves. This is not a strange phenomenon, because many and perhaps all foreign proteins provoke a reaction in a living organism. Chicken albumin injected into a rabbit will immunize the rabbit against this substance. A reaction will occur in the rabbit on further inoculation with chicken albumin, but the reaction is very specific. If a rabbit immunized against chicken albumin is treated with duck albumin, no reaction will occur. The living organism can discriminate critically between such substances.

An Rh-positive (*R*–) father and an Rh-negative (*rr*) mother may (through dominance of *R*) have an Rh-positive child. When an Rh-positive fetus is carried by an Rh-negative mother, an immunization may occur in the mother. It has been presumed that very small quantities of fetal blood get through the placenta and mix with the maternal blood or that the mixing may occur during the birth process. Fetal blood develops independently in the fetus and no obvious mixing occurs between the mother's blood and that of the fetus during prenatal development. The first child of parents with this genetic background is nearly always normal. Unless the mother has, at some time earlier in her life, received a transfusion of Rh-positive blood or in some other way has been exposed to the Rh factor, there would have been no stimulus to the cells of her body to produce antibodies. Ordinarily, at least one pregnancy and sometimes several are required to sensitize the mother. Several families are known in which the mother is Rh-negative and the father is homozygous Rh-positive but only the youngest of seven or eight children showed evidence of incompatibility. In these families, six or seven pregnancies were required to sensitize the mother.

In one case, brought to the attention of the author, the seventh child of a couple was still-born and showed symptoms of Rh incompatibility. Subsequent serological tests of the parents showed that the father was Rh-positive and the mother was negative. Then the parents and obstetrician remembered some difficulty associated with the sixth pregnancy, but the infant had recovered completely from the ill effects. Differences in the response of mothers may depend on the amount of blood exchanged. Interactions among blood constituents, such as ABO and Rh, may also be involved. The genotype of the father may add another element of uncertainty. If he is heterozygous, only half of the children would be Rh-positive *Rr*,

**TABLE 8.6 Symbols used by Fisher, Race, and others compared with those used by Wiener in the Rh blood-group system**

| Fisher and Race Notations | Wiener Notations | | Approximate Frequencies of Phenotypes in Caucasian Populations |
|---|---|---|---|
| Genes | Type | Genes | |
| *CDe* | $Rh_1$ | $R^1$ | 41% |
| *cDE* | $Rh_2$ | $R^2$ | 14% |
| *cDe* | $Rh_0$ | $R^0$ | 3% |
| *CDE* | $Rh_z$ | $R^z$ | Rare |
| *cde* | rh | *r* | 39% |
| *Cde* | rh′ | *r′* | 1% |
| *cdE* | rh″ | *r″* | 1% |
| *CdE* | $rh_y$ | $r^y$ | Very rare |

and half would be negative *rr* like the mother.

The clinical name for the disease resulting from Rh incompatibility is "hemolytic disease of the newborn." Most obvious symptoms are anemia, jaundice, and fluid accumulation in the tissues of the embryo (fetal hydrops). Clinically, the disease has been recognized for a long time, but the cause was not known until 1940 when the Rh factor was discovered. Undoubtedly, some still-born babies and infant deaths in past generations resulted from Rh incompatibility. The genetic combination associated with the ill effects occurs when the father is Rh-positive and the mother is Rh-negative.

About 85 percent of the white population of Western Europe and North America is Rh-positive, and about 15 percent is Rh-negative. Erythroblastosis occurs less frequently in the general population than would be expected on the basis of gene frequency and probability. Only a small proportion of the pregnancies occurring from the matings between Rh-positive men and Rh-negative women have produced symptoms of the disease. Two explanations are suggested: (1) the wide variation in degree of severity, and (2) the predominance of small families. Parents with only one or two children may never know of their Rh incompatibility.

### Other Blood Group Systems

Several other blood antigens (Table 8.5) have now been discovered which are unrelated genetically to the blood-group systems discussed so far. These were named for the people in whom the antigens were first discovered. The antibody that defines the Lutheran blood groups was first reported in 1945 from the serum of a patient who had received many transfusions. Gene $Lu^a$ was found to be inherited as a dominant and $Lu^b$, discovered later, was found to have a similar dominant mode of inheritance. $Lu^a$ and $Lu^b$ are now recognized as a pair of codominant alleles. About 92 percent of Caucasians are $Lu^b$.

The Kell system is a large and important one including three pairs of alleles, $K/k$, $Kp^a/Kp^b$, and $Js^a/Js^b$, which may be closely linked with each other, and a very infrequent gene tentatively designated $K^\circ$. This system was originally described in terms of two alternative phenotypes, Kell positive and Kell negative controlled by alleles $K$ and $k$. About 9 percent of Caucasian people but only 1 to 2 percent of Negro people were found to be Kell positive ($KK$ or $Kk$). The system became more complex when the second pair of alleles $Kp^a$ and $Kp^b$ was discovered. Alleles $Js^a$ and $Js^b$ were formerly known as the Sutter group and were given symbol designations appropriate for that group, but now have been shown to belong to the Kell system. $Js^a$ is dominant and is confined almost entirely to Negroes. A rare antigen K° (Peltz) and corresponding antibody anti-Ku are now included in the Kell system.

Duffy antibodies were first discovered in 1950. A pair of alleles $Fy^a$ and $Fy^b$ was first described. The third allele, $Fy$ and later (1965) the fourth allele $Fy^x$ were added to the series. $Fy$ is common among Negroes but very rare in Caucasians. $Fy^a$ and $Fy^b$, on the other hand, are found in a high proportion of Caucasians but rarely in Negroes. $Fy^a$ is present in a high proportion of Japanese, Koreans, and others of the Mongolian race.

The two major alleles of the Kidd group $Jk^a$ and $Jk^b$ are codominant. The third, $Jk$ is recessive to both $Jk^a$ and $Jk^b$ and is very rare. In Caucasians, $Jk^a$ and $Jk^b$ are about equal in frequency, but in other races marked differences occur in relative distribution. $Jk^a$ is present in about 90 percent of American Negroes.

The Diego system is represented by antigens $Di^a$ and $Di^b$. Phenotypes, Diego positive and Diego negative, can be detected. A single pair of alleles $Di^a$ and $Di^b$ is postulated with $Di^a$ dominant over $Di^b$. The gene $Di^a$ is almost completely confined to members of the Mongolian race. About 10 percent of Japanese people are Diego positive but virtually no Caucasians carry this antigen. The antigenic determinant for antigen $Di^b$ is present in nearly all Caucasians thus far tested.

Auberger antibodies were discovered in a woman in Paris in 1961. More than 80 percent of the people tested were found to have the corresponding antigen. These studies have led to the postulation of a pair of alleles $Au^a$ and $Au$ with $Au^a$ dominant over $Au$. Auberger positive people are expected to be $Au^aAu^a$ or $Au^aAu$ whereas Auberger negative people would be $AuAu$.

The I antigen, first described in 1958, was found in all adult human beings tested and was at first known as a "public" or species antigen. With more extensive studies, however, only a very few adults were found to be completely devoid of this antigen but different people showed marked variation in antigen strength. When people of different ages were tested, the I antigen was found to be weak in newborn and young children but stronger in older people. This antigen is inherited, but it is not useful as a marker because of alteration by age and environmental factors.

A blood antigen $Xg^a$ controlled by a dominant sex-linked gene $Xg^a$ was discovered in 1962. This gene and its allele $Xg$ have become important for mapping the human X chromosome. All other blood-group genes previously discovered were autosomal. $Xg^a$ is located near the end of the short arm of the X chromosome. It has proved useful as a marker gene in studies designed to identify the positions of other sex-linked genes and to provide information concerning the source of abnormal deleted and translocated chromosomes.

The new blood group named "Dombrock" was first described in 1965 from antibodies (anti-$Do^a$) obtained from a transfused patient. An antigen $Do^a$ has now been detected in a few people and a pair of alleles $Do^a$ and $Do$ is postulated for this blood group.

Data showing the relative frequencies of different alleles in segments of the population represent a valuable tool for tracing the ancestry of human groups. Evidence is now available to show that gene frequencies reflect the ancestral history of populations in geographical areas of the world. Phenotypes associated with blood alleles are simple, stable, and readily detectable with simple tests. They lend themselves well to population studies (Chapter 18). Beginnings have already been made in comparing gene frequencies of different present-day populations and determining their possible ancestral relations.

### *Antigenic Substances in Other Organisms*

Long lists of specific gene-controlled antigens have been discovered in cattle, sheep, chickens, and other animals. Many variations have been found as the typing program has now been extended to different breeds of cattle. More than 160 different antigenic responses (phenogroups) have been associated with the B locus alone in cattle. Presumably, all phenogroups are dependent on separate alleles. In sheep, some 50 phenogroups have been associated with the B locus. More than 20 alleles have been found at the B locus in chickens. This number will undoubtedly be increased when more breeds are tested. When all other loci carrying blood factors are included, a tremendous number of different combinations is possible. Individual cows, sheep, or chickens may be identified with great precision.

Antigens similar to those found among human beings have been identified in the blood of other organisms. A-type agglutinogens have been found in the chimpanzee; A, B, and AB in the orangutan; and A in the gibbon. Antibody absorption tests indicate that the factors A and B for these three species are similar to those of man. New-world monkeys (Platyrrhina) and lemurs have a substance similar but not identical with the B antigen in man. The chimpanzee has a single gene that behaves like the heterozygous combination (*M/N*) in the MN antigenic series in man. Three blood groups can be distinguished in cats with a genetic system similar to those in man.

Species differences between pearlneck and ring doves were detected by antigenic properties of the blood. Each species was found to have specific substances as well as substances common to both. The hybrids resulting from interspecific crosses between these two doves had a special hybrid substance, probably resulting from an interaction between substances of the two species.

Other tissues and body fluids besides the blood also carry antigens. A "secretor" gene similar to *Se* in man by which A and B antigens can be detected in tears, saliva, urine, semen, gastric juice, and milk occurs in other animals. For example, antigens may be transmitted through the milk of horses and through the yolk in chicken eggs.

## SERUM PROTEINS

In addition to the variations in blood-group antigens under genetic control, many inherited variations have been detected in serum or plasma proteins. Samples of serum have been obtained from many people and laboratory methods have been employed for the separation and identification of proteins in the blood sera. The procedure most commonly used is the starch-gel electrophoresis technique developed by Smithies in 1955. A drop of fluid containing a mixture of proteins is placed at the base of a starch-gel column. When an electric field is applied to the column, the different proteins migrate at a characteristic rate depending on their net electric charge as well as on the size and shape of their molecules. After the migration has been in progress for a given period of time, the positions of the various proteins are made observable by special staining techniques.

When, for example, starch-gel electrophoresis is applied to a sample of normal blood serum, the different serum proteins migrate at a particular rate and take characteristic positions at a given time, as illustrated diagrammatically in Fig. 8.9. With the "normal" pattern established as a standard, samples from different individuals are tested. Protein variants can be detected by comparison with the "normal." From samples of different people, differences are sometimes observed in the rate of migration resulting in altered patterns. Such alterations in proteins may result

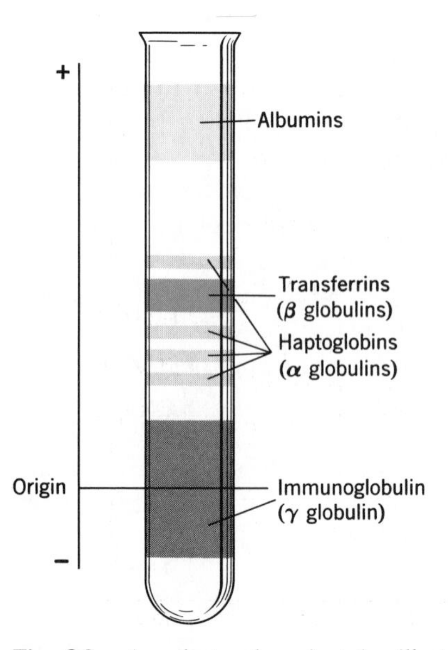


**Fig. 8.9** An electrophoresis tube illustrating the separation of serum proteins by starch gel electrophoresis.

from a substitution of one or more amino acids resulting in a changed protein with different properties. In some samples of serum, a band representing a protein is entirely missing; in others, subdivisions at different locations are observed. Many serum proteins have been identified. Three types with particular genetic interest, haptoglobins, transferrins, and immunoglobulins will be cited here as examples. Each of these types is determined by a system of alleles at a single locus.

### *Haptoglobins*

Haptoglobins are alpha globulins. Three main types of haptoglobins, Hp1-1, Hp2-1, and Hp2-2, can be separated by starch-gel electrophoresis as shown diagrammatically in Fig. 8.10. A pair of codominant alleles, $Hp^1$ and $Hp^2$, has been postulated to account for the three phenotypes. Hp1-1 is produced by allele $Hp^1$ in homozygous condition ($Hp^1Hp^1$), Hp2-1 by the heterozygote ($Hp^1Hp^2$) and Hp2-2 by the allele $Hp^2$ in homozygous condition.

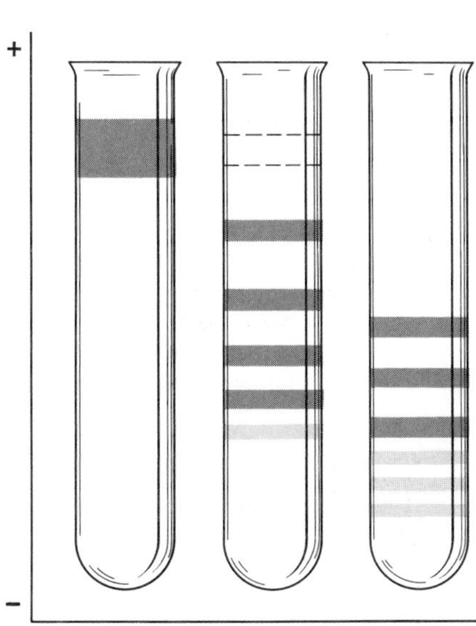


**Fig. 8.10** Electrophoresis tubes illustrating the separation patterns of the three common haptoglobin types, Hp 1-1, Hp 2-1, and Hp 2-2.

### *Transferrins*

Transferrins are beta globulins. They have the vital function of transporting plasma iron to the bone marrow and tissue storage areas and binding this metal in compounds. Iron is a component of hemoglobin, myoglobin, cytochrome, and several important enzymes. Transferrins were detected by electrophoresis and identified with letters of the alphabet. The common form is designated as C. All of the 14 other forms that have been discovered are comparatively rare. All known transferrins seem to have the same ability to bind and transport iron. The gene $Tf^c$ has been associated with the C form of transferrins. Individuals homozygous for this gene ($Tf^cTf^c$) have a single electrophoretic band. Those heterozygous have two bands. Different known forms of transferrins are probably controlled by a series of codominant alleles, but more data are necessary to establish this pattern of inheritance for all transferrins.

### *Immunoglobulins*

Several different human gamma globulins have been recognized and given phenotypic designations such as $Gm^a$ and $Gm^b$. They are believed to be controlled by a series of *Gm* alleles, more than 10 of which have been identified. These alleles, like several others of the blood-group and serum-protein gene systems cited in this chapter, are polymorphic in the human population. They are thus useful in tracing the ancestral history of isolates and races of man, as will be further shown in Chapter 18. In one sample of 1284 Danish people, for example, 56 percent were $Gm^a$. Another phenotype, called "Gm-like," which is presumably produced by another *Gm* allele, is not found in Caucasians but is found in Negroes. *Gm* alleles have been found in varying frequencies in different ethnic groups. Some primates carry *Gm* factors but none have been discovered in mammals lower in the phylogenetic scale, indicating that the *Gm* factors are of relatively recent evolutionary origin.

The globulins (including haptoglobins, transferrins, and gamma globulins) have had an evolutionary history that parallels the phylogenetic tree established from other lines of evidence for animals and plants.

## SUMMARY

Series of three or more alternative genes at the same locus are multiple alleles. Many examples of multiple alleles have been discovered and, undoubtedly, many more remain to be found. Additional alleles may be produced continuously by mutation. Several systems of alleles and some combinations with nonallelic genes have been discovered in the blood groups and serum proteins of man and other animals. Some of these (for example, Rh factor) are related to the health of individuals and their progeny. These systems are better known genetically than any other group of human traits. They are therefore useful in providing marker genes for linkage studies and for identifiable traits from which gene frequencies may be obtained for comparisons of populations.

## REFERENCES

Briles, W. E., C. P. Allen, and T. W. Millen. 1957. "The B blood group system of chickens." *Genetics,* **42,** 631–648.

Chown, B., M. Lewis, and H. Kaita. 1965. "The Duffy blood group system in Caucasians: evidence for a new allele." *Amer. J. Human Genet.,* **17,** 384–389.

Giblett, E. R. 1962. *The plasma transferrins. Progress in medical genetics.* A. G. Steinberg and A. G. Bearn, (eds.) Vol. II. Grune and Stratton, New York.

Grüneberg, H. 1952. "The genetics of the mouse." *Bibliographia Genetica,* **15,** 1–650. The Hague. (The agouti series and other series of alleles in mice.)

Hadorn, E. 1961. *Developmental genetics and lethal factors.* John Wiley and Sons, New York. (Chemical and functional basis of allelism.)

Harris, H. 1961. "Inherited variations in human plasma proteins." *Brit. Med. Bull.,* **17,** 217–223.

Race, R. R., and R. Sanger. 1962. *Blood groups in man.* Blackwell, Scientific Publications, Oxford.

Sager, R., and F. J. Ryan. 1961. *Cell heredity.* John Wiley and Sons, New York. (Chemical aspects of allelism and compound loci.)

Steinberg, A. G. 1962. *Progress in the study of genetically determined human gamma globulin types (the Gm and Inv groups). Progress in medical genet.* A. G. Steinberg and A. G. Bearn (eds.) Vol. II. Grune and Stratton, New York.

Stormont, C. 1959. "On the applications of blood groups in animal breeding." *Proc. X Intern. Cong. Genet.,* **1,** 206–224.

Watkins, W. M. 1966. "Blood-group substances." *Science,* **152,** 172–181. (Sugar residues that determine blood group specificity.)

Wiener, A. S., and I. B. Wexler. 1958. *Heredity of the blood groups.* Grune and Stratton, New York.

# *Problems*

**8.1** What was the contribution of each of the following to the terminology and basic concept of allelism: (a) Bateson, (b) Johannsen, (c) Morgan, Bridges, and Sturtevant?

**8.2** One inbred variety of plants has white flowers and another variety of the same species has red flowers. How could we find out whether a single pair of alleles or more than a single pair is involved in determining the different flower colors?

**8.3** Why are mutant (alternative) genes essential for identifying wild-type alleles and locating the positions of gene loci on chromosomes?

8.4 (a) How do multiple alleles originate? (b) How should groups of multiple alleles be symbolized? (c) To what extent do they represent alterations of the same phenotype?

8.5 The following, listed in order of dominance, are four alleles in rabbits: $c^+$, colored; $c^{ch}$, chinchilla; $c^h$, himalayan; and $c$, albino. What phenotypes and ratios would be expected from the following crosses: (a) $c^+c^+ \times cc$; (b) $c^+c \times c^+c$; (c) $c^+c^{ch} \times c^+c^{ch}$; (d) $c^{ch} \times cc$; (e) $c^+c^h \times c^+c$; and (f) $c^hc \times cc$?

8.6 In mice, a series of five alleles has been associated with fur pattern. These alleles are, in order of dominance, $A^Y$ (homozygous lethal) for yellow fur; $A^L$, agouti with light belly; $A^+$, agouti; $a^t$, black and tan; and, $a$, black. For each of the following crosses, give the coat color of the parents and the phenotypic ratios expected among the progeny. (a) $A^YA^L \times A^YA$; (b) $A^Ya \times A^La^t$; (c) $a^ta \times A^Ya$; (d) $A^La^t \times A^LA^L$; (e) $A^LA^L \times A^YA$; (f) $Aa^t \times a^ta$; (g) $a^ta \times aa$; (h) $A^YA^L \times Aa^t$; and (i) $A^Ya^t \times A^YA$.

8.7 If a series of four alleles is known to exist in a given diploid ($2n$) species, how many would be present in: (a) a chromosome? (b) a chromosome pair? (c) an individual member of the species? (d) On the same basis, how many different combinations might be expected to occur in the entire population?

8.8 Assume that in a certain animal species four alleles ($c^+$, $c^1$, $c^2$, and $c$) have their locus in chromosome I and another series of two alleles ($d^+$ and $d$) have their locus in chromosome II. How many different genotypes with respect to these two series of alleles are theoretically possible in the population?

8.9 Assume that, in a certain animal species, four alleles ($c^+$, $c^1$, $c^2$, and $c$) have their locus in chromosome I and another series of three alleles ($d^+$, $d^1$, and $d$) have their locus in chromosome II. How many different genotypes with respect to these two series of alleles are theoretically possible in the population?

8.10 A series of multiple alleles in a certain species of fish which breeds readily in the laboratory was listed by Myron Gordon as follows: $p^o$, one spot; $P^m$, moon complete; $P^c$, crescent; $P^{cc}$, crescent complete; $P^{co}$, comet; $P^t$, twin spot; and $P$, plain. (a) How many combinations of these alleles might be expected to occur in the population? (b) How could the allelic nature of these genes be indicated by genetic methods?

8.11 In several plants, such as tobacco, primrose, and red clover, combinations of alleles in eggs and pollen have been found to influence the reproductive compatibility of the plants. Homozygous combinations such as $S_1S_1$ do not develop because $S_1$ pollen is not effective on $S_1$ stigmas. $S_1$ pollen, however, is effective on an $S_2S_3$ stigma. What progeny might be expected from the following crosses (seed parent always written first): (a) $S_1S_2 \times S_2S_3$; (b) $S_1S_2 \times S_3S_4$; (c) $S_4S_5 \times S_4S_5$; and (d) $S_3S_4 \times S_5S_6$?

8.12 In man, a series of alleles has been associated with the blood typing groups as follows: $A$, A type; $A^B$, B type; $AA^B$, AB type; and $aa$, O type. What phenotypes and ratios might be expected from the following crosses: (a) $AA \times A^BA^B$; (b) $AA^B \times aa$; (c) $Aa \times A^Ba$; and (d) $Aa \times aa$?

8.13 A case was brought before a certain judge in which a woman of blood group O presented a baby of blood group O, which she claimed as her child, and brought suit against a man of group AB whom she claimed was the father of the child. What bearing might the blood type information have on the case?

**8.14** In another case, a woman of blood group AB presented a baby of group O which she claimed as her baby. What bearing might the blood-type information have on the case?

**8.15** If the active substances in A, B, H, and $Le^a$ antigens are qualitatively identical, how can antigenic specificity of these substances be explained?

**8.16** (a) What is the possible relation between the H substance and the A and B substances? (b) What genotype is associated with the Bombay phenotype? (c) What genotype is associated with the $Le^b$ phenotype?

**8.17** An Rh-positive man (*RR*) married an Rh-negative (*rr*) woman. Their first child was normal and their second child had the hemolytic disease of the newborn. (a) What genetic explanation might be offered? (b) What prediction might be made concerning future children by this couple?

**8.18** An Rh-positive man (*Rr*) married an Rh-negative (*rr*) woman. Their first child was normal and their second child showed the effects of Rh incompatibility. What prediction might be made concerning future children of this couple?

**8.19** If the two genes $M$ and $N$ are alleles and the three genes $A$, $A^B$, and $a$ are alleles in a different chromosome, (a) list the genotypes that are theoretically possible in the population. (b) How could these be useful in human problems of identity and paternity?

**8.20** The number of cases reported in the United States with symptoms of Rh incompatibility is less than expected on the basis of the proportion of couples in the population expected to have the genetic constitution for this incompatibility. How might this difference be explained?

**8.21** A blood sample introduced as evidence in legal proceedings in which a Negro and a Caucasian were involved was found to be A, Fy, $Js^a$ and $Jk^a$, and Gm-like. Did the blood probably come from the Negro or the Caucasian?

**8.22** In legal proceedings involving an Englishman and a Japanese man, a sample of blood was AB, $Di^a$, and $Fy^a$. From which of the individuals concerned did the blood most likely originate?

**8.23** What practical applications are associated with the blood antigens in (a) medical practice? (b) human genetics studies? (c) identification of particular individuals?

**8.24** In what different ways have animal studies aided and supported human antigen investigations?

**8.25** Distinguish haptoglobins, transferrins and immunoglobulins from each other. How do they differ from blood antigens?

# *Chromosome Structural Modifications and Position Effects* | 9

In 1917, C. B. Bridges observed that a sex-linked recessive gene in Drosophila came to expression when it was presumed to be in a heterozygous condition. He postulated that a section of the homologous chromosome containing the dominant allele was missing; that is, that a deficiency had occurred in a chromosome. When a recessive gene presumed to be homozygous did not come to expression, Bridges postulated that a dominant allele was present in another place in the chromosome set; that is, that a duplication of a chromosome section had occurred. Rearrangements of sections within chromosomes (inversions) and exchanges of parts between entirely different chromosomes (translocations) were postulated by A. H. Sturtevant and Bridges to explain various genetic irregularities. Many years elapsed, however, before the predicted structural changes could actually be observed through the microscope.

In 1922 and 1926, attached-X chromosomes and attached-X and -Y chromosomes were discovered in Drosophila. H. J. Muller and Edgar Altenburg in 1928 induced structural changes in Drosophila chromosomes with X-rays and then detected translocations. The first cytological demonstration of plant chromosome rearrangements was made in maize by Barbara McClintock in 1930. She worked with the pachytene and other meiotic prophase stages that present large chromosomes for microscopic observation. She eventually demonstrated that irregular configurations made by chromosome rearrangements in the pairing process led to four different kinds of structural changes: (1) deficiencies (parts of chromosomes lost or deleted), (2) duplications (parts added or duplicated), (3) inversions (sections detached and reunited in reverse order), and (4) translocations (parts of chromosomes detached and joined to nonhomologous chromosomes). Demonstrations were later made in Drosophila with giant polytene chromosomes.

Structural modifications of chromosomes are common in nature and have apparently played a significant role in evolution. They occur spontaneously, that is, without any known cause. The frequency of structural changes is increased by ionizing radiations and chemical mutagens.

## BREAKAGE AND JOINING OF CHROMOSOME PARTS

A brief review of chromosome anatomy and the chromosome cycle will enable us to appreciate the nature and effect of structural rearrangement. During metaphase, when chromosomes are most easily observed, they are discrete rods or ovals, but in early prophase and late telophase they are long thin threads. A coiling process occurs in the transition from prophase to metaphase. The threads uncoil during telophase. The remarkable process of DNA replication presumably occurs either in interphase or in the early meiotic prophase.

In cells of higher organisms chromosomes occur in pairs, one member having come originally from each parent. Chromosomes normally do not appear in paired arrangement, however, except during the brief period of synapsis, which is a part of the meiotic process. In other stages, the maternal and paternal member of each set are present but unpaired in the same nucleus. A few exceptional cases are known in which chromosome mates are continuously attracted to each other and stay together in pairs. Continuous somatic pairing in giant polytene chromosomes of larval Diptera is an example.

Structural changes presuppose breaks in the chromosomes. More than one break can occur in a single chromosome or set of chromosomes, and the broken parts may then reunite in new arrangements. Any broken end may presumably unite with any other broken end, thus potentially resulting in new linkage arrangements. The loss or addition of a chromosome segment may also occur in the process. More than one type of aberration may occur at the same time. For example, a section may be broken off and lost during the formation of an inversion or translocation, and thus simultaneously produce a deficiency.

The observation of chromosome aberrations is a major problem for the cytogeneticist because members of a pair usually lack any visible means of identifying different areas along their length. Maize chromosomes are exceptions. They have become one of the most favorable materials for microscopic study because meiotic prophase chromosomes have deep-staining bodies, called heteropyknotic knobs (Fig. 9.1), distributed along their

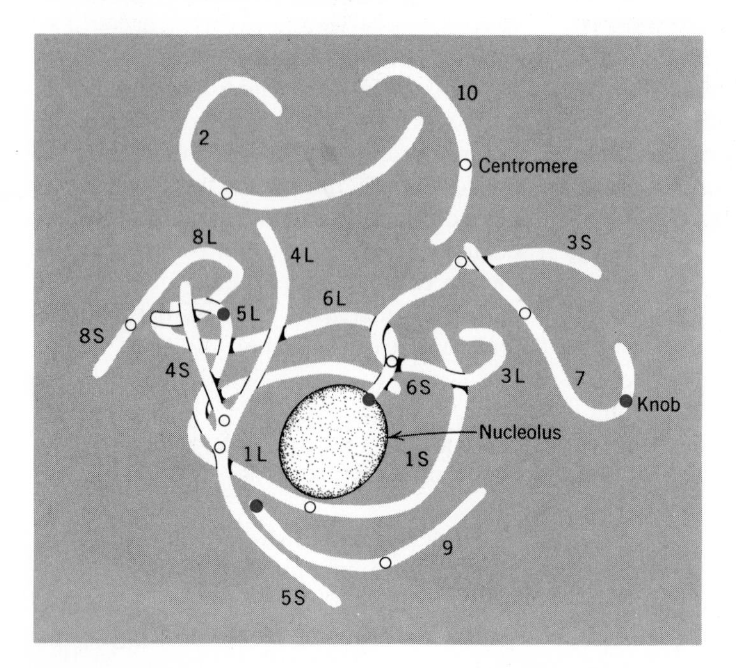


**Fig. 9.1** Ten chromosomes of maize, showing centromeres and most common knobs. Long and short arms of some chromosomes are identified. (From M. M. Rhoades, *Journal of Heredity* **41**:59–67, 1950)

length. With the aid of visible markers, many chromosome changes have been detected in maize. The acetocarmine smear method, first applied to other plant materials by J. Belling in 1921, greatly facilitated studies of the maize chromosomes. This technique permits whole chromosomes to be fixed, stained, and spread on a microscope slide in one operation. It provides a way to compare individual chromosomes within a genome, as well as whole sets from different organisms. The ten maize chromosome pairs were first described in the meiotic prophase stages by McClintock on the basis of a series of studies that utilized the acetocarmine method.

## GIANT POLYTENE CHROMOSOMES IN DIPTERA

Large coiled bodies about 150 to 200 times as large as gonad cell chromosomes were observed in the nuclei of glandular tissues of dipterous larvae as early as 1881 by E. G. Balbiani. He described banded structures in the nuclei of cells of larval midges in the genus Chironomus but did not attach any particular significance to the observation. Three years later, J. B. Carnoy made further morphological observations, and in 1912 F. Alverdes traced the development of these structures from

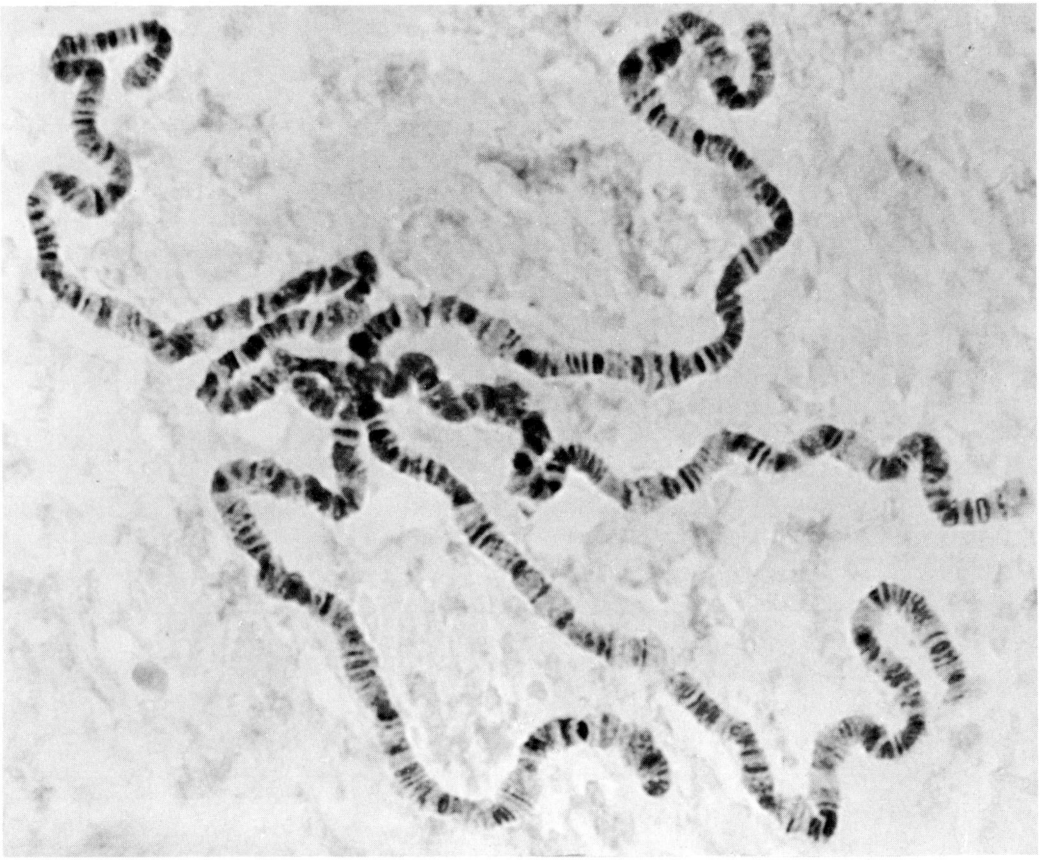

**Fig. 9.2** Salivary gland chromosomes of *Drosophila melanogaster*. (Courtesy of Berwind P. Kaufmann, Department of Zoology, University of Michigan and *Journal of Heredity* **30:**179–190, 1939.)

the early embryo to a late larval stage. In 1930, D. Kostoff suggested a relation between the bands of these structures and the linear sequence known to occur among genes. The anatomical significance of the nuclear bodies was further studied by E. Heitz and H. Bauer in 1933 in the genus Bibio, a group of March flies whose larvae feed on the roots of grasses. These authors identified the bodies as giant chromosomes occurring in pairs. They described the morphology in detail and discovered the relation between the salivary gland chromosomes and other somatic and germ-cell chromosomes. They also demonstrated that comparable elements occurred in the giant chromosomes and in the chromosomes of other cells of the same organism.

It is largely through the work of T. S. Painter that Drosophila salivary gland chromosomes (Fig. 9.2) were first used for cytological verification of genetic data. Painter related the bands on the giant chromosomes to genes, but he was more interested in the morphology of the chromosomes and implications concerning speciation than in the association of chromosome sections with particular genes. Bridges, beginning in 1934, made extensive and detailed investigation of the salivary gland chromosomes and, in the course of his investigations, developed a tool of practical usefulness in relating genes to chromosomes. In applying this

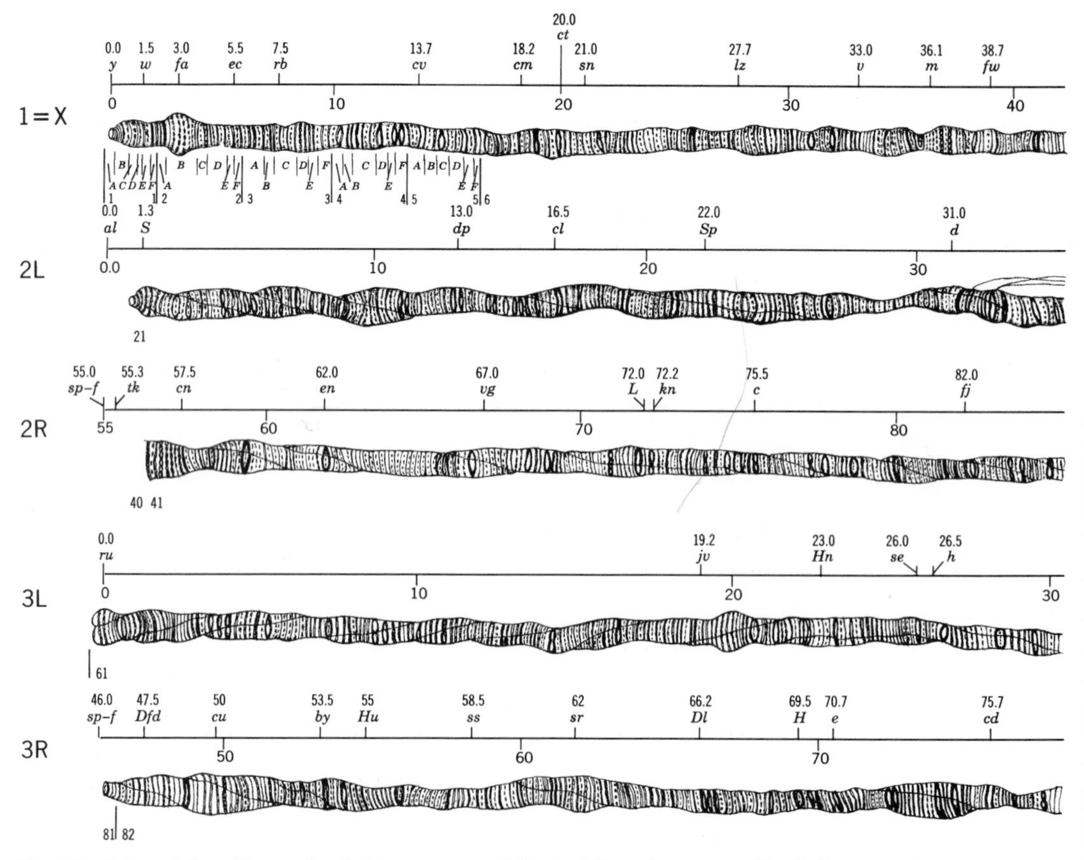


**Fig. 9.3** Map of the salivary gland chromosomes of *Drosophila melanogaster*. The linkage map is superimposed on the cytological map. On the left end of the first (X) chromosome the num-

method to *Drosophila melanogaster,* he prepared a series of cytological (chromosome) maps (Fig. 9.3) to correspond with the linkage maps already available. This project of constructing maps of all four chromosomes of *D. melanogaster* was in progress at the time of his death in 1938.

## *Features of Polytene Chromosomes*

The unusual size of the salivary gland chromosomes is explained at least superficially by the type of growth that occurs in larval glandular tissues in dipterous insects. Salivaries and other glands grow by enlargement rather than by duplication of individual cells. This can be demonstrated by cell counts and measurements taken at different stages in development of a larva. As a larva develops, the chromosome threads (chromonemata) in the cells duplicate themselves repeatedly, producing bundles. A great many chromonemata, having originated by duplication of chromosomes in the original cells involved in the formation of the gland, are present in a single giant chromosome. The chromosomes are thus polytene or many stranded, cable-like structures. Bands running crosswise on the giant chromosomes represent an accumulation through continuous duplication of basophilic stainable regions (chromomeres). Giant polytene chromosomes thus correspond in linear structure with other chromosomes of the

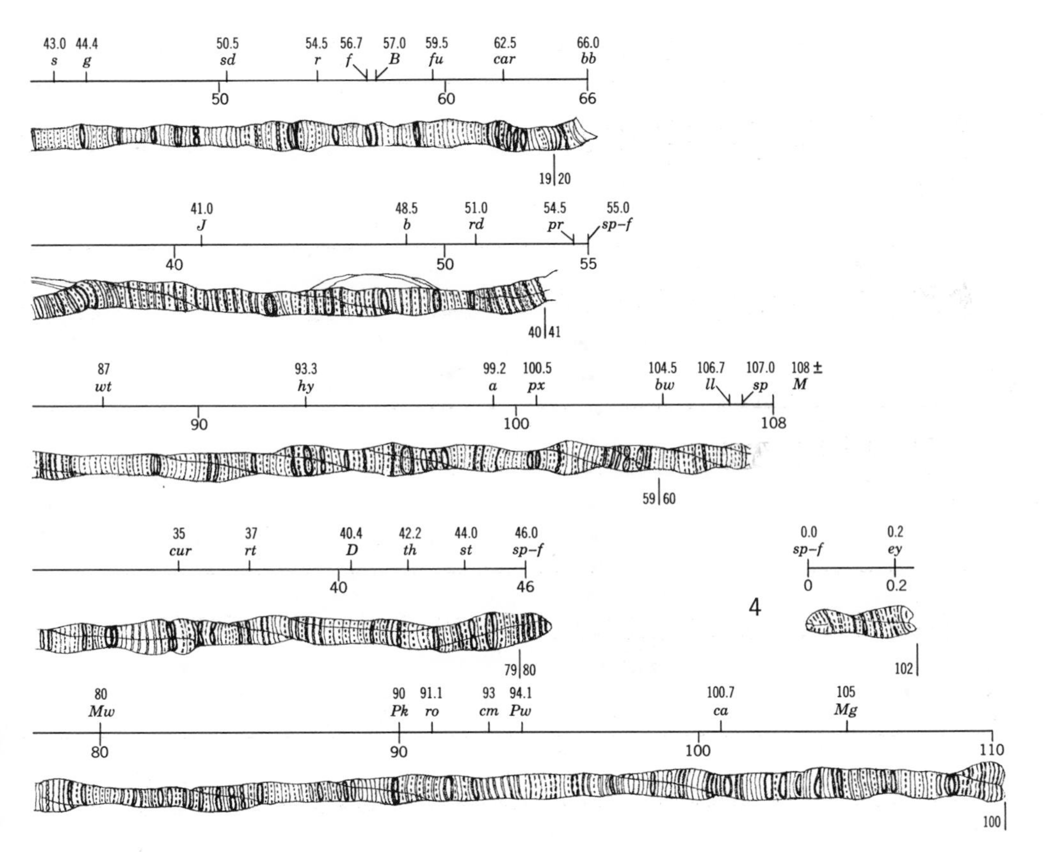


bering system used to identify particular bands is illustrated. (From Bridges, *Journal of Heredity,* **26:**60–64, 1935.)

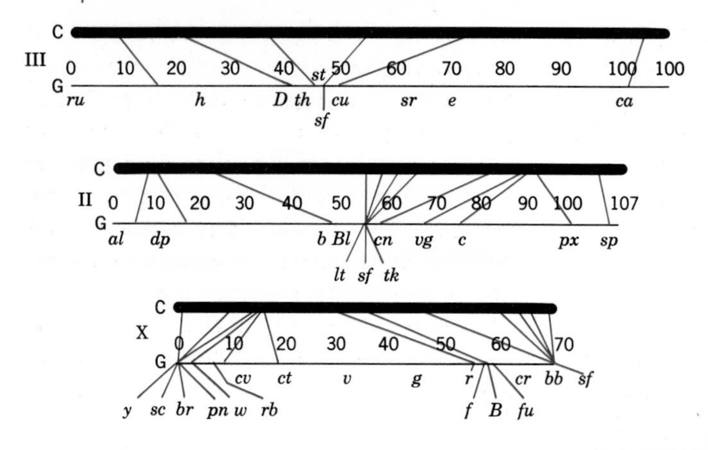


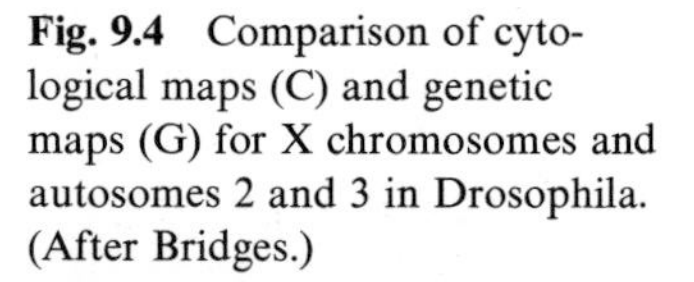
**Fig. 9.4** Comparison of cytological maps (C) and genetic maps (G) for X chromosomes and autosomes 2 and 3 in Drosophila. (After Bridges.)

same species. The difference is that the duplicate strands are held together in bundles through a special process and they do not separate out to new cells through cell division. Giant chromosomes are constructed basically like other chromosomes with DNA and protein in each strand.

Another feature of the giant salivary chromosomes that makes them valuable for study is their continuous state of somatic synapsis. Most homologous chromosomes in somatic cells are not actually paired, and those in germ cells come together in synapsis for only a brief period during the meiotic prophase. Salivary chromosomes, on the other hand, are constantly in synaptic pairs and thus are comparable with chromosomes of the meiotic prophase. If one member of a pair is altered by deficiency, duplication, inversion, or translocation, an irregularity occurs in pairing. Characteristic and observable irregularities make it possible to recognize different kinds of chromosome modifications and to identify their location on the chromosome.

### *Applications of Polytene Chromosomes*

Polytene chromosomes allow comparisons between cytological chromosome maps and linkage data maps. Cytological maps are obtained by placing the genes in their visually observed positions on the chromosome. By contrast, linkage maps are deduced from crossover data. When the two types of maps were prepared for *D. melanogaster,* they were remarkably parallel (Fig. 9.4) except for one major difference. Linkage maps did not include or allow proper spacing in parts of the chromosome where few genes are located and crossing over does not occur at the usual frequency. Parts of chromosomes (heterochromatin) near the spindle fiber attachment regions and some other sections along the chromosomes were found to cross over less frequently than other parts near the free ends of the chromosomes.

In the salivary gland preparations of *D. melanogaster,* the major portion of heterochromatin of all chromosomes coalesces into one central body. In a female cell, a chromocenter is formed when the heterochromatin sections of the four paired chromosomes in the nucleus join together. The entire Y chromosome of the male is included in the chromocenter. When the heterochromatin arrangement is taken into account, salivary gland chromosomes are remarkably similar to chromosomes found elsewhere in larvae or in adult flies. About 5000 single cross bands have been noted on the four pairs of salivary gland chromosomes in *D. melanogaster.* This number is considered a minimum approximation of the number of genes in that animal.

Some genes have been associated with individual bands. Bridges' system (Fig. 9.3) of designating parts of chromosomes with numbers, subdivisions with letters, and numbering bands within subdivisions had made it possible for investigators to discuss precise locations. In this system, fairly uniform divisions are numbered in order throughout each entire chromosome set from 0 at the beginning of the X chromosome to 102 at the end of chromosome 4. Subdivisions within the areas are identified with letters from *A* to *F*, and bands within subdivisions are numbered from left to right. For example, the gene (*w*) for white eyes is in bands 3C 2. In linkage units this gene is located at 1.5 in the X chromosome. Linkage data do not correspond exactly with cytological locations, as shown in Fig. 9.4, but the linear sequence of genes can be verified from salivary preparations.

The main use of polytene chromosomes is the location of genes and the identification of structural changes in the chromosomes. They are also useful for studying effects of environmental agents on chromosomes. M. Diaz and C. Pavan (1965), for example, have demonstrated effects of infection by protozoa and viruses on particular areas of polytene chromosomes. Disintegration of particular sections as compared with uninfected cells and the formation of nucleolarlike bodies were observed. Polytene chromosomes are also used for physiological studies of gene action (mRNA synthesis), which will be discussed in Chapter 15.

Chromosome modifications, particularly missing sections or deficiencies, are useful tools for locating genes on chromosomes. In general, chromosome locations are detected by (1) identifying from microscopic observation the deleted section in the salivary chromosome, and (2) results of appropriate matings. Test matings must be designed in such a way that genes along the chromosome are heterozygous. When recessive genes in such an arrangement express themselves, a plausible explanation is that the region in the homologous chromosome carrying the dominant allele has been deleted. The term *pseudodominance* has been used to describe the expression of a recessive gene that occurs because the dominant allele, which would ordinarily suppress it, is missing.

## DEFICIENCIES

A single break near the end of a chromosome may result in a terminal deficiency. If two breaks occur, a section may be deleted and an intercalary deficiency created. Terminal deficiencies would seem less complicated and more likely to occur than those involving two breaks, but the great majority of deficiencies detected thus far are of the intercalary type; that is, the type inserted within the chromosome. No truly terminal deficiencies have been found in Drosophila, although they have been described in maize. In either type of deficiency, the chromosome set is left without the genes carried in the deleted portion unless the deleted part becomes fused to a chromosome that has a spindle fiber attachment. If a chromosome section becomes detached from the part containing the centromere, it cannot move to the pole of the spindle during cell division. Such a section lags in the dividing cell and is excluded from the chromosome group when the nuclear membrane forms around the chromosomes of a daughter cell.

When an intercalary part of a chromosome is missing, a buckling effect may be observed microscopically in the paired salivary gland chromosomes (Fig. 9.5). The mechanism is illustrated diagrammatically in Fig. 9.6. Large deficiencies are more

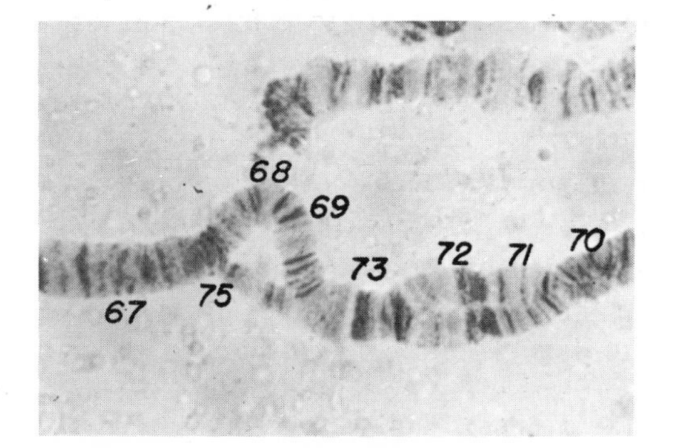


**Fig. 9.5** Salivary gland chromosomes illustrating a heterozygous deficiency of sections 68 and 69. These sections are present in another part of the chromosome, but in the segment shown one member of the pair is deficient. (From C. D. Kastritsis and D. W. Crumpacker, *Journal of Heredity* **58**:1–12, 19, 1967.)

readily detected than small ones, but with good optical equipment and patience on the part of the investigator, it is possible to see single bands of the salivary preparations and thus to identify minute heterozygous deficiencies. By identifying the part of the polytene chromosome in which the buckle occurs and then studying the phenotype of flies carrying a recessive gene in the homologous chromosome opposite the deficiency, it is possible to identify the spatial position of the gene on the chromosome. Chromosome deficiencies have greatly facilitated the checking of linkage maps. Precise locations of many genes on the actual chromosomes are now known in *D. melanogaster* and other species of Diptera because of the effective use of this technique.

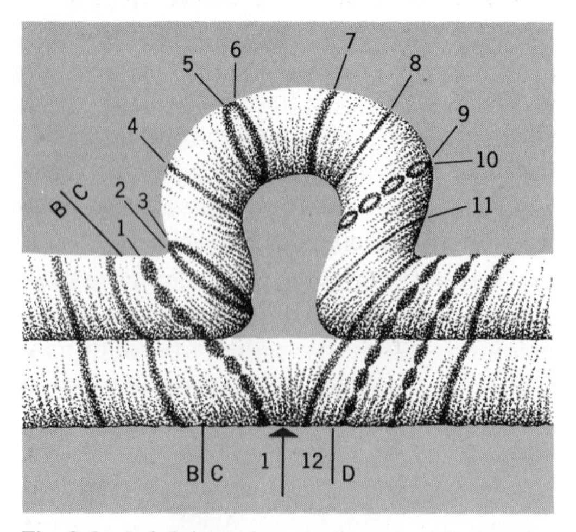


**Fig. 9.6** A deficiency loop in the paired X-chromosomes from a salivary gland cell of a larva heterozygous for *Notch*. Only a short section of the chromosome pair is shown. In this figure, subsection C of section 3 is presented. Note that bands 3C2 through 3C11 are missing from the lower chromosome. (Redrawn from *Principles of Human Genetics,* 2nd edition, by Curt Stern. San Francisco: W. H. Freeman and Company. Copyright © 1960.)

A somatic cell that has lost a small chromosome segment may live and produce other cells like itself, each with a deleted section of a chromosome. Phenotypic effects sometimes indicate which cells or portions of the body have descended from the originally deficient cell. If, on the other hand, the deficient cell is a gamete that is subsequently fertilized by a gamete carrying a nondeficient homologue, all cells of the resulting organism will carry the deficiency in heterozygous condition. Recessive genes in the region of the deficiency but on the nondeficient chromosome may express themselves (pseudodominance). Heterozygous deficiencies usually decrease to some extent the general viability of the flies that carry them. Flies carrying deficiencies in homozygous condition usually die. Some very small homozygous deficiencies, however, have been found to be viable in Drosophila. Such deficiencies are known to occur in the region in which the *w* (white eye) and *fa* (facet eye) genes are located near the end of the X chromosome.

An early example of a deficiency, which illustrates the general characteristics of such chromosome aberrations, was encountered in May 1916 by Bridges. A sex-linked lethal that arose in a culture of *D. melanogaster* was shown from linkage data to be in the region of the recessive gene *v* for vermilion colored eyes (at 33 units from the left end of the X chromosome). When females heterozygous for the lethal were outcrossed to vermilion males, all the daughters receiving the chromosome from the mother carrying the lethal had vermilion eyes. Since the gene ($v$) was recessive and the mothers were known not to carry it, the lethal was presumed to be a deficiency that included the $v$ locus and carried the wild type allele ($v^+$). Expression of the vermilion phenotype was attributed to pseudodominance. The $v$ gene, which came to expression in the females, originated with the males, and no $v^+$ allele was contributed from the mother to offset the expression of vermilion. The lethal action in homozygous condition and pseudodominance of $v$ when the chromosomes were heterozygous suggested that a chromosome segment had been lost, that is, that a deficiency had occurred.

Other sex-linked genes in the vicinity of $v$, including *tb* (tiny bristles) at 35.8 and *m* (miniature wings) at 36.1, failed to show pseudodominance. Therefore these loci were outside the area covered by the deficiency. At the time these studies were made, salivary gland chromosomes were not yet being used as tools for identifying chromosome sections with genes. Bridges attempted to locate the deficiency on the chromosomes of gonadal cells but was unable to do so. He did, however, postulate from evidence suggesting the shortening of the linkage map that this deficiency occupied one to three linkage units. The salivary chromosome technique has made it possible to identify precisely such deficient areas.

A deficiency in a mammal was reported by W. H. Gates in connection with a study of so called "waltzing mice." A recessive gene ($v$) was known to produce a peculiar nervous abnormality. Mice carrying the gene in homozygous condition would move about erratically until they became exhausted. Homozygous strains of waltzing mice are maintained in many laboratories in which genetic studies are conducted. When waltzers ($vv$) are mated with normal homozygous ($v^+v^+$) mice, no waltzers are expected in the immediate progeny because the gene $v^+$ is dominant over $v$. Large numbers of such matings were made by Gates and others, and, as expected, no waltzers appeared.

In one litter of seven however, resulting from a cross between a homozygous normal female and a waltzer male, Gates observed one waltzer female. This cross is illustrated diagrammatically as cross 1, Fig. 9.7. When the $F_1$ waltzer was mated (cross 2) successively with two different waltzer males, eleven progeny were obtained, all of which were waltzers. The same $F_1$ waltzer female later produced three litters by normal males (cross 3). A total of thirteen progeny was obtained. All the individuals were normal. Finally, this $F_1$ female was mated to her son (cross 4), known from appropriate tests to carry one $v^+$ gene. From this mating, seven young were produced, five normal and two waltzers. These results were explained on the basis of a deficiency including the $v$ locus, which originated in the female of cross 1 and was transmitted to her daughter. A deficiency recently discovered in man has been associated with the cri-du-chat (or cat-like cry) syndrome. Major symptoms expressed in children are a cat-like cry and microcephally (small head and low mentality). The deficiency includes part of the short arm of chromosome No. 5 (see Figs. 10.9 and 10.20).

## DUPLICATIONS

Duplications represent additions of chromosome parts arranged in such a way that sections are longitudinally repeated. They provide a means for studying the effects of different numbers and arrange-

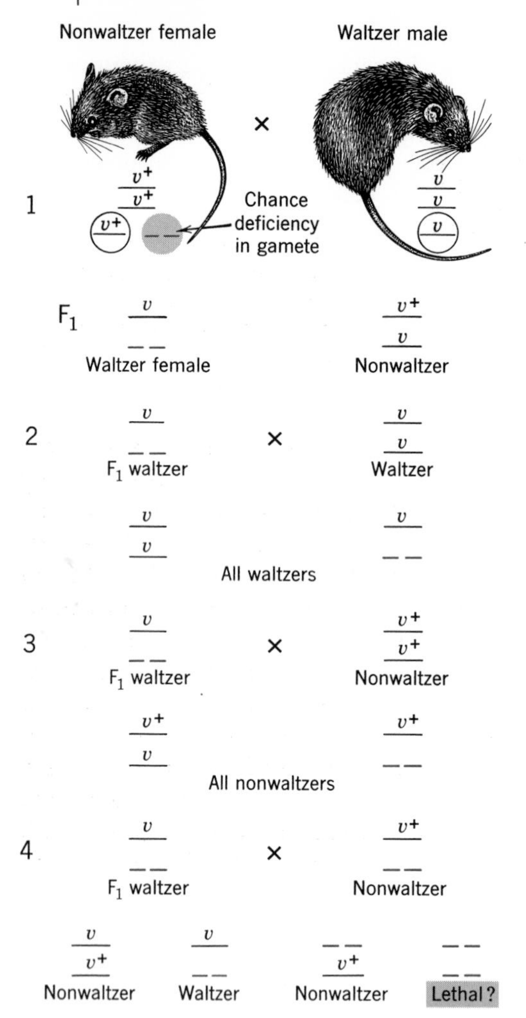


**Fig. 9.7** Diagram of cross between a female nonwaltzer and a male waltzer mouse and successive crosses between an $F_1$ female and different males. Results indicated that a chromosome deficiency had occurred. (After W. H. Gates.)

ments of chromosome segments or genes that otherwise occur only singly or in allelic pairs. Some chromosome segments behave as dominants with respect to certain phenotypes and some as recessives. Others show intermediate inheritance and still others have cumulative effects. Duplications provide a means for determining effects of chromosome segments when three, four, or more similar sections are present in individual animals or plants. In 1919, Bridges found a case in Drosophila in which a presumably homozygous recessive gene did not express itself, and he postulated that a dominant allele was located elsewhere in the chromosome set.

The first duplication to be critically examined involved the *B* (*bar*) locus in the X chromosome of Drosophila. In the presence of a single *B* (heterozygous), the eye is somewhat smaller than the normal eye (Fig. 9.8), and the sides are straighter, giving an oblong or bar appearance. In the homozygous condition, the eye is considerably smaller. Bridges and Muller discovered independently that the bar phenotype was the result of a duplication involving a part of the X chromosome already present in the wild-type flies. They were able to observe not only the effect of a duplication producing bar eye, but also a reduplication resulting in an extreme decrease in the size of the eye, which was called "double bar." By using the salivary chromosome technique, they located segments of the chromosome actually involved in the duplication. The different phenotypes and the corresponding segments of the salivary gland chromosome pairs are illustrated in Fig. 9.9. Section 16*A* is present in flies with the wild-type eye. When this section is duplicated, it produces the bar phenotype. When the segment is reduplicated in such a way that section 16*A* is represented three times in a single chromosome, the double-bar phenotype results.

A quantitative relation was observed between the number of chromosome segments (16*A*) and the size of the eye. Each additional duplicate segment made the eye smaller. Other duplications have since been found in Drosophila which work in the opposite direction suppressing the effects of mutant genes and making the fly appear more normal with respect to certain traits. Further studies demonstrated that duplications need not be perpetuated

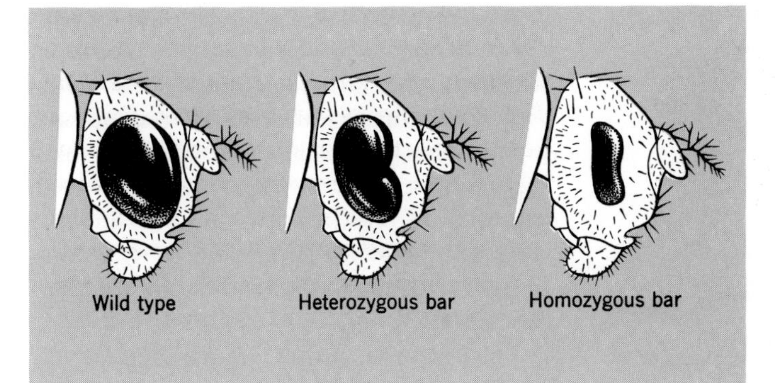


**Fig. 9.8** Bar eye of *Drosophila melanogaster* compared with wild type. (Left) Wild-type eye; (center) bar eye of a heterozygous (B/+) female; (right) homozygous (B/B) female.

in the immediate vicinity of the section duplicated to exert an influence. Sometimes chromosome fragments become attached to entirely different chromosomes. Through assortment of such chromosomes in the gametes, duplications may be carried to succeeding generations.

## INVERSIONS

Inversions occur when parts of chromosomes become detached and reinserted in such a way that the genes are in reversed order. Some inversions presumably result from entanglements of the threads during the meiotic prophase and chromosome breaks that occur at that time. For example, a certain segment may be broken in two places and the two breaks may be in close proximity because of a loop in the chromosome. When they rejoin, the wrong ends may become connected. The part on one side of the loop connects with a broken end different from the one with which it formerly connected. This leaves the other two broken ends to become attached, as illustrated in Fig. 9.10. The part within

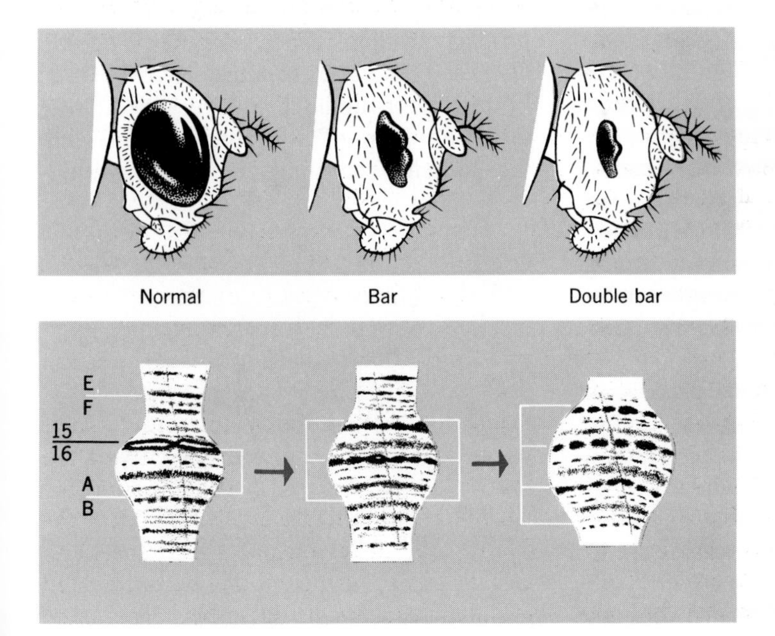


**Fig. 9.9** Diagrammatic representation of wild-type eye, bar and double bar in *Drosophila melanogaster* above corresponding chromosome segments as seen in salivary gland preparations. (After Bridges.)

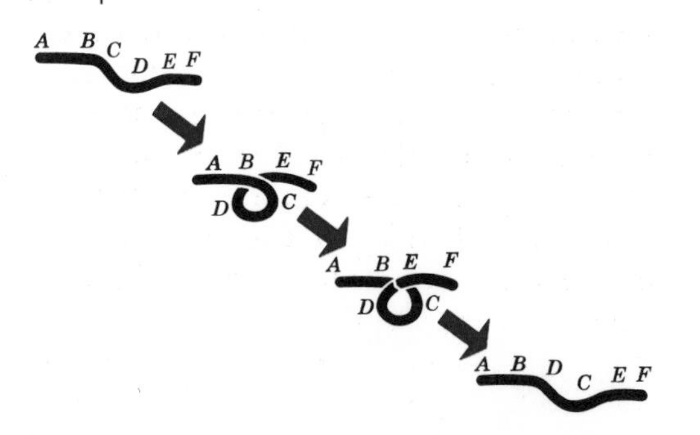


**Fig. 9.10** Diagram illustrating the mechanism by which some inversions might be produced.

the loop thus becomes turned around or inverted. It is not known whether all inversions occur in this way, but this is a plausible explanation for many chromosome inversions.

Inversions may be perpetuated in the pairing process at meiosis and segregated into viable gametes. As indicated in earlier chapters, chromosome pairing is essential to the production of fertile gametes. The mechanism by which homologous chromosomes heterozygous for inversions accomplish such pairing in the meiotic sequence is remarkable. The part of the uninverted chromosome corresponding to the inversion forms a loop. A similar loop is formed by the inverted section of the homologous chromosome but in reverse direction. For example, if the loop of the uninverted section is formed with the gene sequence in a clockwise direction, the inverted part will form in a counter clockwise direction. In this way, corresponding parts come together even though one of the sections is inverted, as illustrated diagrammatically in Fig. 9.11.

Inversions have been associated with the suppression of crossing over. Before Drosophila chromosomes were studied extensively, investigators had already identified genetic crossover suppressors in this organism. These were first considered to be genes that somehow interfered with crossing over. It was later shown that the locations of inversions and crossover suppressors coincided and that the apparent suppression of crossing over was associated directly with inversions. It was shown further that the main process was not a suppression of crossing over, although instances of physical crossing over may be reduced. The principal effect was that crossover gametes that did occur were not recovered.

The mechanism through which an inversion can remove the crossover gametes has been described in chromosomes with the centromere outside the inverted area (paracentric; Fig. 9.12) and in those with the centromere inside the loop (pericentric; Fig. 9.13). As shown in the illustrations, chromosomes that carry paracentric inversions cannot cross over within the loop without producing fragments of chromosomes lacking centromeres (acentric) and chromosome complexes with two centromeres (dicentric). These result either in fragments that lag in the center of the spindle, or chromatid bridges that tie together the two homologues involved and interfere with the division process. In either case, chromosomes do not separate properly to their respective poles. The fate of these cells varies in animals and plants. Following a single crossover within the inversion loop of a maturing plant cell, the gametes receiving crossover chroma-

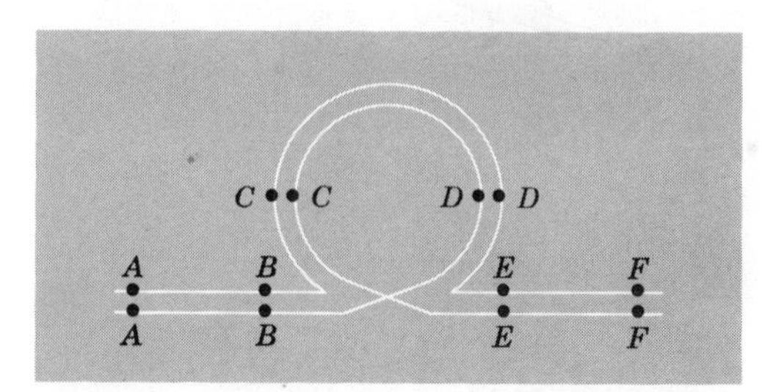


**Fig. 9.11** Diagram representing a pairing of an uninverted chromosome with a chromosome in which an inversion has occurred. A loop may be observed in salivary gland preparations of flies which carry heterozygous inversions.

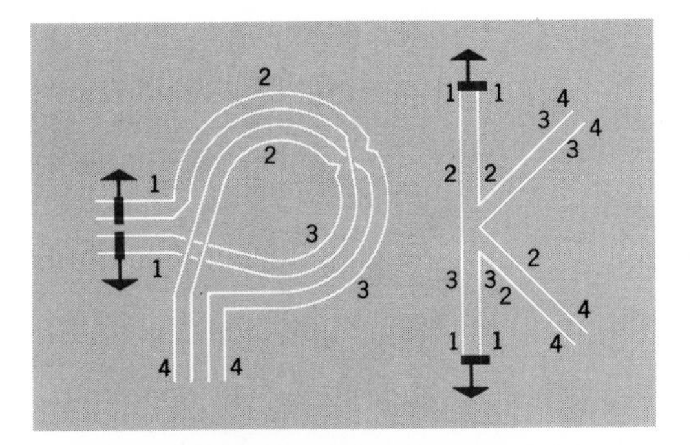


**Fig. 9.12** Diagram of meiotic metaphase and anaphase illustrating mechanism through which a paracentric inversion acts as a "crossover suppressor." Dicentric (1 2 3 1) and acentric (4 3 2 4) chromosomes, which are also unbalanced, are formed by crossover chromatids.

tids are inviable. If no gametes receiving crossover chromatids survive, crossing over is effectively suppressed. In animals, unbalanced zygotes produced by abnormal gametes die, thus eliminating crossover chromatids from the members of the population.

An imbalance of chromosome parts resulting from crossing over in the presence of pericentric inversions causes gamete inviability. Irregular unbalanced chromosomes are produced by crossing over in the inverted area. One of the chromatids illustrated (Fig. 9.13) has chromosome parts designated as 1 2 3 1 instead of 1 2 3 4. Another chromatid has 4 3 2 4

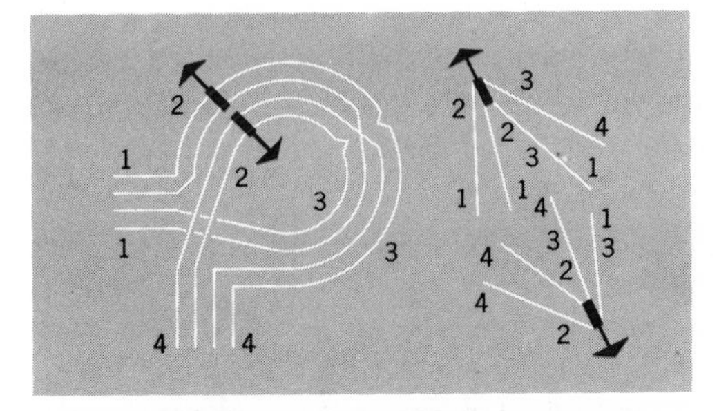


**Fig. 9.13** Diagram illustrating the "crossover suppressor" action of a pericentric inversion. The resulting chromatids are out of balance and therefore zygotic lethals result.

instead of 1 3 2 4, which would be the sequence for the inverted chromosome. This chromosome irregularity is associated with genic imbalance. Most of the crossover chromatids result in inviable gametes or zygotes. Therefore, the number of crossover gametes recovered is greatly reduced. The apparent suppressing effect of inversions on crossing over can thus be explained mostly on the basis of secondary results that follow crossing over in inverted segments.

Polytene chromosomes of Drosophila have been especially useful in detecting heterozygous inversions. A characteristic loop in these chromosomes is illustrated by an actual photograph in Fig. 9.14. Loops in giant chromosomes of salivary gland tissues presumably resemble those in meiotic prophase chromosomes where observation is much more difficult.

Chromosomes with inversions have practical application in maintaining Drosophila stocks. They are used as balancers, that is, chromosomes that can be placed opposite homologous chromosomes carrying certain genes that are homozygous inviable or lethal. Crossing over is suppressed in such chromosomes and it is possible to maintain a gene heterozygous, which could not be kept in homozygous condition. In laboratory stocks carrying several mutants, it is advantageous to keep the chromosomes intact without crossing over. However, because recessive genes are not expressed when they are in heterozygous condition, frequent checks must be made to insure against loss of the gene from the stock. Appropriate outcrosses are conducted occasionally to check for the presence of the gene or genes in the stock. The mechanism through which some laboratory stocks are kept balanced and heterozygous was discussed in Chapter 7 under "Balanced Lethal Mutations."

J. T. Patterson and W. S. Stone have shown that differences in chromosome

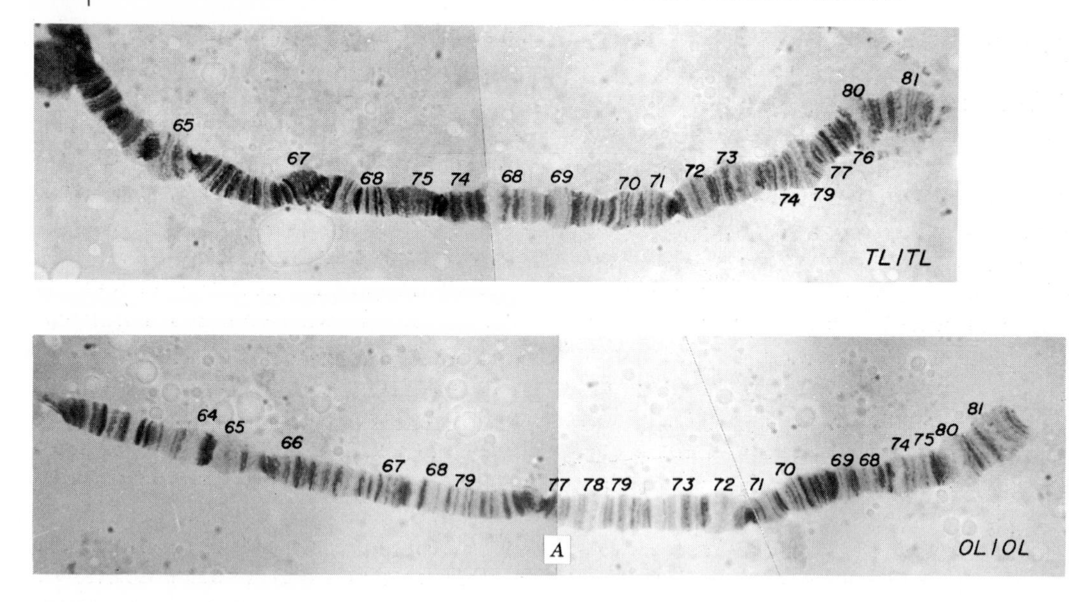


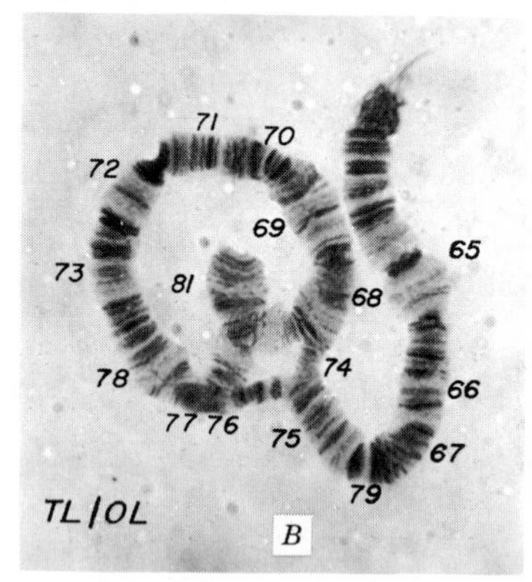


**Fig. 9.14** Salivary gland chromosomes illustrating an inversion. *A*, homozygous chromosomes TL/TL and OL/OL. *B*, heterozygote, TL/OL with inversion loop. (Courtesy C. D. Kastritsis and D. W. Crumpaker and *Journal* of *Heredity* **58:**113–130, 1967.)

complements between different races and different species of Drosophila depend on the number, extent, and location of inversions. Inversions have evidently occurred spontaneously in nature and have become established in populations. Furthermore, the degree of separation between taxonomic groups is correlated with the number of inversions present. Whether this is true in organisms other than Drosophila is not known. No other group has been studied as completely as Drosophila, and further observations are necessary before comparisons can be drawn.

## TRANSLOCATIONS

Sometimes parts of chromosomes become detached and reunited with nonhomologous chromosomes. These rearrangements are called translocations. The definition has been extended to include exchanges between different nonhomologous parts of the same chromosome pair. Exchanges between the X and Y chromosomes, for example, are considered to be translocations. Reciprocal translocations occur when parts of chromosomes belonging to members of two different pairs become exchanged. Part of chromosome I, for example, may be detached from its linkage group and attached to chromosome II, while the part removed from chromosome II becomes attached to chromosome I. Reciprocal translocations have been described in a number of plants and are important factors in the evolution of certain plant groups, for example, Datura and Oenothera. Translocations do not ordinarily involve a loss or an addition of chromosome material but only rearrangements of chromosome parts that were already present. They reduce crossing over mainly by interfering with chromosome pairing.

Translocations can be detected from genetic data by noting altered linkage arrangements brought about by exchanges of parts between different chromosomes. If, for example, gene *a* is ordinarily linked with *b* and *c*, following translocation it may be linked with *s* and *t*, which are ordinarily in a different linkage group. It should be noted here that evidence such as this based on translocations provides further support for the theory that genes are in chromosomes. Historically, evidence from this source, along with the studies of nondisjunction and other observations, supported the chromosome theory of inheritance.

Another indication of heterozygous translocations is pollen or ovule sterility. The reason for the sterility is that some kinds of gametes possible from a plant carrying a heterozygous translocation are unbalanced and inviable. Such plants are called "semisterile." The imbalance causing the sterility occurs when chromosomes separate to the poles in meiosis. Some gametes are deficient in chromosome parts and some carry duplications.

Cytological evidence for translocations can be obtained from microscopic studies of polytene chromosomes in Drosophila and meiotic prophase stages in plant materials. A translocation between the second and third chromosomes in *Drosophila melanogaster* is illustrated from salivary chromosomes in Fig. 9.15. The cross configuration marked by arrows is a characteristic cytological pattern for translocations. Pollen mother cells carrying heterozygous translocations show rings of four or more chromosomes instead of regular pairs. New structural arrangements created by the translocations result in particular configurations. Homologous parts pair together, and if homologous parts happen to be located on entirely different chromosomes, these chromosomes are held together during synapsis.

Characteristics of translocations and a method of detecting them are illustrated further from an actual study on barley. The alleles ($r^+$ and $r$) for rough and smooth awns and those ($s^+$ and $s$) for long and short rachilla hairs are in linkage group 7. Alleles ($n^+$ and $n$) for hulled and hull-less and those ($l^+$ and $l$) for lax and club head are in group I. When the progeny of a certain plant were classified, the results indicated that *s* was linked with *n*. This genetic evidence suggested that a translocation joining chromosomes 1 and 7 had occurred. When the plants were observed in the field and studied in the laboratory, at least 30 percent of the pollen was found to be sterile. Further investigations showed that many ovules also were sterile. Cytological studies of pollen mother cells (Fig. 9.16), showed one quadripartite ring and five bivalents instead of the seven bivalents usually observed in barley preparations. This cytological evidence demonstrated that a reciprocal translocation had occurred. The explanation for the altered linkage grouping and semisterility, and the mechanism of gamete and zygote formation involving the chromosomes carrying the translocation are illustrated in Fig. 9.17.

It has been demonstrated in some plants

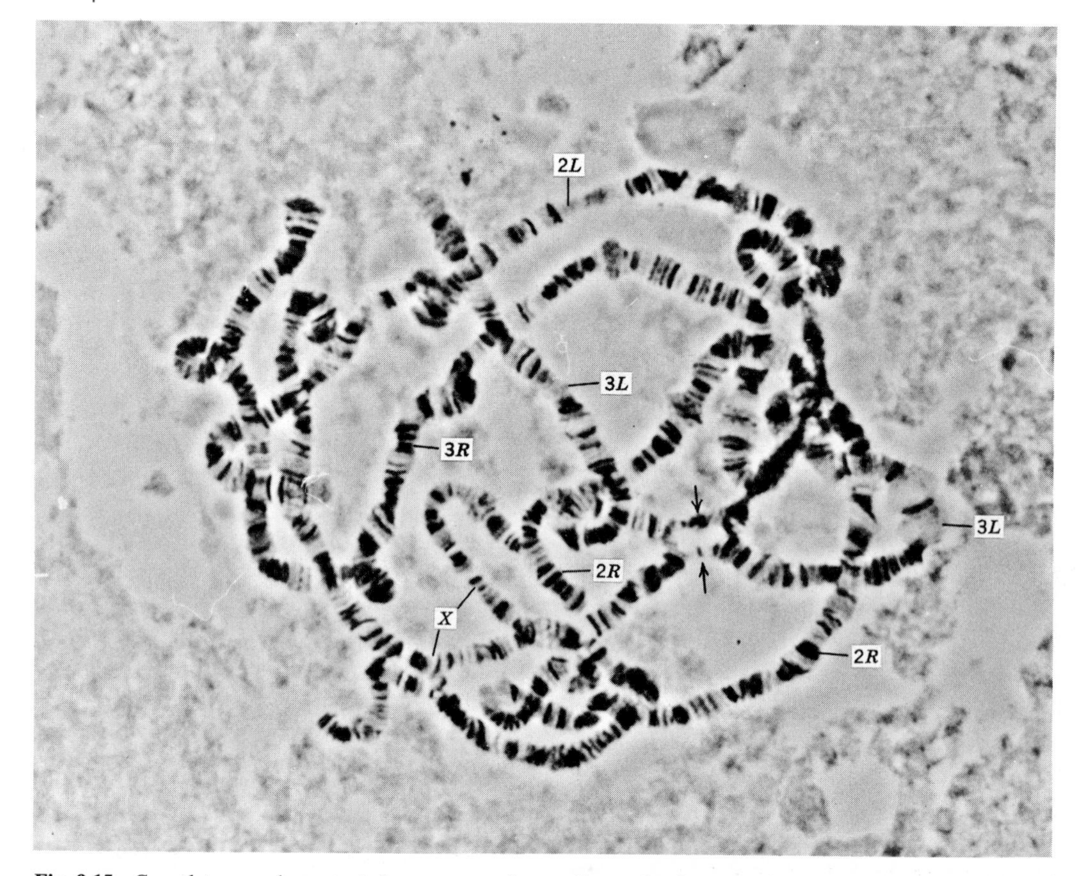


**Fig. 9.15** Complete complement of chromosomes from salivary gland preparation of *Drosophila melanogaster* showing a translocation between the right arm of chromosome 2 and the left arm of chromosome 3. Break points are marked with arrows. Chromosomes are identified as follows: left arm of 2nd, 2L, right arm of 2nd, 2R, left arm of 3rd, 3L, right arm of 3rd, 3R. X chromosome, X. (Courtesy of Burke H. Judd.)

that complex groupings of chromosomes result from this type of rearrangement. In the pairing that occurs in meiosis, chromosomes and chromosome parts must find their mates and pair properly. If the mate of a certain chromosome segment happens to be translocated to a nonhomologous chromosome, these two chromosomes will be held together during pairing. Rings and sometimes chains of chromosomes are thus produced. This is the probable explanation for the chromosome complex that occurred in the evening primrose (Oenothera), which was studied by Hugo de Vries and which permitted him to elaborate the mutation theory (Chapter 7).

Only a relatively small number of plants and animals have been studied cytologically. On the basis of these studies, however, it would seem that translocations occur and become established more commonly in plants, whereas inversions, judging by the Drosophila data, are more common among animals.

Many of the examples used here to illustrate structural modifications of chromosomes have come from plants such as maize where the chromosomes are large,

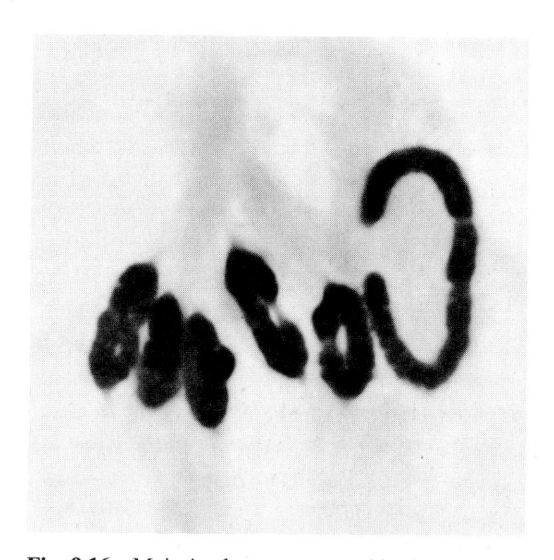

**Fig. 9.16** Meiotic chromosomes of barley translocation. Five bivalents and 1 possessing a reciprocal quadrivalent are evident. (Courtesy of W. S. Boyle.)

comparatively few in number, and lend themselves well to cytological investigation. The giant polytene chromosomes of diptera have made these insects especially useful for cytogenetic studies. Examples could be cited in many other higher plants and animals, and a large body of cytological data is accumulating for molds, yeasts, and protozoa.

## POSITION EFFECTS

When a chromosome rearrangement involves no change in the amount of genetic material, but only in the order of the genes, the term *position effect* is used to describe any associated phenotypic alterations. Along with gene mutations, position effects represent a source of genetic variation; however, the extent to which chromosome rearrangements such as inversions and translocations are associated with new phenotypic variation is open to question. In this regard, it must be remembered that chromosome modifications, particularly inversions, curtail recombination and thus would be expected generally to restrict genetic variation.

Nevertheless, several well-established position effects are on record. The first came from the work done by Sturtevant and Bridges on the bar-eye duplication in Drosophila (Fig. 9.18). They found a quantitative relation between the number of chromosome sections (16*A*) present and the size of the eye. Further critical experi-

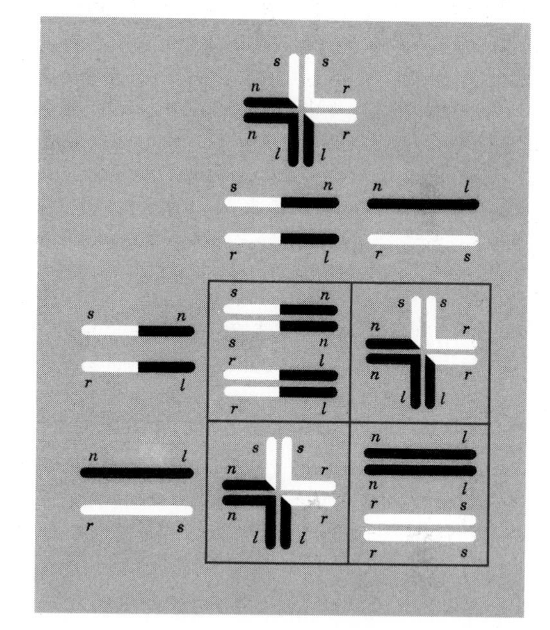

**Fig. 9.17** Diagram illustrating explanation developed to account for the results of barley crosses. A reciprocal translocation had occurred between chromosomes 1 and 7, bringing the genes *n* and *s* into the same linkage group. The crosslike configuration at the top of the diagram represents the pairing of the translocated chromosomes (only 2 of the 4 strands are shown). Two viable male and 2 viable female gametes of the selfed plant are represented at the top and left, respectively, of the checkerboard square. In the 4 squares of the checkerboard, some zygotes from the selfed plant are illustrated with the chromosomes as they would appear at synapsis. The 2 zygotes which have crosslike configurations are heterozygous for the translocation and produce plants which are partially sterile, i.e., semisteriles, because of the deficiencies and duplications of chromosome parts occurring in the gametes. (Data from R. W. Woodward and W. S. Boyle.)

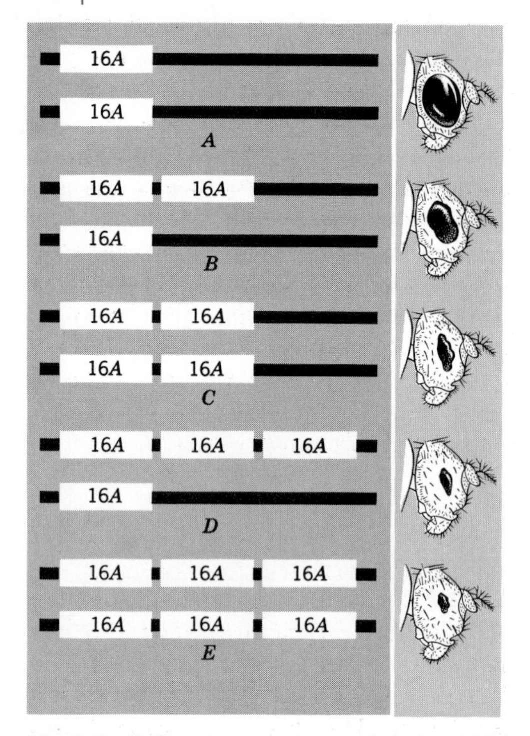


**Fig. 9.18** Different arrangements of section 16*A* in *D. melanogaster* X chromosome and resulting phenotypes. *A*, wild-type female; *B*, bar female, heterozygous; *C*, bar female, homozygous; *D*, double-bar female, heterozygous showing position effect; *E*, double-bar homozygous. (After Morgan, Sturtevant, and Bridges.)

ments, however, showed that it is not a strictly proportional relation. The arrangement of the chromosome segments with respect to each other, as well as their presence or absence, influences the size of the eye. When section 16*A* was duplicated in such a way that two extra similar sections were present side by side in the same chromosome, the effect was different from that produced by one extra segment in each member of the pair (homozygous). The effect of different arrangements was demonstrated by manipulating the chromosomes through appropriate matings and counting the facets in the eyes of the resulting female flies.

When section 16*A* was duplicated and the extra segment occurred in homozygous condition (Fig. 9.18*C*), the number of facets in the eyes averaged 68. When the same chromosome parts were present, but the sections 16*A* were side by side (Fig. 9.18*D*), however, the eyes averaged 45 facets. When the sections were homozygous (Fig. 9.18*E*), small eyes with an average of 25 facets occurred and were called "ultra-bar" eyes. The difference between (Figs. 9.18*C* and 9.18*D*) depends not on the presence or absence of certain genes, but rather on the arrangement of position of the genes with respect to each other. Therefore, the phenomenon was interpreted as a position effect.

Several well-established and many possible position effects have now been described in Drosophila, but the mechanism involved required further investigation. E. B. Lewis has shown that all known position effects fall into two classes: (1) stable and (2) variegated. Stable position effects are uniform phenotypic effects resulting from changes of specific segments of chromosomes. The bar-eye position effect is an example. Variegated position effects result in the diversification of a trait usually evidenced in a particular structure or area of the body. Specks of different colors, for example, may occur in the eyes of Drosophila following rearrangements of the *w* (white eye) locus. Inversions or translocations that place $w^+$ near heterochromatin may cause white variegation or mosaicism for eye color.

Several eye-color combinations depending on genotype and environmental conditions have resulted from different experiments with Drosophila. In some cases, red color patches occur on a light background and, in others, light patches occur on a red background. Variegated-type position effects in Drosophila are associated with chromosome structural changes in which a gene or chromosome area in euchromatin is transferred to a region in or near heterochromatin. Some chemical anomaly is apparently associated with the change in position of chromosome segments.

In general, if a euchromatin segment is relocated by chromosome structural change next to heterochromatin, activity of its genes will be depressed. Action of a gene normally occurring in a heterochromatin region will also be depressed if the gene is moved to a euchromatin region. Because gene action is altered by moves in both directions, the established chemical environment to which a gene is adjusted rather than a direct effect from heterochromatin would seem to be involved. This explanation of position effects was supported by experiments of H. J. Becker on Drosophila eye development. With X-rays he induced mitotic exchanges of eye-color genes at time intervals during development. Because each affected sector was made up of the cell progeny of a single cell carrying an exchange product, it was possible to trace the developmental sequence of the tissue composing the eye. Becker then induced structural changes in chromosomes and found that alterations in the position of genes created position effects that appeared the same phenotypically as the results of X-ray disturbance, which had been induced. The interpretation was that either X-ray disturbance or chromosome modification or perhaps any kind of alteration of genetic structure with reference to chemical background would result in mosaic sectors in variegated eyes.

The explanation for this type of position effect is based on the movement of the gene to an altered or different chemical environment following rearrangement. This implies that a gene is not completely independent in producing its effects, but rather that the action (or end products) of a given gene is influenced by its neighboring genes or chromosome environment.

Most of the evidence thus far obtained on variegated-type position effects has come from Drosophila, but similar phenomena probably occur in Oenothera and some other plants. Catcheside has described a case in Oenothera in which a gene ($P^5$) that produces broad red and narrow green stripes on the sepals was translocated to a different chromosome. Variegated patches of red occurred in place of the broad red stripe. This situation may be similar to those described in Drosophila. Other possible examples of variegated-type position effects have been suggested in Datura and maize.

## ALTERATIONS IN FINE STRUCTURE OF THE GENE

The Russian geneticist N. P. Dubinin (in 1939) recognized step allelism (that is, the graded effect of different alleles) in Drosophila. This discovery foreshadowed the idea that "genes" could be subdivided. Tangible evidence for compound or complex loci became available when it was shown that certain chromosome areas in Drosophila, formerly considered to be single genetic units, could be subdivided by crossing over. Complex loci have now been discovered in Neurospora, maize, and several other higher organisms as well as in bacteria and viruses. Complex gene structure may be basic to all organisms.

Investigations demonstrating subdivisions of the gene began in 1940, when C. P. Oliver obtained unexpected results from a cross between Drosophila mutants carrying the genes $lz^g$ and $lz^s$, which were presumed to be alleles and which had been represented in exactly corresponding positions on a chromosome pair $\frac{(lz^g)}{(lz^s)}$. All progeny from this cross were expected to have the characteristic (lozenge) phenotype, which is a narrow ovoid eye (Fig. 9.19), but a few were wild type. It was then

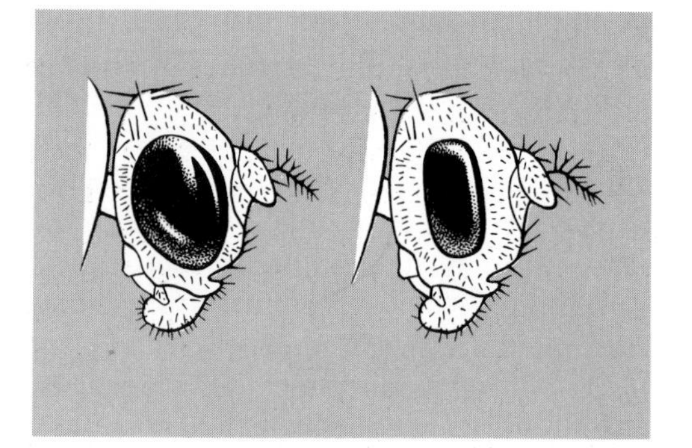

**Fig. 9.19** Lozenge eye in Drosophila. (Left) Wild type eye, (right) lozenge eye.

postulated that the two genes were not in identical positions on homologous chromosomes but were located in slightly different areas, $\frac{lz^g +}{+ lz^s}$. Crossovers had presumably occurred, placing $lz^g$ and $lz^s$ on the same homologue $\frac{lz^g\ lz^s}{+\ +}$ and each in heterozygous condition. M. M. and K. C. Green pursued the investigation of the *lz* locus and showed that at least three recombinational units, shown diagrammatically in Fig. 9.20 with their combination effects, were separable by crossing over. Markers representing these segments were symbolized as $lz^{BS}$, $lz^{46}$, and $lz^g$, and at first were described as pseudoalleles occupying slightly different positions on the chromosome. Several different states of the same genetic unit, which could not be separated by crossing over, were recognized in each of the three sites. Vermilion *v* and forked *f* loci were later found to be complexes of closely linked sites which ordinarily behaved as traditional alleles but were separable very infrequently by crossing over.

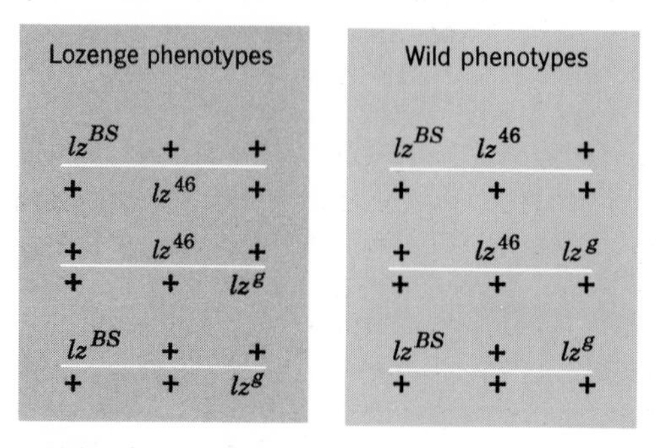


**Fig. 9.20** Diagram illustrating combinations at the *lz* complex locus in Drosophila with the phenotypes of various combinations. (After M. M. Green and K. C. Green.)

The area of the first chromosome where the genes for white and apricot eye color are located was found by several investigators to be a complex of five sites. The gene for apricot eye color was previously considered to be an allele of the gene *w* for white eye and was originally symbolized $w^a$. When flies with white eyes were mated with those having apricot eyes, the eye color of the $F_2$ generation showed simple monohybrid ratios expected for a single sex-linked gene. The two genes were not separated by early crossover tests and there was no reason to question their allelic relationship with each other. When large experiments involving thousands of flies were conducted with improved techniques, however, the loci for white and apricot were separated and the symbol for the apricot gene was changed to *apr*. A few individuals from crosses that ordinarily produced only apricot and white were found to have wild-type red eyes. These were explained on the basis of crossing over. With accumulated crossover data, the distance between the two sites was placed at about 0.01. It has now been shown that recombinations occur between *apr* and $apr^4$, indicating that these presumed alleles occupy different sites.

To test the hypothesis of complex loci, as opposed to the possible mutation explanation, markers were placed on either side of the area in which the white (*w*) and apricot (*apr*) genes were located and further crosses were made. The gene *y* for yellow body color, at 1.5 units on one side of *w*, and the gene *spl* for split bristles, located at 1.5 units on the other side, were

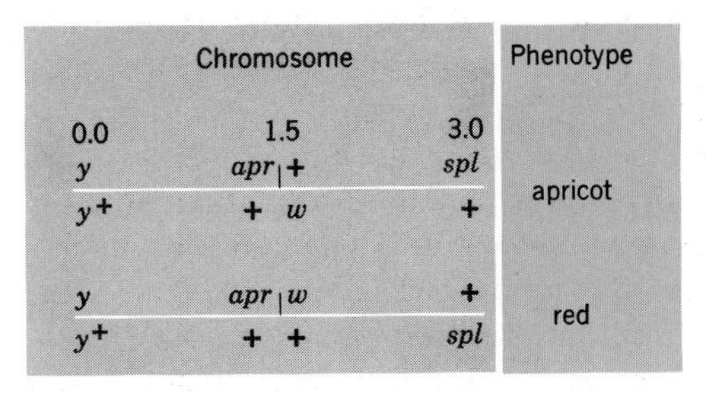


**Fig. 9.21** Diagram showing the two arrangements of the sites, *w* and *apr*, and the phenotypic effects. (After E. B. Lewis.)

placed in the chromosomes in heterozygous condition. These outside markers were found to change places in the exceptional red-eyed flies demonstrating that crossing over had actually occurred and bringing the two wild-type genes together on the same homologue, as illustrated in Fig. 9.21. When the *w* and *apr* genes were together on the same chromosome and the wild (+) alleles were on the homologous chromosome (*cis* arrangement), the eyes were red. When the two mutant genes were opposite each other (*trans* arrangement), the eyes were apricot.

## COMPLEX LOCI AND COMPLEMENTARITY IN PRODUCTION OF PHENOTYPES

Why did the *w* and *apr* genes behave differently in different positions? There is no direct answer to this question at present, but one hypothesis is that the production of red pigment is a two-step chemical process. One gene may control one step while the other gene in close proximity may control another step in the reaction. When the two genes $w^+$ and $apr^+$ occur next to each other on the same chromosome, they produce the normal red eye color. When they are opposite each other, however, chemical blocks occur that stop the reaction at one or more points. This is a type of position effect because the position of the genes with respect to each other rather than their presence or absence determines the end result.

Several other cases of complex loci have been demonstrated or suggested in Drosophila, which include the following loci: *bx* (bithorax), *Sb* (stubble bristles), *N* (notch wing), *g* (garnet eye color), *sn* (singed bristles), *dp* (dumpy wing), and *S* (star, an eye shape and surface character).

Experimental materials other than Drosophila have now provided demonstrations of complex loci. Many biochemical mutants are available in Neurospora, and special tools have been devised to facilitate investigations. Numerous mutants can be induced and detected by irradiating spores and sorting out mutants with filtration and plating techniques. Mutations influencing a particular phenotype may then be grouped and analyzed together.

Another evidence of complex loci, that of complementarity in production of phenotypes, has been explored in these investigations. Complementary interaction between alleles indicates complex loci even when recombination between them has not been observed. Tests have been developed to determine which mutants within a given locus will complement each other and produce wild types. A test is accomplished by mating different mutant types and observing the phenotypes in the progeny. When data from appropriate crosses were analyzed, much information suggesting complex loci was obtained. The *Td* region in *Neurospora crassa,* for example, which controls the final step in tryptophan synthesis, has been shown to be a complex of several sites in linear order.

Complex loci have been reported in maize at the *A* locus, which controls pigment production; the *R* locus, which controls pigmentation; and the *wx* locus, which influences the nutritive content of the seed. In the wasp, Mormoniella, a complex similar to that of the *R* locus in maize has been discovered. Complex loci have been found in cotton and suggested in mice and pigeons. Impressive demonstrations have also been made in yeast and in the bacterium, Salmonella.

Five sites, for example, have been located in the cystine *C* locus of Salmonella. When outside markers were introduced with appropriate crosses (by transduction) of Salmonella, the results suggested that crossing over, similar to that indicated in the apricot eye-color study in Drosophila, had occurred. Selective media techniques and large numbers of organisms available from crosses have made it possible to study complex loci much more efficiently in bacteria and in viruses than in higher forms, as shown in Chapter 12.

The discovery of possible complex loci in a wide variety of plants and animals has made it necessary to once again reconsider the definition of a gene. It is no longer sufficient to define the gene in general terms like a bead on a string or a discrete body separated by distinct boundaries on the chromosome. Chromosome areas must now be visualized as groups or clusters of sites capable of complementarity in function and separation by crossing over. Sizes and numbers of genes are no longer central questions in genetics because the nucleotide of the Watson and Crick model has become the basic unit. More and more refined techniques have revealed subsections of subsections in the fine structure of the gene, but the ultimate relation between the chromosome locus in higher organisms and DNA remains unknown. Even though complications arise when attempts are made to define the gene in all of its aspects, the gene concept is a good one and it should be retained. It is only necessary to indicate the level or order of magnitude of the DNA unit, when the term is used. The unit in the physical world, the atom, has now been subdivided, but the concept of the atom remains useful and valid. Similarly, in the biological world, the gene as a unit of inheritance continues to be a useful and valid concept even though the unit has been subdivided and now must be considered in the chemical rather than the physical sense.

It should be pointed out that, in spite of the abundant evidence for complex loci, the genes that have significance in inheritance are separated by some distances on the chromosomes and are more independent functionally than the sites of complex loci described above. They do not usually influence the visible expressions of their neighboring genes unless breaks occur to place them in new positions with respect to each other. Only those genes in very close proximity and those that are moved to heterochromatin regions by chromosome structural changes show well-established position effects. Ordinarily, genes in the same general chromosome area act on entirely different structural or functional characteristics of the body. For example, seven genes with entirely different end results have been located by linkage studies near the end of the X chromosome in *D. melanogaster* (Fig. 9.22). The gene *y* makes the body color yellow, *ac* removes some bristles and hairs from the body, *l* is a lethal that, in homozygous condition, kills the fly (the mode of action is not known), *tw* twists the abdomen about 30 degrees like a left-hand screw, *br* makes the wings broader and shorter than wild type, *pn* gives the eye a prune color, and *gt* (giant) makes the larva, pupa, and

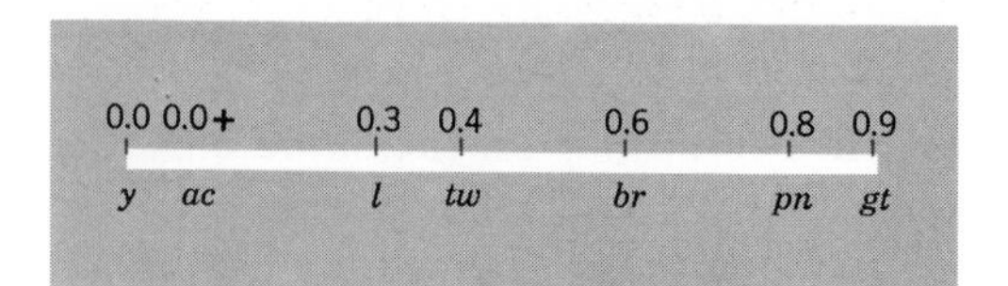


**Fig. 9.22** Chromosome map of the end of the X chromosome showing 7 genes within one crossover unit, which act on 7 different characters in the fly.

adult larger than wild type. Here seven genes, all located within one crossover unit on the linkage map, influence seven different characteristics.

The functional gene still remains the unit of inheritance for practical purposes. Complex loci were discovered when techniques became available in particular organisms for exploring the fine structure of the gene. The first evidence came from Drosophila studies in which presumed alleles were found to be pseudoalleles, that is, closely linked genetic units that behaved ordinarily as if they were alleles but were not in exactly corresponding positions. They could be separated by crossing over. Virus studies then showed that many sites were present in a particular locus. Now studies of gene structure are being extended to bacteria, molds, flies, and maize, and it appears that complex gene structure is basic to all organisms.

## SUMMARY

Structural modifications of chromosomes occur in plants and animals and have apparently played a significant role in evolution. Polytene chromosomes in Diptera and large meiotic prophase chromosomes in plants, especially maize, have been used extensively in identifying structural changes. Breaking and rejoining of chromosomes results in modifications such as deficiencies, duplications, inversions, and translocations.

Stable position effects are uniform phenotypic changes resulting from specific transfer of a chromosome segment. Variegated position effects are caused by a shift of genetic material to a new location usually involving heterochromatin. Refined methods have made possible a subdivision of some gene loci into much smaller recombinational units. Several loci have been found to be complex, including a few to many sites. Position effects have been recognized at the level of the fine structure of genetic material. In the *cis* arrangement, certain sites show complementarity, suggesting a step by step chemical sequence in the production of certain phenotypes.

## REFERENCES


Bridges, C. B. 1935. "Salivary chromosome maps with a key to the banding of the chromosomes of *Drosophila melanogaster.*" *J. Hered.,* **26,** 60–64.

Bridges, C. B. 1936. "The bar "gene" a duplication." *Science,* **83,** 210–211.

Burnham, C. R. 1962. *Discussions in cytogenetics.* Burgess Publishing Co., Minneapolis. (Extensive data concerning chromosome structural changes.)

Darlington, C. D. 1965. *Cytology.* J. and A. Churchill, London. (Compilation of volumes under the title, "Recent advances in cytology" which have been published over the years and now are brought up to date.)

Dobzhansky, T. 1936. "Position effects on genes." *Biol. Rev.,* **11,** 364–384.

Dobzhansky, T. 1951. *Genetics and the origin of species,* 3rd ed. Columbia University Press, New York.

Dobzhansky, T., and A. H. Sturtevant. 1938. "Inversions in the chromosomes of *Drosophila pseudoobscura.*" *Genetics,* **23,** 28–64.

Gates, W. H. 1927. "A case of nondisjunction in the mouse." *Genetics,* **12,** 295–306.

Hannah, A. 1951. "Localization and function of heterochromatin in Drosophila melanogaster." *Advances in Genetics.* M. Demerec (ed.) Vol. 4. Academic Press, New York.

Levitan, M. 1954. "Position effects in natural populations." *Amer. Nat'l.,* **88,** 419–423.

Lewis, E. B. 1950. "The phenomenon of position effect." *Advances in Genetics.* M. Demerec (ed.) Vol. 3. Academic Press, New York.

McClintock, B. 1941. "The stability of broken ends of chromosomes in *Zea mays.*" *Genetics,* **26,** 234–282.

Painter, T. S. 1927. "The chromosome constitution of Gates' 'nondisjunction' (*v-o*) mice." *Genetics,* **12,** 379–392.

Painter, T. S. 1934. "Salivary chromosomes and the attack on the gene." *J. Hered.,* **25,** 464–476.

Patterson, J. T., and W. S. Stone. 1952. *Evolution in the genus Drosophila.* The Macmillan Co., New

York. (An elaborate discussion of the relation between chromosome rearrangements and the evolution of Drosophila.)

Sturtevant, A. H. 1925. "The effects of unequal crossing over at the bar locus in Drosophila." *Genetics,* **10,** 117–147.

Swanson, C. P., T. Merz, and W. J. Young. 1967. *Cytogenetics.* Prentice-Hall, Englewood Cliffs, New Jersey.

White, M. J. D. 1954. *Animal cytology and evolution,* 2nd ed. Cambridge University Press, Cambridge, England.

# *Problems*

**9.1** (a) What genetic evidence first suggested chromosome structural changes? (b) Why did it take so many years to obtain cytological verification for the genetic evidence? (c) How was cytological verification obtained?

**9.2** Compare the methods now available for cytogenetic studies of the fruit fly with those available for maize.

**9.3** What characteristics of Drosophila salivary gland chromosomes make them especially suitable for cytogenetic studies?

**9.4** What are the advantages of the acetocarmine smear technique as compared with fixing, sectioning, and staining methods for chromosome studies?

**9.5** Formulate a plausible explanation for the origin of the giant salivary gland chromosomes in the developing larva of the fly. What do the cross bands represent?

**9.6** What is the difference between a linkage and a cytological chromosome map?

**9.7** Describe or illustrate with appropriate sketches how a recessive gene may be expressed through pseudodominance.

**9.8** How can the extent of a chromosome deficiency be determined (a) genetically, (b) cytologically?

**9.9** If a trait such as "waltzing" in mice known to depend on a single recessive gene (*v*) should appear in an animal considered to be heterozygous for the gene, how could it be determined (a) genetically and (b) cytologically whether a mutation had occurred or a deficiency was present in the chromosome opposite *v*?

**9.10** Describe or illustrate with sketches the appearance of the following heterozygous chromosome modifications in salivary preparations: (a) deficiency, (b) duplication, (c) inversion, and (d) reciprocal translocation.

**9.11** How can (a) paracentric and (b) pericentric inversions act as "crossover suppressors?" Describe or illustrate. (c) Is crossing over really suppressed?

**9.12** What (a) genetic and (b) cytological evidence would indicate that a translocation was present in a plant material such as barley?

**9.13** How is pollen sterility associated with translocations? Illustrate.

**9.14** In a Drosophila salivary chromosome section, the bands have a sequence 1 2 3 4 5 6 7 8. The homologue with which this chromosome must pair has a sequence 1 2 3 6 5 4 7 8. (a) What kind of a chromosome change has occurred? (b) Describe or draw a diagram to illustrate the possible pairing arrangement.

**9.15** Other chromosomes have sequences as follows: (a) 1 2 5 6 7 8; (b) 1 2 3 4 4 5 6 7 8; and (c) 1 2 3 4 5 8 7 6. What kind of chromosome modification is present in each? Illustrate with diagrams the pairing of these chromosomes with their normal homologues in salivary preparations.

**9.16** Chromosome I in maize has the sequence A B C D E F, whereas chromosome II has the sequence M N O P Q R. A reciprocal translocation resulted in the following arrangements A B C P Q R and M N O D E F. Diagram the expected pachytene configuration and describe the causes of the pollen sterility that might be expected.

**9.17** How could a phenotypic effect, such as the number of facets in expressions of bar eye in Drosophila, be demonstrated as a position effect?

**9.18** (a) How do variegated position effects originate and (b) how can they be explained?

**9.19** (a) What kind of data is necessary to identify complex loci? (b) Why was the discovery of complex loci not made before the middle of the present century?

**9.20** What advantages have (a) Drosophila, (b) Neurospora, and (c) Salmonella for investigations of complex loci?

**9.21** (a) What is the significance of the discovery of complex loci? (b) In view of current trends in the direction of molecular dimensions of genetic material, how should the traditional gene concept be regarded?

# Variations in Chromosome Number | 10

Somatic cells of higher plants and animals usually have chromosomes in pairs (2*n*); that is, two of each kind of chromosome are present in each cell. Mature germ cells, having undergone reduction division, normally have one member of each pair (*n*). Many individual plants and animals, however, have local areas of somatic tissue characterized by a multiple of the basic chromosome number. A doubling process in cell division is the usual explanation for these deviations.

With the exception of sex differences, somatic doubling, and minor variations that occur in natural and experimental populations, all members of a species of plants or animals have the same basic chromosome number. Chromosome number can be overemphasized as a criterion for species identification, but it represents a valid characteristic to be used along with others for distinguishing species. The range or reported chromosome numbers in animals extends from 2 pair in a rhabdocoel *Gyratrix hermaphroditus* and some mites, midges, and scale insects, to more than 100 in some butterflies and Crustacea. The Crustacean, *Paralithodes camtschatica,* for example, has 208 chromosomes or 104 pairs (Fig. 10.1). The reported range in plants is from 2 pairs in the small composite plant *Haplopappus gracilis* to several hundred in some ferns. A species of fern-like plants of the genus Ophioglossum is reported to have 768 chromosomes. Chromosome numbers of a few well-known plants and animals are listed in Table 10.1.

Whereas all individuals within a species, with the exceptions noted above, have the same chromosome number, different species within a genus often have different numbers. Cytological investigations of chromosomes help to unravel problems of species formation. The evolutionary path of a certain species can be followed in some cases by comparing numerical and structural relations of its chromosomes with those of other species within the genus. The essential genetic material is a major factor in determining evolutionary patterns, but the chromosome number it-

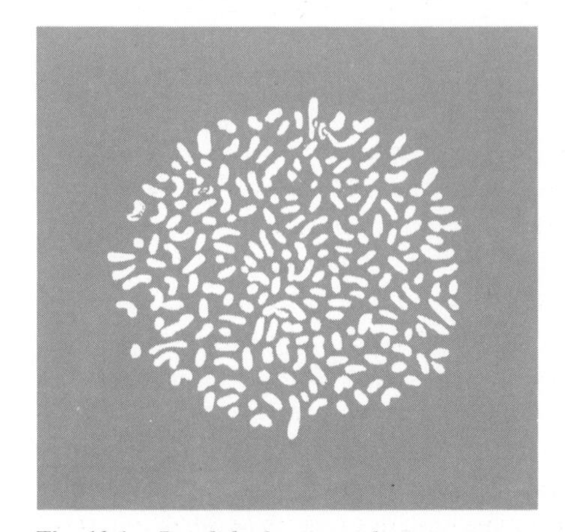

**Fig. 10.1** *Paralithodes camtschatica,* spermatagonial set (208 chromosomes). From Niiyama (1934).

**TABLE 10.1 Chromosome numbers of some common animals and plants**

| Species | Number of Chromosome Pairs |
|---|---|
| *Plants* | |
| Garden pea, *Pisum sativum* | 7 |
| Sorghum, *Sorghum vulgare* | 10 |
| Maize, *Zea mays* | 10 |
| Johnson Grass, *Sorghum halepense* | 20 |
| Alfalfa, *Medicago sativa* | 16 |
| Barley, *Hordeum vulgare* | 7 |
| Oats, *Avena sativa* | 21 |
| Tomato, *Lycopersicon esculentum* | 12 |
| Tobacco, *Nicotiana tabacum* | 24 |
| Trillium, *Trillium erectum* | 5 |
| *Animals* | |
| Gypsy moth, *Lymantria dispar* | 31 |
| Mouse, *Mus musculus* | 20 |
| Rabbit, *Oryctolagus cuniculus* | 22 |
| Cow, *Bos tarus* | 30 |
| Horse, *Equus caballus* | 32 |
| Donkey, (ass) *Equus asinus* | 31 |
| Dog, *Canis familiaris* | 39 |
| Monkey, *Macaca rhesus* | 21 |
| Gorilla, *Gorilla gorilla* | 24 |
| Chimpanzee, *Pan troglodytes* | 24 |

self represents merely the number of packages into which the genetic material is divided. Chromosome number is probably more constant, however, than any other single morphological characteristic that is available for species identification.

Changes in the number of chromosomes may be reflected in phenotypic variations, which constitute a useful tool for identifying the influence of individual chromosomes. If, for example, phenotypically distinguishable individuals with different chromosome numbers can be identified in natural populations or produced experimentally, it is sometimes possible to determine the effect of adding or removing certain chromosomes. Some plants with increased chromosome numbers have phenotypic changes in morphological or physiological characteristics which are of practical importance to man. Grape and tomato plants with chromosome numbers above $2n$ are larger and produce more desirable fruit than do corresponding varieties with the usual $2n$ number.

Classifications of chromosome changes are arbitrary and superficial because these changes are necessarily interpreted in terms of obvious additions or eliminations of parts of chromosomes, whole chromosomes, or whole chromosome sets. The presently accepted classification system, therefore, is merely a working tool. Two main classes are euploidy and aneuploidy ("ploid," Greek for unit; "eu," true or even; and "aneu," uneven). Euploids have chromosome complements consisting of whole sets or genomes. The chromosome number of euploid organisms is basically represented by the monoploid ($n$). Euploids with chromosome numbers above the monoploid level may be diploid ($2n$), triploid ($3n$), tetraploid ($4n$), or have some other "polyploid" number.

## ANEUPLOIDY

The first critical study of aneuploid plants was made by Blakeslee and Belling using the common Jimson weed *Datura stramonium,* which normally has 12 pairs of chromosomes in the somatic cells. In 1924, these investigators announced the discovery of a "mutant type" having 25 rather than 24 chromosomes. At the meiotic metaphase, one of the 12 pairs was found to have an extra member; that is, one trisome was present along with 11 disomes. This originally discovered trisomic plant differed from wild-type plants in several specific ways. Conspicuous deviations were observed in shape and spine characteristics of seed capsules. The chromosome complement with one extra member in addition to the regular set was illustrated by the formula $2n + 1$. Theoretically, because the complement was composed of 12 chromosome pairs differing in the genes they carried, 12 distinguishable trisomics were possible in Jimson weeds. Through experimental breeding, Blakeslee and his associates succeeded in producing all 12 possible trisomics. These were grown in Blakeslee's garden and each was found to have a distinguishable phenotype that was attributed to an extra set of the genes contained in one of the 12 chromosomes.

It was possible to identify some genes with their chromosomes, and to establish further that certain genes are located in particular chromosomes. One of the 12 trisomic types of Jimson weed, known as Poinsettia, had several distinguishing traits, including seed capsules that differed from those of other trisomic types. An extra chromosome carrying the alleles $p^+$ and $p$ for purple and white flower, respectively, was always present in Poinsettia plants. Thus, any one of three chromosome arrangements ($p^+p^+p^+$, $p^+p^+p$, and $p^+pp$) was found to produce purple Poinsettia plants whereas only one ($ppp$) gave rise to white plants. Normal ($2n$) plants had two chromosome arrangements ($p^+p^+$ and $p^+p$) for purple and one ($pp$) for white.

Trisomics have interesting complications when undergoing meiosis. Two chromosomes ordinarily go to one pole and one goes to the other in the reduction division of megasporogenesis, thus giving rise to different kinds of gametes, some with two and some with one member of the trisome. Recessive genes are not as likely to occur in completely homozygous arrangements in trisomic complexes as in normal diploid plants. Therefore, they come to expression less frequently. Trisomic ratios (for example, 5:1, 17:1, and 35:1) reflect increased proportions of progeny carrying wild-type alleles.

In the Jimson weed, extra chromosomes may be transmitted through the egg because developing megaspores tolerate extra chromosomes, and form gametes with relatively little loss of viability. When additional chromosomes above the $n$ number enter developing microspores, however, the resulting spores cannot successfully compete against those with the normal haploid complement. Therefore, only haploid pollen grains become functional. These differences in the results of megasporogenesis and microsporogenesis lead to trisomics such as the Poinsettia plants cited above. A cross between two purple Poinsettia plants ($p^+p^+p \times p^+p^+p$) may be constructed as illustrated in Fig. 10.2. Female gametes are of four kinds, two haploid and two carrying an extra chromosome. They occur in the proportion:

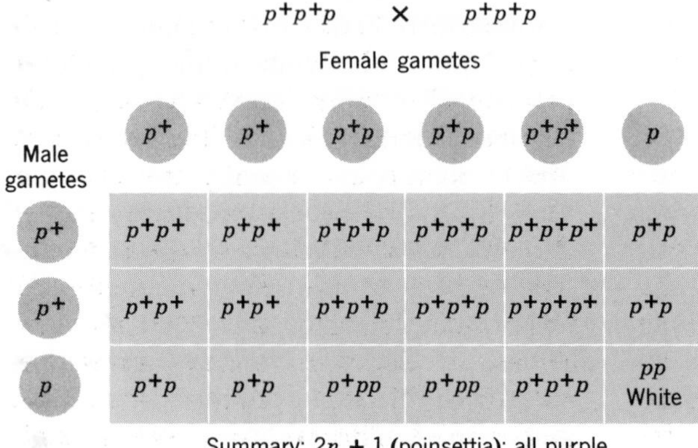


**Fig. 10.2** Diagram of cross between two purple trisomic plants of the genus *Datura*.

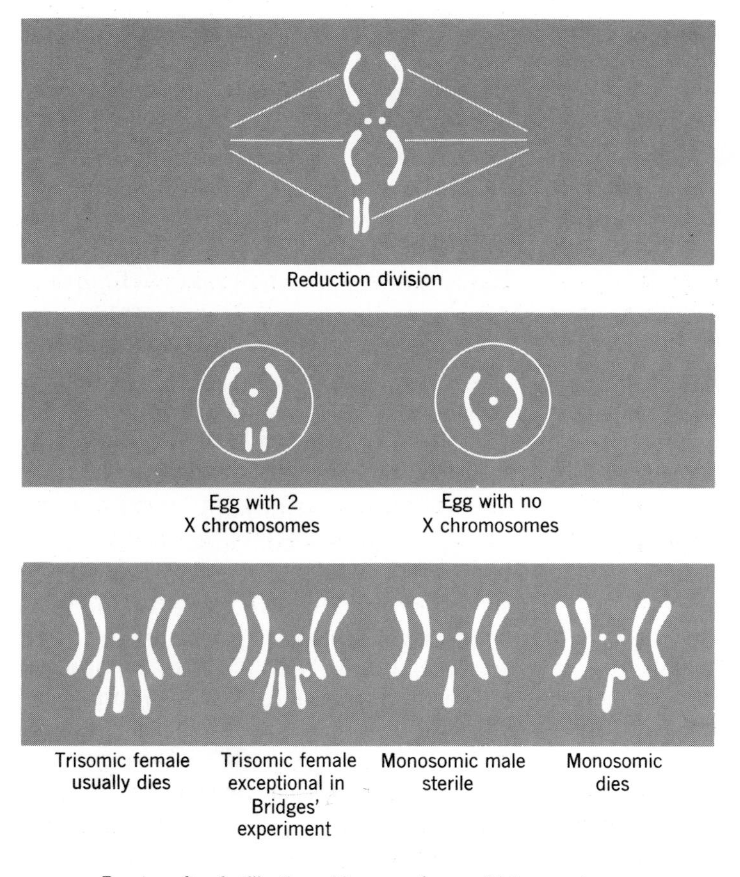


**Fig. 10.3** Diagram illustrating nondisjunction in Drosophila, and monosomics and trisomics resulting from fertilization by wild-type males. The trisomic females with 2 X chromosomes and a Y chromosome and the monosomic male with one X gave the exceptional results in Bridges' experiment.

$2p^+$, $2p^+p$, $1p^+p^+$, and $1p$. Because male gametes receiving extra chromosomes are nonfunctional, only two kinds, $p^+$ and $p$, occurring in the proportion $2p^+$ and $1p$, were involved in fertilization. All Poinsettia $(2n + 1)$ plants resulting from the cross carried at least one $p^+$ gene and had purple flowers. The $2n$ plants occurred in the proportion of 8 purple to 1 white.

Aneuploidy in animals was illustrated in Bridges' example of trisomic X chromosome (Chapters 4 and 5). From crosses between white-eyed female fruit flies and red-eyed males from which only red-eyed daughters and white-eyed sons were expected, Bridges found a few white-eyed daughters and a few red-eyed sons. He explained the mechanics of aneuploid formation on the basis of a failure of the X chromosomes to separate or disjoin in the reduction division. This nondisjunction produced some eggs with two X chromosomes and others with none (Fig. 10.3).

When fertilized with normal sperm, eggs with two X chromosomes produced two kinds of trisomics, XXX and XXY. The metafemales (XXX) (Fig. 10.4) were always sterile and usually inviable, but the XXY combinations produced females phenotypically indistinguishable from wild-type females. These were the unexpected white-eyed females that Bridges saw. Zygotes with normal pairs of autosomes but single X or Y chromosomes were monosomics whereas those with a single X produced the exceptional red-eyed males,

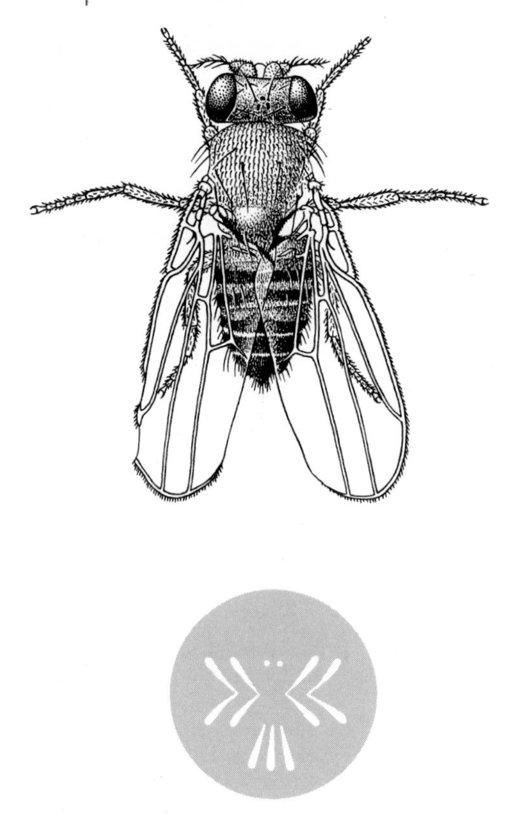

**Fig. 10.4** Above, metafemale; below, chromosome complement of metafemale with XXX.

which were normal in appearance but were sterile. Zygotes with a single Y chromosome were inviable.

Later investigations by Bridges showed that other chromosomes besides the X (I chromosome) could be added or eliminated. When, however, the II and III chromosomes were lost or added, the resulting cells were always inviable. Each of these large chromosomes was essential to the life of the cell. Chromosome IV, on the other hand, is very small and could be lost or added without seriously affecting the viability of the flies. Through the addition of a fourth chromosome to the wild-type complement (Fig. 10.5), a trisomic ($2n + 1$) called triplo-IV was obtained. A monosomic ($2n - 1$) called haplo-IV was obtained through the elimination of one fourth chromosome. Phenotypes of the triplo-IV and haplo-IV reflected the numbers of fourth chromosomes present. In general, haplo-IV flies were small with slender bristles. They also deviated in several minor respects from the wild type. Triplo-IV flies were slightly larger than the wild type with bristles that were appreciably more coarse than those of wild type flies.

Chromosome IV genes, such as *ey* for eyeless (a phenotype characterized by small or missing eyes), behave differently with different chromosome combinations, as expected. When $2n$ eyeless flies (*eyey*) were outcrossed with haplo-IV (Fig. 10.6), the $F_1$ generation consisted of normal $2n$ and eyeless haplo-IV flies. When eyeless flies were crossed with triplo-IV, none of the first-generation progeny was eyeless. About half were triplo-IV and half were normal (diplo-IV) as expected. When $F_1$ triplo-IV females were crossed with eyeless (*eyey*) males as shown in Fig. 10.7, the progeny consisted of about half triplo-IV and half $2n$. Normal and eyeless phenotypes were present in a ratio of about 5/6 to 1/6, respectively. This trisomic ratio is explained on the basis of the extra chromosome present in the triplo-IV flies.

Presumably, trisomy occurs in other organisms but extensive investigation of trisomics and monosomics has been essentially limited to such materials as Jimson

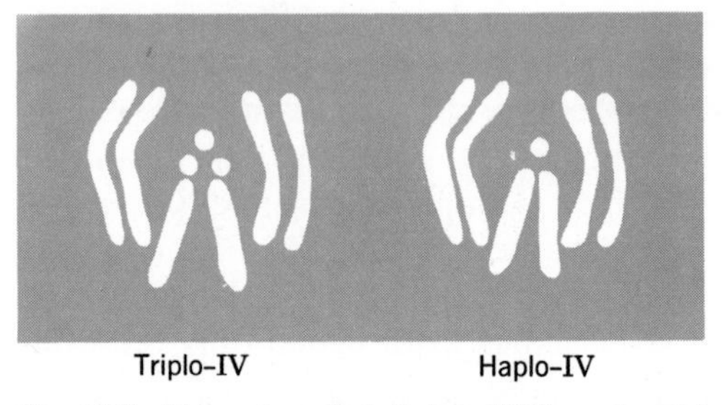


**Fig. 10.5** Trisomic called "triplo-IV," produced by the addition of a fourth chromosome, and monosomic called "haplo-IV," resulting from elimination of one fourth chromosome in Drosophila.

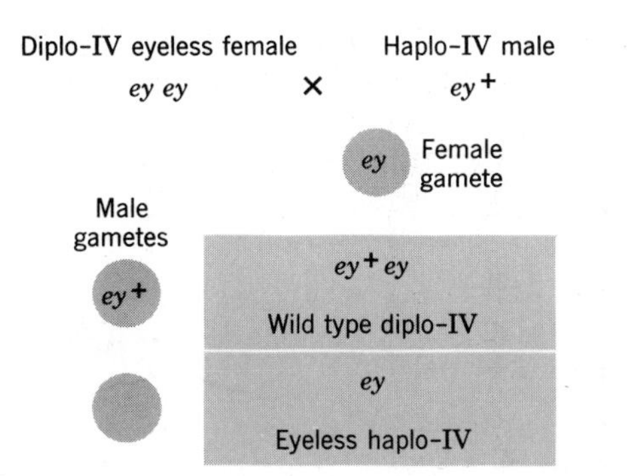


**Fig. 10.6** Diagram of cross between a diplo-IV eyeless female and a haplo-IV male.

weeds, tobacco, maize, wheat, tomatoes, and fruit flies, which produce viable combinations. Aneuploids more complex than trisomics have been produced in some species, but ordinarily they are highly inviable. Tetrasomics ($2n + 2$) have been identified in wheat, but no phenotypic characteristics were observed by which the tetrasomics could be distinguished from trisomics.

Another variation that could be expected to occur in an aneuploid series is the complete absence of a certain kind of chromosome ($2n - 2$). Plants in which a chromosome pair is completely missing are called nullisomics. These may be produced occasionally in nature but probably seldom survive long enough to be recognized or to perpetuate the chromosome type. E. R. Sears experimentally produced all of the 21 possible nullisomics in wheat, *Triticum aestivum*. By associating certain phenotypes with corresponding chromosome arrangements, the geneticist makes use of nullisomics in determining the chromosome carrier of certain genes. Nullisomics have been used effectively in locating several different genes in wheat.

### *Chromosome Number in Man*

For many years before 1956 the chromosome number in man was recorded as 48. Suitable material for human chromosome studies was difficult to obtain, and the older techniques were not satisfactory for critical chromosome counts. Human chromosomes are small, and in earlier preparations they overlapped on the microscope slide and were extremely difficult to distinguish. New methods of chemical treatment are now employed for fixing tissues with a minimum of distortion. Chemical treatment has also been developed for spreading chromosomes on the microscope slide, thus making it possible to identify each individual chromosome. Tissue culture methods have facilitated studies of cell division in living cells and have made metaphase stages available for chromosome counts. Recent developments in surgical treatment for cancer and other diseases have made more fresh human

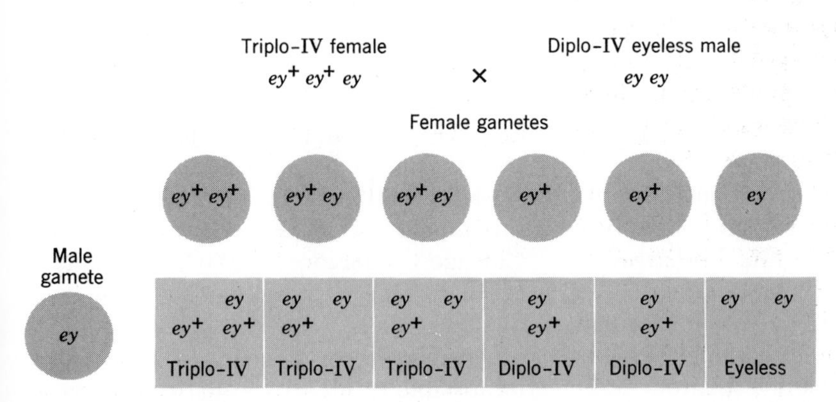


**Fig. 10.7** Diagram of cross between a triplo-IV female and a diplo-IV eyeless male.

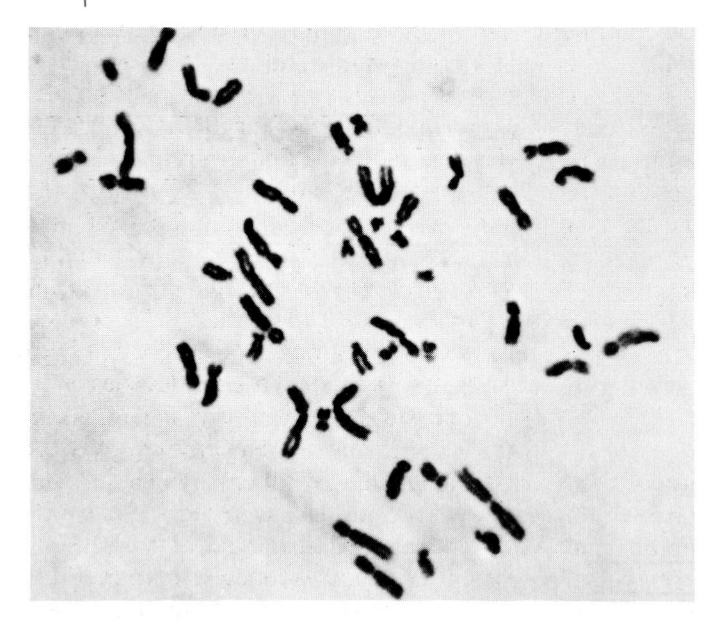

**Fig. 10.8** Human chromosomes. 46 mitotic metaphase chromosomes from a cell in culture derived from skin biopsy from a male child. (Photograph by Ernest H. Y. Chu, Oak Ridge National Laboratory.)

tissue available and modern techniques have provided better preparations for study. Testicular specimens have become particularly useful for chromosome investigations. Methods of freezing and fixing tissues have improved their value as cytological material.

In 1956, two cytologists, J. H. Tjio and A. Levan, working in Sweden, published a paper on the chromosome number in man, giving 46 as the $2n$ number (Fig. 10.8). Their counts were made from tissue culture preparations of lung tissue representing four different human embryos. A pretreatment with certain solutions spread the chromosomes of dividing cells and made it possible to observe each chromosome separately. The investigators examined 265 dividing cells and concluded that the chromosome number in human embryo lung tissue was 46. Two more embryos were later included in the investigation and similar results were obtained. The lung tissue of all six Swedish fetuses had the same chromosome number. In the same year, two English investigators, C. E. Ford and J. L. Hammerton, reported 23 pairs of chromosomes in testicular preparations of each of three adult Englishmen. In 1961, S. Makino and M. S. Sasaki studied 1422 cells from 54 different human embryos, ages 2 to 7 months, and found virtually all to have 46 chromosomes. Many specimens have now been obtained from widely separated parts of the world and the number 46 has become well established as the $2n$ number. No persistent difference in chromosome number has been detected among races or ethnic groups of mankind.

A group of cytogeneticists met at Denver, Colorado in 1960 and adopted a system for classifying and identifying human chromosomes. Chromosome length and the position of the centromere were the criteria for classification. The Denver classification, with refinements made at the London Conference (1963) and the Chicago Conference (1966), has become a standard for chromosome studies. In spite of standardized preparations and numerous specimens for comparison, it has been impossible to identify consistently every chromosome pair. The 22 pairs of autosomes have, however, been divided successfully into 7 groups identified with letters A to G (Fig. 10.9). Numbers 1 to 22 are associated with the autosomes in descending order by length. All autosomes can be placed satisfactorily within a group but the numbering within the groups is more or less tentative. The X chromosome is difficult to distinguish from members of the C group and the Y chromosome shows considerable variability in different preparations.

### *Aneuploidy in Man*

More recent studies on individuals have related chromosome numbers below and above 46 with intersex conditions and other irregularities manifesting physical, reproductive, and mental abnormalities. Participants in the Chicago Conference agreed on a system of nomenclature for identifying numerical and structural chromosome alterations. In a description of a karyotype, the first item to be recorded is the total number of chromosomes, including the sex chromosomes, followed by the sex chromosome constitution and any autosomal aberrations. A complement of 44 autosomes and one X, for example, is symbolized 45,X (Fig. 10.10). This monosomic chromosome complement has been associated with an abnormal female condition known for many years as Turner's syndrome and which occurs in one of about 5000 people in the general population. The most obvious adult symptoms in the syndrome are ovarian agenesis, incomplete or faulty development of the ovaries, short stature, low-set ears, hypoplasia, abnormal jaw formation, webbed neck, and

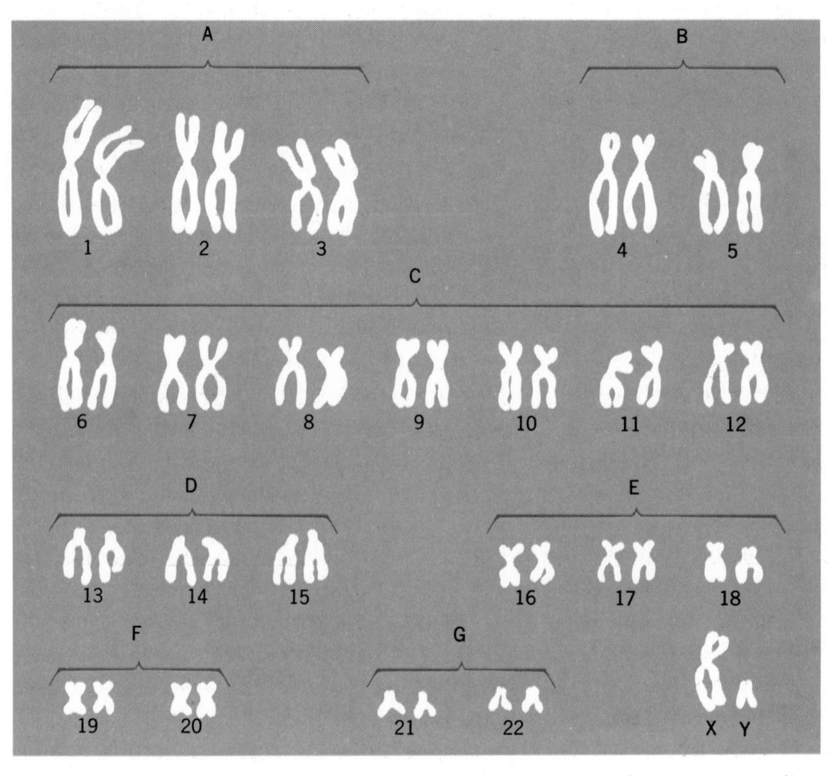


**Fig. 10.9** Human metaphase chromosomes classified in seven major groups according to criteria established at Denver (1960), London (1963), and Chicago (1966) conferences.

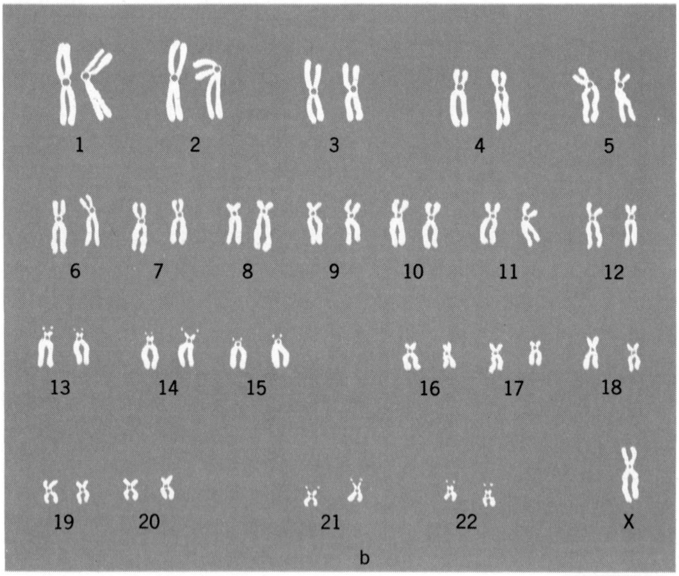

Fig. 10.10 Chromosomes associated with Turner's syndrome, 45, X chromosomes.

shieldlike chest. Microscopic sections of ovaries of adult patients have indicated that fibrous streaks of tissue represent all that is present of the ovaries. Symptoms associated with Turner's syndrome can also be recognized in infants (Fig. 10.11).

When the Y chromosome is present in addition to the usual female complement, a trisomic (47,XXY) is produced (Fig. 10.12) making a total of 47. An abnormal male complex known as Klinefelter's syndrome is associated with the chromosomal trisomic. This condition, estimated roughly to occur in one of 500 live births, is characterized by testicular dysgenesis (defective development of the testicles). Individuals with this syndrome are phenotypically males but some tendency toward femaleness can be recognized, particularly in secondary sex characteristics. Such symptoms as enlarged breasts, underdeveloped body hair, small testes and small prostate glands are a part of the syndrome. Usually mental retardation is also recognized. Studies of Klinefelter's syndrome along with other abnormal sex chromosome conditions give evidence that the Y chromosome in human beings is male determining.

Other irregular combinations of sex chromosomes also have been recognized. About one percent of all mentally defective women in institutions have been shown to be trisomic for the X chromosome (47,XXX). The few individuals that have been studied with tetrasomic X chromosomes (48,XXXX) are all mentally defective females. In the general population, a trisomic X chromosome occurs in the proportion of about one per 1000. Individuals with the "triple X syndrome" are comparable in some ways to Drosophila metafemales (XXX). In Drosophila, however, such individuals are strikingly abnormal and sterile, whereas human XXX individuals are visibly indistinguishable from individuals with the normal XX arrangement.

The best-known symptoms associated with this syndrome are abnormalities associated with functional processes such as menstruation. One patient cited by P. A. Jacobs was a 37 year-old female who reported that the first suggestion of an abnormality was highly irregular men-

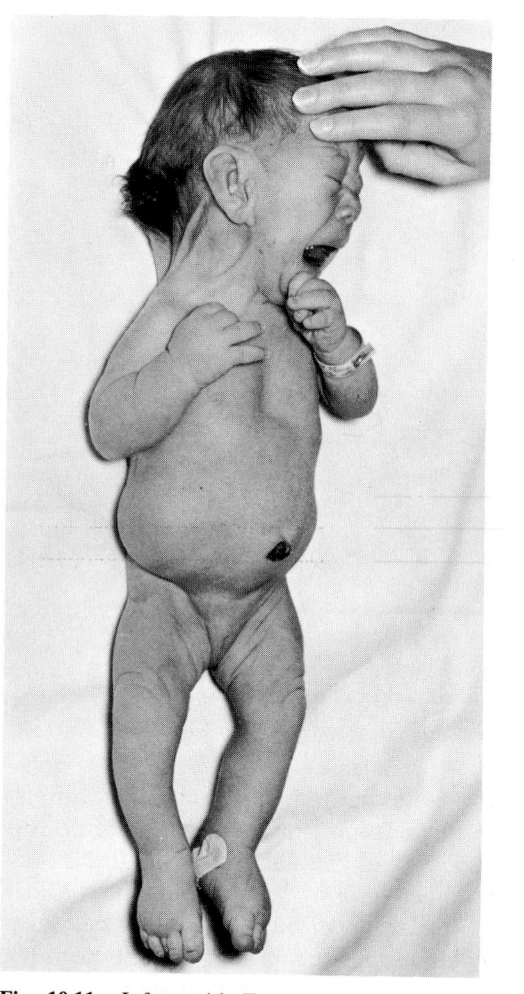

**Fig. 10.11** Infant with Turner's syndrome (45, X chromosomes). Note webbed neck, puffy hands and feet. (Courtesy of Irene A. Uchida.)

struation. When the abdominal wall was opened the ovaries appeared as if they were post menopausal. Microscopically, they showed deficient ovarian follicle formation. Of 63 cells observed, 51 had 47 chromosomes; the extra chromosome was an X. Nondisjunction in the production of the egg from which this woman developed was postulated as the mechanism for the occurrence of the extra chromosome. When the somatic cells of this woman were studied cytologically, further evidence for X chromosome trisomy was obtained. Buccal smears prepared according to the Barr technique (Chapter 5) showed two sex chromatin bodies in the epithelial cells as expected if three X chromosomes were present.

Figure 10.13 illustrates the results of a study by Dr. Irene A. Uchida and her associates in which XXX trisomy was detected. A cell with two sex chromatin bodies is shown along with the chromosomes. In this same individual (Fig. 10.14) autosomal trisomy for a member of the E group, probably chromosome 18 (48,XXX?18), was found. Symptoms associated with this trisomy also form a syndrome characterized by malformation of the skull, short neck, webbed toes, chest deformity, and heart abnormality. The patient in Uchida's study was an infant with a long narrow head, crumpled abnor-

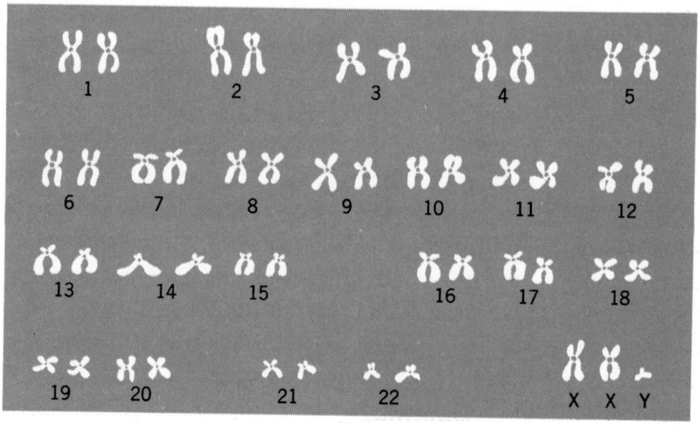

1 2 3 4 5
6 7 8 9 10 11 12
13 14 15 16 17 18
19 20 21 22 X X Y

**Fig. 10.12** Chromosomes associated with Klinefelter's syndrome, 47, XXY chromosomes.

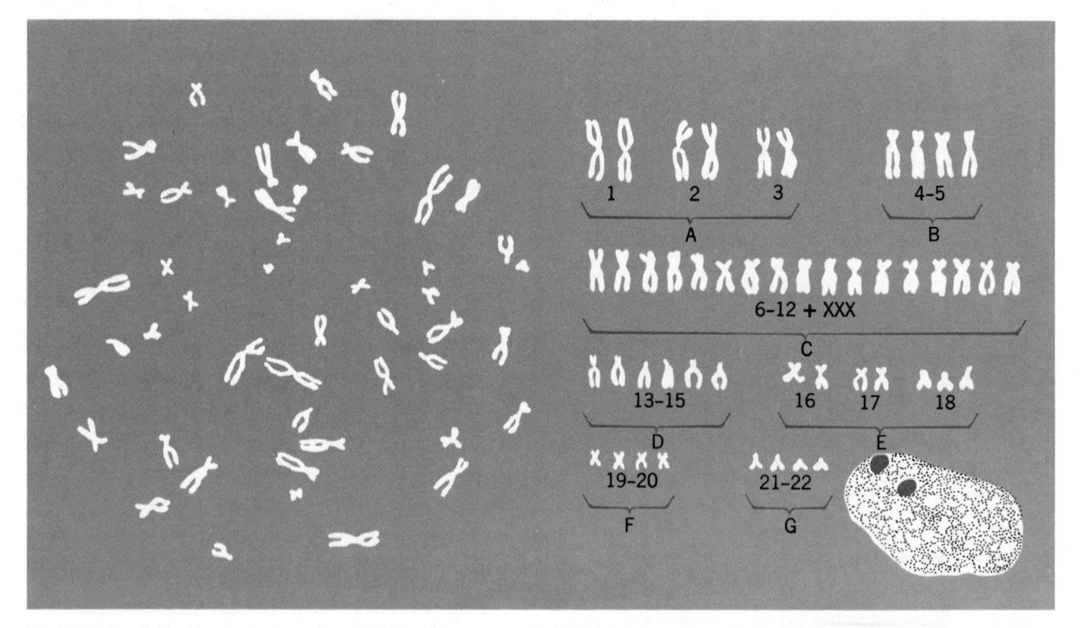


**Fig. 10.13** Cell of patient showing 48 chromosomes (48, XXX E). Karyotype on the right shows an extra X chromosome and an extra member of the group probably no. 18. Two sex chromatin bodies are visible in the nucleus shown in the lower right-hand corner. (Courtesy of Irene A. Uchida.)

mal ears, receding mandible, short sternum, small hips, left rocker-bottom foot, and right club foot. Fingers of both hands were abnormally flexed in such a way that the index and little fingers overlapped the central two fingers. Internal abnormalities in this patient included an overactive and enlarged heart. In addition, the patient (like others with this trisomy) had simian creases in the palms of the hands, single creases on the fifth fingers, and no distal flexion creases on the other fingers. This dermatoglyphic pattern is characteristic of No. 18 trisomy and is also recognized in individuals with some other chromosomal irregularities. It is a common characteristic of apes and monkeys. Another of Uchida's patients (Fig. 10.15) with chromosome 18 trisomy shows a characteristic elfin appearance with small nose and mouth, receding mandible, and abnormal ears.

The incidence of trisomy 18 has been variously estimated in different studies from one in 5000 to one in 500. Samples in these studies have been small and it is not known whether racial or other population groups differ in incidence. Older women are more likely than younger women to have babies with this deformity. This is to be expected if the primary cause of trisomy is nondisjunction in meiosis and if older women are more prone to this chromosome irregularity than younger women.

Another syndrome associated with trisomy of an autosomal chromosome was formerly known as "mongolism" but is now designated Down's syndrome. It was named after Langdon Down who first described the symptoms in 1866. The individuals he studied, and those with the same syndrome who have since been observed, were short in stature (about four feet tall); they had characteristic slanting eyes (thus the earlier name "mongolian"), stubby hands (particularly the fifth digit),

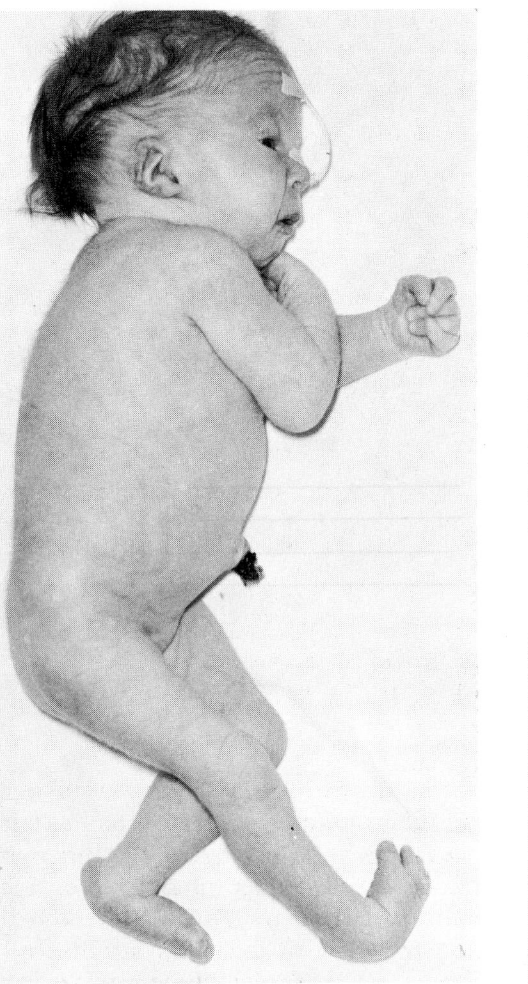

**Fig. 10.14** Infant with trisomic X and trisomic No. 18 (48, XXX?18). Note abnormal ears, receding mandible, flexion deformity of fingers, small hips, left rockerbottom foot, and right club foot. (Courtesy of Irene A. Uchida.)

broad, short skull, large tongues, with a characteristic furrowing, and general loose jointedness, observed particularly in the ankles. They were characterized as low in mentality.

A small chromosome in the G group, presumably No. 21 (Fig. 10.16), is added to the normal complement in all cases where Down's syndrome is recognized. Chromosome No. 21 has been difficult to distinguish from No. 22 and it is not known which of these two is involved. On the basis of size, No. 21 is presumed to be associated with Down's syndrome. Both 21 and 22 have small satellites that can be observed in the best of preparations for microscopic study making this feature unsuitable for distinguishing between the two. Trisomy of No. 21 is apparently the result of primary nondisjunction, which occurs at the reduction division in the meiosis of the mother. Paired chromosomes do not separate properly to the poles at anaphase and, as a result, one egg receives two No. 21 chromosomes and the first polar body receives no No. 21 chromosomes.

Down's syndrome occurs once in about

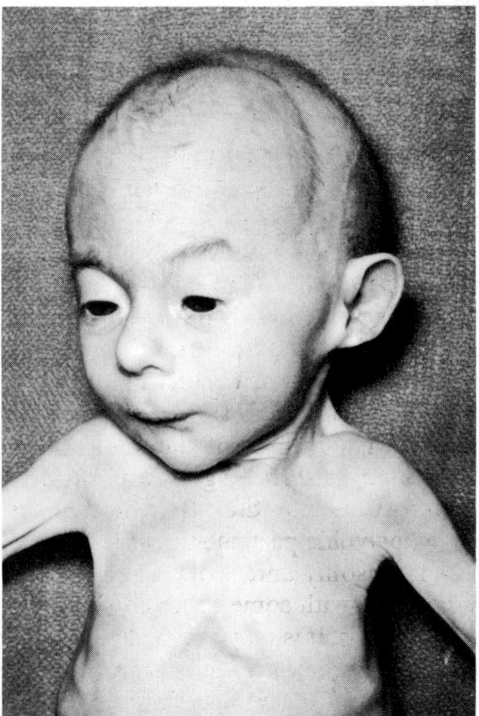

**Fig. 10.15** Facial features associated with trisomy of No. 18 (47, XX18). Note elfin appearance, small palpebral fissures, small nose and mouth, and receding mandible and abnormal ears. (Courtesy of Irene A. Uchida.)

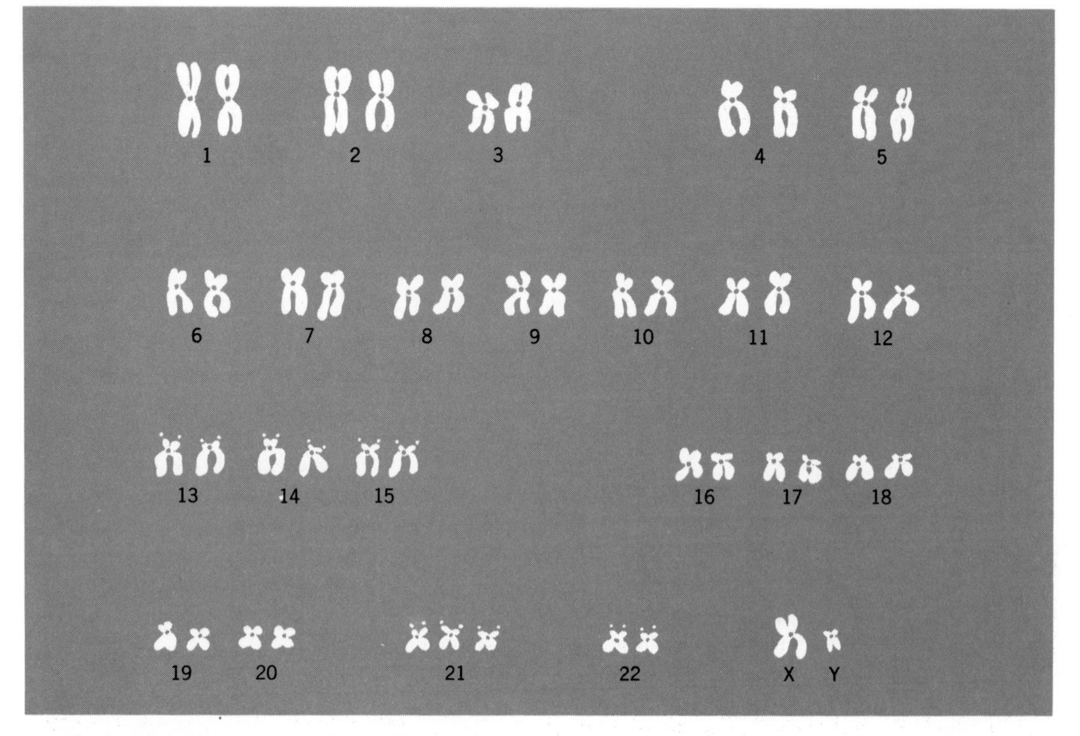


**Fig. 10.16** Extra chromosome (47, XYG) of G group associated with Down's syndrome.

700 births among European people. Older mothers have a higher incidence than younger mothers. About 40 percent of Down's syndrome victims are born to women over 40 years of age, whereas this group of mothers produces only about 4 percent of all babies born in the general population. The mean maternal age for all babies born in the population according to Penrose is 28.5 years compared with a mean age of 36.6 years for mothers of babies with Down's syndrome. The greater incidence among older mothers may be associated with the long delay in completion of meiosis. Potential eggs in the ovary begin the meiotic process before birth and proceed to primary oöcyte stage. They then remain dormant until shortly before ovulation occurs. Cells of a woman 40 years of age have thus remained in an inactive stage for about twice as long as those of a woman 20 years old. This long period of quiescence may explain at least partially why nondisjunction occurs more frequently in older than in younger mothers.

A patient with Down's syndrome, who illustrates typical facial features—that is, slanting eyes, open mouth with large tongue, small protruding ears, and broad skull—is shown in Fig. 10.17. The hand (Fig. 10.18) of a Down's syndrome patient shows the simian crease on the palm and single crease on the little finger. Some patients have a total of only 46 instead of 47 chromosomes, but in such cases a translocation has been found to join chromosome No. 21 with another chromosome in the same complement.

A special case should be cited in which an extra chromosome or more, probably a chromosome fragment of No. 21, is associated with a specific disease. This is the Philadelphia chromosome (Fig. 10.19)

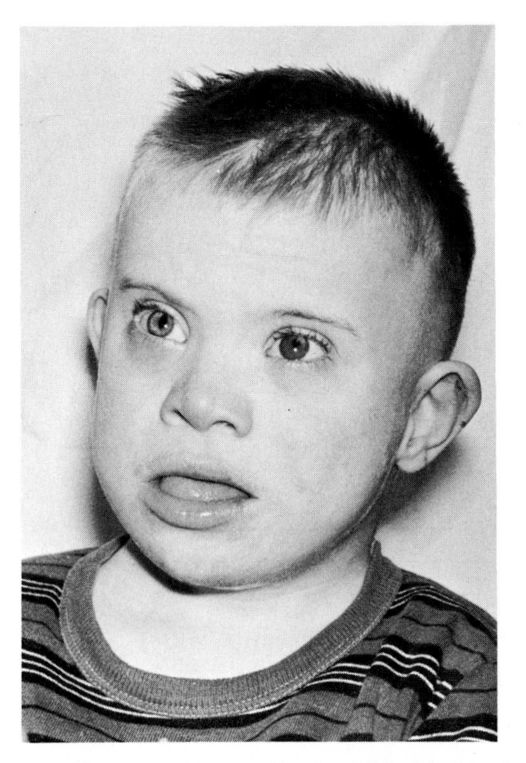

**Fig. 10.17** Facial features of a child with Down's syndrome. Note slanting eyes, open mouth with large tongue, small protruding ears, and broad head. (Courtesy of Irene A. Uchida.)

which is found in leucocytes of patients with chronic granulocytic leukemia. It is apparently a deleted part of chromosome No. 21 and serves as an identification marker in the bone marrow cells of people who have this particular kind of leukemia. A deletion of part of the short arm of chromosome No. 5 is associated with the cri-du-chat syndrome characterized by microcephaly, a small head and mental disorder (Fig. 10.20). Children with this abnormality have a cat-like cry.

Several other trisomic chromosome arrangements have been associated with syndromes. Examples with an extra chromosome from the B, D, and E group, which differ from the example cited above, are on record. One additional chromosome in the D group is associated with a cleft lip (Fig. 10.21). Most, and perhaps all, cases of aneuploidy in man can be explained basically by nondisjunction at meiosis, as illustrated in Fig. 10.22. More complex arrangements of the sex chromosomes (such as 48,XXXY, 48,XXYY, 49,XXXXY, and 47,XYY, males and 48,XXXX and 49,XXXXX females) are now on record. Irregular numerical chromosome arrangements cited thus far have been associated with structural and mental abnormalities in the patients concerned.

## *Chromosomal Mosaics*

Chromosomal mosaics have been detected in man as in other animals. These are individuals who have at least two cell lines with different karyotypes derived from the same zygote. Mosaics originate from a chromosome irregularity after fertilization. A chromosome may lag in a mitotic division and become incorporated in the same nucleus with the chromosome from which it divided. One daughter cell

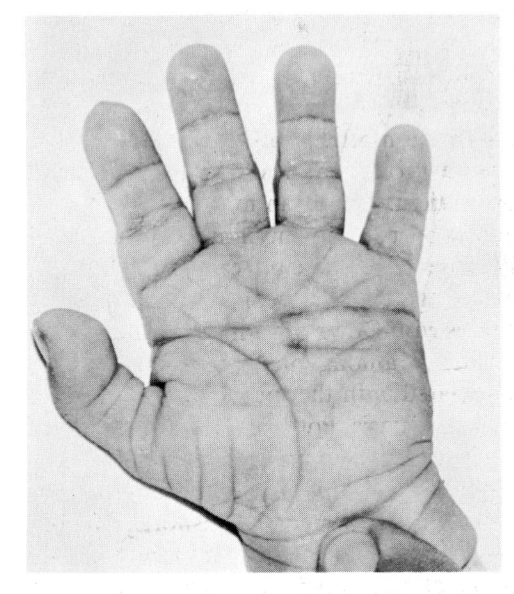

**Fig. 10.18** Hand of child with Down's syndrome showing simian crease on palm and single crease on little finger. (Courtesy of Irene A. Uchida.)

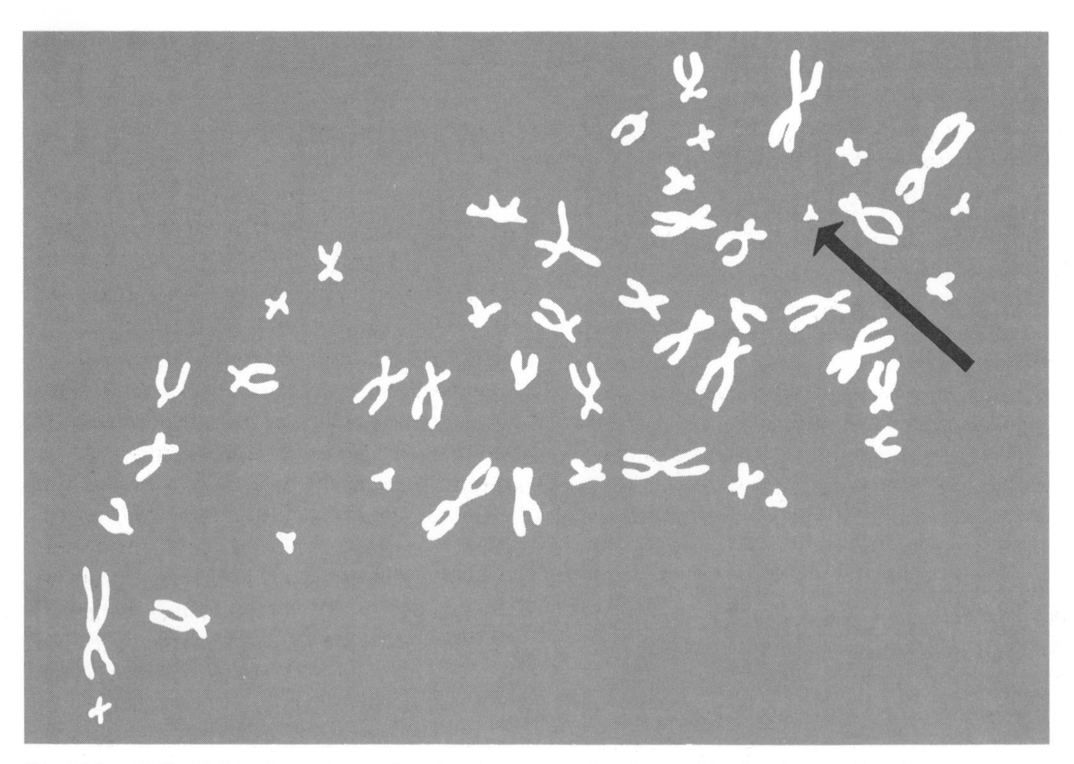

**Fig. 10.19** Philadelphia chromosome, found in leucocytes of patients with chronic granulocytic leukemia.

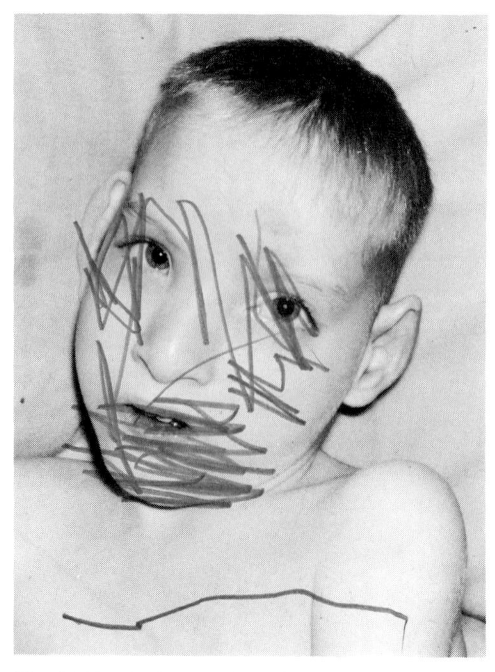

**Fig. 10.20** Patient with cri-du-chat syndrome which is associated with a deletion of part of the short arm of chromosome No. 5. Associated with microcephaly and cat-like cry. (Courtesy of Irene A. Uchida.)

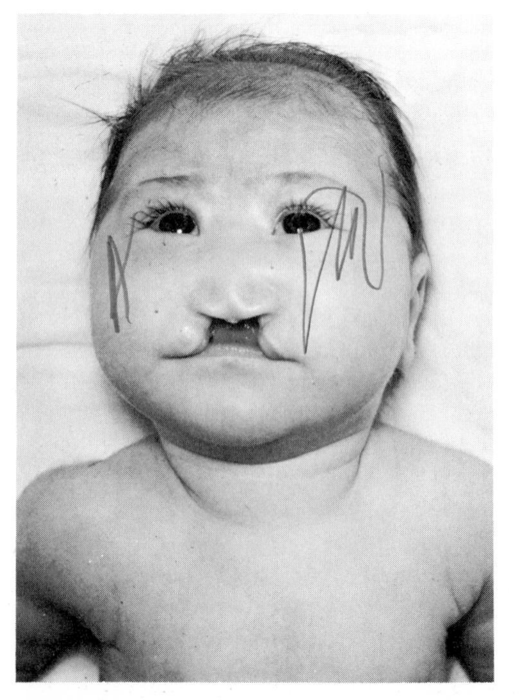

**Fig. 10.21** Child with trisomy for a member of the D group of chromosomes (47, XYD?) showing characteristic cleft lip. (Courtesy of Irene A. Uchida.)

would thus receive one too many and the other would be one deficient, as illustrated in Fig. 10.23. Each cell would give rise to a cell line with the irregular chromosome number. Proportions of cells representing the different cell lines would vary in different tissues, making the extent of the mosaicism and the effect on the organism difficult to predict.

Many sex chromosome mosaics have been detected in human beings. Each has at least two cell lines with different sex chromosome arrangements. The main phenotypic characteristic is extreme variability. Some sex chromosome mosaics that have been reported are: XO/XX, XO/XY, XX/XY, XXY/XX, XX/XXX, XXX/XO, XXXX/XXXXY, and several other combinations reflecting two or three cell lines. Mild to severe phenotypic symptoms have been associated with these sex chromosome mosaics.

## EUPLOIDY

In contrast to aneuploids, which differ from standard $2n$ chromosome complements in single chromosomes, euploids differ in multiples of $n$. Monoploids ($n$) carry one genome, that is, one each of the normally present chromosomes. The $n$ chromosome number is usual for gametes of diploid animals, but unusual for somatic cells. Monoploidy is seldom observed in animals except in the male honey bee and other insects in which male haploids occur.

Plants have a gametophyte stage in their cycle which is characterized by the reduced ($n$) chromosome number. In higher plants, this stage is brief and inconspicuous, but in some lower plant groups it represents the major part of the cycle. Occasionally, plants in natural populations or experimental plots can be recognized as mono-

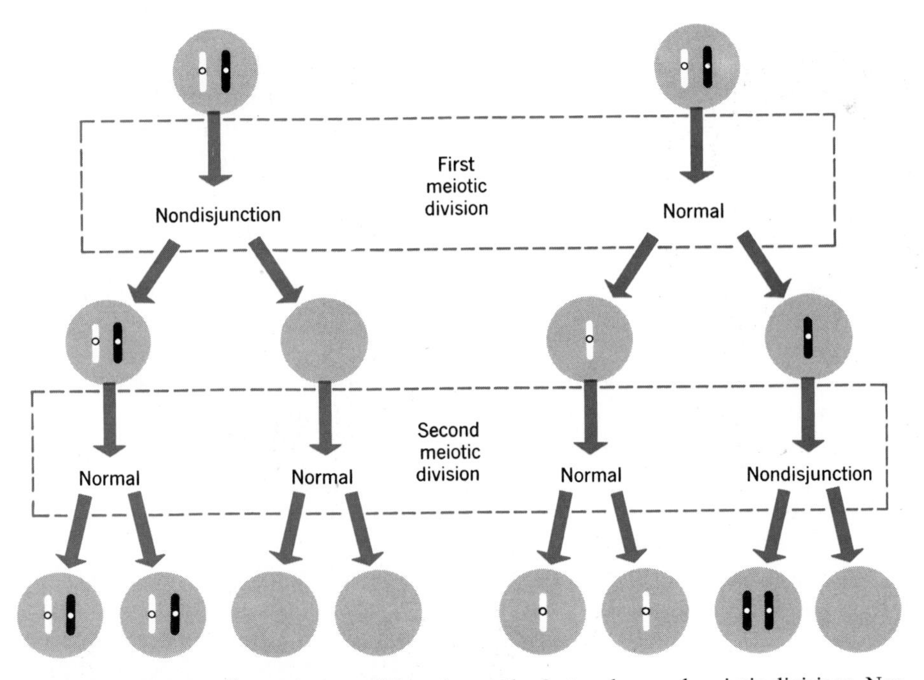


**Fig. 10.22** Diagram illustrating nondisjunction at the first and second meiotic divisions. Nondisjunction at meiosis I produces gametes containing both or neither of the members of homologous pairs of chromosomes. Nondisjunction at meiosis II produces gametes containing (or lacking) two identical chromosomes both derived from the same member of the homologous pair.

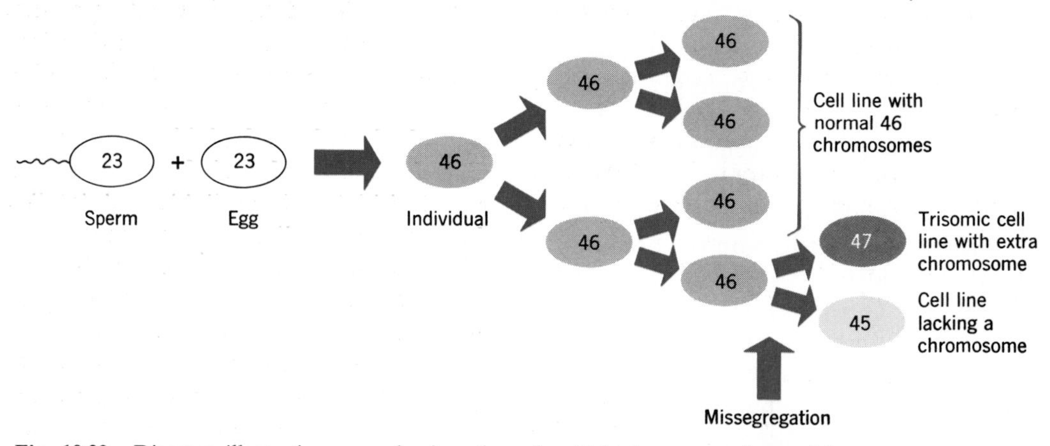


**Fig. 10.23** Diagram illustrating a mechanism through which chromosomal mosaicism may occur. A normal individual with 46 chromosomes is formed when sperm and egg unite. During the third cell division missegregation gives rise to a cell with 47 chromosomes and a cell with 45 chromosomes. Each of these cells initiates a cell line, thus forming a mosaic individual with cells carrying different numbers of chromosomes.

ploids by observation and verified by cytological procedures. These plants are usually frail in structure with small leaves, low viability, and a high degree of sterility. Sterility is attributed to irregularities at meiosis. Obviously, no pairing is possible because only one set of chromosomes is present. Therefore, if the meiotic process succeeds at all, the dispersal of chromosomes to the poles is irregular and the resulting gametes are highly inviable. Because monoploids undergo no segregation and carry a single set of genes, they are invaluable experimental tools when they can be produced successfully. Microorganisms in general are useful to geneticists because they are propagating monoploids.

The diploid with two genomes ($2n$) is most common among euploids. Normal chromosome behavior in animals and plants is based on diploids, which are used in the following examples as standards for comparison.

## POLYPLOIDY

Organisms with three or more genomes are polyploids. Polyploidy is common in the plant world. Fully one-half of all known plant genera contain polyploids, and about two-thirds of all the grasses are polyploids, but polyploids are rarely seen in animals. One reason is that the sex balance in animals is much more delicate than that in plants. As we noted in Chapter 5, the addition of chromosomes above the diploid number gives rise to intersexes that do not reproduce. Sterility in animals is virtually always associated with a departure from the diploid number. The few animals (such as the brine shrimp, *Artemia salina*) that show evidence of polyploidy utilize parthenogenesis to escape the hazard of anomalous gametes.

An exceptional case of triploidy in salamanders related to *Ambystoma jeffersonianum* has been reported. Female salamanders of this particular group having large erythrocytes and erythrocyte nuclei, produced some triploid larvae with 42 chromosomes whereas those with small erythrocytes and erythrocyte nuclei produced diploid larvae with 28 chromosomes. Field observations and laboratory studies indicated that distinct, persisting populations of triploid females had become established in parts of the range occupied by this species complex.

Although animals composed entirely of polyploid cells are rare, many diploid animals have polyploid cells within certain tissues of their bodies. In teleostean embryos, for example, giant nuclei, presumably polyploid, have been observed in many species. Giant polyploid nuclei occur in particular tissues of a wide range of diploid animals.

### *Polyploidy in Plants*

Two basic irregular processes have been discovered by which polyploids may evolve from diploid plants and become established in nature. (1) Somatic doubling: cells sometimes undergo irregularities at mitosis and give rise to meristematic cells that perpetuate these irregularities in new generations of plants. (2) Reproductive cells may have an irregular reduction or equation division in which the sets of chromosomes fail to separate completely to the poles at anaphase. Both sets thus become incorporated in the same nucleus resulting in a doubling of chromosome number in the gamete. Both of these irregularities occur in nature. Once polyploidy is established, intercrossing among plants with different chromosome numbers may give rise to numerous chromosome combinations that are then under the influence of natural selection. All degrees of viability are encountered, from lethal combinations to those that compete favorably with diploids in particular environmental situations.

Two main kinds of polyploids, auto- and allopolyploids, may be distinguished on the basis of the source of chromosomes. Autopolyploids occur when the same genome is duplicated. Apparently, it is a rather frequent occurrence in single cells of many plants, but these cells usually do not survive. Among salamanders, autopolyploidy is common in nature. Allopolyploids result when different genomes come together through hybridization. Usually it is impossible to determine whether the genomes are alike and therefore whether the polyploids are auto- or allopolyploids unless information from ancestral history is available and detailed chromosome studies are performed.

The presence of varying numbers of quadrivalents (that is, four homologous chromosomes instead of the usually two pairing with one another in synapsis) suggests autopolyploidy. Unequal segregation of chromosomes in quadrivalents is one reason why autopolyploids possess varying degrees of sterility. In the meiotic prophase, chromosomes must pair with one another throughout their entire length. When four similar chromosomes are present, they usually pair with different chromosomes at different places along their length, thus complicating the meiotic process and frequently resulting in unequal disjunction and other meiotic irregularities, thus giving rise to inviable cells. Unequal chromosome pairing is not the whole basis for sterility in autopolyploids. Unequal disjunction occurs and there are other, perhaps more important factors, but none of these is well enough established to permit discussion here. Chromosomes in some autopolyploids appear to pair properly and form bivalents rather than quadrivalents.

Some plant groups have a series of chromosome numbers based on a multiple of a basic number. In the genus Chrysanthemum, for example, the basic number is 9, and species are known that have 18, 36, 54, 72, and 90 chromosomes. In Solanum, the genus of nightshades including the potato, *S. tuberosum,* the basic number is 12. Members of this genus include species with 24, 36, 48, 60, 72, 96, 108, 120, and 144 chromosomes. In spite of such conspicuous examples, however, where autopolyploidy would appear superficially to be involved in the origin of plants with different chromosome numbers, it is doubtful that autopolyploidy alone has played a major role in the evolution of plant groups. Inviability and sterility would seem to preclude the perpetuation of true autopolyploids in nature. Autopolyploidy combined with allopolyploidy however, resulting in "autoallopolyploids" has apparently been an important process in the evolution of some plants.

Triploids ($3n$) with three genomes occur sporadically as a result of fertilization between unreduced ($2n$) and normal ($n$) gametes. Failure of reduction occurs commonly in many diploid plants, resulting in gametes with more than a single genome. Triploids do not ordinarily become established in nature because of irregularity during meiosis, which results in sterility and low survival. Plants that can be vegetatively reproduced, however, may be preserved as triploids. Gravenstein and Baldwin apples are perpetuated by grafting and budding and thus maintain their triploid characteristics. Tulips with three sets of chromosomes ($3n$) are also propagated by vegetative means. Triploids occurring in grasses, vegetables, and flower garden varieties are less stable and less fertile than corresponding diploids.

Tetraploids ($4n$) have four genomes. They most frequently originate by doubling of diploids, but many arise through intercrossing among various polyploids. They also may result from the duplication of somatic chromosomes following irregularities at mitosis. If the spindle does not develop properly in the mitotic sequence of a diploid, and cell division fails to follow chromosome duplication, a single nuclear membrane may develop around the two sets of chromosomes that ordinarily would produce daughter nuclei. The resulting restitution nucleus contains four sets of chromosomes instead of the usual two. If this tetraploid cell perpetuates itself through normal mitosis, the increased chromosome number may become established in a group of cells or tissues within the organism. When such plants are capable of vegetative reproduction, they may be manipulated to produce whole tetraploid plants. Failure at reduction division in the oöcytes of some plants results in tetraploids. Chromosome irregularity is rare in mature pollen because developing male gametes that have irregular chromosome numbers do not compete favorably with normal gametes.

The low fertility and marked phenotypic variation associated with chromosome irregularity are illustrated in Fig. 10.24. A cross was made between Polish wheat *T. polonicum,* a tetraploid with large, amber kernels, and Marquis, a hexaploid with hard, red kernels. The entire $F_2$ from the cross is shown in the illustration. Only a

**Fig. 10.24** Heads of wheat resulting from a cross between Polish with 28 chromosomes and Marquis with 42 chromosomes. These are the only heads produced from an extensive experiment, indicating the low fertility encountered in crosses between plants with different chromosome numbers.

few plants were produced from an extensive experiment and those observed showed wide variation.

Tetraploids occasionally have greater commercial value than corresponding diploids. In some cases, the plants themselves are larger and more deeply colored, and they may bear larger fruits and seeds. Sometimes tetraploids have larger cells with correspondingly larger nuclei than do diploids. Stomata and epidermal cells are often larger, fewer, and arranged in different patterns as compared with those of diploids. Distinctive physiological characteristics also make tetraploids more valuable commercially than diploids; some grow better in a wider range of habitats. Fruits of tetraploid tomatoes have a higher vitamin C content than do those of diploids. Kernels of yellow tetraploid maize are reported to contain more vitamin A than those of the corresponding diploids.

Both autopolyploidy and allopolyploidy have occurred in various plant groups, and some present-day plants have resulted from such a combination. The distinction between allo- and autopolyploidy in natural populations is therefore a matter of degree. Allopolyploids originate through hybridization. Some polyploid species that were self-established in nature have genomes that correspond more or less completely to the combined chromosome complements of different but related diploid plants. Some authors have referred to these as amphidiploids. Presumably, such polyploids encompass hybridization somewhere in their ancestral history. Allopolyploidy thus represents a method by which new species may be formed immediately in nature, whereas autopolyploidy alone results in cell-division anomalies and "dead ends" with reference to evolution.

### *Polyploidy and Plant Evolution*

As suggested earlier in this chapter, polyploidy combined with interspecific hybridization provides a mechanism by which new species may arise suddenly in nature. E. Anderson has shown this process to be important in the evolution of many plant groups. In one of his investigations, the blueflag, *Iris versicolor* with 108 chromosomes, was shown to have the doubled chromosome complement of a hybrid derived from a 72-chromosome iris of the Mississippi Valley and a 36-chromosome arctic iris from Alaska. Evidently these species, now separated geographically, had grown near each other at some time in their ancestral history. E. B. Babcock concluded, from his elaborate analysis of 196 species of Crepis, that polyploidy was involved in the formation of about 8 percent of the species in that genus.

Early in the nineteenth century, some seeds of the American marsh grass, *Spartina alterniflora,* were accidentally transported by ship to Bayonne, France, and Southampton, England. The American species became established in the same localities where a European marsh grass, *S. stricta,* was growing. A new marsh grass, *S. townsendii,* commonly called Townsend's grass, was later identified in these localities. By 1907 it had become common along the coast of southern England and northern France. Townsend's grass was more vigorous and aggressive than either the American or the European species and had crowded out the native grasses in many places. It therefore was intentionally introduced into Holland to help support the dikes and it was also imported into other localities for similar purposes. Townsend's grass was considered to be a hybrid between the American and European species but, unlike most hybrids, it was fertile and true breeding. The European grass had 56 chromosomes, the American species 70, and Townsend's grass 126. These facts suggested that a cross had occurred in which allopolyploidy was involved. Townsend's grass had the sum of the diploid chromosomes carried by the two species. This evidence, along with the high fertility and intermediate appearance, indicated that the new plant arose from natural hybridization and doubling of chromosomes. The chromosome doubling had presumably given the hybrid its properties for fertility and survival.

In an early experiment, the Russian cytologist G. D. Karpechenko synthesized what might be considered a new species from crosses between two common vegetables belonging to different genera, the radish, *Raphanus sativus,* and the cabbage, *Brassica oleracea.* Although these plants were only distantly related, they were enough alike to be crossed successfully. Both had 9 pairs of chromosomes. The diploid hybrid had 18 pairs of chromosomes, 9 from each parent, but it was sterile and could not perpetuate itself, largely because of the failure in pairing between the unlike chromosomes in meiosis. Some unreduced gametes were formed, however, and in the $F_2$ population Karpechenko recovered some tetraploids. When the chromosomes of the $F_1$ hybrid were doubled in this way, a fertile polyploid named Raphanobrassica was produced with 18 radish and 18 cabbage chromosomes. Because two sets of chromosomes were now present from each parental variety, pairing was quite regular. Normal gametes were produced and a high degree of fertility was obtained. This experiment had theoretical significance because it demonstrated a method by which fertile interspecific hybrids could be produced. It also suggested the possibility of incorporating desirable genotypes from two different species into a new polyploid species. Seed capsules of the parents, the sterile hybrid, and the tetraploid plants of Karpechenko's experiment are shown in Fig. 10.25. Unfortunately from the practical standpoint, Raphanobrassica had the foliage of a radish and the root of a cabbage. The cross gave hope, however, that more practical results could follow similar combinations in other plants.

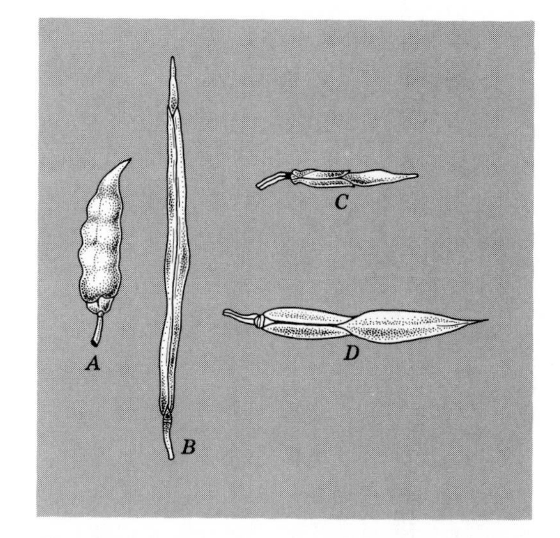


**Fig. 10.25** Seed pods of (*A*) radish (Raphanus), with 18R chromosomes; (*B*) cabbage (Brassica); with 18B chromosomes; (*C*) sterile diploid hybrid with 9R + 9B chromosomes; and (*D*) tetraploid resulting from chromosome doubling, with 18R + 18B chromosomes. (After Karpechenko)

The primrose, *Primula kewensis,* is an allotetraploid with 36 ($2n$) chromosomes. It was derived from a cross between two diploids *P. floribunda* ($n = 9$) and *P. verticillata* ($n = 9$). Plants from these two species could be crossed readily, producing hybrids with 18 chromosomes in their vegetative cells, 9 from *P. floribunda* and 9 from *P. verticillata,* but the hybrids were sterile. A branch on a hybrid plant had developed from a cell in which the chromosome number was doubled (36). This branch was propagated and it gave rise to a fertile primrose plant with cells containing 36 chromosomes. In Fig. 10.26, metaphase chromosomes of the two diploid parents, the sterile diploid hybrid, and the fertile tetraploid hybrid are shown. The figwort, *Digitalis mertonensis* (56 chromosomes), is likewise an allotetraploid, having arisen

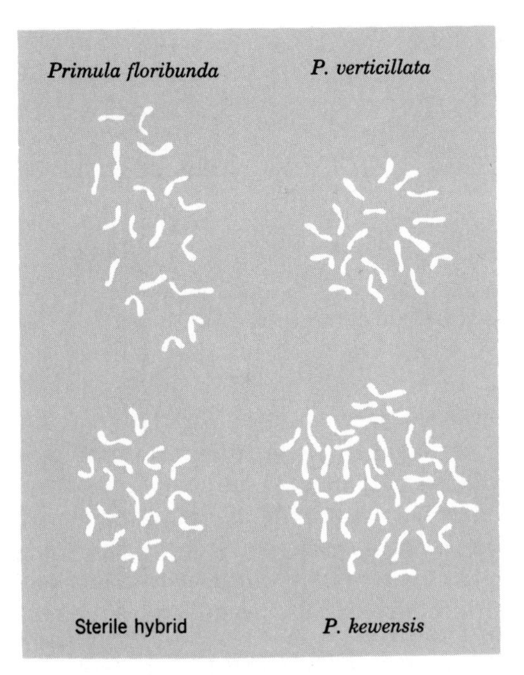


**Fig. 10.26** Chromosomes of *Primula floribunda, P. verticillata,* the sterile hybrid, and the allotetraploid, *P. kewensis*. The 2 parents and the hybrid each have 18 chromosomes, whereas the fertile tetraploid *P. kewensis* has 36 chromosomes.

from a cross between *D. purpurea* ($n = 28$) and *D. ambigua* ($n = 28$).

Müntzing, working with diploid and tetraploid species of Galeopsis, found that one of the tetraploids, *G. tetrahit* with 32 chromosomes, could be synthesized from crosses involving the diploid species, *G. pubescens* and *G. speciosa* ($2n = 16$). *G. tetrahit* is not a strict amphidiploid but arose from a backcross between a triploid $F_2$ plant with 24 chromosomes and one of the parents, *G. pubescens*. The increase in chromosome number was due to the functioning of unreduced gametes. These observations and experimental verification have substantiated the function of polyploidy in the evolution of some plant groups. Among the most interesting aspects of such work were the duplications in the laboratory of natural processes that have been involved in the origin of species. Several species that already exist in nature have been synthesized in the laboratory.

### *Induced Polyploidy*

Polyploids have been induced experimentally by several methods in a number of different plants. Any mechanism that interferes with spindle formation during mitosis might result in a doubling of the chromosomes. Induced polyploidy was first demonstrated by subjecting certain growing plants to a higher than usual temperature. Maize and some other plants responded to temperature treatment, and the chromosome number of certain cells was increased. Some of these cells gave rise to germinal tissue and whole plants were propagated. Other such cells were cultured artificially and polyploid plants were produced. Another early method used in tomatoes was that of decapitation. When the bud was removed, some shoots developing from scar tissue would be tetraploid. These were propagated and whole plants with $4n$ chromosomes were produced.

The method of inducing polyploidy in plants that has become most widely used was developed by Blakeslee, A. G. Avery, and B. R. Nebel in 1937. These investigators found that an alkaloid, colchicine, extracted from the autumn crocus plant, *Colchicum autumnale,* could produce a disturbance in spindle formation during cell division. When root tips or other growing plant parts were placed in appropriate concentrations of colchicine, chromosomes of treated cells duplicated themselves properly, but spindle formation was inhibited. Therefore, the cytoplasmic phase of cell division did not occur. Restitution nuclei with different numbers of chromosomes were produced in the treated tissue. Some cells occurred with completely doubled chromosome number. When these cells were propagated, tetraploid plants were produced and tetraploid seed was obtained.

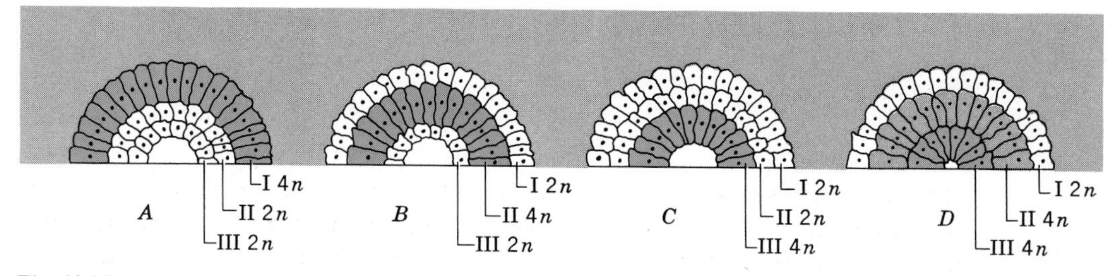


**Fig. 10.27** Diagrams illustrating 3 cell layers found in the stem tips of a plant. These diagrams illustrate a mechanism by which chromosome doubling may be reflected in various parts of the plant, including the reproductive cells.

In some plants, new growing areas at the stem tips and lateral buds have three distinct cell layers, as illustrated in Fig. 10.27. Cells from each layer are much alike in early stages of development, but later they give rise to separate tissues in stems, leaves, and other organs. The outer layer (I) becomes the epidermis, the middle layer (II) gives rise to the reproductive cells (eggs and pollen), and the inner layer (III) produces the internal parts of stems and leaves. Colchicine placed in the medium of the growing tips may interfere with division and result in transformation of $2n$ cells into $4n$ cells in one or more layers. Cells usually divide vertically in such a way that the number within a given layer is increased. In examples *A*, *B*, and *C*, the $4n$ cells are restricted to the first, second, and third layer, respectively. Sometimes cells divide horizontally and the daughter cells enter a new layer. Thus, a doubled ($4n$) cell in layer III may give rise to a $4n$ cell in layer II, as shown in *D*. This pattern of irregularity may extend $4n$ cells to the reproductive tissue and thus provide a means of perpetuating $4n$ cells in a new plant. By propagating tetraploid tissue, it is possible to produce tetraploid plants.

Other chemicals (for instance, acenaphthene and indole acetic acid) have been employed for the doubling of chromosome number in some plants. The action of these reagents on plant cells, however, is not clear. C. L. Huskins and L. M. Steinitz found in their studies on roots of the oyster plant, *Rheo discolor*, that indole-3-acetic acid stimulated mitosis in regions in which cells ordinarily divide infrequently. The reagent merely induced cells that were already polyploid to divide and did not produce initial chromosome doubling.

### *Experimental Production of Polyploids*

Among the cultivated varieties of wheat, three different chromosome numbers are represented: 14, 28, and 42. For example, the primitive small-grained einkorn type of Europe and Asia, *Triticum monococcum*, has 14 chromosomes in its vegetative cells. Its yield is low and it is of comparatively little value. An emmer wheat, (durum) *T. dicoccum*, grown chiefly in northern Europe but also in the United States, has 28 chromosomes. It has thick heads with large hard kernels and is used mainly for macaroni, spaghetti, and stock feed. The bread wheats, *T. estivatum*, have 42 chromosomes. J. Percival (1863–1949) of England postulated that bread wheat came from a cross between emmer wheat and goat grass (Aegilops), which is native to the Babylonian region where bread wheat originated.

When techniques for artificial chromosome doubling became established, investigations on the origin of bread wheat were resumed and Percival's theory was confirmed. Experimental evidence obtained by E. S. McFadden, E. R. Sears, and H.

Kihara has established the origin of one type of bread wheat, *T. spelta*. These investigators doubled the chromosome numbers of an emmer wheat and of a wild goat grass, *Aegilops squarrosa,* with colchicine and made a cross similar to the one that had apparently occurred in nature. The hybrid had 42 chromosomes, 28 from the wheat parent and 14 from the goat grass parent. It was phenotypically similar to primitive forms of bread wheat. The decisive genetic test was made by crossing the synthesized wheat with *T. spelta*. Hybrids were fertile and evidenced normal chromosome behavior. These experiments indicated that a moderately useful wheat and a useless weed had, at sometime in the past, hybridized in nature and produced forerunners of man's valuable plant crop, wheat.

Analysis of the possible origin of New World cotton provides another example of polyploidy occurring in nature which can be duplicated in the laboratory. Interspecific crosses can be made between distinct species of cotton, Gossypium. The hybrids show a wide range of vigor and fertility, making the material favorable for studies of speciation. Three cytological groups have been found to correspond with the major world distributional areas. Old World cotton has 13 pairs of large chromosomes. American cotton, which originated in Central or South America, has 13 pairs of small chromosomes. New World cotton (the cultivated long-staple type) has 26 pairs, 13 large and 13 small. Evidently, hybridization and chromosome duplication occurred somewhere in the ancestry of this type of cotton. J. O. Beasley used the colchicine technique and succeeded in doubling the chromosomes of a hybrid between Old World and American cotton. The resulting hybrids, with four sets of chromosomes (amphidiploids), crossed readily among themselves and produced fertile plants resembling New World cotton. The process by which the valuable polyploid cotton may have originated in nature was thus duplicated in the laboratory. More detailed chromosome studies are now in progress to determine whether the origin was ancient or more recent and to analyze the genetic and cytological relations among different kinds of cotton.

Interesting experiments that make use of induced polyploidy and cytological analysis in certain grasses have been conducted by W. S. Boyle, A. H. Holmgren, and their associates. A completely sterile perennial grass was observed in Cache Valley, Utah, and in several other locations. On the basis of its sterility and morphological characteristics, the grass was tentatively identified as a natural hybrid between two genera in the tribe Hordeae. Examination of the Hordeae species in the vicinity of the hybrids indicated that the two parents were probably *Agropyron trachycaulum* and *Hordeum jubatum* (Fig. 10.28). Cytological studies on the two presumed parents and the hybrid supported this view. Both *A. trachycaulum* and *H. jubatum* were found to be allotetraploids ($2n = 28$). During meiosis of both species, normal pairing of chromosomes occurred to form 14 paired chromosomes (bivalents). The sterile hybrid was also a tetraploid with the same chromosome number ($2n = 28$), but its chromosome behavior during the meiotic process was highly irregular (Fig. 10.29). Fourteen unpaired chromosomes (univalents) and 7 bivalents were frequently observed at metaphase in pollen mother cells. Many lagging chromosomes remained in the center of the spindle during anaphase, and numerous small micronuclei, reflecting chromosome irregularity, were observed following division. No viable pollen was produced. These observations indicated that meiotic irregularity was a major factor in the sterility.

Sterile hybrids were produced through

**Fig. 10.28** Spikes of parents and hybrid from cross. *A*, *Agropyron trachycaulum;* *B*, $F_1$ hybrid; *C*, *Hordeum jubatum*. (Courtesy of W. S. Boyle.)

controlled reciprocal crosses between *A. trachycaulum* and *H. jubatum,* thus confirming the predicted parentage. The hybrids were then treated with colchicine. Some stalks or culms with doubled chromosome numbers (octoploids) were produced and set seed. All this seed was viable and produced fertile plants considered to be autoalloploids. This name was applied because both auto- and allopolyploidy had entered into the formation of the fertile octoploid. Chromosome studies indicated that the two parents carried a genome in common. Therefore, the genomic formulas of the parents were represented as *AABB* and *AACC*. The sterile hybrid was *AABC* and the colchicine-induced octoploid was *AAAABBCC* (Fig. 10.30).

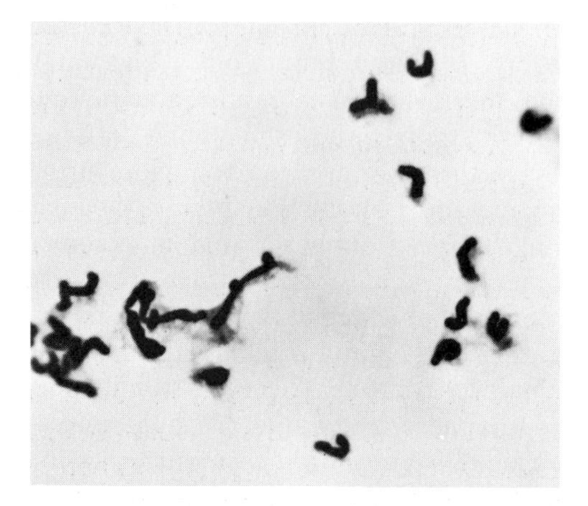

**Fig. 10.29** Chromosomes of the sterile hybrid between *A. trachycaulum* and *H. jubatum* during meiosis. Seven bivalents and 14 single chromosomes were frequently found as in this photograph. (Courtesy of W. S. Boyle.)

### *Practical Applications of Polyploidy*

Although induced polyploidy has not been exploited to a great extent, practical applications may become more common as additional data are accumulated. By artificially induced polyploidy, disease resistance and other desirable qualities have been incorporated into some commercial crop plants. Tobacco, *Nicotiana tabacum,* for example, was susceptible to the tobacco mosaic virus, whereas *N. glutinosa* appeared at first observation to be resistant. Further investigation however, showed that in *N. glutinosa* the virus killed the cells that were invaded and the virus particles became isolated in the dead cells. The apparent resistance thus was attributable to hypersensitivity. When the two tobacco species were crossed, the hybrid was found to be "resistant" to the virus but totally sterile. When the chromosomes were doubled, it was possible to secure a fertile polyploid, "resistant" to the virus.

Some varieties of plants that serve man's purposes more effectively than others have now been identified as polyploids. Many polyploids were selected and cultivated because of their large size, vigor, and ornamental values, before their chromosome numbers were known. Giant "sports" from twigs of McIntosh apple trees that were found to be tetraploid ($4n$) were

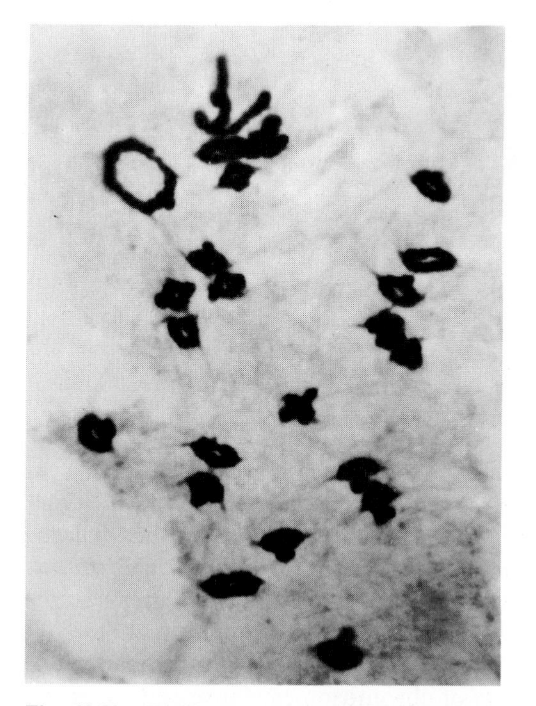

**Fig. 10.30** Diakinesis stage of colchicine-induced octoploid. In this photograph the following chromosome associations are present: 1 ring of 4; 22 rings of 2; 3 rods of 2; and 2 single chromosomes, making a total of 56. (Courtesy of W. S. Boyle.)

propagated into whole trees, which produce extra large fruit. The texture of the giant apples is as fine as that of diploids. They are inferior in yield, but mass selection of seedlings may overcome this difficulty. Bartlett pears, several varieties of grapes, and cranberries have also produced sports with giant fruits. Some of these show promise of practical usefulness. With colchicine treatment, a number of polyploids have been developed artificially. This technique has provided a way to explore the mechanism involved in polyploid formation and to make use of the good qualities of polyploids. Tetraploid ($4n$) maize is more vigorous than the ordinary diploid, and produces some 20 percent more Vitamin A. Its fertility is somewhat reduced, but this drawback responds to selection. Polyploid watermelons have been developed by colchicine treatment by Kihara and others. The tetraploid with 44 chromosomes is large and has practical value. Triploid watermelons with 33 chromosomes are especially desirable because they are sterile and have no seeds.

It is possible to produce $4n$ plants from injured parts of tomato seedlings. $4n$ plants can also be produced from seed but these are usually weak and sterile. Tetraploid clover has several desirable characteristics, but the seeds are usually abortive and infertile. If this difficulty can be overcome in some way, $4n$ clover may attain practical usefulness. Among the cereal crops, all tetraploid barley thus far produced is autotetraploid and of no value. In oats and wheat, on the other hand, the polyploids are allopolyploids and represent the best commercial strains. Among the flower garden varieties, $4n$ marigolds and snapdragons are widely cultivated.

Polyploid plants respond to artificial selection and hybridization, as do diploid species. The recent history of plant breeding has been characterized by a marked improvement in many polyploid plant crops. The yield of wheat, for example, has increased appreciably. This has been accomplished by developing disease-resistant strains and breeding for increased hardiness and greater efficiency under various environmental conditions available in wheat growing areas. A constant threat to the wheat crop is rust, a fungus that attacks the stems and leaves of the growing plants and destroys the ripening grain. Spores are borne by wind, and when conditions are right they spread like fire through wheat fields. The disease can be combated by developing rust-resistant strains and by eradicating barberry bushes, which are hosts to the spores during the spring months. But the rust keeps evolving new varieties that destroy previously resistant grain, thus perpetuating the job of plant breeders.

**Fig. 10.31** Wheat kernels illustrating the advantage of rust resistance. Left, rust-resistant wheat; right, rust-susceptible wheat, similar in other respects to the strain represented at left. (Courtesy of Utah State Experiment Station.)

The advantage of incorporating rust resistance is illustrated in Fig. 10.31. The larger kernels at the left are from a new strain of rust-resistant spring wheat. At the right are shown kernels of wheat, similar in other respects, but not resistant, which are dwarfed from the infection with stem rust. The number of kernels of grain per plant as well as the size of the kernels is decreased by rust infection. Investigators in experiment stations are constantly alert for new rusts. When a new one is found, the standard wheat varieties are tested against it. If they are not resistant, breeding programs are initiated immediately to develop new strains resistant to that particular rust.

## SUMMARY

A particular chromosome number is a characteristic of cells of plant and animal species. The normal range in different organisms extends from one pair to several hundred chromosomes. Euploids have whole sets ($n$ or multiples of $n$) of chromosomes. Aneuploids deviate from the base number by one, two, or a few chromosomes (for example, $2n + 1$; $2n - 1$). Human beings have 23 pairs of chromosomes. Irregularities in number such as loss of one or the gain of one or more have been associated with abnormal syndromes. Nondisjunction of chromosomes in meiosis will account for most of the aneuploid variations. Irregular mitotic division will account for chromosome mosaics in individual organisms.

Polyploids, which are multiples of whole sets of chromosomes (for example, $2n$, $3n$, $4n$), are common among plants but uncommon among animals. In some plant groups, polyploidy has been an important factor in evolution. By using colchicine and some other agents that interfere with cell division, polyploids can be induced. Some polyploids have more desirable phenotypes than corresponding diploids and therefore have practical value.

## REFERENCES

Allen, G. 1960. "Symposium on cytology and cell culture genetics of man." *Amer. J. Human Genet.*, **12,** 95–138.

Anderson, E. 1949. *Introgressive hybridization.* John Wiley and Sons, New York.

Bergsma, D. 1966. Chicago Conference: standardization in human cytogenetics. *Birth Defects,* **2(2),** 1–20.

Blakeslee, A. F. 1941. "Effect of induced polyploidy in plants." *Amer. Natur.*, **75,** 117–135. (Colchicine treatment for inducing polyploidy.)

Bridges, C. B. 1916. "Nondisjunction as proof of the chromosome theory of heredity." *Genetics,* **1,** 1–52.

Burnham, C. R. 1962. *Discussions in cytogenetics.* Burgess Publishing Co., Minneapolis.

Chu, E. H. Y., and N. H. Giles. 1959. "Human chromosome complements in normal somatic cells in culture." *Amer. J. Human Genetics,* **11,** 63–79.

Clausen, J., D. D. Keck, and W. H. Hiesey. 1945. "Experimental studies on the nature of species. II. Plant evolution through amphiploidy and autoploidy, with examples from Madiinae." Carnegie Inst. Wash. Publ. 564.

Dawson, G. W. P. 1962. *An introduction to the cytogenetics of polyploidy.* Blackwell Scientific Publications, Oxford.

Demerec, M. (ed.). 1947. *Advances in Genetics.* Vol. I. Academic Press, New York. (This volume includes a concise review of cytogenetics and speciation in Crepis by E. B. Babcock, a discussion of the origin and evolution of maize by P. C. Mangelsdorf, a classification of polyploids by G. L. Stebbins, Jr., and a review of the origin and cytogenetics of New World cotton by S. G. Stephens.)

Ferguson-Smith, M. A. 1961. "Chromosomes in human disease." Chapter 8 in *Medical Genetics.* Steinberg, A. G. (ed.), Grune and Stratton, New York.

McFadden, E. S., and E. R. Sears. 1946. "The origin of *Triticum spelta* and its free-threshing hexaploid relatives." *J. Hered.,* **37,** 107–116.

McKusick, V. A. (ed.). 1961. *Medical genetics 1958–1960.* C. V. Mosby Co., St. Louis. (Human chromosome studies are included.)

Müntzing, A. 1961. *Genetic research.* Stockholm Lts Förlag. (Chapter 25 is a discussion of polyploidy.)

Sasaki, M. S., and S. Makino. 1962. "Revised study of the chromosomes of domestic cattle and the horse." *J. Hered.,* **53,** 157–162.

Sears, E. R. 1948. "The cytology and genetics of wheats and their relatives." *Advances in Genetics,* Vol. 2. M. Demerec (ed.), Academic Press, New York.

Stebbins, G. L., Jr. 1950. *Variation and evolution in plants.* Columbia University Press, New York.

Stebbins, G. L. 1951. "Cataclysmic evolution." *Sci. Amer.,* **184(4),** 54–59. (Modern wheat, cotton, and tobacco evolved rapidly by hybridization and chromosome doubling.)

Stevenson, A. C. (ed.) British Medical Bulletin. September 17(3). Grune and Stratton, New York.

Sutton, H. E. 1965. *An introduction to human genetics.* Holt, Rinehart, and Winston, New York.

Swanson, C. P., T. Mertz, and W. J. Young. 1967. *Cytogenetics.* Prentice-Hall, Englewood Cliffs, New Jersey.

Uchida, I. A., A. J. Lewis, J. M. Bowman, and H. C. Wang. 1962. "A case of double trisomy: trisomy No. 18 and triplo-X." *J. Pediatrics,* **60,** 498–502.

Uchida, I. A., K. Patau, and D. W. Smith. 1962. "Dermal patterns of 18 and D. trisomics." *Amer. J. Human Genet.,* **14,** 345–352.

Whittinghill, M. 1965. *Genetics and its foundations.* Rinehold, New York.

Yunis, J. J. (ed.). 1965. *Human chromosome methodology.* Academic Press, New York.

# *Problems*

**10.1** What is the significance of chromosome numbers in (a) taxonomy; and (b) studies of evolution in plants and animals?

**10.2** The Poinsetta type of Datura carries an extra member of the chromosome set ($2n + 1$) in which the genes for purple ($p^+$) and white ($p$) flower color are located. From the following crosses, give the expected proportions of purple and white. (Female parent is always written first. Female gametes may carry either 1 or 2 chromosomes of this set, but viable pollen carries only a single chromosome.) (a) $p^+p^+p \times p^+p^+p$; (b) $p^+p^+p \times p^+p$; (c) $p^+pp \times p^+p^+p$; and (d) $p^+pp \times p^+p$. (e) How do trisomic ratios differ from the usual Mendelian ratios?

**10.3** Triplo-IV fruit flies have an extra member of the fourth chromosome in which the gene *ey* is located. Give the expected results from a cross between triplo-IV flies of the genotype $ey^+ey^+ey$ and diplo-IV, $ey^+ey$, flies in terms of (a) $2n$ and $2n + 1$; and (b) eyeless and normal eye phenotypes.

**10.4** How can aneuploidy be used as a tool to identify genes with chromosomes?

**10.5** Why are tetrasomics and nullisomics found in nature less frequently than trisomics?

**10.6** What values, potential if not realized at present, could monoploids have for genetic studies?

**10.7** Why were critical chromosome studies in man not carried out before 1956?

**10.8** (a) Why is it difficult to identify individual human chromosomes? (b) What criteria were used by the groups at Denver, London, and Chicago to distinguish chromosomes?

**10.9** (a) What evidence concerning the influence of the Y chromosome on sex determination in man can be obtained by comparing the characteristics of XO, XXY, and XXX individuals? (b) Compare the influence of the human Y chromosome on sex determination with that of Drosophila and Melandrium Y chromosomes (see Chapter 4).

**10.10** According to the Lyon hypothesis (Chapter 5) all but one X chromosome in multi-X individuals degenerate and form sex chromatin bodies. How many sex chromatin bodies would be expected to occur in a cell from a person with (a) Turner's syndrome, (b) trisomic X, and (c) Down's syndrome (47,XXG)?

**10.11** How can human trisomy be explained?

**10.12** What is the (a) theoretical and (b) practical significance of the Philadelphia chromosome?

**10.13** If Down's syndrome occurs in 1/700 births in the general population (a) what is the chance that two cases will be recorded in a city hospital in the same day? (b) If the number of live births for a given year in a country is 42,000,000, how many would be expected to have Down's syndrome? (c) If 40 percent of the babies with Down's syndrome are born to mothers over 40 years of age and mothers in this age group produce 4 percent of all children, what is the chance that a given woman in this age group would have a baby with Down's syndrome?

**10.14** If nondisjunction of chromosomes No. 21 is known to have occurred in the division of a primary oöcyte in a particular woman and the two 21 chromosomes had remained together in the division of the secondary oöcytes, what is the chance that a mature egg arising from this secondary oöcyte will receive the two No. 21 chromosomes?

**10.15** If Down's syndrome occurs in about 1/700 and Turner's syndrome occurs in about 1/5000 in the general population, and each is separately and randomly distributed in the population, what is the chance that a baby will be born with both of these abnormalities?

**10.16** If X chromosome trisomy occurs in 1/1000 of the general population and No. 18 trisomy occurs in 1/3000, and each is separately and randomly distributed, what is the chance that a baby, such as the one described by Uchida, will be born with both abnormalities? (b) If the mother is over 40 years old and if the increased occurrence of nondisjunction makes mothers in this age group ten times more likely to have babies with each of these abnormalities, what is the probability of the two trisomies occurring in the same baby?

**10.17** Polyploidy is rare in animals, yet some tissues in the bodies of certain diploid animals show evidence of polyploidy. Why do numbers above $2n$ persist in somatic tissues when they do not occur in the whole animal?

**10.18** Describe two methods by which polyploidy might occur in nature.

**10.19** (a) How may autopolyploidy and allopolyploidy originate? (b) Evaluate the significance that each might have in evolution.

**10.20** Why do tetraploids behave more regularly in meiosis than triploids, and perpetuate themselves more readily in populations?

**10.21** How does colchicine treatment result in chromosome doubling in plants?

**10.22** What (a) practical and (b) theoretical significance may be associated with colchicine-induced polyploidy?

**10.23** How could polyploidy be a significant factor in the evolution of such plants as cotton and wheat?

**10.24** How might new species be produced through a combination of polyploidy and hybridization?

**10.25** Why is chromosome irregularity associated with low fertility in plants?

**10.26** Give a plausible explanation for the origin of (a) *Triticum spelta;* (b) *Raphanobrassica;* (c) *Spartina townsendii;* (d) *Primula kewensis;* and (e) New World cotton.

**10.27** A plant species *A*, which has 7 chromosomes in its gametes, was crossed with a related species *B*, which has 9. Hybrids were produced but they were sterile. Microscopic observations of the pollen mother cells of the $F_1$ showed no pairing of chromosomes. A section of the hybrid that grew vigorously was propagated vegetatively and a plant was produced with 32 chromosomes in its somatic cells. What steps might have been involved?

**10.28** A plant species $A$ ($n = 5$) was crossed with a related species $B$ with $n = 7$. Only a few pollen grains were produced by the $F_1$ hybrid. These were used to fertilize the ovules of species *B*. A few plants were produced with 19 chromosomes. They were highly sterile but following self-fertilization produced a few plants with 24 chromosomes. These plants were different in phenotype from the original parents and the progeny were fertile. What steps might have been involved?

# *Cytoplasmic Inheritance and Maternal Effects* | 11

The transmission of hereditary traits through nuclear genes and chromosomes has been amply demonstrated. Nuclear elements are undoubtedly the most important and very nearly the universal genetic materials. Nevertheless, throughout the history of genetics, sporadic reports have indicated that extranuclear or cytoplasmic elements might act as agents for hereditary transmission. Most examples originally attributed to extranuclear inheritance have been explained by other mechanisms. Some that appeared at first to depend on cytoplasmic factors were shown by further investigations to be ultimately controlled by nuclear genes. In a few cases, however, cytoplasmic DNA has been shown to exist and to function as an information-carrying genetic material.

True cytoplasmic inheritance is defined as inheritance based on independent DNA elements in the cytoplasm. Very few cases of such inheritance completely independent of nuclear genes are known. Maternal effects, which are often difficult to distinguish from true cytoplasmic inheritance, are defined as influences arising in some way from the genes or tissues of the mother. They are transmitted in the egg, sometimes through a cytoplasmic body, but they are controlled by the genes of the mother rather than by those of the developing embryo.

The most useful criterion for initially screening examples in diploid plants and animals which may represent extrachromosomal inheritance from those which depend on Mendelian genes and chromosomes is the difference in results from reciprocal crosses. In Mendelian or chromosomal inheritance, genes from the male and female parent contribute equally to the genetic constitution of the progeny. For example, when females from strain A of a particular animal or plant species are crossed with males from strain B of the same species, usually the offspring produced is comparable to those of the reciprocal cross between females from B and males from A. When a significant difference is detected in the results of reciprocal crosses, cytoplasmic inheritance or a maternal effect may be suspected.

Ordinarily, most of the cytoplasm in a zygote of a diploid organism came from the egg rather than from the sperm or pollen. This has been verified in many diploid animals and a number of plants including maize, *Zea mays;* four-o'clock, *Mirabilis jalapa;* and primrose, *Primula sinensis.* In the willow herb, Epilobium, and the evening primrose, Oenothera, a small amount of cytoplasm is carried by the pollen and a trivial but persistant increment of paternal cytoplasmic (plastid) inheritance has been detected. Some other plants (for instance, the catnip, *Nepeta cataria*) have a much higher proportion of cytoplasm transmitted by the pollen. Among the flowering plants, examples can be found in which nearly as much cytoplasm is contributed by the pollen gamete as by the seed parent gamete to the zygote. In some haploid microorganisms, equal amounts of cytoplasm may come from the male and female. Nevertheless, a difference in the results of reciprocal crosses has been the most useful initial test for suspected cytoplasmic inheritance and maternal effects.

Progress has been slow because it is so difficult to obtain mutational changes or comparisons between standard or "wild-type" and altered or mutant phenotypes. Another difficulty in dealing with maternal inheritance arises from the fact that all traits are transmitted directly from the mother and none come from the father. It is thus impossible to apply the usual method of genetic analysis and follow the segregation of the genes in succeeding generations. If an abnormal or mutant trait is transmitted solely through the maternal line, the mechanism of inheritance is difficult to interpret.

Although the overwhelming majority of heritable variation in higher organisms is controlled by the DNA in the nucleus, the evidence now available does not exclude independent control by the cytoplasm of certain genetic functions. Evidence for cytoplasmic DNA has come mainly, but not exclusively, from plants and microorganisms. Plastid characteristics, male sterility in plants, streptomycin resistance in Chlamydomonas, enzyme-controlled yeast characteristics, killer particles in Paramecium, genoids producing $CO_2$ sensitivity in Drosophila, coiling in snails, eye color in beach hoppers, and the breast-cancer-producing milk virus in mice are the main examples in which cytoplasmic DNA has been indicated. In a few cases (for instance, with some plastid characteristics), inheritance may be controlled by independent plasmagenes or symbionts in the cytoplasm, but most instances are dependent to some extent on nuclear genetic material.

## PLASTID CHARACTERISTICS

The most firmly established cases of true cytoplasmic inheritance are those that involve plastid characteristics. Carl Correns and his associates first described these apparent deviations from Mendelian heredity in 1908, and many examples have been substantiated since that time.

Plastids are minute cytoplasmic organelles in plant cells. Most important are the chloroplastids, which carry chlorophyll, which is basic to the photosynthetic process and is usually responsible for a plant's green color. Plastids arise from smaller cytoplasmic particles (plastid primordia) that contain DNA. They duplicate themselves independently of other cell parts and are distributed more or less equally during cell division. Although some plastids or their primordia are included in the cytoplasm of the egg, few if any are transmitted in the pollen of most plants. Thus, some plastid characteristics are controlled by cytoplasmic inheritance independently of the nuclear genes inherited from the maternal or seed parent.

Nuclear genes, however, are involved in the overall presence or absence of chlorophyll in plants. This is illustrated by albino seedlings, which occur when the plastids entirely lack chlorophyll. In barley, for example, the albino condition is dependent on a recessive nuclear gene *an*, which may be transmitted either through the egg or pollen. Many variations in plant colors depend directly or indirectly on chromosomal genes. Some phenotypes, in which the leaves are mosaics of pale green or even white and dark green areas, are apparently independent of nuclear genes and their occurrence is controlled by the cytoplasm of the maternal line. Some variations in plastids can be traced to mutational changes that occur in the DNA of the plastid primordia and are entirely independent of nuclear genes. Both spontaneous and induced mutations in these cytoplasmic bodies have been reported.

The most widely accepted explanation for mottled or variegated leaves, branches, or whole plants is that two kinds of plastids (or plastid primordia), normal and mutant, are present. Normal green plastids give rise, through independent multiplication followed by cell division, to normal plastids, and mutant forms give rise to abnormal mutant plastids. Daughter cells are ordinarily similar to the parent cells from which they have arisen. Sometimes, in rapidly dividing cells, the multiplication of plastids does not keep pace with cell division and the reduced numbers make chance distribution effective in changing the characteristics of daughter cells. The chance distribution of plastids resulting in different kinds of daughter cells is illustrated in Fig. 11.1. A cell with a small number of abnormal plastids may give rise to a green cell with mostly normal plastids and a nearly colorless cell with all or nearly all abnormal plastids. Daughter

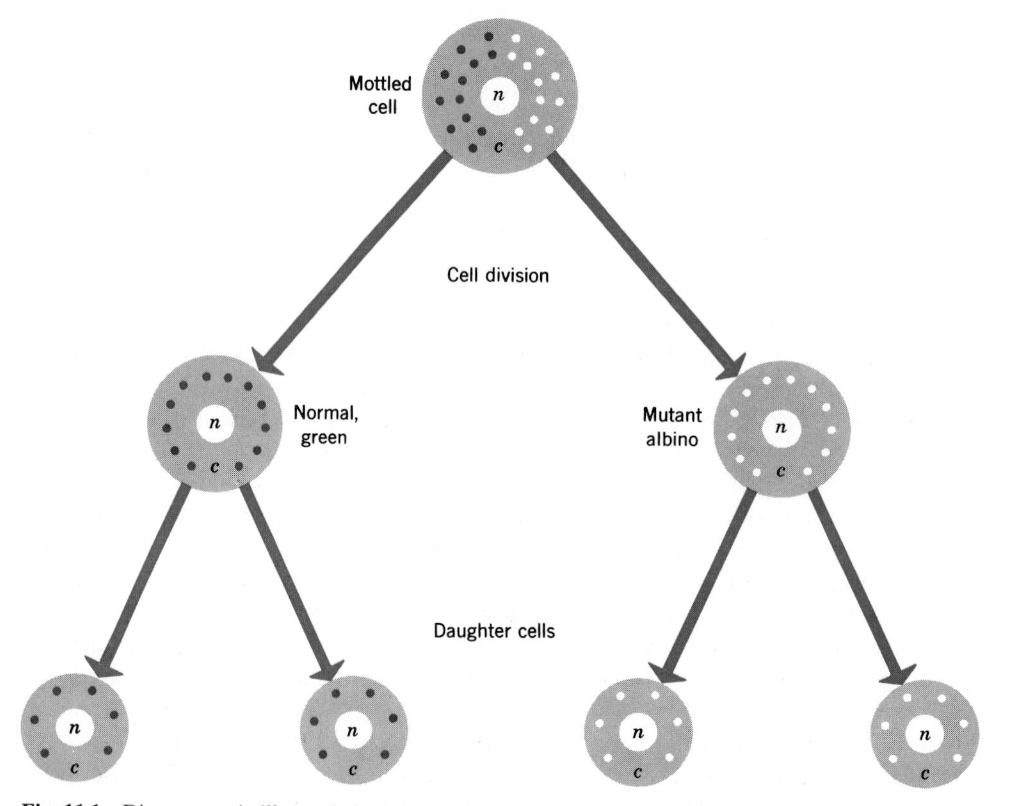


**Fig. 11.1** Diagrammatic illustration of the segregation of plastids in cell division; $n$ = nucleus, and $c$ = cytoplasm.

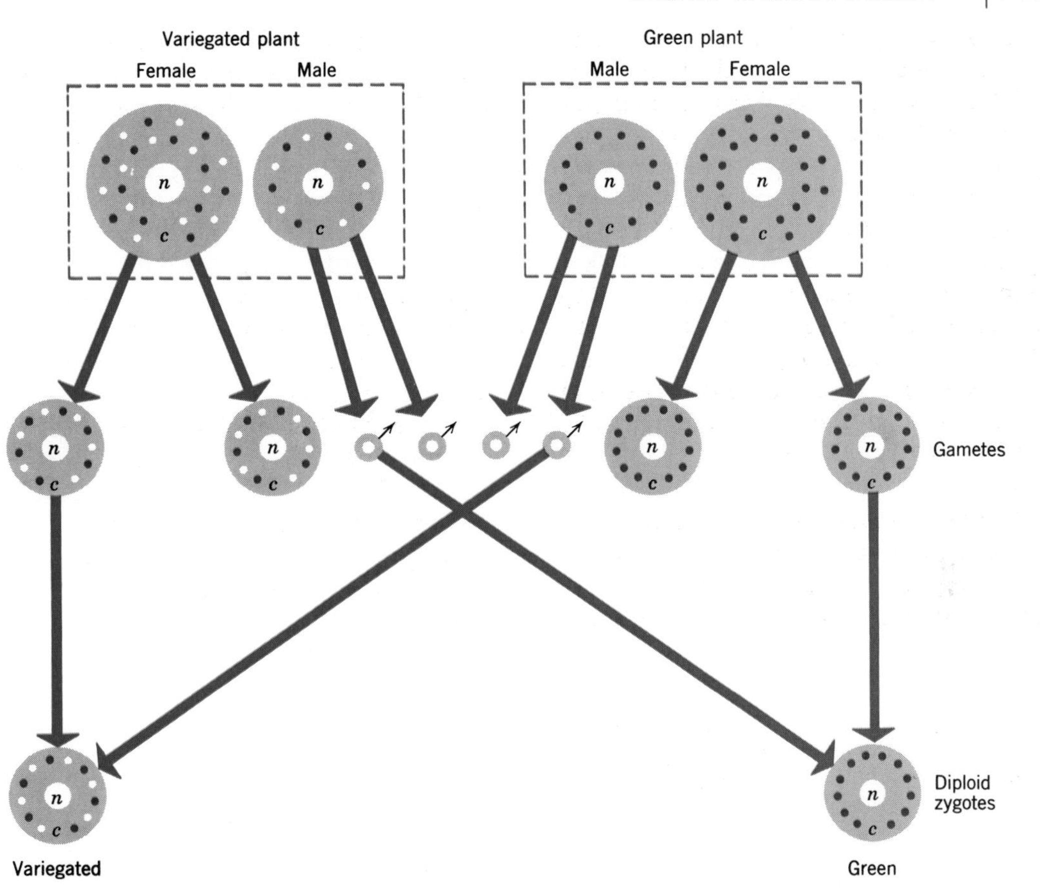


**Fig. 11.2** Diagrammatic illustration of maternal plastid inheritance in a diploid plant such as Mirabilis which has little or no cytoplasm in pollen gametes; $n$ = nucleus, and $c$ = cytoplasm.

cells with only abnormal plastids and those with only normal plastids divide to form cells of their own kind.

Observations in plants such as maize, however, have not supported the hypothesis of mixed normal and abnormal plastids segregating in cell division. Furthermore, too many cell-division cycles seem to be required before phenotypic changes are observable, to account for color variations on the basis of the segregation of mature plastids. One modified hypothesis places the determining factor at the level of a maternally inherited plasmagene that segregates in cell division and gives rise at a later time to the modifications that can be observed phenotypically. An alternative hypothesis assigns the basic abnormality to the cytoplasm itself rather than to individual plastids. This postulates that abnormal or diseased cytoplasm effects the size and general efficiency of developing plastids, resulting in gradations of chlorophyll production (and therefore color) in individual mature plastids which are reflected in color patterns of whole plants or plant sectors.

Ovules as well as somatic cells of mottled plants (for instance, the four-o'clock, *Mirabilis jalapa*) may carry both abnormal nearly colorless and normal green plastids in their cytoplasm (Fig. 11.2). The mottled effect is transmitted through the maternal line generation after generation. Because the pollen of the four-o'clock has little if any cytoplasm, its influence on the variegation is negligible. Single plants with green, white, and variegated branches or sectors may produce seed that perpetuates each of the three types. Seeds borne on white branches contain only primordia for colorless plastids, those on green branches only green, and those borne on variegated branches might contain either colorless or green or a combination of both.

In some other plants, such as the primrose, *P. sinensis,* chimeras are sometimes formed with parts of plants containing chlorophyll and parts without. The parts with abnormal plastids lacking chlorophyll can rely on the green part of the plant for the products of photosynthesis and thus continue to live. Each part may produce reproductive cells and thus transmit its type of plastids through female gametes. Plastid inheritance, independent of chromosomal genes, has been detected in many different plants including the willow herb, Epilobium, which has been studied extensively by Peter Michaelis, and several mosses investigated by Ditter von Wettstein.

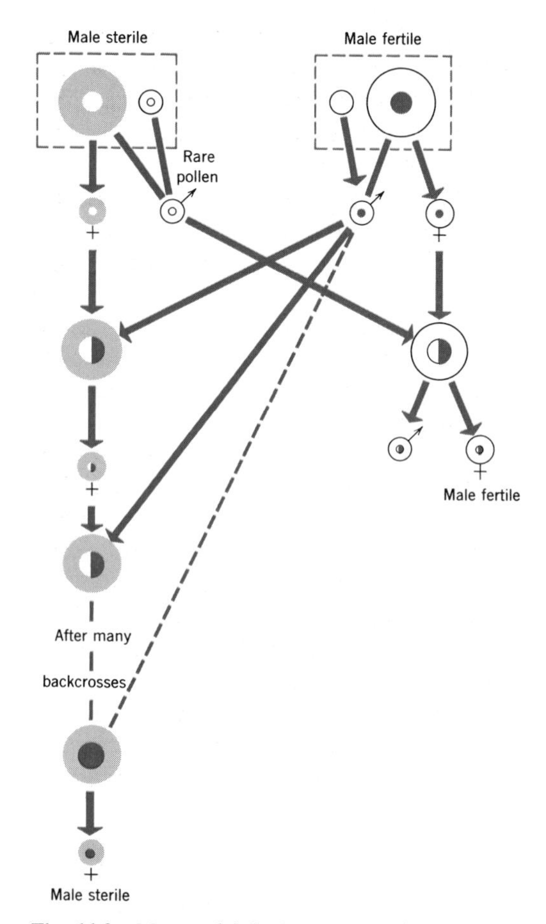


**Fig. 11.3** Maternal inheritance of male sterility in maize. (After Rhoades.)

## MALE STERILITY IN PLANTS

Another example of cytoplasmic inheritance is associated with pollen failure. This occurs in many flowering plants and results in male sterility. In maize, wheat, sugar beets, onions, and some other crop plants, fertility is controlled, at least in part by cytoplasmic factors. Male sterility is also controlled in some plants by nuclear genes. Critical observations and tests must be made to determine the mechanism of inheritance in individual cases.

A classical example of maternal inheritance of male sterility was discovered by M. M. Rhoades in maize (Fig. 11.3). A particular male sterile variety produced only male sterile progeny when fertilized with pollen from normal maize plants. The male sterile seed parent plants were then backcrossed repeatedly with pollen fertile lines until all chromosomes from the male sterile line had been substituted for those of the male fertile line. Male sterility persisted, indicating that inheritance was maternal and was not controlled by chromosomal genes. As the investigation progressed, a small amount of pollen was obtained from the male sterile line making reciprocal crosses possible. Inheritance was maternal regardless of the direction in which the cross was made. Male sterility, in this case, was attributed to cytoplasmic plasmagenes transmitted by female gametes.

The cytoplasmic effect is not entirely independent, however, because specific nuclear genes are now known to suppress maternally inherited male sterility in maize. A single dominant chromosomal gene will restore pollen fertility in the presence of cytoplasm which ordinarily would result in sterility. In one experiment, pollen abortion occurred only when a specific kind of cytoplasm was present along with a dominant gene for male sterility and the homozygous recessive allele was present at a suppressor locus.

Male sterility is of practical importance in making crosses on a large scale. Hybrid plants have certain advantages over inbred plants. They are produced commercially in maize, cucumbers, onions, wheat, and other plants for the purpose of obtaining hybrid vigor (Chapter 20). In plant breeding programs involving plants capable of self-fertilization, the tedious process of removal of pollen (emasculation) can be avoided if it is possible to obtain a male sterile line for use in crosses.

## STREPTOMYCIN RESISTANCE IN CHLAMYDOMONAS

In 1954, when Ruth Sager placed green algae (Chlamydomonas) cells on a culture medium containing the antibiotic streptomycin, most of the cells were killed but about one per million survived and multiplied, each to form a streptomycin-resistant colony. In other words, a mutant form of this alga with resistance to streptomycin was being selected from the predominantly streptomycin-susceptible cells. Subsequently, many mutations were identified in Chlamydomonas, but most of these were shown by appropriate test crosses to be changes in nuclear genes. Such mutations were merely being demonstrated by associations with the antibiotic. The approximately 10 percent that were maternally inherited and nonchromosomal, however, were found to be induced by sublethal concentrations of the drug.

Eventually, nonchromosomal mutants could be recovered from almost every colony. Streptomycin was not specific for a particular change but induced several kinds of alterations in the treated colonies. Nonchromosomal changes gave the same phenotypes as chromosomal changes, but their frequency of occurrence was much greater than the frequency of chromosomal gene changes.

Reciprocal crosses (Fig. 11.4) demonstrated that antibiotic resistance, when controlled by nonchromosomal factors, was maternally inherited. Mating types in this sexual unicellular alga are controlled by chromosomal genes, which were identified by the investigators as $mt^+$ and $mt^-$ or simply + and − (instead of female and male). All progeny from each mating were like the + mating type with respect to relative streptomycin resistance. When the + mating type was resistant, all progeny were resistant and when the + mating type was nonresistant, all progeny were nonresistant. These results of reciprocal crosses demonstrated maternal inheritance and a single contrasting pair of traits. Other nonchromosomal genes, *sr* for streptomycin resistance and *sd* for streptomycin dependence, were postulated to control these two alternative characteristics. The *sr* gene behaves as a dominant. Cells containing both *sr* and *sd* genes could survive either with or without streptomycin. Occasionally, the Chlamydomonas nonchromosomal genes do not show strict maternal inheritance but are transmitted from both parents to the progeny. When this occurs, subsequent segregation permits the investigator to follow the pattern of inheritance. Under these conditions, the genes *sr* and *sd* seemed to segregate as would members of a pair of chromosomal alleles. The two genes present in the same

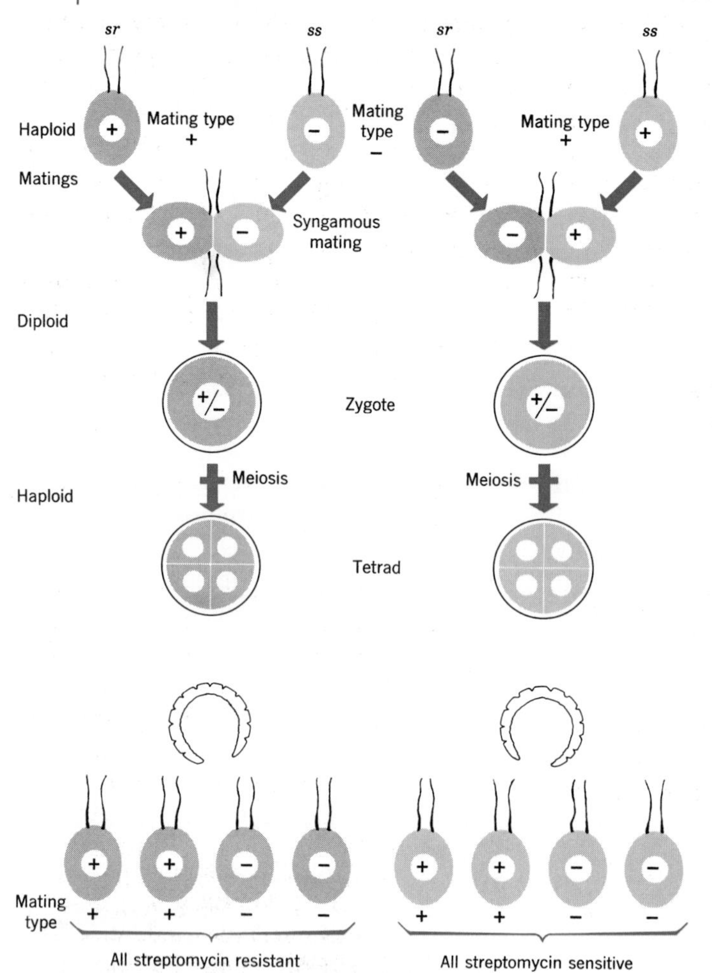


**Fig. 11.4** Inheritance of resistance to streptomycin. The plus and minus signs refer to mating type, which is inherited as a single gene difference. The progeny is with rare exceptions always like the plus parent in its reaction to streptomycin, but in these crosses the mating type difference segregates 1 : 1 in every tetrad. Based on Ruth Sager and F. J. Ryan, *Cell Heredity* (John Wiley & Sons, 1961).

parent cell segregated to different daughter cells.

Another pair of nonchromosomal genes, $ac_1$ and $ac_2$, was induced in the same strain of Chlamydomonas. These mutations blocked photosynthetic activity. The mutants required acetate in the medium for growth. These genes were also found to behave as a pair of alleles. Segregation began in the first few cell divisions after meiosis, indicating that the number of copies of each gene is very low, perhaps only one.

With two pairs of nonchromosomal genes available in the same system, it was possible to check for evidence of linkage as contrasted with that for independent combinations. Crosses of the dihybrid type $ac_1sd \times ac_2sr$ were allowed to grow for a few vegetative multiplications. Each cell was then classified for its segregating markers, both nonchromosomal and chromosomal (that is, mating type and others known to be chromosomal). Both the $ac_1/ac_2$ and the *sr*/*sd* pairs of genes were observed to segregate early but not always in the same division. After four or five mitotic doublings, equal numbers of parental ($ac_1sd$ and $ac_2sr$) combinations had been obtained. The results indicated that the two pairs of nonchromosomal genes were carried on different particles. This was a demonstration of recombination of nonchromosomal genes.

Extranuclear DNA has been detected in cellular organelles such as chloroplasts and mitochondria of Chlamydomonas and other organisms. These organelles thus could carry primary genetic information. But even so, the presence of DNA in bodies identified with genetic functions does not preclude the possibility that cells may also contain additional genetic systems in the cytoplasm which may or may not depend on DNA.

## CYTOPLASMIC FACTORS IN YEAST

Much information has been accumulated about yeast genetics. Mendelian segregation has been established, and mutations have been demonstrated. In addition, B. Ephrussi and several other investigators have shown clearly that the cytoplasm as well as the nucleus influences morphological and physiological characteristics of yeast cells.

In one investigation, a red-colored strain was obtained from white yeast through treatment with mustard gas. A single chromosomal gene mutation was at first considered adequate to account for the changed phenotype. When the red mutants were propagated vegetatively, however, some white cells appeared. A cytoplasmic factor was therefore postulated to explain the color difference. The hypothesis established to explain the mechanics of this occurrence was based on a chance distribution of color-producing cytoplasmic constituents through continued vegetative reproduction of an organism with a constant genotype.

In another investigation, it was shown that about one percent of the cells of baker's yeast were dwarfs. These cells were unable to utilize glucose efficiently because they lacked the proper enzyme. Dwarfs originated sporadically from apparently normal cells, but in the presence of certain chemicals the proportions of dwarfs increased appreciably. The frequency of occurrence under all conditions was far greater than was explainable by the highest frequency of gene mutation which could be expected. Furthermore, any given cell might produce either normal or abnormal progeny through vegetative reproduction. Therefore, the segregation of particulate cytoplasmic elements was postulated to account for the dwarfs.

## OTHER POSSIBLE MECHANISMS OF CYTOPLASMIC INHERITANCE

New knowledge about the chemical and physical properties of cells, and about their relationships with inheritance processes, has suggested many possible cases of cytoplasmic involvement in hereditary mechanisms. Slow-growing strains of yeast and Neurospora, for example, have been found to be deficient in cytochrome, a compound involved in cell respiration. The slow-growing characteristic has been shown, in several different strains, to be maternally inherited.

Cytochrome is located in mitochondria. These are cytoplasmic bodies known to be essential to the life of the cell and the organism. Mitochondria reproduce by replication of preexisting mitochondria. Furthermore, they contain DNA and exhibit genetic continuity. A well-known class of extrachromosomal mutations involving mitochondria give rise to respiratory-deficient mutants of yeast and Neurospora. These are slow-growing organisms that have resulted from alterations of mitochondrial DNA. The chemical composition and functional characteristics of a mitochondrial protein are changed by such a mutation. Results of reciprocal crosses and other experimental criteria demonstrate that the respiratory deficiency trait is inherited maternally.

Centrioles are tubule-producing cytoplasmic structures observed in cells of higher animals, protozoa, and lower plants with flagellated sperm. Like mitochondria they are extrachromosomal, self-replicating, DNA-containing organelles. In animal spermiogenesis, a centriole produces the flagellum of the sperm. In differentiation of ciliated epithelial cells, repeated reduplication of centrioles results in the formation of basal bodies that give rise to cilia and also serve as kinetic centers for these cilia. Centrioles are associated with the cell-division spindle of animal cells but they probably do not have a fundamental relation with spindle formation. No direct connection has been observed between the centrioles and the spindle tubules. Plants with nonflagellated sperm have cell-division spindles but no centrioles.

## $CO_2$ SENSITIVITY FACTOR IN DROSOPHILA

A true-breeding strain of Drosophila was found by L'Heritier and Teissier to be sensitive to carbon dioxide ($CO_2$). Appropriate observations have shown that most Drosophila can be subjected for hours to contact with pure $CO_2$ without any permanent injury. Sensitive flies, when exposed briefly, become uncoordinated in a characteristic way, with some of their legs becoming paralyzed. Results of reciprocal crosses showed that the trait was inherited mainly, but not exclusively, through the maternal line. Sensitivity can be induced in wild flies by injecting an extract prepared by crushing sensitive flies, diluting with Ringer's solution, and centrifuging the resulting suspension. A viruslike particle called a genoid or a sigma particle has been identified in the cytoplasm of somatic and reproductive cells of sensitive flies.

Genoids are transmitted primarily through the egg cytoplasm but also, under certain conditions, through the sperm. They multiply in the egg cytoplasm. Their perpetuation depends on an initial supply of genoids, suitable temperature (about 20° C; they are heat-labile at high temperatures), and a favorable genotype. They do not require a particular gene but can accommodate themselves to different genotypes, even those of different species of Drosophila.

Mutations may occur in genoids themselves; one has been reported which makes genoids incapable of being transmitted by males. This cytoplasmic particle is viruslike in its behavior and has the properties of a plasmagene, an inheritable self-reproducing body in the cytoplasm of the cell having the properties of genes but nonchromosomal. By replacing each of the chromosomes in the sensitive strain with homologous chromosomes from a resistant strain, it was shown that inheritance of the trait is extra-nuclear.

## KILLER PARTICLES IN PARAMECIUM

T. M. Sonneborn and his associates have investigated a persistent extranuclear effect in protozoa. Some races of *Paramecium aurelia* produce a substance that has a lethal effect on members of other races of the same species. Paramecia from races capable of producing the substance were called "killers." When killers were subjected to low temperatures and poor food, the killing capacity was gradually lost. The toxic effect was also decreased after repeated cell divisions. It was at first postulated that separate entities in the cytoplasm were responsible for the production of a toxic substance. From mathematical calculation, it was estimated that about 400 particles would be required to make

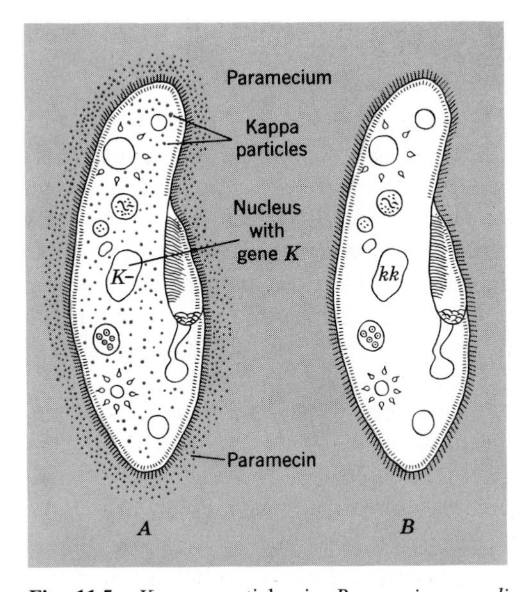


**Fig. 11.5** Kappa particles in *Paramecium aurelia*. *A*, killer with kappa particles inside and paramecin in the liquid medium outside the organism. Gene *K* is present in the nucleus. *B*, sensitive organism with no kappa particles, no paramecin, and genes *kk* in the nucleus. (After T. M. Sonneborn.)

killers effective. After the hypothetical calculations were completed, the killers were observed microscopically and particles called "kappa" were observed in about the expected numbers. These particles have now been shown to contain DNA, RNA, and protein. Two kinds of kappa were distinguished, a replicating form and a killer form.

A toxic substance called "paramecin," which is produced by the killer particles, is diffusible in the fluid medium. When killers were allowed to remain in a medium for a time and were then replaced by sensitives, the sensitives were killed. Paramecin has no effect on killers. Kappa particles were at first considered to be completely independent cytoplasmic units, that is, plasmagenes. Further investigation, however, showed that they were perpetuated only in organisms carrying a nuclear gene *K*, which either provided directly for the production of kappa or established the kind of environment necessary for the particles to multiply. Relations among *K* and *k* genes, kappa particles, and paramecin in the killers and sensitives are illustrated in Fig. 11.5.

By using appropriate techniques (to avoid killing the mate), killer and nonkiller Paramecia were mated with each other. From the divisions that followed these matings, killers produced only killers and sensitives only sensitives. This suggested that the nuclear genes that were exchanged during the mating process had no effect. It was observed that sometimes the mating process (conjugation) persisted much longer than usual. While the mates were attached, a larger than usual connection was established between the conjugants, and the exchange of some cytoplasm as well as nuclear material could be observed, as illustrated in Fig. 11.6. When prolonged

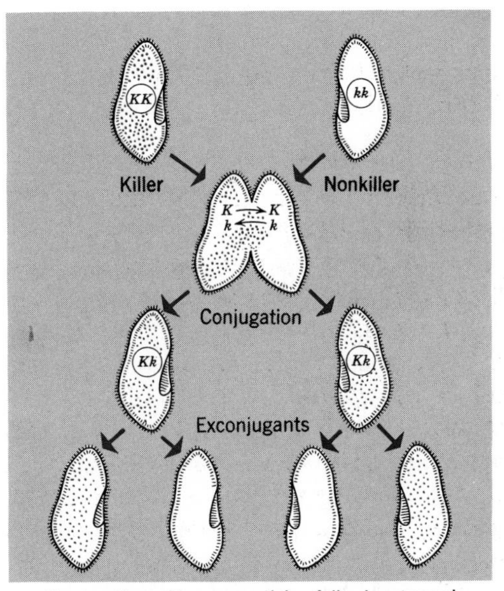


**Fig. 11.6** Diagram illustrating the transfer of kappa particles from killers to nonkillers during prolonged conjugation. After several cell divisions following conjugation, the particles were dispersed to the extent that some organisms had enough to express the killer trait and some did not. (After Sonneborn.)

conjugation occurred, the nonkillers became killers. Cytoplasm carrying kappa particles had been transferred and carried the killer trait to the nonkiller protozoa.

After several rapid cell divisions of killers, the kappa particles became so dispersed that some organisms had enough particles to be effective as killers, but others did not. After fifteen divisions, no kappa was left in the cytoplasm of some Paramecia. A method of separating kappa from organisms carrying the gene *K* was developed by feeding killers abundantly and inducing them to divide more rapidly than the kappa could be produced. Nonkiller Paramecia, carrying *K* but lacking kappa particles, were thus obtained from killers. Furthermore, nonkillers could be converted into killers if placed in the same container with crushed killers from which the paramecin had been removed. Kappa evidently was incorporated under favorable conditions into the cytoplasm of nonkillers.

When these methods were applied and kappa was introduced into the cytoplasm of an organism with the genotype *kk*, it was maintained for seven generations but eventually was lost. On the other hand, when all kappa was removed from an organism carrying the gene *K*, that organism could regain kappa only if it was introduced from another killer. Kappa particles have now been transferred through feeding to other ciliate protozoa such as Didinium, demonstrating that the particles are symbionts not restricted to Paramecia for sustenance. It has been shown further that kappa can thrive in the cytoplasm without the gene *K* being in the nucleus, but under this condition cells cannot reproduce more kappa particles. Another "mate killer" substance called "mu" has been found to exist in the cytoplasm of organisms carrying the nuclear gene *M*. No toxic substance is liberated into the medium, but paramecia with mu may kill sensitives with which they conjugate.

## COILING IN SNAILS

Eggs and embryos are expected to be influenced by the maternal environment in which they develop. Even those removed from the body of the mother at an early stage receive the cytoplasm and nutrients in the egg from the mother and special influences on gene action may have already emanated from the mother. Certain potentialities of the egg are known to be determined before fertilization, and in some cases these have been influenced by the surrounding maternal tissue. Their existence is commonly suggested from the results of reciprocal crosses.

One of the earliest to be investigated and best-known examples of a maternal effect was that of the direction of coiling in snails, *Limnaea peregra.* Some strains of this species have dextral shells, which coil to the right, and others have sinistral shells, which coil to the left. This characteristic is determined by the mother rather than by the genes of the developing snail. The gene $s^+$ for right-handed coiling is dominant over its allele $s$ for coiling to the left.

When crosses (Fig. 11.7) were made be-

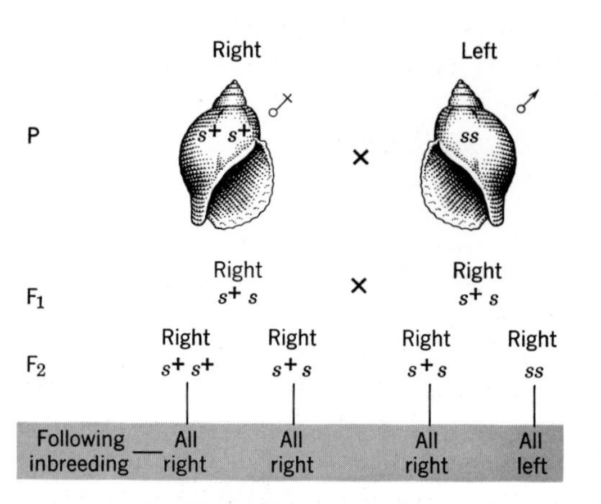


**Fig. 11.7** Diagram of a cross between a female snail coiled to the right and a male coiled to the left, illustrating a maternal effect. (Data and interpretation from Boycott et al. and Sturtevant.)

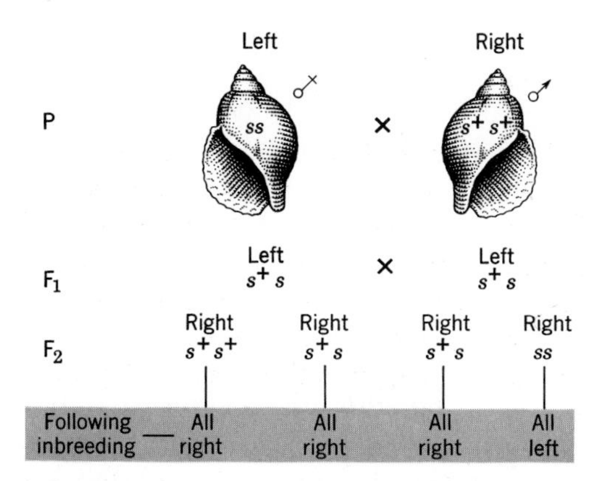


**Fig. 11.8** Diagram of cross between female snail coiled left and male coiled right, illustrating a maternal effect. (Data and interpretation from Boycott et al. and Sturtevant.)

tween females coiled to the right and males coiled left, the $F_1$ snails were all coiled to the right. The usual 3:1 ratio was not obtained in the $F_2$ and the expected phenotype for *ss* was not expressed. Instead, the pattern determined by the mother's genes was expressed. When *ss* individuals were inbred, progeny that coiled to the left were produced. However, when the $s^+s^+$ and $s^+s$ snails were inbred, they produced offspring that coiled to the right. From the reciprocal cross between left-coiling females and right-coiling males (Fig. 11.8), all the $F_1$ progeny were coiled to the left. The $F_2$ all coiled to the right, but when each $F_2$ snail was inbred, those with the genotype *ss* produced progeny that coiled to the left.

Further investigation of coiling in snails has shown that the spindle formed in the metaphase of the first cleavage division influences the direction of coiling. The spindle of potential sinistral snails is tipped to the left, but that of dextral snails is tipped to the right. This difference in the arrangement of the spindle is controlled by the genes of the mother, which act on the developing eggs in the ovary. They determine the orientation of the spindle, which in turn influences further cell division, and results in the adult pattern of coiling. The actual phenotypic character, therefore, is influenced directly by the mother, with no immediate relation to the genes in the egg or the sperm. Most other snail traits, however, do not show the maternal effect pattern. The striping color pattern, for example, is also determined in the early embryo, but this characteristic is controlled directly by chromosomal genes of both parents and is not influenced by a maternal effect. In this example, comparable color patterns are obtained from the results of reciprocal crosses.

## EYE COLOR IN BEACH HOPPER

A maternal effect on the intensity of eye color has been observed in the crustacean, Gammarus, sometimes called water flea or beach hopper. A pair of alleles, *A* and *a*, acting in Mendelian fashion determine whether a representative of this species will have dark or light eyes. No appreciable difference has been detected in the results of reciprocal crosses. When *AA* females are crossed with *aa* males, the first generation young all have dark eyes and the eyes remain dark when the adult stage is reached. From the reciprocal cross (that is, *aa* females mated with *AA* males), the young have light eye color like their mothers, but the adults have dark eyes. The dark pigment is produced from kynurenine in *A*-individuals. Since kynurenine is diffusible, it can be transferred from *A*-mothers to their progeny. Little or no kynurenine is present in the progeny of *aa* mothers, but the pigment can be built during the developmental period by progeny carrying *A* genes.

Similar observations have been made of the flour moth, Ephestia. In this insect, it has been possible to implant *aa* ovaries into *AA* females and then mate the females to *aa* males. The *aa* offspring from such females have dark eyes at first, but as development proceeds, the dark phenotype, which was dependent on the mother, was replaced by the light one controlled by the genes of the embryo. This pattern suggested that the eggs were influenced by a diffusible substance retained in the ovaries of their originally *AA* mothers.

Many other examples of maternal effects in invertebrates have been reported. These include shape and color characteristics in the eggs of the silk worm moth *Bombyx mori* reported by Toyama, and the tumorous head trait characterized by abnormal growths on the head region of *D. melanogaster,* which was studied by several investigators.

## MILK FACTORS IN MICE

An extrachromosomal factor controlling the susceptibility of mice to mammary cancer was identified by J. J. Bittner. It behaved like a virus and was transmitted through the milk of the mother to young mice. Mice receiving it from their mothers would, on reaching maturity, be considerably more susceptible to breast cancer than other mice of similar genotypes that were foster fed by mothers free from the milk factor. Appropriate foster-feeding experiments showed that it was something in the milk rather than any other possible influence which was responsible for the high susceptibility to mammary cancer. Certain nuclear genes were necessary, however, for the production of the milk factor.

Both the dba and A strains of inbred mice carry the milk factor. About 90 percent of the mice in these strains have breast cancer at 18 months of age. Other inbred strains, such as C57 black, have a very low incidence of mammary tumors and cancer. When crosses were made between female dba mice carrying the milk factor and males from strains free from the factor, about 90 percent of the female progeny had breast tumors by the time they reached 18 months of age. From the reciprocal cross between females from a strain without the milk factor and males from a mammary tumor line, none of the progeny had breast tumors at the end of 18 months. When the progeny from breast cancer mothers were foster fed by mothers from noncancerous strains, no tumors appeared. These results established a maternal inheritance dependent on a factor carried in the milk.

More recent studies have shown that the factor is transmitted also by body fluids other than milk, including saliva and semen. Since it may also be transmitted by the fluids of the male, the susceptibility may have a paternal as well as a maternal transmission. This discovery in mice has stimulated interest and speculation concerning the possibility of a milk factor in other animals, including human beings. If evidence for such a factor in mankind were discovered, it would undoubtedly influence the decision of some mothers as to whether they would nurse their female babies.

Maternal effects are common in mammals and must be considered in planning breeding programs for domestic animals. The embryo is carried and nourished by the mother for a period of several weeks or months before birth, which allows ample time for the mother's genotype to exert some influence.

## SUMMARY

Most heritable traits are associated with chromosomal genes, but cytoplasmic bodies or influences may be involved in various ways in transmission. A few traits have been found to depend on cytoplasmic DNA, which behaves more or less independently of chromosomal genes. These may be initially detected by analyzing the results of reciprocal crosses. Some plastid characteristics, such as presence or absence of chlorophyll, are maternally inherited. They represent the best examples of true cytoplasmic inheritance. Male sterility in maize and other crop and flower garden plants is controlled by cytoplasmic factors, but in some cases the sterility may be masked by chromosomal genes. Other examples of cytoplasmic inheritance include streptomycin resistance in Chlamydomonas, and size and color characteristics of yeast. Genoids associated with $CO_2$ sensitivity in Drosophila and kappa particles in Paramecium seem to be symbionts that have become well established. They are transmitted through the cytoplasm but, in the case of kappa, a nuclear gene or some introduced factor is required to provide the proper environment for reproduction of these bodies in the cell. Direction of coiling in snails and eye color in beach hoppers depend on chromosomal genes of the mother and therefore are classified as maternal effects. The milk factor in mice is a virus. It is transmitted in the milk of female mice that carry particular chromosomal genes, and it increases the susceptibility of young mice to mammary cancer as they approach 18 months of age.

## REFERENCES

Duvick, D. N. 1965. "Cytoplasmic pollen sterility in corn." *Advances in Genetics.* M. Demerec (ed.) Vol. 13. Academic Press, New York.

Ephrussi, B. 1953. *Nucleo-cytoplasmic relations in microorganisms: their bearing on cell heredity and differentiation.* The Clarendon Press, Oxford.

Goldschmidt, R. B. 1955. *Theoretical genetics.* University of California Press, Berkeley. (Cytoplasmic influences and maternal effects, and suggested chemical relations between genes and characters.)

Jinks, J. L. 1964. *Extrachromosomal inheritance.* Prentice-Hall, Englewood Cliffs, New Jersey.

L'Heritier, P. 1951. "The $CO_2$ sensitivity problem in Drosophila." *Cold Spring Harbor Symp. on Quant. Biol.,* **16,** 99–112.

Michaelis, P. 1954. "Cytoplasmic inheritance in Epilobium and its theoretical significance." *Advances in Genetics.* M. Demerec (ed.) Vol. 6. Academic Press, New York.

Rhoades, M. M. 1933. "The cytoplasmic inheritance of male sterility in *Zea mays.*" *J. Genet.,* **27,** 71–93.

Sager, R. 1965. "Genes outside the chromosomes." *Sci. Amer.,* **212,** 70–79.

Sager, R. 1965. "On the evolution of genetic systems." *Evolving genes and proteins.* V. Bryson and H. U. Vogel (eds.) Academic Press, New York. (Suggestion that cytoplasmic genetic systems may be of continuing evolutionary importance in providing flexibility for organelle growth in a changing environment.)

Sager, R. 1966. "Mendelian and non-Mendelian heredity: a reappraisal." *Proc. Royal Soc.,* **B164,** 290–297.

Sager, R., and F. J. Ryan. 1961. *Cell Heredity.* John Wiley and Sons, New York. (Examples of cytoplasmic and maternal inheritance.)

Seecof, R. L. 1962. "$CO_2$ sensitivity in Drosophila as a latent virus infection." *Cold Spring Harbor Symp. Quant. Biol.,* **27,** 501–512.

Sonneborn, T. M. 1960. "The gene and cell differentiation." *Proc. Nat'l. Acad. Sci.,* **46,** 149–165. (Influences of genes and cytoplasm in differentiation in *Paramecium aurelia.*)

Weier, T. E., and C. R. Stocking. 1952. "The chloroplast: structure, inheritance, and enzymology II." *Bot. Rev.,* **18,** 14–75. (Detailed review including a discussion of plastid inheritance.)

Wettstein, D. von. 1961. "Nuclear and cytoplasmic factors in development of chloroplast structure and function." *Canad. J. Botany,* **39,** 1537–1545.

Woodward, D. O., and K. D. Munkres. 1966. "Alteration of a maternally inherited mitochondrial structural protein in respiratory deficient strains of Neurospora." *Proc. Nat'l. Acad. Sci. U. S.,* **55,** 872–880.

## Problems

**11.1** Since the early part of the present century, examples of possible cytoplasmic inheritance have been reported. Most of these have eventually been explained on the basis of mechanisms other than strict cytoplasmic inheritance. Evaluate the current status of the case for cytoplasmic inheritance with examples.

**11.2** In most animals, a larger amount of cytoplasm is carried by the egg than by the sperm. Likewise, the egg in plants carries more cytoplasm than the pollen. How could this difference affect the expression of inherited traits (a) dependent on chromosomal genes; and (b) dependent on nonchromosomal genes.

**11.3** Reciprocal crosses sometimes give different results in the $F_1$. This may be due to (a) sex-linked inheritance; (b) cytoplasmic inheritance; or (c) maternal effects. If such a result were obtained, how could the investigator determine experimentally which category was involved?

**11.4** Explain how single plants such as four-o'clocks could have green, pale green, and variegated sectors. If such sectors reached sexual maturity, what color characteristics would each type be expected to transmit through male or female gametes?

**11.5** What practical applications could be made with male sterile lines of onions, wheat, and other crop plants?

**11.6** Review the evidence for mutation, segregation, and recombination of nonchromosomal genes in Chlamydomonas.

**11.7** How could (a) genoids and (b) kappa particles have become established in their host organisms, Drosophila and Paramecium, respectively, in evolution?

**11.8** In snails of the genus Limnaea, coiling is influenced by a maternal effect. (a) Give the phenotypes that could be associated with the following genotypes in individual snails and give the reason for each answer: $s^+s^+$, $ss^+$, and $ss$. (b) What might be said about the female and male parents and grandparents of snails represented by each of the three genotypes?

**11.9** Diagram a cross between a female snail with dextral coiling (that is, coiling to the right) with the genotype $s^+s^+$, and an inbred $ss$ male with sinistral coiling. Carry the cross to the $F_2$ and represent the expected results from inbreeding each of the $F_2$ snails. Explain the results.

**11.10** In the beach hopper of the genus Gammarus, pigment of the eyes is influenced in early stages by the genotype of the mother but later by the genes of the individual hopper. Give the expected results of the following crosses in young and adult stages: (a) dark females ($AA$) $\times$ light males ($aa$); and (b) light females ($aa$) $\times$ dark males ($AA$). (c) Give a plausible explanation for the change that sometimes occurs from light eyes in young organisms to dark eyes in later stages.

**11.11** When ovaries from light-colored ($aa$) flour moths of the genus Ephestia are implanted into dark ($AA$) females, which are then mated to $aa$ males, the $aa$ progeny have dark eyes when first hatched but they gradually become lighter. Give a plausible explanation for such a change in eye color.

**11.12** Females in certain strains of mice have a strong tendency toward mammary tumors when they become mature. How could it be determined whether (a) a nuclear gene, (b) an extranuclear factor, or (c) an environmental factor was involved?

**11.13** In a Drosophila stock that originated from a field collection and had been maintained by inbreeding for many generations, a new phenotype was observed. Some flies had irregularly shaped eyes. Outline experiments to determine whether the new phenotype was (a) a nonhereditary environmental modification; (b) a maternal effect; or (c) a mutation dependent on a single gene.

# II

# *Nature and Function of Genetic Material*

# Genetic Material and Genetic Coding | 12

Genes carry from cell to cell and from generation to generation the information that specifies the characteristics of the plant or animal. They accomplish their function through (1) a replication process that results in more units like themselves and (2) an information transfer process that results in the synthesis of enzymes and other macromolecules that function in the metabolism of the cell. Although genes were first postulated from their end effects, as expressed in altered phenotypes, they are now known for what they are chemically and for what they do in directing the synthesis of proteins. Most biochemists who were interested in genetics during the early years concentrated on the protein part of the chromosome in their search for the gene. Now the emphasis has shifted to the nucleic-acid components, deoxyribonucleic acid (DNA) and ribonucleic acid (RNA).

## DNA, THE GENETIC MATERIAL

### *Transformation*

Direct evidence that DNA is genetic material—that is, the chemical of which genes are composed—came from investigations on pneumococcus (*Diplococcus pneumoniae*) bacteria beginning in the 1920's. Many types of pneumococcus can be distinguished by morphological and serological characteristics. Type specificity is a genetically controlled property of the organism. The most obvious point of difference between colonies is the carbohydrate capsule coat, which determines the appearance of each colony that is formed when cultures are grown on blood agar. Some colonies are smooth, because the cells have polysaccharide capsules, and some are rough, with no capsules. The capsules also impart antigenic specificity and virulence for the disease pneumonia. When these cells are introduced into mice or other susceptible mammals, a severe illness usually follows. The colonies that have a rough appearance and no capsules are not virulent. When mice are inoculated with avirulent cells, no ill effects occur. Characteristics of these two kinds of colonies are summarized in Table 12.1. Sometimes virulent cells lose their capsules through spontaneous mutation and become avirulent.

Frederick Griffith in England used this background information in designing experiments to study the effects of virulent and avirulent pneumococci. In a series of experiments (in 1928), he introduced heat-killed virulent cells into one group of mice, avirulent cells into another group, and avirulent cells mixed with heat-killed virulent cells into a third group. The first two groups were not affected by the injections, but mice in the third group be-

**TABLE 12.1 Characteristics of smooth and rough colonies of Pneumococcus raised on blood agar**

| Appearance | Size | Virulence | Capsule |
|---|---|---|---|
| Smooth | Large | Virulent | Present |
| Rough | Small | Avirulent | Absent |

came ill, as illustrated in Fig. 12.1. Griffith thus made the remarkable discovery that a fatal case of pneumonia could be produced if mice were given a mixture of live, avirulent organisms, and virulent but killed organisms. Something in the dead organisms was apparently transferred to the live cells and carried over to the mice. This phenomenon was at first called the "Griffith effect" and later became known as transformation.

Techniques were refined and experiments were designed by several investigators to test the transforming principle more critically. When the cells of the rough form of pneumococcus Type II, which had arisen by spontaneous mutation from Type II smooth, were combined with heat-killed cells of Type III smooth, a few cells could be shown to have the serological properties as well as the virulence of Type III smooth. Transformation in this experiment went toward the type from

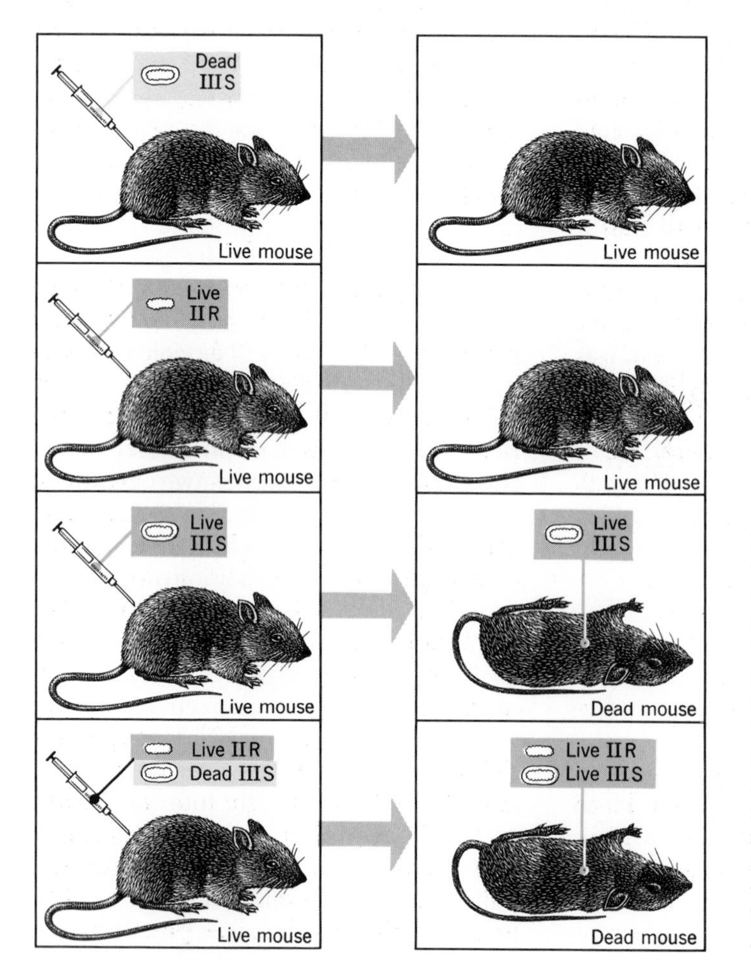


**Fig. 12.1** Diagram illustrating the Griffith experiment that demonstrated the principle of transformation. When smooth, Type III pneumococci were killed and introduced into mice no ill effect occurred. Likewise, when rough Type II living cells were introduced the mice were not affected. Living Type III cocci killed the mice. When killed Type III material was introduced with living Type II (avirulent) cocci the mice were killed. A dead substance had been incorporated into a living organism.

which the heat-killed cells were derived, demonstrating that a transfer had been made from the killed cells to the live cells. Later experiments were carried out *in vitro,* that is, in the test tube rather than in the mouse. These showed that debris or an extract from the donor cells could carry the transforming principle and thus removed an alternative explanation proposed from the earlier investigation that the live avirulent cells somehow restored the dead cells to viability. *In vitro* studies led to the determination of the biochemical nature of the transferred material.

In 1944, O. T. Avery, C. M. MacLeod, and M. McCarty published the results of their extensive investigations, which had been conducted over a period of some ten years. Through long and tedious experiments, they eliminated every other possibility and identified the transforming substance as the chemical, deoxyribonucleic acid (DNA). When DNA extracted from one strain of pneumococcus was highly purified and allowed to penetrate the cells of another strain, the recipient organisms developed certain characteristics of the donor strain. The chemically (DNA) transmitted traits were continued generation after generation, indicating that the genetic material as well as the phenotype of recipient organisms had been changed. Evidently the DNA, which presumably was pure, could be incorporated into the genotype of the recipient bacterium.

When the transformed cells were cultured, they remained encapsulated, and extracts prepared from them had the same transforming ability as those of the original encapsulated strain. It was thus demonstrated that *in vitro* transformation resulted in a hereditary change similar to that which Griffith had demonstrated *in vivo,* that is, in the living organism. This now classical experiment of Avery and his associates resulted in two important conclusions: (1) DNA is the genetic material in pneumococci, and (2) DNA differs from the end product or trait that it determines (the polysaccharide capsule).

Transformation is now known to also occur in *Hemophilus influenzae* (a minute rod-shaped pathogen), *Bacillus subtilus* (a common soil bacterium, *Shigella paradysenteriae* (the causative agent for a diarrhia resembling mild dysentery), and several other organisms. The transformation principle, therefore, is not unique to pneumococcus, but has general significance, at least in bacteria. In some instances it has been possible, through transformation, to transfer genetic material from one bacterial species to another. Streptomycin resistance, for example, has been transferred from pneumococci to streptococci. This suggests that bacteria causing one disease might transfer resistance to antibiotics to other types of bacteria, thus increasing the problems of disease control.

### *DNA Activity in a Virus*

By using radioactive tracers, A. Hershey and M. Chase (1952) provided further direct proof that DNA is the genetic material in certain bacterial viruses. These investigators were studying the bacteriophages that attack the bacterium, *Escherichia coli.* They prepared a chemically defined medium containing phosphoric acid and sulfuric acid as the only sources of phosphorus and sulfur. Known quantities of radioactive isotopes of phosphorus ($P^{32}$) and sulfur ($S^{35}$) were added to the medium. The *E. coli* grown on the medium incorporated the $P^{32}$ and $S^{35}$ into their chemical constituents. When phage particles infected the radioactive bacteria (Fig. 12.2), they incorporated the labeled DNA. Phage proteins do not contain appreciable amounts of phosphorus and only the DNA was labeled with $P^{32}$. Similarly, the protein envelope around the

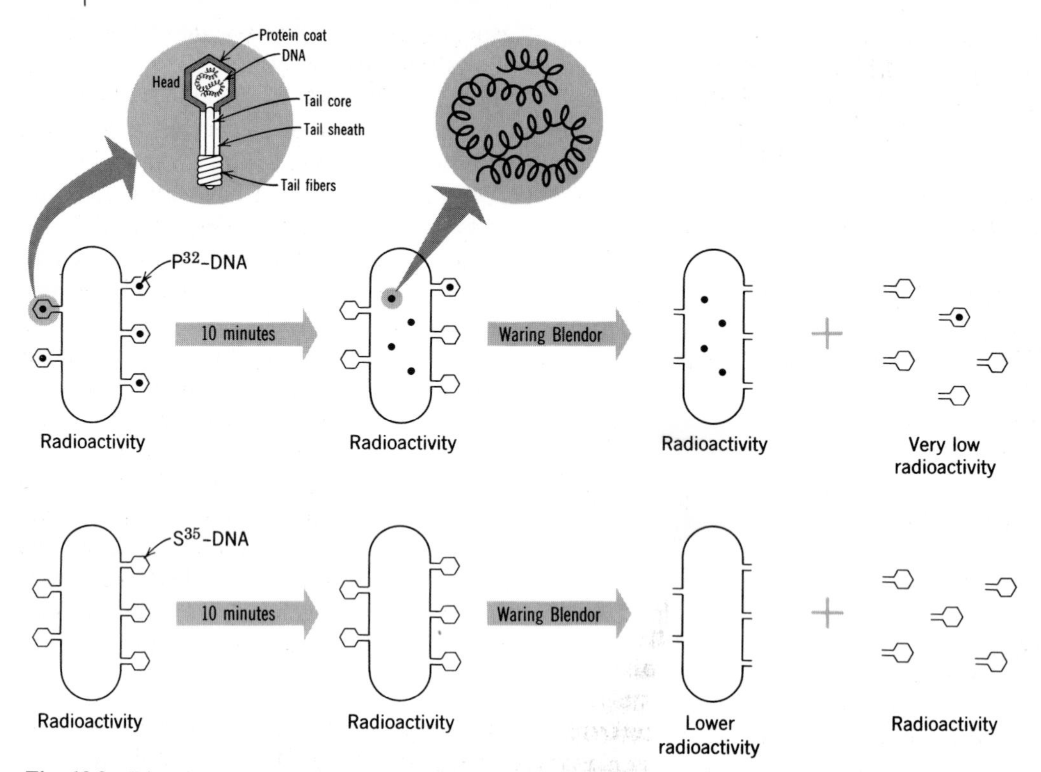


**Fig. 12.2** Diagram of Hershey and Chase experiment demonstrating that only phage DNA enters the bacterial host cell after infection. Cells were infected with $P^{32}$-labeled phage, and after being allowed time for infection, they were agitated in a Waring Blendor which sheared off the phage coats. Radioactivity was measured at each step in the procedure. Very little of the original $P^{32}$ radioactivity was lost from the cells. Thus, the phage DNA had been incorporated into the host cells. When phage were labeled with $S^{35}$ in their proteins, and the same experiment performed, the results were very different. Most of the radioactivity was found in the supernatant with the phage protein; very little entered the cells. (Based on Ruth Sager and F. J. Ryan, *Cell Heredity,* John Wiley and Sons, 1961.)

phage was selectively labeled with $S^{35}$. DNA contains virtually no sulfur and was not labeled with $S^{35}$. By this method it was possible to differentially label the phage DNA and phage protein of the virus.

After phage growth, the virus particles were separated from the host cells by centrifugation. The radioactive viruses were next introduced to nonradioactive bacterial cultures where they attacked the bacteria. Subsequently, the viruses were separated from the host cells by agitation and the content of $P^{32}$ and $S^{35}$ in the host and parasite was determined. The phosphorus label was found to be associated with the bacterial cells and the sulfur label was in the protein coats left in the medium. This indicated that the DNA had penetrated the cells but that the protein coat of the phage was left outside the wall of the bacterium and had been separated completely from the bacterial cell by agitation. Only the labeled DNA was passed on to the next generation.

Significantly, it was concluded that when the DNA of a virus particle entered a host cell, essentially all of the protein part remained outside and therefore it did not represent the genetic material. Only the DNA of the virus was in the bacterium while the fundamental process of viral DNA replication was being accomplished. After the DNA part of the virus was reproduced within the bacterial cell, new protein was synthesized and then became associated with the DNA units. New infective virus particles were thus formed. When the host (bacteria) lysed, numerous infectious virus particles emerged, ready to enter other bacterial cells and repeat the cycle. The interpretation of the Hershey and Chase experiments has been fully confirmed by further studies including electron micrographs of the infection process. These experiments, taken together, demonstrated beyond doubt that DNA is genetic material.

## DNA AS THE UNIVERSAL GENETIC MATERIAL

Transformation experiments demonstrated that DNA is the genetic material in pneumococcus and other bacteria. The Hershey and Chase experiments showed that DNA specifies hereditary traits in certain viruses. Other studies and logical extrapolations have indicated that DNA has widespread and nearly universal significance as *the* genetic material. It is a complex chemical which has now been studied extensively by biochemists and biophysicists as well as geneticists.

DNA is a constant part of chromosomes and it has the properties that are expected to characterize genes. By means of a specific staining technique (Feulgen reaction), DNA was located in the chromosomes of interphase cells as well as in those undergoing the division process. Furthermore, it eventually was shown that DNA is confined to the chromosomes and certain cytoplasmic bodies, that is, chloroplastids and mitochondria.

The concentration of DNA in a given cell is comparatively uniform and constant. This was demonstrated when radioactive phosphorus ($P^{32}$) was incorporated into the DNA of dividing cells. The cells with the labeled DNA were then maintained as nondividing cells and checked periodically for change in amount of DNA. Very little change was detected. This indicated that DNA remains constant and does not respond to the metabolic activities of the cells.

DNA was thus shown to be a stable chemical, as would be expected of the material that preserves information and carries it from cell to cell. The remarkable stability and constancy of DNA can be indicated further when the amount per cell is measured in different cells of the same organism and in cells of different kinds of organisms. In haploid eggs and sperm, for example, the quantity is just

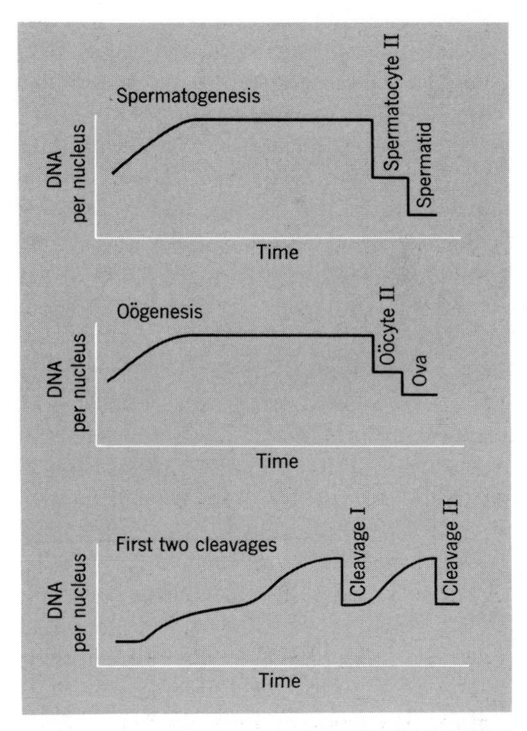


**Fig. 12.3** Relative concentrations of DNA in cells of grasshopper during stages of meiosis and mitosis (After H. Swift in *International Review of Cytology*, Vol. 2, Academic Press, Inc., New York.)

half that in diploid somatic cells of the same species. Furthermore, cells of different size in the same organism, which through irregular cell division have become tetraploid (*4n*) and octoploid (*8n*), carry 2 and 4 times more DNA, respectively, than do diploid (*2n*) cells. During mitosis and meiosis the DNA content drops abruptly with each separation of the daughter chromosomes, as illustrated in Fig. 12.3. The parallel between DNA content fluctuations and the chromosome cycle substantiates the role of DNA as chromosomal material.

## WATSON AND CRICK MODEL

While the investigations that resulted in the chemical identification of DNA as genetic material were in progress, and especially following the report of Avery and his associates (1944), attempts were made to explain the physical and chemical nature of DNA. As early as 1938, X-ray diffraction pictures of nucleic acid indicated that the main chemical components in the molecule (organic bases) were stacked on each other. Preliminary models were prepared to illustrate the data being accumulated. Some of these early models represented the bases in ascending steps resulting in a ladderlike configuration. All of this information was available to J. D. Watson and F. H. C. Crick when they undertook the task in the early 1950's of developing a model that would account for all the data bearing on the chemical and physical nature of DNA.

Watson and Crick envisioned various structural arrangements in attempts to fit a structure to the data. They eventually proposed a model for DNA which could not, at that time, be fully supported from experimental data, but which has since gained strong support. Their model was based on linear sequences of nucleotides, each composed of a pentose sugar, a phosphate, and an organic base (Fig. 12.4). Four kinds of nucleotides were recognized, each including a different nitrogenous base: adenine, thymine, cytosine, or guanine (Fig. 12.5). These investigators received a Nobel prize in 1962 for the model and hypothesis that they presented in 1953, which had been substantiated in the intervening years.

The physical criteria used in building up the model were derived from X-ray diffraction pictures produced by M. H. F. Wilkins (also a 1962 Nobel prize recipient) and his coworkers, using isolated DNA.

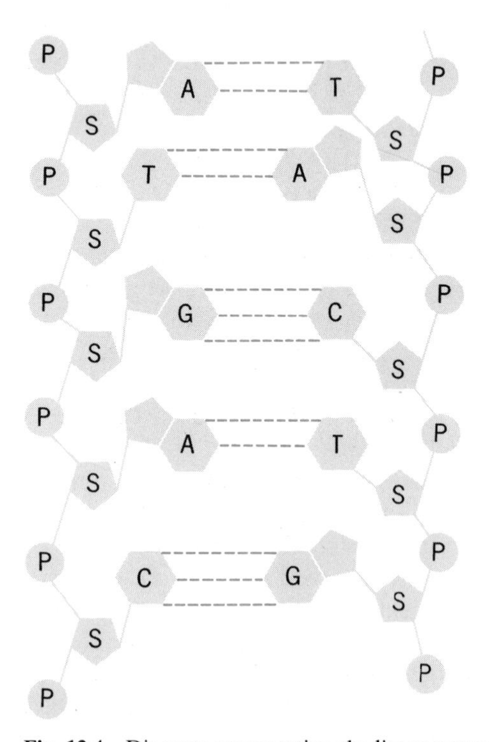


**Fig. 12.4** Diagram representing the linear sequence of nucleolides as proposed in the DNA model of Watson and Crick. Each nucleotide is composed of a phosphate (P), a sugar (S) and an organic base: adenine (A), thymine (T), guanine (G), or cytosine (C). The phosphate-sugar rims in the configuration are held together firmly by chemical bonds but the two organic bases in each cross link are connected less firmly with each other by hydrogen bonds (After Crick).

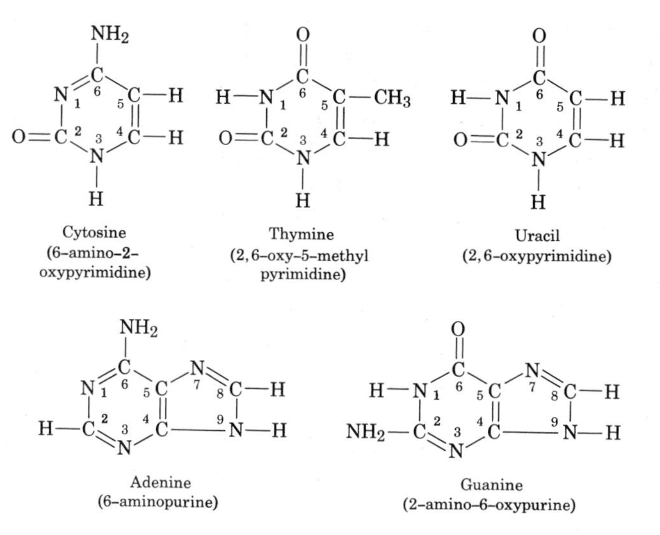


**Fig. 12.5** Structural formulas for organic bases in DNA and RNA. Four bases: cytosine, thymine, adenine, and guanine are in DNA. In RNA thymine is replaced by uracil.

Their X-ray diffraction pictures were crude compared with those subsequently developed, but they did show that the DNA molecule was in the shape of a helix (Fig. 12.6). The early pictures also were suitable for making measurements of the spacing between the bases. Examinations of isolated nuclei and sperm heads proved that the same structure found in the isolated DNA also exists in the cell. These pictures indicated that DNA molecules were composed of two or three strands forming helices.

Chemical analyses used by Watson and Crick were those of Chargaff and his associates, which showed that a 1:1 relation existed between adenine (a purine) and thymine (a pyrimidine), and between cytosine (a pyrimidine) and guanine (a purine). This relation did not exist between the two purines or the two pyrimidines. These investigators found the same basic chemical pattern in DNA from many sources. The Watson and Crick model is illustrated schematically in Fig.12.6. The relatively rigid long strands that form the spirals around an axis are made up of phosphates and pentose sugars. Crosswise, the strands are less rigidly connected by the organic bases through hydrogen bonds. Adenine and thymine are connected by two H bonds, while cytosine and guanine are connected by three. In each cross link, the bases are arranged in such a way that a certain purine is bonded to a certain pyrimidine, adenine-thymine and cytosine-guanine. Pairs of organic bases may be arranged in any order. Within the length of one spiral, that is, within 34 Å, 10 base pairs are located.

Although Watson and Crick relied heavily on the work of others, they made enormous contributions themselves. They put together the X-ray diffraction, chemical, and physical data and created a model that incorporated the functional requirements of the genetic material. Watson and Crick were the first scientists to propose a double helix with polarity and complementarity of the paired bases. They represented hydrogen bonds in the appropriate positions to specify the bases.

In the early 1950's, the Watson and Crick initial publication was one of a group of three short papers published in the same volume (**171,** 1953) of *Nature* under the heading, "Molecular Structure of Nucleic Acids." The second paper was the one by Wilkins and associates presenting the X-ray diffraction data used by

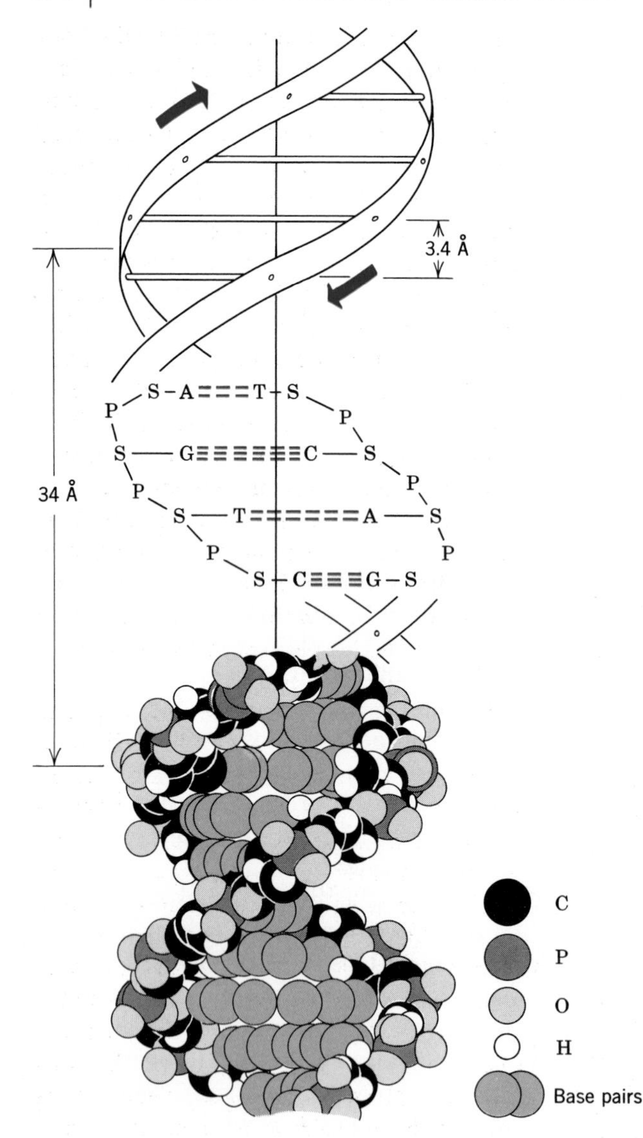


**Fig. 12.6** Diagram illustrating the Watson and Crick Model for DNA. Three representations of the two-stranded double-helical structure of DNA to same scale. Symbols are the usual chemical symbols and those for nucleic acid bases, with S for sugar and P for phosphate residues. Bottom: Space-filling model. Middle: Less detailed representation. Top: Schematic representation with the rungs in the twisted ladder depicting base pairs. (Carl P. Swanson, *The Cell,* Second Edition, © 1964, p. 72. Redrawn by permission of Prentice-Hall, Inc., Englewood Cliffs, New Jersey.)

Watson and Crick (see the references at the end of this chapter). The third was by R. E. Franklin and R. G. Gosling entitled, "Molecular Configuration of Sodium Thymonucleate."

## REPLICATION OF GENETIC MATERIAL

Replication is a basic process by which living things perpetuate their kind. Each DNA molecule uses its own structure as a template and takes from its substratum the necessary materials for replication.

The most widely accepted modern explanation of the mechanics of gene replication is based on the Watson and Crick model for DNA. According to this model, the basic structure of DNA has two strands or chains coiled around a common axis and held together by hydrogen bonds between pairs of organic bases: adenine-

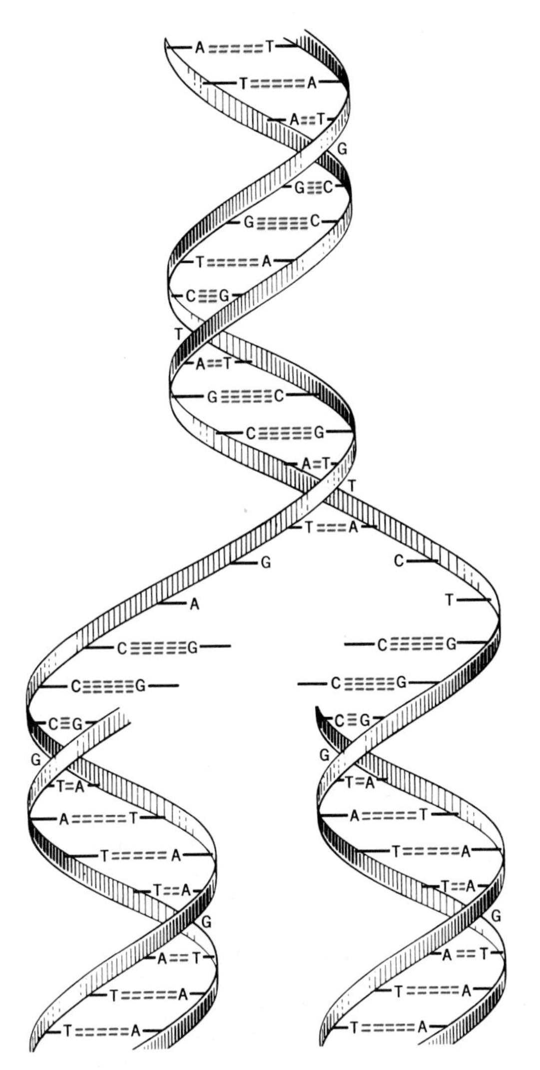

**Fig. 12.7** Proposed replication of DNA. As the double-stranded parent DNA unwinds, the separated strands serve as templates for the alignment of nucleotides, which combine to form new strands complementary to the parental strands.

thymine and cytosine-guanine. One member of each pair must be a purine and the other a pyrimidine in order to maintain a connection and form a cross link between the two strands. Any sequence of pairs of bases can fit into the structure, and in long molecules many different combinations are possible, but a given arrangement remains fixed in a particular molecule. The arrangement of bases is fundamental to the coding system (Chapter 13) and determines the differential action of different genes.

In the Watson and Crick model, each of the two original strands is the complement of the other. When duplication occurs, the hydrogen bonds between the bases break and the strands replicate as they unwind, as illustrated in Fig. 12.7. Each strand acts as a model or template for the formation of a new complementary chain. Two pairs of chains thus appear where before only one pair existed. Furthermore, each chain is a complement of the one from which it was specified, carrying genetic qualities determined by the original structure. This complementarity is maintained because of the pairing relations that exist between bases; that is, adenine pairs only with thymine and cytosine pairs only with guanine.

Strong support for the Watson and Crick explanation for DNA replication came from an experiment of M. S. Meselson and F. W. Stahl, which also demonstrated semiconservative replication; that is, the original DNA strands remain after each forms a new complementary strand. These investigators allowed bacteria to reproduce in a medium in which the only source of nitrogen was a heavy stable isotope $N^{15}$. During the reproductive process, the DNA of the bacteria became labeled with heavy nitrogen. The bacteria were then transferred to a medium containing only ordinary nitrogen, $N^{14}$. At the end of each of the next two generations, the proportion of $N^{15}$ to $N^{14}$ was measured. The results are illustrated in Fig. 12.8. After one generation in the $N^{14}$ medium, the proportion was half $N^{15}$ and half $N^{14}$. After the second generation, the proportion was three light to one heavy. In each replication the new strand incorporated the $N^{14}$ in the medium but the $N^{15}$ label was retained in the DNA strands originally labeled. These studies indicated that the

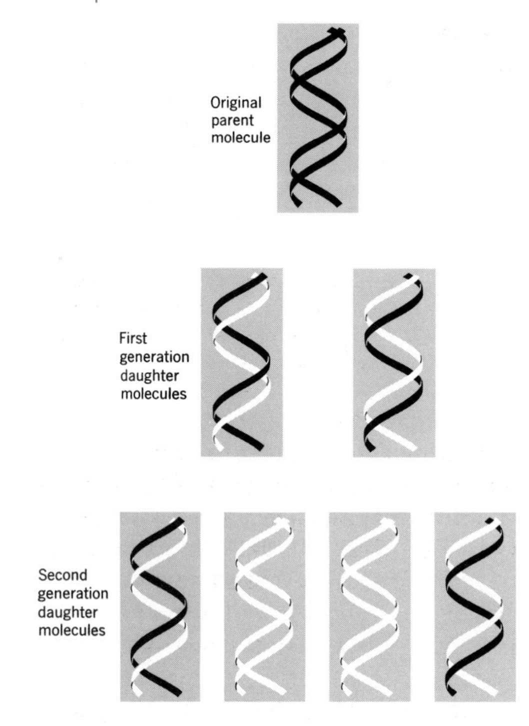


**Fig. 12.8** Semiconservative replication of DNA. Note that each first-generation daughter molecule consists of one old and one new strand of DNA. The same is true for second (and succeeding) generations, but only the labeled strands are detectable. For further description, see text. (From Meselson and Stahl: *Proc. Nat. Acad. Sci.*, **44**:671–682, 1958.)

original strand was maintained during each replication. The replication process was, therefore, semiconservative.

Arthur Kornberg, Nobel prize winner, has studied the chemistry of DNA synthesis and has synthesized DNA *in vitro* with an enzyme, DNA polymerase. These studies have done much to clarify the nature of the biochemical processes involved in DNA replication, but several questions remain to be answered. A critical one is: how do the *in vitro* observations relative to DNA replication relate to the formation of genes and chromosomes in living cells? The DNA strands are at the molecular level and in a different order of magnitude as compared with chromosomes and other structures seen in higher organisms with the light microscope. Most of the data concerning the replication of DNA has come from studies on bacteria and viruses.

Based on the Watson and Crick model, many different chemical arrangements could be established and replicated. If, for example, the four bases are identified with letters—adenine (A), cytosine (C), guanine (G), and thymine (T)—many combinations could be put together, as illustrated in the three series below, each representing a characteristic double helix.

| A-T | G-C | T-A |
|---|---|---|
| C-G | C-G | A-T |
| G-C | T-A | C-G |
| T-A | A-T | G-C |
| T-A | C-G | T-A |
| G-C | G-C | C-G |
| C-G | C-G | G-C |
| T-A | G-C | A-T |
| A-T | T-A | C-G |
| G-C | A-T | T-A |
| • • | • • | • • |
| • • | • • | • • |
| • • | • • | • • |

The great number of bases that are present in any given molecule permit a tremendous number of arrangements ($4^n$ where $n$ is the number of base pairs). DNA in one virus particle, for example, contains some 200,000 base pairs. Higher forms of life contain many times more in each cell. An occasional error or misfit in the replication process could explain alterations or mutations in the genetic material.

### *Different Quantities of DNA Required for Different Activities*

Now that the chemical nature of the gene is known, different quantities of DNA can be associated with the different activities—mutation, recombination, and protein synthesis—previously associated with the gene. Benzer has suggested terms for identifying the gene more precisely in terms of its different functions. The smallest element of DNA capable of mutation, a single base contained in a nucleotide, is called a *muton;* and the smallest indivisible unit of DNA, also a single base, which gives rise to a new form by recombination, is called a *recon.* Units of DNA which carry the information necessary for the synthesis of one enzyme are *cistrons.* Investigations of Benzer and others on the *r*II locus in $T_4$ bacteriophage (Chapter 14) indicate that a cistron includes about 1500 nucleotides. The cistron is the best equivalent of the conventional Mendelian gene. Alleles such as those described in Chapter 8 are cistrons.

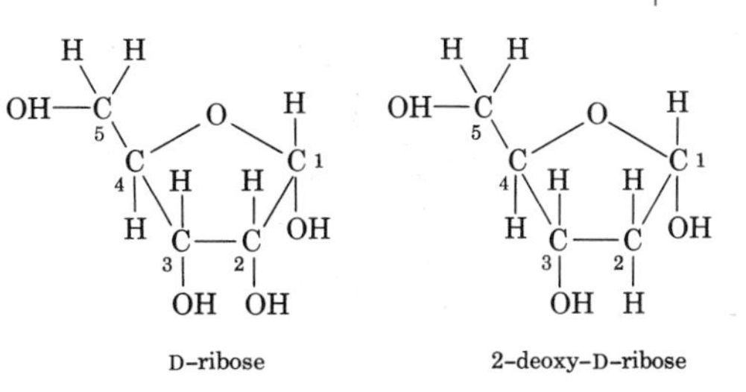


**Fig. 12.9** Structural formulas for sugars found in RNA and DNA. D-ribose is a part of the RNA molecule and 2-deoxy-D-ribose with one less atom of oxygen (see position 2) is in DNA.

## RNA IN TRANSCRIPTION AND TRANSLATION OF GENETIC INFORMATION

Ribonucleic acid (RNA) has important functions in living things. It is located in the nucleus and also in the cytoplasm, particularly in the cytoplasmic structures called ribosomes. Only RNA is present in some viruses and in these particles it fulfills the genetic function that is ordinarily restricted to DNA. In all cells, RNA participates actively in cell metabolism. The turnover rate changes with the metabolic activity of the cell. In essence, the information that DNA carries is transmitted through RNA, which directs protein synthesis in the ribosomes within the cytoplasm of the cell.

The RNA molecule is single-stranded rather than double-stranded. It contains ribose (Fig. 12.9) instead of deoxyribose sugar and the organic base uracil instead of thymine. Like DNA, RNA gives a maximum absorption of ultraviolet light with a wavelength of about 260 millimicrons. Also like DNA, RNA stains with basic dyes. RNA can be demonstrated with cytochemical tests in which RNase (an enzyme that acts on RNA) is introduced to break down the cytoplasmic basophilia. Three kinds of RNA have important functions in the transcription and translation of genetic information: (1) messenger-RNA, (2) transfer-RNA, and (3) ribosomal-RNA.

Messenger-RNA (m-RNA) is synthesized with the aid of an enzyme, RNA polymerase, in the nuclei along one strand of double-stranded DNA, as illustrated in Fig. 12.10. The attachment of RNA polymerase to a DNA molecule opens up a section of the double helix, thereby allowing free bases on one of the DNA strands to pair with complementary bases and thus provide a transcription of the base sequence. For example, on the new RNA strand, thymine (T) of DNA is represented in m-RNA by adenine (A), cytosine (C) is represented by guanine (G), and adenine by uracil (U). As RNA polymerase moves along the DNA template, the growing RNA strand peels off, allowing hydrogen bonds to reform between two complementary strands. The m-RNA transcription passes to the cytoplasm where it becomes associated with the ribosomes. Information from nuclear DNA is translated during protein synthesis.

Another kind of RNA, called transfer-RNA (t-RNA), is involved in the translation function. It is single-stranded, like

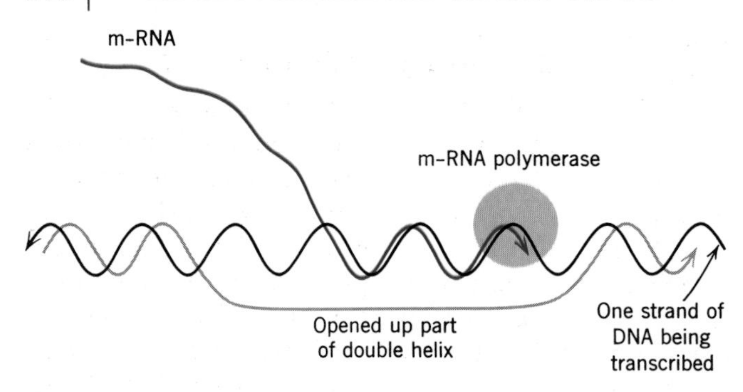


**Fig. 12.10** DNA transcription by messenger-RNA. (After Watson, *Molecular Biology of the Gene,* W. A. Benjamin, Inc., 1965.)

m-RNA, but the molecules are much smaller than those of m-RNA. This RNA is a selecting and transporting agent. Two or more specific t-RNA's exist for each amino acid. Molecules of t-RNA (Fig. 12.11) are adapted to seek out particular amino-acid molecules that have been synthesized in the cell and that have been activated by enzymes. The free ends of certain t-RNA molecules are adapted to connect with specific amino acids. Elsewhere in the t-RNA molecule, a series of bases is located which specifies a site on the m-RNA strand. The t-RNA molecules bring particular amino acids to the appropriate place on the ribosome-m-RNA complex and assist in assembling them into polypeptides.

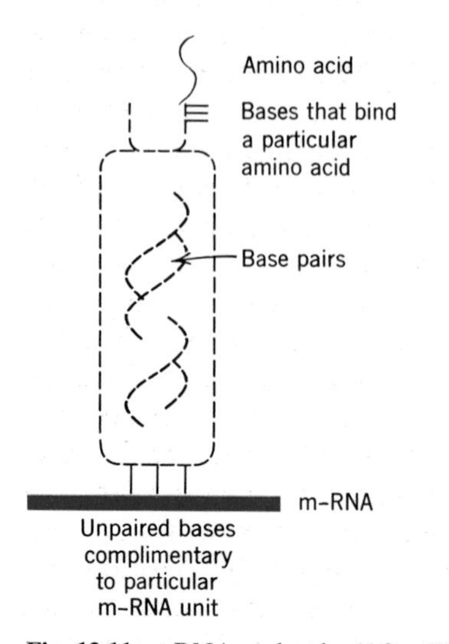


**Fig. 12.11** *t*-RNA molecule. (After Watson, *Molecular Biology of the Gene,* W. A. Benjamin, Inc., 1965.)

A third kind of RNA is a component of ribosomes and is called ribosomal-RNA (r-RNA). This RNA joins the ribosomes to m-RNA. Unlike m-RNA and t-RNA, r-RNA is nonspecific. It makes up part of the structure of the ribosome which functions as an assembly plant for amino acids operating according to specifications of m-RNA transcripts. Roughly half of the volume of each ribosome is r-RNA, and half is protein. Proportions of RNA and protein in ribosomes vary greatly in different organisms. Chains of ribosomes observed in electron micrographs of materials such as mammalian reticulocytes are called polysomes.

## BASE TRIPLETS AND THE GENETIC CODE

Genetic coding, which is basic to the transmitting of information relative to protein synthesis, involves the sequence arrangement of organic bases in the DNA molecule. The Watson and Crick model for DNA is fundamental to the currently accepted explanation of coding. By experiments with *E. coli,* an enzyme source was discovered which would promote the synthesis of proteins in a test tube. Another significant technical advance was the artificial synthesis of different kinds of m-RNA-like polymers. This tool provided a technique by which a synthetic m-RNA could be tested to see what kind of polypeptide it would specify.

Experiments based on these two technical advances resulted in the deciphering of the genetic code. The first step was to determine the kind of "language" in which the information is coded. How can four organic bases carry the information required for the synthesis of particular proteins in living systems? The "letters" in the "language" were found to be the bases, the "words" (codons) are groups of bases, and the "sentences" and "paragraphs" equate with groups of codons. How many bases make up a codon? Several lines of evidence have now provided an answer to this question.

A series of early experiments, which gave evidence for codons consisting of three bases rather than 2, 4, or some other number, was conducted by F. Crick and his associates on the B cistron in the *r*II region of bacteriophage $T_4$. Mutations induced with acridine dyes resulted in insertions or deletions of single nucleotides; that is, units in the DNA sequence consisting of one phosphorus, one sugar, and one base. When a single insertion or deletion, or two insertions or deletions were induced, the cistron was inactivated and the mutant trait was expressed. When, however, three mutations of the same type were induced in sequence, the normal phenotype was often restored. Furthermore, mutants of opposite kinds suppressed each other and the wild-type phenotype was restored. The results were interpreted to indicate that the m-RNA message is read from one position along a linear sequence in units of three bases. Other more direct evidence for the triplet arrangement of the codon will be discussed later in this chapter.

### *Deciphering the Genetic Code*

In 1961, M. W. Nirenberg and J. H. Matthaei reported the production of a synthetic RNA, polyuridylic acid (poly-U), consisting of molecules with only one base, uracil. This was accomplished with the aid of an enzyme, polynucleotide phosphorylase. The investigators added this synthesized RNA to a cell-free extract containing protein-synthesizing enzymes from *E. coli* together with a mixture of the twenty common amino acids.

To make such a cell-free extract, the investigators allowed the bacteria to grow rapidly by providing a suitable nutrient medium and optimal temperature conditions. When large numbers of bacteria had been produced, the investigators harvested the bacteria by centrifugation. Bacterial cells were then broken by gently grinding them in a mortar with a pestle in the presence of finely divided aluminum oxide. Cell contents containing all the enzymes necessary for protein synthesis, energy sources, and other necessary factors were prepared in a test tube.

When poly-U was added to such a cell-free extract, a small proteinlike molecule was produced. The incorporation process was traced by repeated experiments, in each of which a single amino acid was labeled with radioactive carbon ($C^{14}$). When the synthesized molecules from the different experiments were checked for radioactivity, it was found that only those from the mixture containing radioactive phenylalanine were radioactive. Further analysis showed that these molecules were made up entirely of repeating units of labeled phenylalanine. Peptide linkages had joined units of the same amino acid, in sequence, making polyphenylalanine. The base sequence, uracil-uracil-uracil (UUU or poly-U), in m-RNA was thus transcribed as amino acid, phenylalanine.

In turn, the m-RNA base sequence was a transcription of the complementary DNA sequence, adenine-adenine-adenine (triplet AAA). Thus, the DNA codon for one amino acid (phenylalanine) had been discovered. It consisted of three bases and was transcribed in the m-RNA by three complementary bases.

The next obvious step was to try to similarly determine the code symbols for other amino acids. Progress was slow at first because it was necessary to prepare a fresh cell-free extract for each experiment and to synthesize a fresh m-RNA. Later, methods were devised by which the enzyme extracts could be stored for long periods of time without loss of activity, and soon agencies were established to prepare synthetic m-RNA's for investigators. These technical advances speeded up the experimental procedures, and several investigators worked out new modifications in conjunction with the many studies that were initiated to decode the information necessary for the synthesis of other polypeptides.

In one of these experiments, polycytidylic acid (poly-C) was introduced into a cell-free system, and the amino acid, proline, was incorporated into a proteinlike substance. Synthesis was discontinued in the system when the m-RNA was depleted and no DNA was present to provide more templates necessary to make more m-RNA. When an appropriate m-RNA was added to the system, protein synthesis was resumed. A stop and go system was now available for testing more synthetic m-RNA's.

Eventually, many combinations of the RNA bases, adenine (A), guanine (G), cytosine (C), and uracil (U) were synthesized and tested. Six varieties of RNA polymer could be formed, each with only two kinds of bases: poly-AC, poly-AG, poly-AU, poly-CG, poly-CU, and poly-GU. When the ratio of bases was carefully adjusted, each polymer was shown to code one or more amino acids. The proportion of one amino acid to another depended on the ratio of bases in the m-RNA.

Techniques of this kind were used effectively by S. Ochoa and his colleagues, who synthesized several copolymers, each with two of the four bases. A synthetic polynucleotide, for example, containing about equal proportions of uracil and cytosine (poly-UC) was found to increase the incorporation of the amino acids phenylalanine, serine, leucine, and proline, suggesting that uracil and cytosine were involved in the coding for these amino acids. If, for example, the poly-UC contained 70 percent of U and 30 percent of C, and the U and C bases were arranged at random, the probability of the triplet sequence UUU would be $0.7 \times 0.7 \times 0.7$, or 0.34. Thus, 34 percent of the triplets would be expected to be UUU. The probability of UUC would be $0.7 \times 0.7 \times 0.3$, or 0.15. Calculations of this type suggested the likely base composition of several triplets. Results of additional experiments indicated that each polynucleotide incorporates a particular set of amino acids. According to the earliest published data, only copolymers that contained uracil served as templates for amino acid incorporation. This seemed strange because no naturally occurring RNA was known to have such a large fraction of uracil.

Several attempts were then made to use polymers that did not contain uracil as templates. Bretscher and Grunberg-Manago found that poly-AC stimulated the uptake of proline, threonine, histidine, and (to a lesser extent) glutamine. Lengyel and his associates found poly-A (m-RNA triplet AAA) to be effective in incorporating lysine in a cell-free rat liver system and also in a cell-free *E. coli* system suggesting again the universality of the code. Polynucleotides that included only uracil and guanine incorporated quite different

**TABLE 12.2 The amino acid code**

| Amino Acid | Abbreviation | DNA Code | m-RNA Transcription |
|---|---|---|---|
| 1. Alanine | ala | CGA CGG CGT CGC | GCU GCC GCA GCG |
| 2. Arginine | arg | GCA GCT GCC TCT GCG TCC | CGU CGA CGG AGA CGC AGG[a] |
| 3. Asparagine | asn | TTA TTG | AAU AAC |
| 4. Aspartic Acid | asp | CTA CTG | GAU GAC |
| 5. Cysteine | cys | ACA ACG | UGU UGC |
| 6. Glutamine | gln | GTT GTC | CAA CAG |
| 7. Glutamic Acid | glu | CTT CTC | GAA GAG |
| 8. Glycine | gly | CCA CCG CCT CCC | GGU GGC GGA GGG |
| 9. Histidine | his | GTA GTG | CAU CAC |
| 10. Isoleucine | ilu | TAA TAG | AUU AUC |
| 11. Leucine | leu | AAT AAC GAA GAG GAT GAC | UUA UUG CUU CUC CUA[a] CUG |
| 12. Lysine | lys | TTT TTC | AAA AAG |
| 13. Methionine | met | TAT TAC | AUA[a] AUG |
| 14. Phenylalanine | phe | AAA AAG | UUU UUC |
| 15. Proline | pro | GGA GGG GGT GGC | CCU CCC CCA CCG |
| 16. Serine | ser | AGA AGG AGT AGC TCA TCG | UCU UCC UCA UCG AGU AGC |
| 17. Threonine | thr | TGA TGG TGT TGC | ACU ACC ACA ACG |
| 18. Tryptophan | try | ACT ACC | UGA[a] UGG |
| 19. Tyrosine | tyr | ATA ATG | UAU UAC |
| 20. Valine | val | CAA CAG CAT CAC | GUU GUC GUA GUG |
| Terminating triplets | | ATT ATC | UAA UAG |

[a] Codon predicted but not yet demonstrated experimentally.

amino acids than those with only adenine and cytosine. Many uracil-free polynucleotides have since been associated with amino-acid incorporation. It is evident that 62 of the 64 possible combinations of the four DNA bases in groups of three (codons) specify amino acids (Table 12.2). Two DNA codons expressed as m-RNA triplets UAA and UAG do not specify amino acids but perform another function, that of punctuating or terminating a particular code message. These were at first called "nonsense" triplets because they did not code for an amino acid but were found to perform an important function as chain terminators.

Experimental evidence now indicates that codons consist only of three adjacent bases and not multiples of three. Codons are lined up linearly and they do not overlap, that is, any one base is a part of only one codon. The three-letter code is always read from a fixed point, that is, from the beginning of a cistron. Furthermore, the code sequence corresponds with the amino-acid sequence, the polypeptide chain being synthesized from the free amino ($NH_2$) end rather than from the carboxyl (COOH) end of the peptide chain.

### *Degeneracy of the Code*

The code has been described as "degenerate" because the same amino acid is coded by more than one base triplet. Leucine, for example, is coded by several different codons. Degeneracy, as used here, does not imply lack of specificity in protein synthesis. It merely means that a particular amino acid can be directed to its place in the peptide chain by more than one base triplet. Degeneracy has apparently been established in the genetic code by natural selection as a mechanism for bolstering stability against natural randomizing influences. The degenerate code stabilizes phenotypes by lessening

**TABLE 12.3 m-RNA codon assignments as designated by Nirenberg and others illustrating the pattern of organization and nature of degeneracy of code**

| | | | | | | | |
|---|---|---|---|---|---|---|---|
| AAU | asn | ACU | thr | AGU | ser | AUU | ile |
| AAC | asn | ACC | thr | AGC | ser | AUC | ile |
| AAG | lys | ACG | thr | AGG | (? arg) | AUG | met |
| AAA | lys | ACA | thr | AGA | arg | AUA | (? met) |
| CAU | his | CCU | pro | CGU | arg | CUU | leu |
| CAC | his | CCC | pro | CGC | arg | CUC | leu |
| CAG | gln | CCG | pro | CGG | arg | CUG | leu |
| CAA | gln | CCA | pro | CGA | arg | CUA | (? leu) |
| GAU | asp | GCU | ala | GGU | gly | GUU | val |
| GAC | asp | GCC | ala | GGC | gly | GUC | val |
| GAG | glu | GCG | ala | GGG | gly | GUG | val |
| GAA | glu | GCA | ala | GGA | gly | GUA | val |
| UAU | tyr | UCU | ser | UGU | cys | UUU | phe |
| UAC | tyr | UCC | ser | UGC | cys | UUC | phe |
| UAG | trm | UCG | ser | UGG | trp | UUG | leu |
| UAA | trm | UCA | ser | UGA | (? trp) | UUA | leu |

the effects of random mutation. It also minimizes the consequences of base-pairing errors occurring in the transcription and translation of the DNA information. A code capable of buffering the effects of mutations and noninherited errors (for instance, those produced by drugs) would increase the reliability of the entire system for gene expression and thus have a selective advantage.

If the code were not degenerate (that is, if each of the 20 amino acids were specified by a single unique codon), the remaining 44 base combinations would not specify amino acids. In this situation, most one-step mutations would lead to triplets that would not specify amino acids. The results would lead to unfinished polypeptide chains expressed in the organisms as defective mutants. A degenerate code with two to six codons for each amino acid and only the minimum number of codons not specifying amino acids would decrease the rate of mutant phenotypes. If, on the other hand, triplets corresponding to the same amino acid shared at least two bases in common, one-step mutations would change the specified amino acid as infrequently as possible. This is the pattern that has been developed in nature. The flexibility of the system and the pattern of organization of codons as assigned by Nirenberg and others is illustrated in Table 12.3. A high proportion of codons for the same amino acid (synonyms) differ in only one base. Mutations that result in no amino-acid substitution (silent mutations) may occur in synonyms with shared doublets. If, for example, a C, G, or A in the third position of the three codons for threonine should mutate to U, the result would be ACU, another codon for threonine.

More recent investigations by Nirenberg and others have provided further evidence for the triplet nature of the code and have shown that the sequence of the three bases in a codon is a significant factor in specifying amino acids. The first and second bases in a triplet are more important than the third in distinguishing amino acids. In one series of experiments, Bernfield and Nirenberg determined the sequence of bases within the codons for phenylalanine, serine, and proline. This was accomplished by following the attachment of $C^{14}$, labeled t-RNA, with chemically defined trinucleotides to the ribosomes. Both UUC and UUU codons were found to specify phenylalanine, UCC and UCU serine, and CCC and CCU proline. A general pattern of degeneracy was proposed in which identical bases in the first and second positions and U or C in the third position serve as codons for the same amino acid. The same relation has been indicated for A and G in the third position; that is, identical bases in the first two positions specify the same amino acid when either A or G is in the third position.

### *Punctuation for Coded Message*

Base sequences, such as UAA and UAG, that do not code for any amino acid were at first considered to be "nonsense" triplets, with no function in protein synthesis. Further study has shown that they perform another function as punctuation codons, that is, start and stop signals or spacers in the coded message. Spacers do not occur between codons. The message at that level is continuous from triplet to triplet but signals initiate and terminate larger sections of the message between functional genes or cistrons.

In one experiment, proteins from *E. coli* were found to contain characteristic $NH_2$-terminal amino acids, predominately methionine, alanine, serine, and threonine. This suggested that the codes for methionine and alanine might be initiation codes for protein synthesis in *E. coli*. Methionine was also found to be the $NH_2$-terminal amino acid for the *E. coli* host-specific bacteriophages. Formylmethionine was found to be the amino-terminal group of the coat proteins of $f_2$ and R17 bacteriophages produced in cell-free systems. For example, an m-RNA triplet (perhaps AUG), which specifies the incorporation of N-formylmethionyl-t-RNA, has been identified as the start signal for synthesis of a virus-coat protein. At the completion of a polypeptide chain, an enzyme provides a stop signal by removing the N-formylmethionine and stopping the synthetic process.

In another investigation designed to identify the mechanism for termination of a polypeptide chain synthesis, a cell-free extract of *E. coli* was employed for the synthesis of different polypeptides. To study the final step in the synthesis, it was necessary to separate polypeptides from peptidyl t-RNA. This was accomplished by chromatography. Polypeptides free from t-RNA were formed with the endogenous m-RNA. This indicated that the normal chain terminating mechanism was operating in this cell-free extract system. With U:A = 2:1, but not with other copolymers studied, a significant amount of peptidyl t-RNA was frequently found in the supernatant fraction. It was therefore considered possible that the release of peptidyl t-RNA into the supernatant fraction had prevented formation of free polypeptides in the UA system. The extent of free polypeptide release with UA was consistent with the suggestion of Brenner that UAA serves as a chain-terminating signal. All the data from this investigation supported the hypothesis that a nucleotide sequence on the m-RNA transcript controls polypeptide chain completion.

## DECODING AN RNA VIRUS

The genetic code carried by RNA has been investigated in the tobacco mosaic virus (TMV) by H. G. Wittmann, H. Fraenkel-Conrat, and several others. These investigators have shown that the same code that has been discovered in bacteriophage, bacteria, and mammalian hemoglobin also applies to RNA viruses. TMV consists of a long single rod-shaped molecule with a radius of about 150 A, a length of about 3000 A and a molecular weight of $4 \times 10^7$ (Fig. 12.12). RNA in TMV is a single chain of some 6500

**Fig. 12.12** Tobacco mosaic virus particles. (Courtesy of Carl Zeiss Company.)

nucleotides surrounded by a tubular protein coat consisting of about 2100 repeating units. In general, the coding mechanism in this RNA virus is similar to that of DNA. The virus retains its infectivity when the protein coat is removed, but infectivity is lost when the RNA core is dissolved with RNase. RNA of the TMV particle also acts as m-RNA and thus directs the protein synthesis of progeny viruses.

Several investigators have studied the amino-acid replacements that result from single base changes in TMV RNA. The experiments showed that TMV protein was a complex of about 2200 single peptide chains, each containing 158 amino acids (Fig. 12.13). Fourteen different amino acids were identified. The TMV studies supported those conducted with DNA organisms and they reiterated that single base changes can cause amino-acid substitutions. The TMV studies thus provide further evidence for a universal code. A code would be universal if the same base triplet codes the same amino acid in all organisms. Samples from widely different groups of living organisms tend to indicate such a universality of the code.

## SUMMARY

The physical element postulated by Mendel as the genetic determiner was shown by transformation studies on bacteria and the experiments of Hershey and Chase on a virus to be deoxyribonucleic acid, or DNA. DNA was consistently found in chromosomes, the places where genes are known to be located. DNA has the properties that genes must have, and it behaves as genetic material is expected to behave. Watson and Crick developed a model of the DNA molecule based on X-ray diffraction studies made by Wilkins and others, and on biochemical analyses by Chargaff and others. This model provides a working pattern of structure associated with the chemical and physical properties of the DNA molecule. DNA is capable of replication preceding cell division, thus carrying information forward from cell to cell. In a given individual, the genetic information incorporated in a DNA molecule is transcribed by m-RNA and translated in the ribosomal process of protein synthesis with the aid of t-RNA. Knowledge accumulated from studies of animals, plants, DNA viruses, and RNA viruses indicates that the code might be universal in all living things. Information carried by DNA is coded in a "language" based on groups of three adjacent bases. All 64 possible codons have been associated with specification of an amino acid or punctuation for the message. The code is degenerate in the sense that more than one codon can specify the same amino acid.

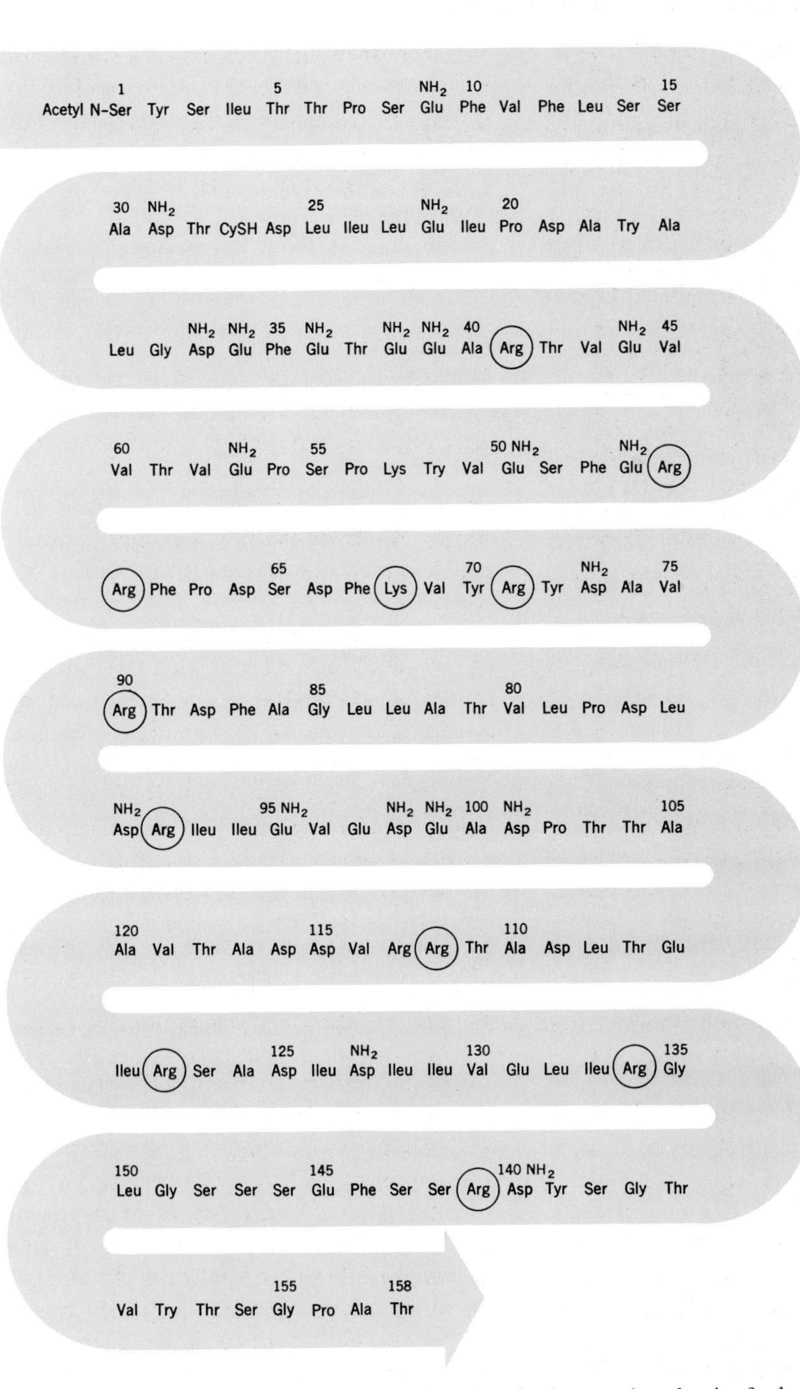


**Fig. 12.13** Sequence of the 158 amino acid residues in the protein subunit of tobacco mosaic virus. The encircled residues indicate the points of splitting by trypsin. (A. Tsugita, D. T. Gish, J. Young, H. Fraenkel-Conrat, C. A. Knight, and W. M. Stanley, "The Complete Amino Acid Sequence of the Protein of Tobacco Mosaic Virus," *Proceedings of the National Academy of Sciences,* Vol. 46, pp. 1463–1469, 1960.)

## REFERENCES


Adams, J. M., and M. R. Capecchi. 1966. "N-formylmethionyl-sRNA as initiator of protein synthesis." *Proc. Nat'l. Acad. Sci. (U. S.)*, **55,** 147–155.

Avery, O. T., C. M. MacLeod, and M. McCarty. 1944. "Studies on the chemical nature of the substance inducing transformation in pneumococcal types." *J. Expyl. Med.*, **79,** 137–158. (Classical study on transformation which provided proof from chemical analyses that DNA is the genetic material.)

Chargaff, E., and J. N. Davidson. 1955. *The nucleic acids,* Vol II. Academic Press, New York. (Extensive chemical analyses of DNA which provided the background for the Watson and Crick DNA model by showing that the amount of adenine equals the amount of thymine and the amount of cytosine equals the amount of guanine.)

Crick, F. H. C. 1962. "The genetic code." *Sci. Amer.*, **207(4),** 66–74. (Virus experiments indicate how genes direct protein synthesis evidence for three bases per codon.)

Hershey, A. D., and M. C. Chase. 1952. "Independent functions of viral protein and nucleic acid in growth of bacteriophage." *J. Gen. Physiol.*, **36,** 39–56. (Experiments which showed that the DNA part of the virus rather than the protein coat is the genetic material.)

Ingram, V. M. 1965. *The biosynthesis of macromolecules.* W. A. Benjamin, New York.

Kornberg, A. 1960. "Biologic synthesis of deoxyribonucleic acid." *Science,* **131,** 1503–1508. Review of Nobel lecture on chemistry of DNA and *in vitro* DNA synthesis.

Levine, R. P. 1962. *Genetics.* Holt, Rinehart, and Winston. New York.

Meselson, M. S. and F. W. Stahl. 1958. "The replication of DNA in *Escherichia coli.*" *Proc. Nat'l. Acad. Sci. (U. S.)*, **44,** 671–682.

Nirenberg, M. W., and J. H. Matthaei. 1961. "The dependence of cell-free protein synthesis in *E. coli* upon naturally occurring or synthetic polyribonucleotides." *Proc. Nat'l. Acad. Sci. (U. S.)*, **47,** 1588–1602.

Sager, R., and F. J. Ryan. 1961. *Cell heredity.* John Wiley and Sons, New York.

Sonneborn, T. M. 1965. "Degeneracy of the genetic code: extent, nature, and genetic implications." In *Evolving genes and proteins.* V. Bryson and H. J. Vogel (eds.) Academic Press, New York.

Swift, H. 1953. "Quantitative aspects of nuclear nucleoproteins." *Intern. Rev. Cytol.*, Vol. II. G. H. Bourne and J. F. Danielli, (eds.) Academic Press, New York. (DNA levels at different stages of meiosis and mitosis.)

Taylor, J. H. 1965. *Selected papers on molecular genetics.* Academic Press, New York.

Terzachi, W., Y. Okada, G. Streisinger, J. Emerick, M. Inouye, and A. Tsugita. 1966. "Change of a sequence of amino acids in phage $T_4$ lysozyme by acridine-induced mutations." *Proc. Nat'l. Acad. Sci. (U. S.)*, **56,** 500–507.

Tsugita, A., D. T. Gish, J. Young, H. Fraenkel-Conrat, C. Knight, and W. M. Stanley. 1960. "The complete amino acid sequence of the protein of tobacco mosaic virus." *Proc. Nat'l. Acad. Sci. (U. S.)*, **46,** 1463–1469.

Wagner, R. P., and H. K. Mitchell. 1964. *Genetics and metabolism.* John Wiley and Sons, New York. (The gene and biochemical genetics.)

Watson, J. D. 1965. *Molecular biology of the gene.* W. A. Benjamin, New York.

Watson, J. D., and F. H. C. Crick. 1953. "A structure for deoxyribose nucleic acid." *Nature,* **171,** 737–738.

Watson, J. D., and F. H. C. Crick. 1953. "Genetical implications of the structure of the deoxyribonucleic acid." *Nature,* **171,** 964–967. (These two papers present a model for the DNA molecule and evidence that DNA is the genetic material.)


# *Problems*

**12.1** What are two general functions that genes must accomplish to fulfill the requirements that have been ascribed to them? How, in general, is each accomplished?

**12.2** Among the different chemicals available, such as carbohydrate, protein, and nucleic acid in the general regions of bacterial cells and virus particles where genes were known to be located, how was the genetic material determined?

**12.3** How did the transformation experiments of Griffith differ from those of Avery and associates? What was the significant contribution of each?

**12.4** How did the phenomenon of transformation support the hypothesis that DNA is the genetic material? How widespread is the occurrence of transformation?

**12.5** How could it be demonstrated that the mixing of heat-killed Type III pneumococcus with live Type II resulted in a transfer of genetic material from Type III to Type II rather than a restoration of viability to Type III by Type II?

**12.6** How could it be demonstrated that transformation in bacteria is the result of a transfer of genetic material rather than a direct interaction of one chemical with another?

**12.7** What was the objective of the experiments cited in this chapter by Hershey and Chase? How was the objective accomplished? What is the significance of this experiment?

**12.8** Are we justified in speaking of DNA as the universal genetic material? What limitations or qualifications should be considered?

**12.9** Distinguish between DNA and RNA (a) chemically, (b) functionally, and (c) locationally in the cell.

**12.10** What background material did Watson and Crick have available for developing a model of DNA? What was their contribution to the building of the model?

**12.11** Why was a double helix chosen for the basic pattern of the molecule? Why were hydrogen bonds placed in the model to connect the bases?

**12.12** How has the Watson and Crick model contributed to genetics?

**12.13** On the basis of the Watson and Crick model, suggest a general mechanism through which replication of DNA could occur.

**12.14** Identify the following terms with reference to function and relative amount of DNA: (a) muton, (b) recon, and (c) cistron.

**12.15** What kinds of experiments resulted in the discovery that three bases make up an m-RNA codon?

**12.16** How do acridine-induced changes in DNA and RNA result in (a) inactive protein? (b) substitution of one amino acid for another in a polypeptide chain?

**12.17** How was the genetic code first decoded? What refinements have since been incorporated in the technique?

**12.18** What experiments demonstrated that base triplets not containing uracil are involved in the transfer of information for protein synthesis?

**12.19** In what sense and to what extent is the genetic code degenerate?

**12.20** Let A, T, C, and G represent adenine, thymine, cytosine, and guanine, respectively. If one strand or helix on the Watson Crick model should have bases in the order GTCATGAC, what would be the order of the bases on the complementary DNA strand?

12.21 If a virus particle contains double stranded DNA with 200,000 base pairs, how many nucleotides would be present? How many complete spirals would occur on each strand? How many atoms of phosphorus would be present? What would be the length of the DNA configuration in the virus?

12.22 If A, T, C, G, and U represent adenine, thymine, cytosine, guanine, and uracil, what letters on the m-RNA transcript would represent the following DNA sequence: TGCAGACA?

# *Synthesis, Genetic Alteration, and Evolution of Proteins*

# 13

Data acquired within the past few years have provided a fairly complete account of genetic coding, indicating how genetic information is carried from cell to cell and from generation to generation. Details of the mechanics of translation and interpretation of genetic information in living systems are not as completely understood as those of transcription but the framework of the processes has been established. The coded specifications transmitted through cellular elements are translated in the synthesis of proteins.

Proteins make up the framework of the tissues in the bodies of living organisms. Most proteins are enzymes and as such have functional significance. Essentially all of the numerous chemical processes carried on in living systems are controlled by enzymes. Many genes are known to act through the agency of enzymes, and it is suspected that most of those not yet investigated have a similar relation with enzymes. Thus, through their particular composition, organization, and enzymatic activity, proteins represent an extremely important group of chemical compounds through which inherited traits are expressed.

Chemically, proteins are giant organic molecules of different shapes and sizes. Molecular weights vary, for example, 6000 for insulin, 13,500 for ribonuclease, 66,200 for hemoglobin, and about 500,000 for very large proteins. Each molecule is composed of amino-acid residues. The number of amino acids per molecule varies from 51 in insulin, 124 in ribonuclease, and 574 in hemoglobin, to perhaps several thousand in the larger protein molecules, which have not yet been successfully analyzed. Although the subunits may number into the hundreds or thousands, only twenty of about eighty kinds of known amino acids are commonly encountered in proteins.

Amino acids contain one or more amino groups ($NH_2$) and one or more carboxyl groups (COOH). The basic structure of common amino acids (except proline) is

$$NH_2-\overset{\displaystyle H}{\underset{\displaystyle R}{\overset{|}{\underset{|}{C}}}}-COOH$$

where R represents any one of a variety of organic groupings, each characteristic of a particular amino acid. Structural formulas for the twenty amino acids commonly found in proteins are given in Fig. 13.1.

In the protein molecule, the amino acids are held together by covalent peptide bonds. Bonding involves elimination of a

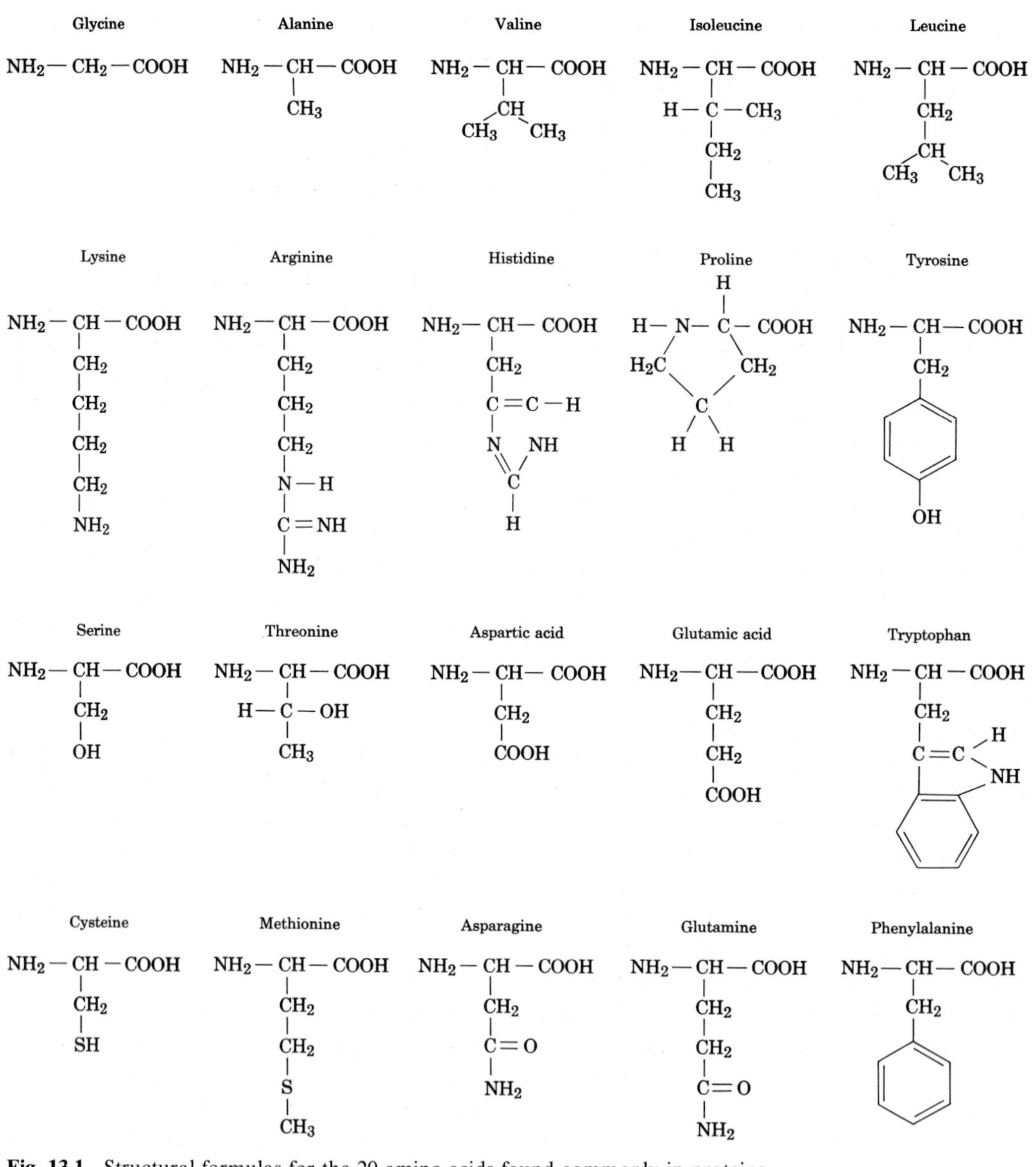


**Fig. 13.1** Structural formulas for the 20 amino acids found commonly in proteins.

hydroxyl from the carboxyl group of one amino acid and a hydrogen from the amino group of another:

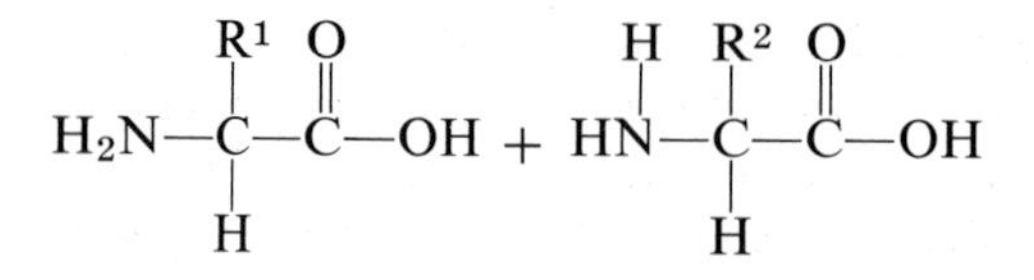

$$H_2N{-}\underset{H}{\overset{R^1}{C}}{-}\overset{O}{\overset{\|}{C}}{-}\underset{}{\overset{H}{N}}{-}\underset{H}{\overset{R^2}{C}}{-}COOH + H_2O.$$

The twenty common amino acids may occur in numerous combinations. Therefore, the number of kinds of proteins possible, is enormous. Some 10,000 proteins may be present in a cell. Only a comparatively few of the potentially large number of different proteins have been identified, and presumably many possible kinds have never occurred in nature.

In addition to their structural significance in living systems, proteins are required for the functioning of living cells and organisms. Hemoglobin, best known of the proteins, is the oxygen carrier in the erythrocytes of vertebrates. Since the great majority of known proteins are enzymes, they are intimately associated as catalysts with numerous chemical reactions in the cell. Enzyme production is controlled by genes, and therefore the vast and intricate metabolic system of an organism is at least indirectly under genetic control. Enzymes composed of single polypeptide chains usually fit the "one-gene-one enzyme" relation. Proteins that include two or more polypeptide subunits, however, may also exhibit enzymatic activity but their relation with genetic units is more complex. Furthermore, enzymes may catalyze more than one specific reaction and interactions may occur among metabolic systems in living cells. Complexities associated with aggregations of polypeptides make the relations between single genes and particular enzymatic activities difficult to demonstrate. Many single genes, however, have now been associated with single chemical processes.

Three major aspects in the mechanics of protein synthesis will be considered here: (1) locations in the cell where the process is accomplished; (2) the mechanism by which the information specifying particular proteins is transmitted from the DNA to the sites where synthesis occurs; and (3) the mechanism by which the parts required for building proteins (that is, the amino acids) are assembled in the proper locations in the cell and incorporated according to specifications into particular proteins.

## RIBOSOMES, CENTERS OF PROTEIN SYNTHESIS

Early studies on protein synthesis, by A. E. Mirsky and others, used nuclei of higher organisms separated from cytoplasmic parts and showed that a small amount of protein was synthesized in the nucleus, but that the greater proportion was manufactured in the cytoplasm. Zamecnik and others incorporated radioactive amino acids into mammalian cell systems that were accumulating protein and observed that the cytoplasmic ribosomes became radioactive. Later, ribosomes from *E. coli* were brought together in a test tube with m-RNA from a phage, an energy generating system, energy-yielding chemicals, and amino acids. Proteins similar to those of the phage coat were synthesized. This indicated that (1) ribosomes were the sites of protein synthesis, and (2) they were nonspecific; that is, they produced the kind of protein they were directed to produce by the m-RNA.

### *Structure and Activity of Ribosomes*

Ribosomes are cytoplasmic bodies composed of protein and ribosomal-RNA. They may be separated intact from cell extracts by differential centrifugation. Single ribosomes may also be separated out from cell extracts by precipitation at *p*H5 and by chromatography. Those involved with hemoglobin synthesis have a molecular weight or particle weight of $4 \times 10^6$ and sediment with a constant of about 80S (Svedberg) units of sedimentation. Ribosomes involved with the synthesis of proteins such as hemoglobin tend to form linear groupings of four or five units called polysomes. These are held together

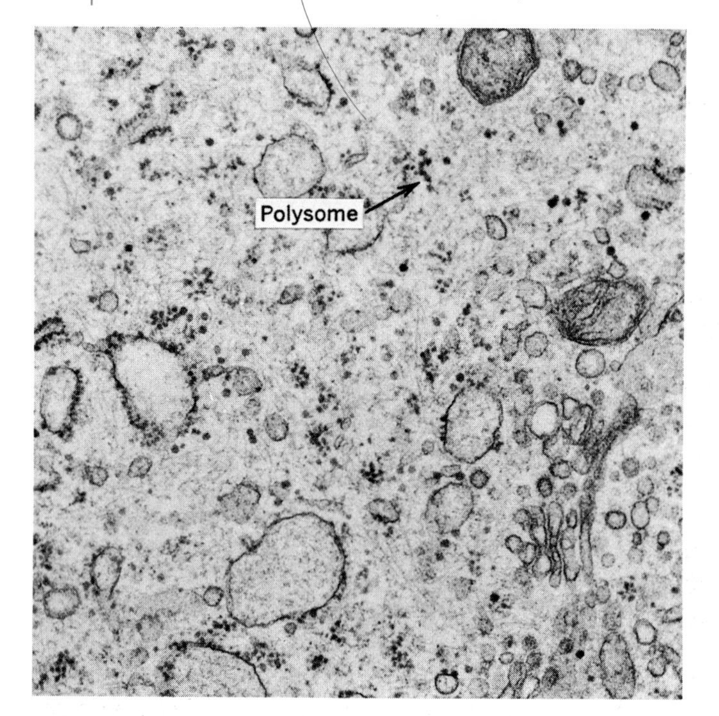


**Fig. 13.2** Photograph showing ribosomes in a follicle cell (Sertoli cell) of the wall of a seminiferous tubule in a lamprey *Lampetra planeri.* Magnification ×31,500. (Courtesy of Hugh P. Stanley.)

by delicate strands of RNA. Polysomes are not observed in all preparations because they readily separate into single ribosomes during the usual methods of preparation. They can be obtained intact after very gentle lysis and sucrose-density gradient centrifugation (Fig. 13.2).

The ribosomes studied most extensively thus far are those from *Escherichia coli.* They are composed of about 60 percent protein and 40 percent RNA. In a comparatively high magnesium ion concentration (1.0mM), 70S and 100S ribosomes with molecular weights of 2.8 and 5.9 × $10^6$, respectively, are observed on electron micrographs. The *E. coli* ribosomes that are most active in protein synthesis under the greatest range of environmental conditions are those with sedimentation constants of 70S. These are composed of 50S and 30S RNA components, which are held intact when the culture medium contains a fairly high concentration of magnesium ion. When the magnesium is decreased, the 70S particles are separated into 50S and 30S RNA subunits, which can then be observed separately. The RNA units, when held intact, are most efficient in performing their two important functions: (1) binding with the m-RNA transcription "tape" carrying the coded message from DNA; and (2) combining with t-RNA, which brings amino acids to the ribosomal assembly plant.

### *Positions and Origin of Ribosomes in Cells*

In *E. coli* the ribosomes active in protein synthesis are dispersed widely throughout the cell. In cells of higher organisms with a distinct separation between nucleus and cytoplasm, the ribosomes are mostly cytoplasmic structures, but they originate in the nucleus. In mammalian reticulocytes, which are involved in the synthesis of hemoglobin, for example, ribosomes are abundant in the cytoplasm. These ribosomes are composed of nearly half RNA;

the remainder is protein. Like the ribosomes of *E. coli,* they are composed of two RNA subunits. About 10 to 20 ribosomal proteins have been indicated. These make up the structural framework and function as enzymes. Ribonuclease is an example of a ribosomal enzyme.

Polysomes, which are made up of chains or clusters of ribosomes, may be observed on electron micrographs of the cytoplasm of cells of higher organisms. In liver cells of adult rats, for example, the polysomes have a spiral arrangement, as shown in Fig. 13.3. Individual ribosomes making up a polysome are held together by strands of RNA 10 to 15 angstroms in diameter. Brief treatment with RNase breaks the connecting links of what is apparently messenger RNA and releases the individual ribosomes.

*E. coli* ribosomes have been studied most extensively because the organisms are easily cultured and their ribosomes are active in protein synthesis. Ribosomes have also been investigated in other microbial systems and in the cells of many higher animals and several higher plants such as pea seedlings, maize root tips, and ripening fruit of the pear. With electron micrographs, ribosomal bodies may be observed in the endoplasmic reticulum of the cell (Fig. 13.2). When the endoplasmic reticulum is ruptured, the ribosomes are suspended freely in the cytoplasm.

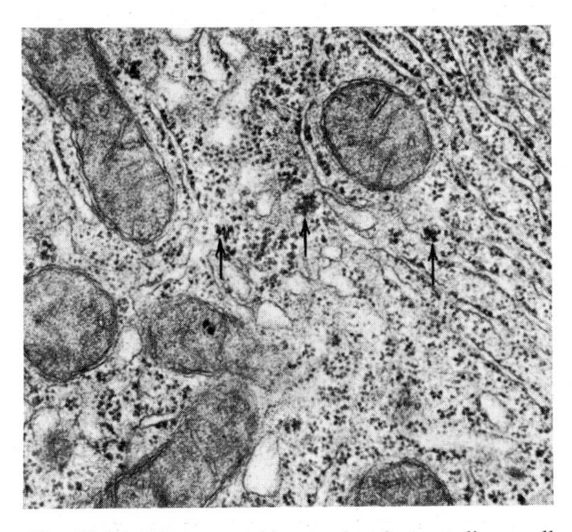

**Fig. 13.3** Electron micrograph of a rat liver cell showing clusters of ribosomes in cytoplasm. Magnification ×30,000. (Courtesy of R. L. Wood.)

The origin of ribosomes in the cell is under control of the genes. About 0.3 percent of the DNA of several different organisms that have been studied has been shown to carry the information required for the synthesis of ribosomal-RNA. F. M. Ritossa and S. Spiegelman and their associates found that, in *Drosophila melanogaster,* the nucleolar organizing (NO) regions on the X and Y chromosomes were the DNA areas responsible for r-RNA synthesis. About 85 percent of the total cellular RNA is r-RNA.

Researches have determined that other cytoplasmic structures besides ribosomes are also involved, although to a lesser extent, in protein synthesis. This observation may be the result of ribosomes located within cytoplasmic organelles, such as mitochondria. Isolated mitochondria have been found to be centers for limited protein synthesis.

Viruses that live only in other organisms make use of the host ribosomes for synthesis of their protein coats. In one investigation, a virus that infected *E. coli* was found to have a unique component. The host DNA was composed of adenine, thymine, guanine, and cytosine, but the DNA of the virus was composed of adenine, thymine, guanine, and hydroxymethyl cytosine. The virus DNA could thus be distinguished readily from the *E. coli* DNA, and it provided a tool for studying the process by which new viruses were synthesized in bacterial cells. In the subsequent experiments, bacteria were first infected with new viral DNA. The viral DNA was replicated by using the facilities of the host bacteria in the regular replication process. Viral m-RNA, which was required to specify the enzymes necessary to make hydroxymethyl cytosine, was also produced. It moved to the host-cell ribosomes where it provided the information for enzyme synthesis. At least thirty different enzymes were involved in the reactions. Viral proteins were produced in the host under the direction of viral DNA acting through viral m-RNA. Each amino acid was incorporated at the proper time into the protein-synthesizing process.

## TRANSMISSION OF GENETIC INFORMATION TO THE LOCATIONS WHERE SYNTHESIS OCCURS

The messenger-RNA hypothesis was established when it was shown that m-RNA could transcribe and carry information from DNA to the site of protein synthesis. The m-RNA is thus an intermediary between the information-carrying DNA and the ribosomes (r-RNA) where proteins are assembled. The DNA message is transcribed as a complementary base sequence with reference to the polynucleotides in a DNA strand. When the m-RNA bases in close association with a DNA strand have been joined together in tandem by an enzymatic reaction, the m-RNA leaves the DNA template or is pulled from it by the ribosomes. The m-RNA unit then becomes associated with ribosomes and specifies the amino-acid sequence in the protein to be formed. The messenger strand ties a series of ribosomes together temporarily as polysomes. Amino acids to be incorporated are brought to the ribosomes by transfer RNA (t-RNA) units. A schematic illustration of protein synthesis is given in Fig. 13.4.

DNA-dependent RNA polymerase is the enzyme that catalyzes a reaction through which m-RNA is formed with specifications transcribed from DNA. In this transfer of information, DNA serves as a template, imprinting its coded information on m-RNA. DNA also acts as a primer or catalyst, as evidenced by the fact that the m-RNA product resulting from controlled experiments greatly exceeds the quantity of DNA introduced.

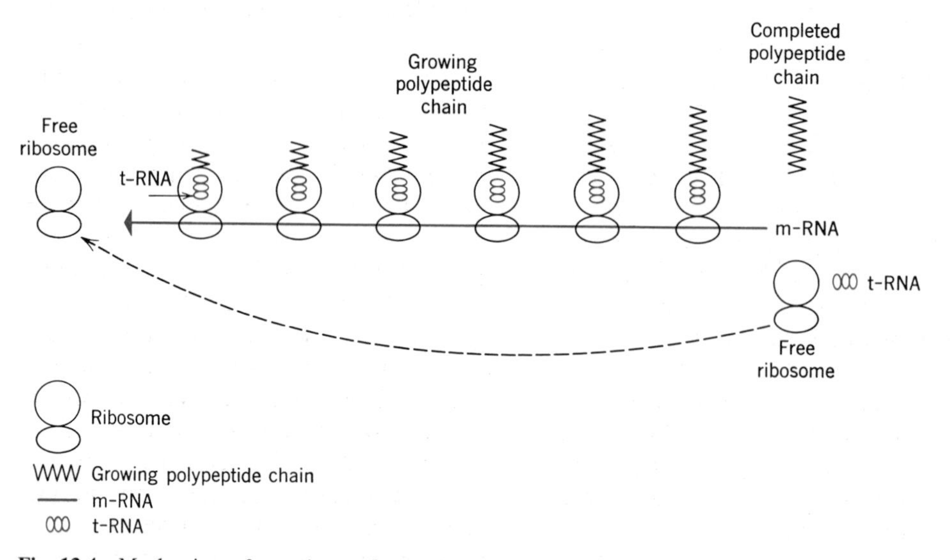


**Fig. 13.4** Mechanism of protein synthesis. (From Watson, *Science* **140**:17–26, 1963. Copyright 1963, *Amer. Assoc. Adv. Sci.*)

The proportions of the different bases in a DNA primer and its m-RNA are comparable. Under appropriate experimental conditions, the coded message was found to be complementary to only one of the two DNA strands. This indicated that the code message carried by m-RNA to the ribosomes was a direct transcription of information that was contained on one strand of DNA.

Further support for the m-RNA hypothesis has come from studies on bacteriophages. When *E. coli* was infected with virus $T_2$, a $T_2$ m-RNA was synthesized that represented the base complement of $T_2$, DNA. More recent investigations with virus $T_4$ have made use of radioactive tracers and have identified an m-RNA in the ribosomes of infected *E. coli* that was specified by a particular DNA virus. These experiments and many others have demonstrated that the ribosome is a manufacturing center for protein, but that it is nonspecific and must be supplied with the proper information from the DNA by m-RNA before it can synthesize a particular protein.

## ASSEMBLING OF AMINO ACIDS FOR INCORPORATION INTO PROTEINS

A crucial step in protein synthesis is that of bringing to the ribosomes the necessary amino acids, which are dispersed in the cell. In man, some amino acids are synthesized in the cell but others ("essential" amino acids) must be supplied in the diet. The transfer of amino acids to the ribosome is accomplished by a kind of RNA called by several names: soluble-, acceptor-, adaptor-, or transfer-RNA. The last of the terms is the most meaningful for a general discussion and the symbol t-RNA is used here to identify transfer-RNA.

A t-RNA molecule combines with a single amino-acid molecule, which originates in another part of the cell. To be reactive, an amino acid must be activated. This is accomplished when the amino acid reacts with an energy-rich molecule of adenosine triphosphate (ATP) also present in the cytoplasm. The amino acid and ATP form an AMP-AA (activated amino acid) complex. The joining of these molecules is made possible only with the aid of an enzyme specific for the amino acid, as illustrated schematically in Fig. 13.5. The real translation of genetic information into protein synthesis is accomplished when a t-RNA picks up an amino acid.

Each t-RNA combines by means of chemical bonding with one amino acid. Following directions from the m-RNA associated with ribosomes, amino acids are joined in proper order to form a particular polypeptide chain. It should be emphasized again that the information determining the sequence in which the amino acids must be assembled to form a particular protein comes from the m-RNA and not from the ribosomes or the t-RNA. Since the immediate function of a t-RNA unit is completed when it delivers an animo acid, the t-RNA is released to move in the cytoplasm and pick up another amino acid which it transports to an m-RNA-ribosome system for incorporation into protein. This process goes on rapidly in a living cell engaged in protein synthesis.

Transfer-RNA molecules appear superficially to be double helices somewhat similar to the double helix of DNA, and X-ray diffraction studies indicate that part of the molecule is helical. Only one strand is present, however, and the double helix occurs from folding. Complete nucleotide sequences have been determined for several t-RNA's. An alanine t-RNA isolated from yeast by R. W. Holley and his associates has short, folded, and therefore, double-stranded regions (Fig. 13.6) but the molecule is considerably smaller than that of either m-RNA or DNA, containing only

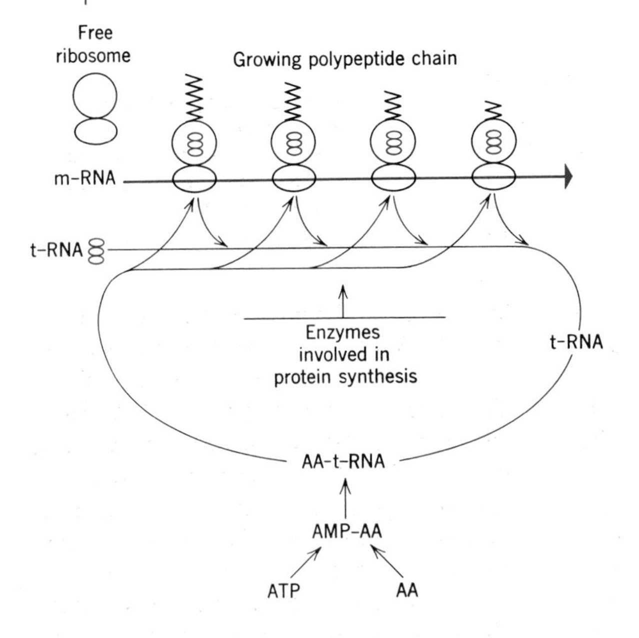


**Fig. 13.5** Activated amino acid complex. (After Watson.)

about 67 nucleotides compared with several hundred to many thousands in m-RNA and DNA. One part of the t-RNA molecule has a connecting link to hold an amino acid and in another part it has a complementary sequence of bases for pairing with a particular part of the m-RNA transcript.

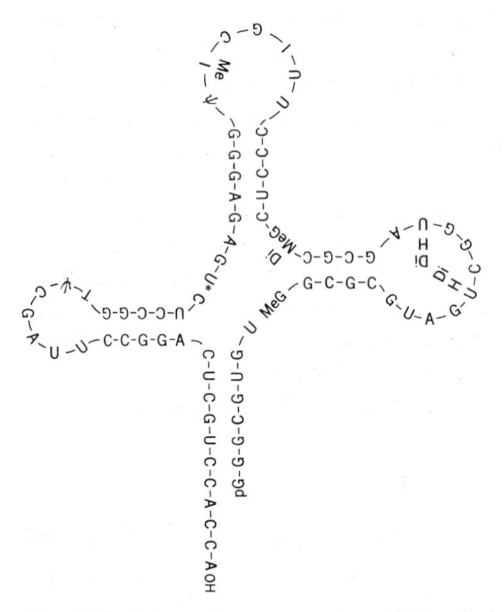

**Fig. 13.6** Schematic representation of the alanine t-RNA with short, double-stranded regions. (After Holley and others, *Science* **147:**1462–1465, 1965, copyright 1965, *Amer. Assoc. Adv. Sci.*)

## MUTATIONS AND AMINO-ACID SUBSTITUTIONS

An explanation of the mechanism and consequences of mutational change at the molecular level is based on the Watson and Crick Model of DNA and the process of protein synthesis. Changes that occur in single base pairs at a genetic locus may result in point mutations. Each of the four bases may occasionally become altered or shifted in such a way that it will pair with a base other than its usual complement. Some environmental agents tend to create unstable conditions in particular bases and thus induce certain specific kinds of alteration. Nitrous acid, for example, acts as a mutagen of extracellular bacteriophages by altering adenine and cytosine. By oxidative deamination, nitrous acid may bring about a substitution of a hydroxy (OH) group for an amino ($NH_2$) group in adenine, as illustrated

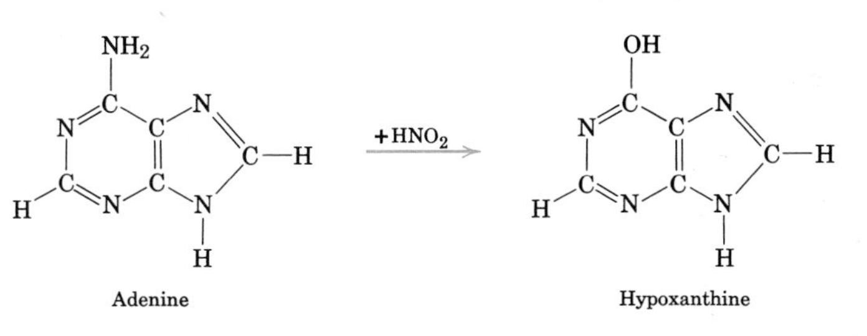


**Fig. 13.7** Change in a single base, adenine, caused by treatment with nitrous acid. By oxidative deamination a $NH_2$ group is changed to an OH group as shown at top of diagram.

in Fig. 13.7. Such a replacement of a single base in DNA constitutes a mutation. Following this alteration, a new arrangement of bases would be carried over in the replication process, as illustrated in Fig. 13.8. In DNA, adenine (A) is ordinarily paired with thymine (T) but in the presence of nitrous acid ($HNO_2$), adenine may be changed to hypoxanthine, which has pairing properties like those of guanine. Hypoxanthine thus specifies cytosine (C), and in the next replication would again specify cytosine, whereas cytosine would specify guanine (G). By this process, an AT base pair could be changed to a GC pair. In this example, thymine (the base opposite adenine in the original pair, which remained unchanged) would continue to specify its complement A, and A would continue to pair with T. A substitution of this kind could lead to a changed triplet on each DNA strand. Similar alterations also occur in RNA viruses in which RNA takes over the functions of DNA. Since both RNA and DNA are polynucleotides, both may be altered by nitrous acid and other mutagens. In the presence of nitrous acid, for example, the RNA base, cytosine, may be changed to uracil (Fig. 13.9).

The effect of nitrous acid is to cause mispairing of single bases in such a way that one purine will be changed to another purine (as illustrated in Fig. 13.7) or one pyrimidine will be changed to another pyrimidine (as illustrated in Fig. 13.8). Changes of this kind are called *transitions*. In other single base changes, called *transversions*, a purine may be replaced by a pyrimidine or a pyrimidine by a purine.

Most of the investigations on the molecular basis of mutations have been carried out on bacteria and bacteriophages, particularly phage $T_4$. In these studies, several physical and chemical agents in addition to nitrous acid have been found to be mutagenic. These have included 5-bromouracil, ultraviolet light, acridines, hydrogen ions, x-rays, and other forms of irradiation and heat.

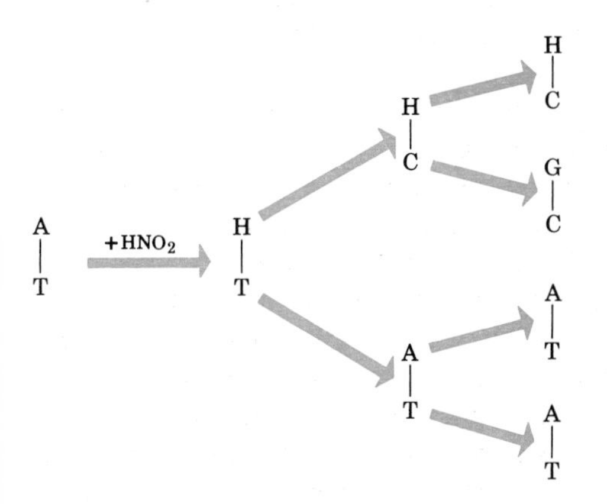


**Fig. 13.8** Changes in base specificity and base pairing resulting from oxidative deamination in the presence of nitrous acid. The pair A-T may give rise to H-C or G-C as shown in upper diagram. (After Sager and Ryan, *Cell Heredity*.)

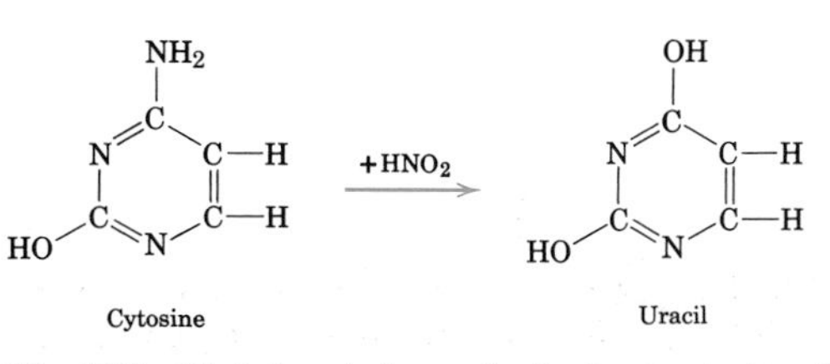


**Fig. 13.9** Mutational change in the base cytosine of RNA following treatment with nitrous acid.

### *Effects of Other Chemical Mutagens*

Bromouracil was found to have no effect on extracellular bacteriophages but mutations were induced in virus-infected *E. coli* in which the virus took over the replicating machinery of the bacteria. This mutagen could be inserted into the DNA chain of the replicating virus by enzymatic activity in the bacterial cell. Mutational changes were apparently occurring as the new strands of DNA were being formed, whereas those changes cited in the previous example, which were induced by nitrous acid, were in bases that had been previously incorporated in the DNA chain and the errors were induced by subsequently altered bases. When bromouracil was introduced, it paired with G, thus replacing C during base incorporation. Once incorporated, the bromouracil replaced T and paired with A. The net result was a transition from guanine to adenine and a base pair change from G-C to A-T. Because replication errors occasionally occur in which bromouracil pairs with G, this mutation is reversible.

A base alteration similar to that induced by bromouracil has been obtained in messenger RNA of bacteriophage-infected *E. coli* cells grown in a medium with 5-fluorouracil. In this example, the fluorouracil was incorporated into m-RNA in place of uracil, and behaved like cytosine in pairing with guanine. When the mutants were maintained on a medium containing 5-fluorouracil, the alteration in some mutants was partially reversed. The altered base, which had behaved like cytosine, changed back to uracil and paired with adenine. The explanation was that the fluorouracil, which had been incorporated at the U sites in m-RNA, occasionally corrected the coding error, thus rendering the change in m-RNA reversible. The mutagen, hydroxylamine, has an effect opposite to that of fluorouracil on m-RNA. Whereas fluorouracil produces a change from U to C, hydroxylamine produced a C to U effect.

### *Alterations With Ultraviolet Light*

Treatment of bacteriophages with ultraviolet light also creates a mutational effect resulting from mispairing of the organic bases. Pyrimidines (thymine and cytosine) are much more sensitive to ultraviolet than purines (adenine and guanine). Furthermore, the effects of ultraviolet alterations on DNA are most evident when replication is in progress, indicating that errors occur during the process of base incorporation. At this time, extraneous bonds between neighboring pyrimidines disrupt the regular duplication process. In one series of ultraviolet-induced mutations, most changes were found to be C to T transitions. The pyrimidine-altered mutants were then induced, by further treatment with ultraviolet and other mutagenic agents, to revert to the original wild type. The mechanism for reversion was shown to be a change in the A-T base pair at the mutant site. Base T was altered to hydroxymethyl-cytosine, which paired with G and replicated as C. A reversible mutational change from a C-G base pair to an A-T and back to a C-G had thus been demonstrated.

## ALTERATION AND EVOLUTION OF PROTEINS

Genetic alterations in proteins have been found to account for the mechanism of hereditary irregularities and molecular variations in plants, animals, and man. A new approach to the study of evolution through molecular biology has also developed. Along with the older and more classical lines of evidence for the pathway of evolution (for instance, paleontology, comparative anatomy, serology, comparative embryology, biogeography, and comparative physiology), molecular biology of the proteins provides impressive supporting evidence. Variation at the molecular level can be evaluated by (1) studying the product of a single gene in different organisms (2) measuring the amount and kind of variation within species and between closely related and more distantly related species, and (3) by estimating gene changes in time. Chemical distinctions between the different kinds of protein have been detected by so-called fingerprinting, the enzymatic separation of polypeptides and identification of amino acids in the peptides by electrophoresis and chromatography. Fingerprints can be compared to determine differences in the amino-acid content of different peptides and, along with other techniques, the precise sequence of amino acids can be discovered. Hemoglobin and cytochrome have been studied extensively by these methods.

### *The Hemoglobin Molecule*

Several different forms of hemoglobin are known to occur in man. Most of them were detected initially by altered electrophoretic mobility; some have been distinguished chemically by fingerprinting and by other procedures. Each is controlled by a particular gene. The human adult hemoglobin A molecule is composed of four polypeptide chains, two identical *alpha* chains and two identical *beta* chains. The alpha chain has 141 amino acids and the beta chain has 146, making a total of 574 amino acids (Fig. 13.10). Nineteen different amino acids are in the hemoglobin molecule. Comparison between the alpha and beta chains shows that numbers 20 (his) and 21 (ala) on the alpha chain have no counterparts on the beta chain, and numbers 1 (val), 39 (gln), 54 (val), 55 (met), 56 (gly), 57 (asn), and 58 (pro) on the beta chain have no corresponding residues on the alpha chain. Among the 137 paired residues, 61 are alike and 76 are different. Comparison between the variation in the nucleotide sequence and that in the corresponding amino-acid sequence shows that a closer relation exists among the genes than among the proteins. This is expected because the genes are coded in a four-letter language (ACGT) but the proteins are in a 20-letter language (20 different amino acids), which magnifies the difference.

Hemoglobin F, with its two alpha and two gamma chains, is present in the blood of the early developing human fetus but it is normally replaced with hemoglobin A during the first six months of neonatal life. Seventy-one percent of the amino acids on the gamma chain are identical with those in corresponding positions on a beta chain. A 39 percent correspondence exists between alpha and gamma chains and a 42 percent correspondence between alpha and beta chains.

### *Abnormal Hemoglobins*

When the beta chain of normal human hemoglobin was broken down piece by piece (Fig. 13.11), the amino acids in the peptide chain designated as part 4 were found to be arranged in the following order: val, his, leu, thr, pro, glu, glu and lys (Fig. 13.12). Hemoglobin S of sickle-cell patients was found to have all eight amino acids in the same order except for number six, glutamic acid, which was replaced by valine. A single gene *Si* is responsible for this amino-acid substitution. All others of the 146 residues of the beta chain were normal. When gene *Si* is present in heterozygous condition, normal hemoglobin A is predominant but a small quantity of abnormal hemoglobin S is also present in the patient. The red cells may be sickle-shaped when oxygen tension is low and the patient is generally in good health. In the presence of the homozygous gene *Si/Si*, hemoglobin A is replaced completely by hemoglobin S and the pa-

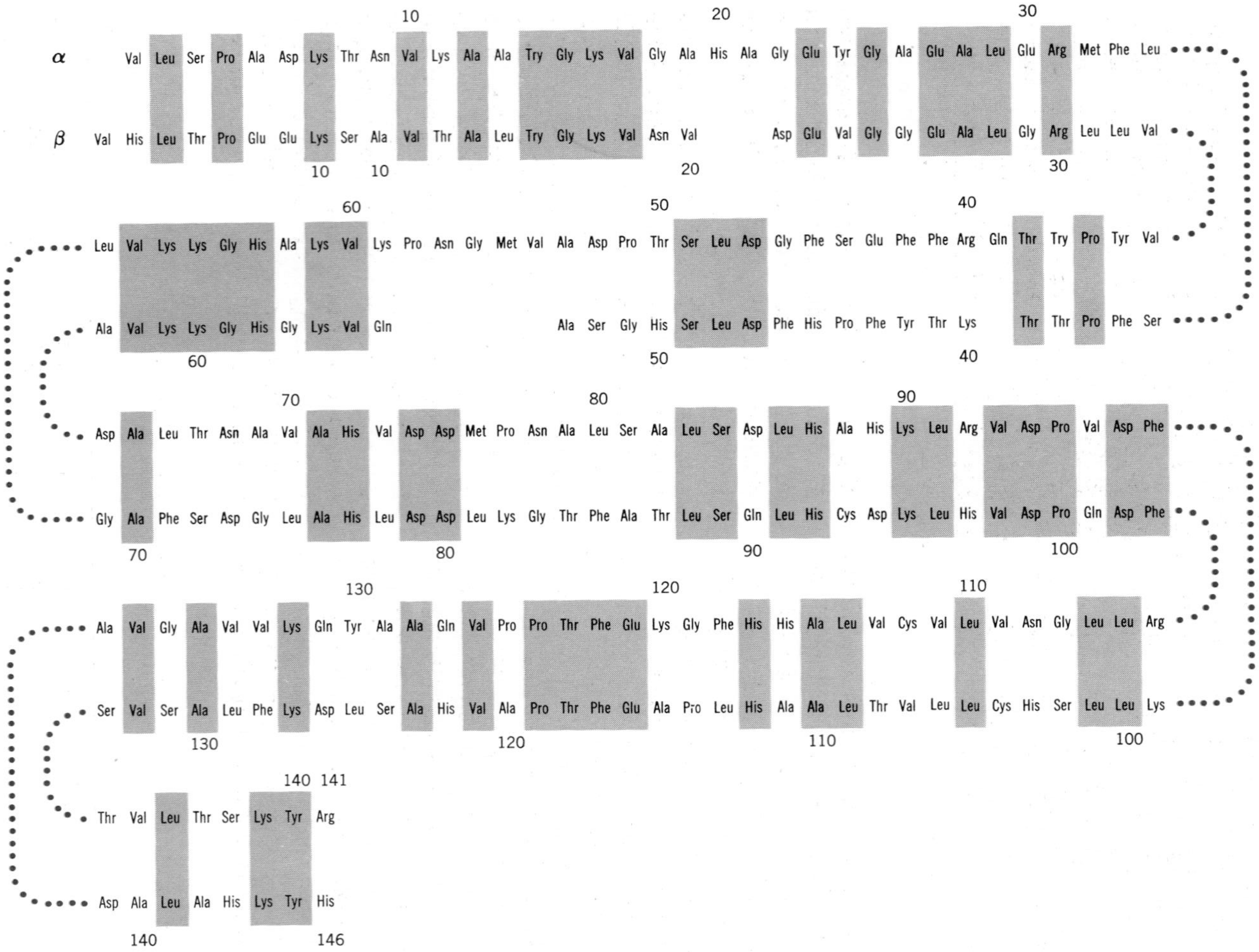

α Val Leu Ser Pro Ala Asp Lys Thr Asn Val Lys Ala Ala Try Gly Lys Val Gly Ala His Ala Gly Glu Tyr Gly Ala Glu Ala Leu Glu Arg Met Phe Leu
(10, 20, 30)

β Val His Leu Thr Pro Glu Glu Lys Ser Ala Val Thr Ala Leu Try Gly Lys Val Asn Val Asp Glu Val Gly Gly Glu Ala Leu Gly Arg Leu Leu Val
(10, 10, 20, 30)

α Leu Val Lys Lys Gly His Ala Lys Val Lys Pro Asn Gly Met Val Ala Asp Pro Thr Ser Leu Asp Gly Phe Ser Glu Phe Phe Arg Gln Thr Try Pro Tyr Val
(60, 50, 40)

β Ala Val Lys Lys Gly His Gly Lys Val Gln Ala Ser Gly His Ser Leu Asp Phe His Pro Phe Tyr Thr Lys Thr Thr Pro Phe Ser
(60, 50, 40)

α Asp Ala Leu Thr Asn Ala Val Ala His Val Asp Asp Met Pro Asn Ala Leu Ser Ala Leu Ser Asp Leu His Ala His Lys Leu Arg Val Asp Pro Val Asp Phe
(70, 80, 90)

β Gly Ala Phe Ser Asp Gly Leu Ala His Leu Asp Asp Leu Lys Gly Thr Phe Ala Thr Leu Ser Gln Leu His Cys Asp Lys Leu His Val Asp Pro Gln Asp Phe
(70, 80, 90, 100)

α Ala Val Gly Ala Val Val Lys Gln Tyr Ala Ala Gln Val Pro Pro Thr Phe Glu Lys Gly Phe His His Ala Leu Val Cys Val Leu Val Asn Gly Leu Leu Arg
(130, 120, 110)

β Ser Val Ser Ala Leu Phe Lys Asp Leu Ser Ala His Val Ala Pro Thr Phe Glu Ala Pro Leu His Ala Ala Leu Thr Val Leu Leu Cys His Ser Leu Leu Lys
(130, 120, 110, 100)

α Thr Val Leu Thr Ser Lys Tyr Arg
(140 141)

β Asp Ala Leu Ala His Lys Tyr His
(140, 146)

**Fig. 13.10** The amino acid sequences of the $\alpha$ and $\beta$ peptide chains of Hb-A. The amino acids enclosed in boxes are identical and occupy corresponding positions along the peptide chains. The amino acids are numerated sequentially from the N-terminus. (After Ingram.)

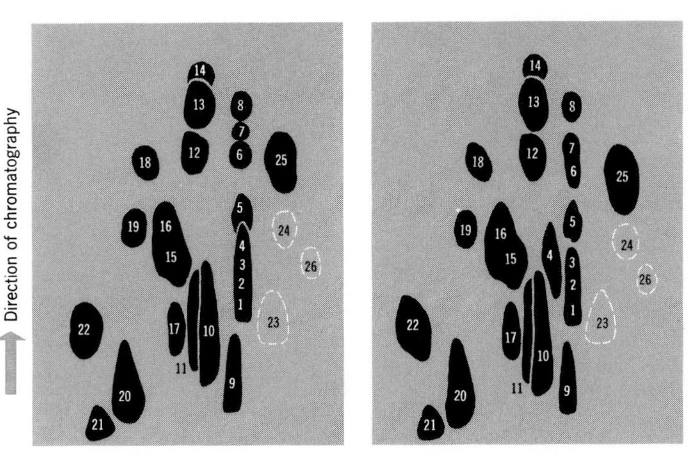


**Fig. 13.11** Peptide fingerprints of hemoglobins A and S. The hemoglobins were first digested with trypsin; then the peptides were subjected to electrophoresis, followed by paper chromatography at right angles. Dotted lines indicate peptides that are visible only after heating. Only peptide No. 4 was found to differ in the two hemoglobins. (After Ingram.)

tient has the severe form of the disease characterized by hemolytic anemia. Hemoglobin S in the cells precipitates when it is deoxygenated and produces crystaloid aggregates that distort blood corpuscles.

Hemoglobin S can also be distinguished from the hemoglobin of people not suffering from the sickle-cell disease by electrophoretic mobility. When placed in an electric field under appropriate conditions, normal hemoglobin with glutamic acid in position six has a negative charge and migrates toward the positive pole, whereas hemoglobin S with valine replacing glutamic acid has no net charge and does not migrate (Fig. 13.13) in the electric field. Another type of hemoglobin, hemoglobin C, with lysine in the number six position on the beta chain has a positive charge and migrates in the direction of the negative pole. Different forms of hemoglobin with single amino-acid substitutions can thus be identified by their differences in electrophoretic mobility as well as the amino acid in position six.

Gene *Si* thus controls the difference between normal and abnormal hemoglobin by substituting valine for glutamic acid in position six in the beta chain. The effect on the erythrocytes and the patient of a single gene substitution that results in a change of two amino-acid residues in a total of 574 would seem to be out of proportion with the magnitude of the molecular change. The amino-acid sequence influences hemoglobin formation resulting in alteration of the three-dimensional structure of the hemoglobin molecule and other effects that follow. One hypothesis for the mechanism states that the genetic substi-

| Kind of Hemoglobin | Amino Acids Numbered in Order | | | | | | | |
|---|---|---|---|---|---|---|---|---|
| | 1 | 2 | 3 | 4 | 5 | 6 | 7 | 8 |
| + | val | his | leu | thr | pro | glu | glu | lys |
| S | val | his | leu | thr | pro | val | glu | lys |
| C | val | his | leu | thr | pro | lys | glu | lys |

**Fig. 13.12** Results of fingerprinting one part (peptide 4) of the beta chain for three kinds of hemoglobin (+, S, and C). The only alteration is in position 6 where glutamic acid of hemoglobin-+ is replaced by valine in hemoglobin-S and lysine in hemoglobin-C.

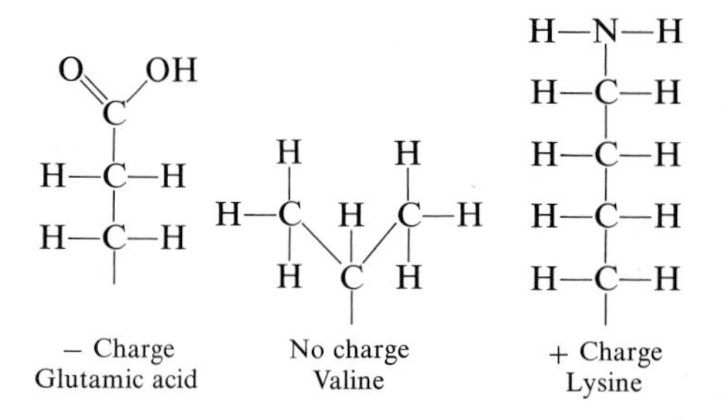


**Fig. 13.13** Structural formulas of carbon chain parts of three amino acids, glutamic acid, valine, and lysine. These amino acids are replaced in the hemoglobin molecule by the substitution of three alleles: $Si^+$, *Si*, and $Si^c$, respectively. The three amino acids behave differently in an electric field.

tution of valine for glutamic acid at the sixth position in the two beta chains allows an intramolecular hydrophobic bond to form. This changes the conformation in such a way that molecular stacking results. Electron micrographs have shown that hemoglobin S molecular threads appear as hollow cablelike structures, thus supporting the stacking theory.

The genes controlling normal hemoglobin ($Si^+$), sickle-cell ($Si^s$), and hemoglobin C ($Si^c$) are all alleles and there is evidence that several other kinds of hemoglobin may also be controlled by other members of the same series of alleles. Gene-controlled substitutions of amino acids are known to occur on both the alpha and beta chains.

In abnormal hemoglobin, a mutation resulting in an alteration in a base sequence has caused the substitution of one amino acid for another and, thus, altered the characteristics of the protein, hemoglobin. Data from studies of cell-free systems indicate that one of the DNA triplets that codes for glutamic acid is CTC. This triplet would code for the complementary GAG in the m-RNA transcript. Substitution of an A for a T (CAC) in DNA (Fig. 13.14) would result in GUG, an m-RNA triplet that codes valine. Substitution of a T for a C (TTC) would produce AAG, an m-RNA triplet that yields lysine. A single base change in the DNA sequence specifying an alteration of one amino acid at a specific point in a particular protein molecule could account for the disease sickle-cell anemia. An actual case of gene-controlled altered hemoglobin can thus be explained by the result of a single DNA base substitution. Pauling has described sickle-cell anemia appropriately as a "molecular disease."

## *Evolution of Hemoglobins*

The hemoglobin molecule has undergone change by mutation in time and now provides an opportunity for comparisons in different levels on the phylogenetic scale. Myoglobin, a protein found in muscle tissue, is presumably the primitive protein that gave rise to the globin part of all hemoglobins. A section of DNA made up of about 486 base pairs was apparently the ancestral information-carrying unit from which all globins in hemoglobin were derived. The following striking similarities in all hemoglobins support the view of common origin: (1) all hemoglobins that

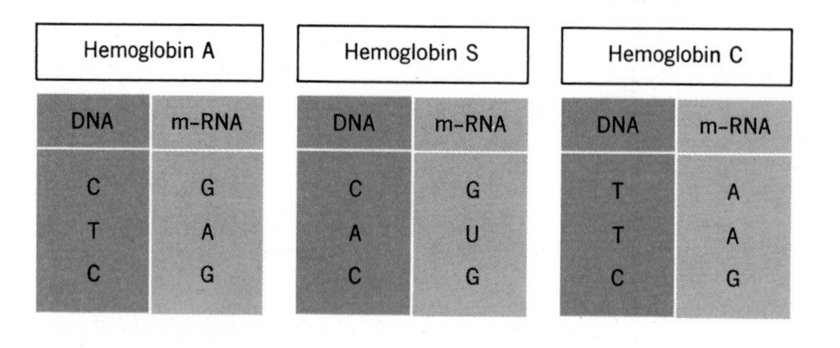


**Fig. 13.14** Substitution of an A in hemoglobin S DNA for a T in hemoglobin A DNA; substitution of a T in hemoglobin C DNA for a C in hemoglobin A DNA.

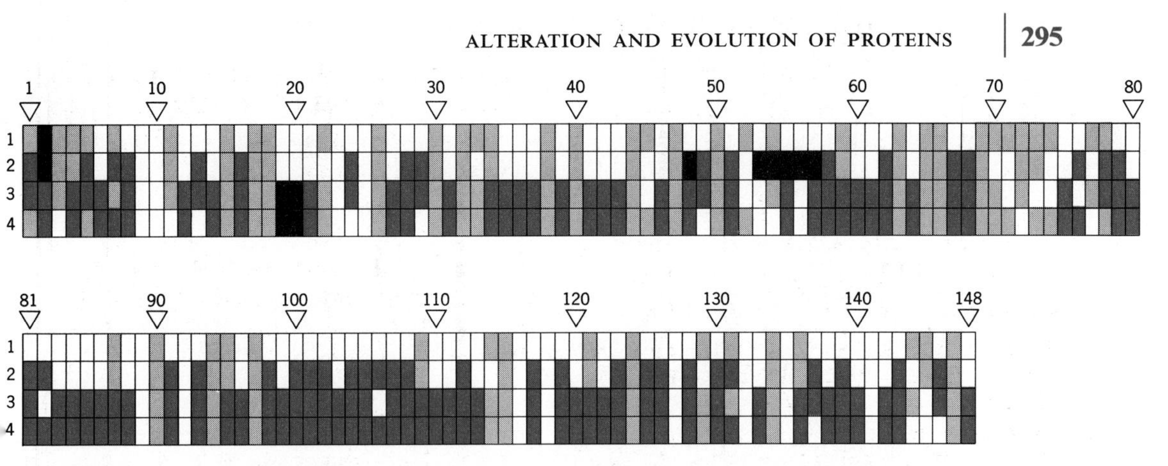


**Fig. 13.15** Amino acid replacements in human globin series: (1) myoglobin. (2) alpha hemoglobin. (3) beta hemoglobin. (4) gamma hemoglobin chains. Gray areas indicate identity of hemoglobin sites with myoglobin; blue areas identity of alpha, beta and gamma hemoglobin sites with each other. Black areas indicate gaps. (Jukes, *Molecules and Evolution,* Columbia University Press, New York, 1966, p. 175.)

have been examined have two histidine residues that are 29 residues apart. These bind the heme group to the polypeptide chain. (2) All the DNA units specifying globin have about 9 loci in common and in the same position. (3) Closely related species (based on other criteria) have very similar hemoglobin and those that are far apart on the evolutionary scale have greater numbers of amino-acid differences in their hemoglobins. (4) The separate chains have different lineages. Greater differences exist between the alpha and beta chains of man than between the alpha chains of man and those of the horse. (5) Examples of single base changes, which control single amino-acid substitutions in either the alpha or beta chain of contemporary human hemoglobins, provide an example of the mechanism through which similar substitutions have occurred in the past. (6) The absence of the terminal six amino acids of primitive myoglobin as compared with modern myoglobin and the alpha, beta, and gamma chains of hemoglobin can be explained by single base changes that produced code-terminating triplets.

A comparison of human myoglobin, and human alpha, beta, and gamma hemoglobin (Fig.13.15) shows 21 widely scattered homologous sites. Many substitutions have occurred in different species but the number of changes is generally parallel with the phylogenetic position of the particular species being compared. This indicates that the hemoglobins and myoglobins have evolved from a single precursor molecule. The combination of four hemoglobin chains connected with the heme prosthetic group has become an efficient oxygen-carrying vehicle, which has been maintained in evolution.

### *The Cytochrome C Molecule*

Cytochrome C is a protein electron carrier that has been identified in many different animals. Far more is known about the primary structure of cytochrome C in different species than about that of the hemoglobins. Some 35 different amino-acid sequences of mammalian type cytochrome C have been compared and found to be remarkably similar. Similarities and differences in such animals as lamprey, tuna, chicken, rabbit, cow, horse, rhesus monkey, chimpanzee, and man have been detected. A comparison of cytochrome C's

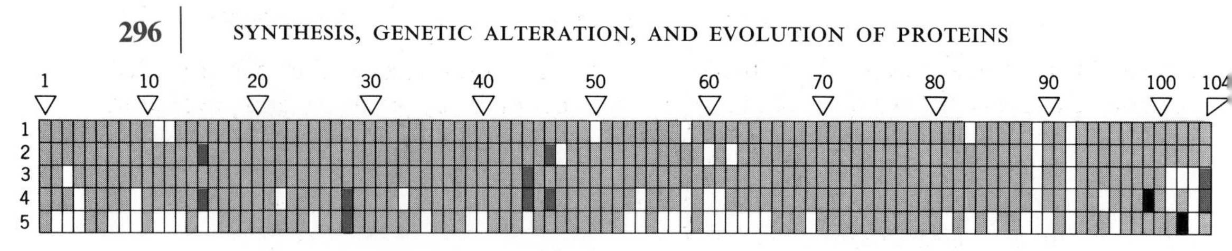


**Fig. 13.16** Amino acid replacements in possible coding sequences for cytochrome C: (1) human, (2) horse, (3) chicken, (4) tuna, and (5) yeast. Gray areas indicate similarities; white areas indicate differences; blue areas indicate differences from (1) but identity of other chains with each other; and black areas indicate gaps. (Jukes, *Molecules and Evolution,* Columbia University Press, New York, 1966, p. 203.)

from man, horse, chicken, tuna, and yeast is illustrated in Fig. 13.16. Most cytochromes have 104 amino acids in their polypeptide chains. Some amino acids are in the same positions in all species studied. Glycine, for example, occurs at eight sites (1, 6, 29, 34, 41, 45, 77, and 84), lysine at six sites, and from one to three of all other amino acids (except serine) are found in all species studied. An identical sequence of 11 amino acids represented by residues 70 to 80 has been found in all samples.

The finding of certain residues in the same place in all samples suggests that they must have important and specific functions. For example, arginine is located in positions 38 and 91 in all samples. Differences as well as similarities, however, are noted in the comparisons among

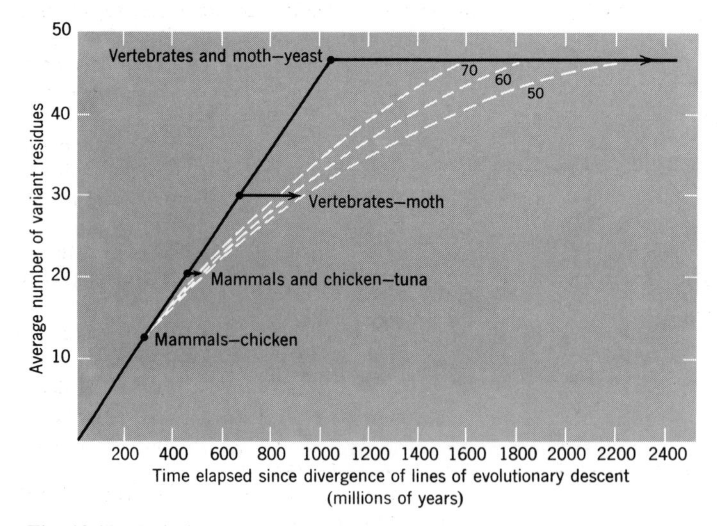


**Fig. 13.17** Relation of number of variant residues among cytochromes C from different classes and phyla of organisms to the time elapsed since the divergence of the corresponding lines of evolutionary descent. The straight line in the figure was calculated on the basis of a value of 280 million years for the time elapsed since the divergence of the mammalian and avian lines of descent, corresponding to a unit evolutionary period of 22.6 million years. The curved lines are drawn through points representing values corrected for the statistically probable number of mutational events required to yield the observed number of variant residues, assuming the occurrence of a total of 50, 60, and 70 variable positions in the protein, respectively, as noted in the figure. The arrows indicate the corresponding corrected times of divergence for the main taxonomic groups considered. (From E. Margoliash and Emil L. Smith, Academic Press, Inc., New York.)

species. In the horse, cow, and rabbit, for example, alanine is in position 15, but man has serine in this position.

The amino-acid sequences in cytochrome C are identical for man and the chimpanzee; man and the rhesus monkey differ in one residue. There are 12 to 13 amino-acid changes between tuna and man. Cytochrome C from man differs from that of yeast in 46 to 48 residues. Assuming that each difference is the result of a single mutational change somewhere in the ancestral history, time estimates are possible for the divergences. A phylogenetic tree (Fig. 13.17) based on the cytochrome C gene alone is much like the trees that have been prepared from other areas of biology.

## SUMMARY

Protein synthesis is the process through which genetic information is interpreted in the organism. Incorporation of amino acids into proteins according to specifications is accomplished mostly on the ribosomes. These structures are nonspecific and capable of making any kind of protein they are directed to make by the controlling m-RNA transcript, which carries the information from the gene (cistron) to the ribosomes. A particular t-RNA picks up a specific amino acid (located elsewhere in the cell) and attaches it to a ribosome assembly line. Here the amino acids are arranged in proper sequence for a particular polypeptide chain.

Investigations on viral, bacterial, and fungal proteins, and human hemoglobin, support the hypothesis that single base changes in DNA can result in single amino-acid substitutions in the corresponding protein. Comparative studies of hemoglobins, cytochrome C's and other proteins have shown a parallel between mutational changes and phylogenetic position of the organisms concerned. This has provided supporting evidence for organic evolution at the molecular level.

## REFERENCES

Anderson, W. F., L. Forini, and L. Breckenridge. 1965. "Role of ribosomes in streptomycin-activated suppression." *Proc. Nat'l. Acad. Sci.* (*U. S.*), **54,** 1076–1083.

Baglioni, C. 1963. "Correlations between genetics and chemistry of human hemoglobin." Chapter IX in *Molecular Genetics,* J. H. Taylor (ed). Academic Press, New York.

Bernfield, M. R., and M. W. Nirenberg. 1965. "RNA codewords and protein synthesis." *Science,* **147,** 479–484.

Bryson, V., and H. J. Vogel (eds.). 1965. *Evolving genes and proteins.* Academic Press, New York. (The article by S. Spiegelman and S. A. Yankofsky, "The relation of ribosomal RNA to the genome," is especially pertinent to this discussion.)

Capecchi, M. R., and G. N. Gussin. 1965. "Suppression in vitro: identification of serine-sRNA as a 'nonsense' suppressor." *Science,* **149,** 417–422.

Clark, B. F. C., and K. A. Marcker. 1966. "The role of N-formul-menthionyl-sRNA in protein Biosynthesis." *J. Mol. Biol.*, **17,** 394–406.

Ganoza, M. C., and T. Nakamoto. 1966. "Studies of the mechanism of polypeptide chain termination in cell-free extracts of *E. coli*" *Proc. Nat'l. Acad. Sci.* (*U. S.*), **55,** 162–169.

Goldberg, A. L., and R. E. Wittes. 1966. "Genetic code: aspects of organization." *Science,* **153,** 420–424.

Holley, R. W. 1966. "The nucleotide sequence of a nucleic acid." *Sci. Amer.*, **214,** 30–39.

Holley, R. W., J. Apgar, G. A. Everett, J. T. Madison, M. Marquisee, S. H. Merrill, J. R. Penswick, and A. Zamir. 1965. "Structure of a ribonucleic acid." *Science,* **147,** 1462–1465.

Horen, R. W. 1963. "The structure of viruses." *Sci. Amer.*, **208(1),** 48–56.

Ingram, V. M. 1965. *The biosynthesis of macromolecules.* W. A. Benjamin, New York.

Jukes, T. H. 1966. *Molecules in evolution.* Columbia University Press, New York.

Nance, W. E. 1963. "Genetic control of hemoglobin synthesis." *Science,* **141,** 123–130.

Pestka, S., and M. Nirenberg. 1966. "Regulatory mechanisms and protein synthesis X codon recognition on 30 S ribosomes." *J. Mol. Biol.*, **21,** 145–171.

Phillips, D. C. 1966. "The three-dimensional structure of an enzyme molecule." *Sci. Amer.*, **215,** 78–90.

Ritossa, F. M., and S. Spiegelman. 1965. "Localization of DNA complementary to ribosomal RNA in the nucleolus organizer region of *Drosophila melanogaster*." *Proc. Nat'l. Acad. Sci.* (*U. S.*), **53,** 737–745.

Sager, R., and F. J. Ryan. 1961. *Cell heredity*. John Wiley and Sons, New York.

Watson, J. D. 1963. "Involvement of RNA in the synthesis of proteins." *Science,* **140,** 17–26.

Watson, J. D. 1965. *Molecular biology of the gene.* W. A. Benjamin, New York.

Yanofsky, C. 1967. "Gene structure and protein structure." *Sci. Amer.*, **216(5),** 80–82.

Yanofsky, C., D. R. Helinski, and B. D. Maling. 1961. "The effects of mutation on the composition and properties of the A protein of *Escherichia coli* tryptophan synthetase." *Cold Spring Harbor Symp. Quant. Biol.*, **28,** 11–24.

Yanofsky, C., B. C. Carlton, J. R. Guest, D. R. Helinski, and U. Henning. 1964. "On the colinearity of gene structure and protein structure." *Proc. Nat'l. Acad. Sci.* (*U. S.*), **51,** 266–272.

Zuckerkandl, E. 1965. "The evolution of hemoglobin." *Sci. Amer.*, **212,** 110–118.

## *Problems*

**13.1** What is the significance of proteins in living organisms? Why is the synthesis of proteins of particular concern to the geneticist?

**13.2** In a general way, describe the molecular organization of proteins and distinguish proteins from DNA, chemically and functionally.

**13.3** At what different locations in the cell may protein synthesis occur? Evaluate the relative importance of these locations.

**13.4** Identify three different major kinds of RNA and give principal locations, characteristics, and functions of each in the living cell.

**13.5** Characterize ribosomes in general as to size, location, function, and chemical makeup.

**13.6** What methods are available for study and comparison of ribosomes?

**13.7** (a) Where in the cells of higher organisms do ribosomes originate? (b) Where in the cells are ribosomes most active in protein synthesis?

**13.8** From what evidence was the messenger-RNA hypothesis established?

**13.9** How is messenger-RNA related to polysome formation?

**13.10** How does r-RNA differ from m-RNA and t-RNA in specificity?

**13.11** How does the t-RNA molecule differ from that of DNA and m-RNA in size and helical arrangement?

**13.12** How does nitrous acid induce mutations? What specific end results might be expected on DNA and m-RNA from treatment of viruses with nitrous acid?

**13.13** Are mutational changes induced by nitrous acid more likely to be transitions or transversions?

**13.14** How does the action and mutagenic effect of 5-bromouracil differ from that of nitrous acid?

**13.15** How does ultraviolet light produce reversible mutations? Which bases are most sensitive to this mutagenic agent?

**13.16** Why is less variation expressed among the genes associated with different hemoglobins than among the corresponding amino acids?

**13.17** How can normal hemoglobin, hemoglobin S, and hemoglobin C be distinguished?

**13.18** If CTT is a DNA base triplet for glutamic acid, what DNA and m-RNA base triplet alterations could account for valine and lysine in position six of the beta hemoglobin chain?

**13.19** Assuming that the beta hemoglobin chain originated in evolution from the alpha chain, what mechanisms might explain the differences that now exist in these two chains? What changes in DNA and m-RNA codons would account for the differences that have resulted in unlike amino acids in corresponding positions?

**13.20** Why is sickle-cell anemia called a molecular disease?

**13.21** Outline the evidence that all human hemoglobin chains are related and that they originated from myoglobin.

**13.22** How does the evidence for evolution of proteins obtained from cytochrome C compare with that from hemoglobins?

**13.23** Is the genetic coding and basic mechanism for protein synthesis thus far discovered almost entirely in *E. coli* and viruses likely to be universal in nature?

**13.24** What constituents are required in a protein-synthesizing system?

# Genetics of Microorganisms

# 14

Present evidence indicates that the same basic pattern of inheritance applies in all living things but specific mechanisms may differ in groups of organisms. Knowledge gained from investigations of microorganisms is both valid and useful in understanding the processes in other organisms and the genetic mechanism for organisms in general. Microorganisms, therefore, have been invaluable in genetic research. From investigations on bacteria and their phages, the genetic code and the mechanisms of transcription and translation have been discovered.

Other organisms could be used for these investigations, but microorganisms have special advantages as experimental materials. Among these are their availability and the ease with which they can be rapidly produced in large numbers. Techniques for fractionating their contents have been developed and basic information concerning their chemistry and organization has been accumulated. Most of the enzyme systems used in biochemical genetics studies have come from microorganisms. These creatures are simpler than other organisms and in many cases fewer interactions occur between the cistrons and the detectable phenotypes. Furthermore, microorganisms occupy a fundamental position at the base of the phylogenetic tree. Molecular continuity in biochemical and genetic mechanisms can be explored more readily in microorganisms than in higher forms. Thus, the models that have been prepared from studies of microorganisms can serve as guides for exploration in other organisms.

It is true that before the mid-twentieth century, microorganisms were thought to reproduce only by asexual means and there was little genetic interest in them except for examples of mutations, which had been studied extensively in these organisms. Some of the most dramatic and exciting genetic experiments now being carried out are those involving bacteria and viruses. The present decade will certainly be recognized in the history of genetic research as a period dominated by studies of microorganisms. Aspects of genetics, in addition to mutation studies, that have progressed rapidly in microorganisms with the introduction of appropriate techniques for their investigation are explorations of proteins, RNA and DNA; recombinations —that is, the origin of new combinations of genes; control of DNA replication; and transduction of bacterial genes by viruses and virus and host relations associated with growth abnormalities and disease.

## EXPLORATIONS OF PROTEINS, DNA AND RNA IN VIRUSES

Bacteriophages have been used extensively in studies of mutations, DNA replication, and coding (Chapters 12 and 13), but in the past they have not been employed to any great extent for investigations of protein synthesis. This is mainly because the proteins synthesized by phage m-RNA and bacterial synthetic mechanism are present only in the head and they are produced in such minute quantities that it is difficult to obtain samples large enough for analysis. It was not until 1964 that sufficient quantities of phage head protein from phage $T_4D$ amber mutants were obtained to determine directly the relation between mutation and the sequence of amino acids in phage polypeptides. Numerous viruses are potentially available. A group of small and relatively simple bacterial viruses, called f viruses, has been introduced as experimental material.

### *f Viruses*

Seven viruses selected from sewage samples formed plaques on donor (male) and not on recipient (female) cells of *E. coli*. The letter "f", for fertility factor, was used to identify the group and the different f viruses were numbered $f_1$ to $f_7$. First in the series, $f_1$ was a long slender filament about 8500 Å (angstroms) in length (almost as long as the bacterial cell that it infects) and about 50 Å wide with a single stretched-out strand of DNA. This virus infects the bacterial cell by attaching to the long hair-like processes or pili on the surface of the bacterium (Fig. 14.1).

The other f viruses ($f_2$ through $f_7$) proved to be small RNA viruses. Currently, the

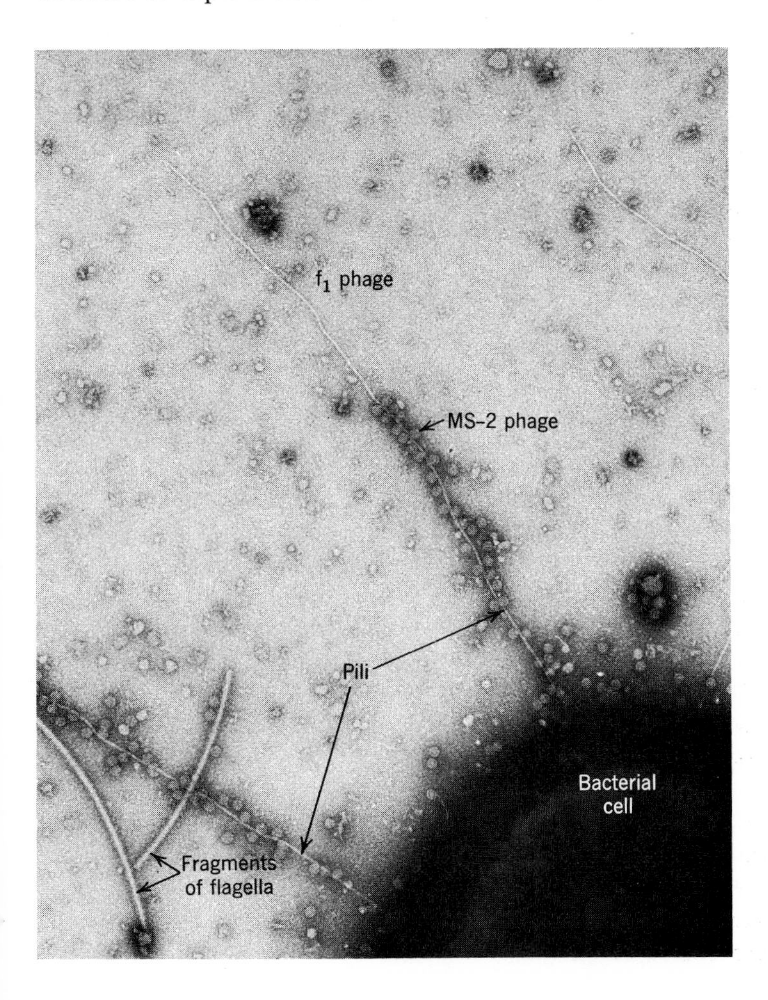


**Fig. 14.1** Pili extending from bacterial cell. DNA phage $f_1$ and RNA phage MS-2 are attached to pili. Magnification ×87,750. (Photograph by L. G. Caro and D. P. Allison.)

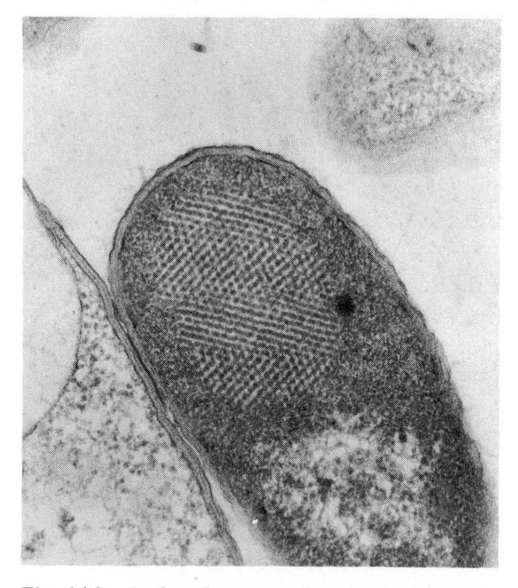

**Fig. 14.2** *Escherichia coli* cell packed with $f_2$ virus particles. Magnification ×125,500. (Courtesy of Norton B. Zinder.)

best known is $f_2$, which is roughly spherical and about 200 Å in diameter with about 3000 base pairs. This is small, indeed, compared with about 300,000 base pairs for the T-even bacteriophages and some ten billion in a human cell. An advantage in studying these RNA viruses is their enormous productivity. Some 20,000 to 40,000 particles may be produced in a single bacterial cell (Fig. 14.2). This virus and others of its kind are some of the most populous organisms on earth. Samples large enough for laboratory study can be obtained in a short time.

The $f_2$ virus particles are attached to pili on the outside of male bacterial cells. In appearance, they are much like the MS-2 viruses shown in Fig. 14.1. Each virus contains an RNA molecule surrounded by a protein coat. The RNA molecule slips out of its coat into a hollow pilus and thence into the bacterial cell. Entrance of the RNA into the cell stimulates the production of the enzyme, RNA polymerase, within the infected bacterium. A double-stranded replicative form of RNA is produced and replication of the ordinarily single-stranded RNA occurs within the bacterial cell. After RNA has accumulated for about 25 minutes in the cell, the process stops; protein-coat molecules appear and the new virus particles are assembled with RNA in the center and protein on the outside. Each RNA molecule requires 150 molecules of coat protein for its cover. The system is regulated so that the proper amount of RNA and protein are produced.

The $f_2$ virus is so small that it could only provide genetic information for the synthesis of four or five proteins. One or perhaps two genes must specify the enzymes required for making more viral RNA. Another gene specifies the protein coat, which is made up of 150 identical molecules of protein, each with 129 amino acids (Fig. 14.3). In addition to the RNA replicating gene or genes and the protein-coat gene, an assembler gene is required in the system. Eventually, the entire biochemical sequence in $f_2$ may be understood.

### *DNA Bacteriophages*

DNA bacteriophages, which have been cited repeatedly in previous chapters, are considerably more complex than the RNA virus $f_2$, but they are among the simplest living forms that go through a life cycle. They appear on electron micrographs as particles with three-dimensional enlarged heads, and short, blunt tails (Fig. 14.4). The head is filled with coiled genetic material (Fig. 14.5), which may be injected into the host bacterial cell. Within a few minutes after entering the host cell, the bacteriophage DNA has taken over the host's facilities for replication and synthesizes more DNA of its own kind. Newly formed bacteriophage particles with DNA from replication of virus DNA and a protein coat from the synthetic processes of the host are liberated by lysis of the host bacterial cell to enter new bacterial cells

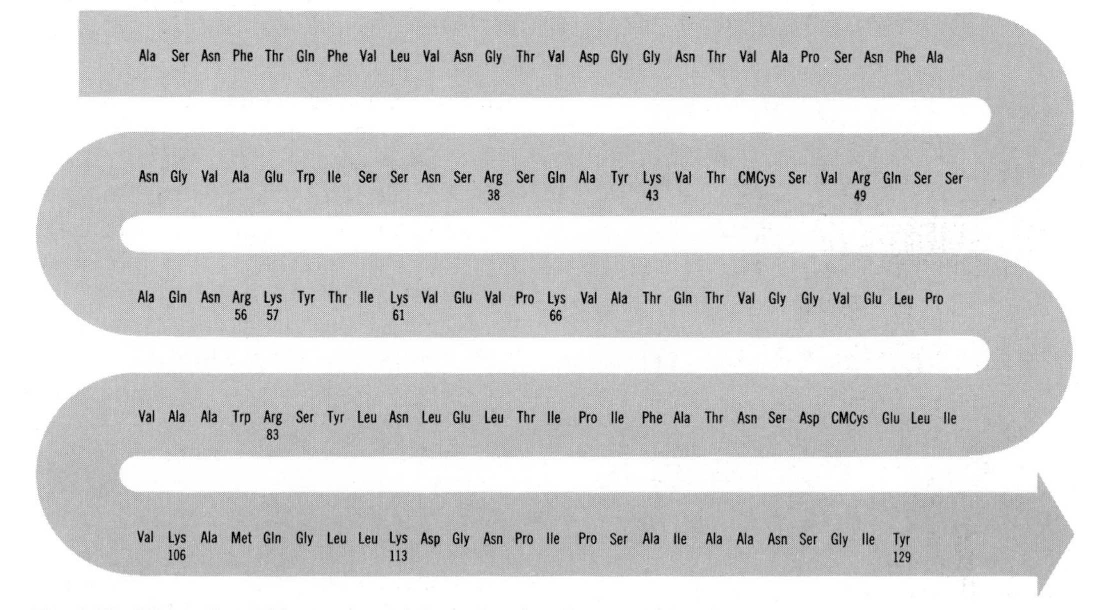


**Fig. 14.3** The amino acid sequence of the reduced carboxymethylated coat protein from the bacteriophage $f_2$. The numbers below each basic residue indicate the position in the protein beginning from the amino-terminus. (From K. Weber and others, *J. Mol. Biol.,* **20:**423–425, 1966. Academic Press, Inc., New York.)

and repeat the cycle. The intimate relation that has thus developed between the phage and the bacterium makes these organisms interesting materials for genetic study.

## RECOMBINATIONS IN VIRUSES

The "T" phages that attack *E. coli* have been employed extensively in recombination studies. Experiments with this material are carried out by spreading a virus suspension over a plate culture of sensitive bacterial cells. Phage particles (Fig. 14.6) become attached by their tails to bacterial cells, and the phage DNA contents are extruded into the cells. The duplication process of the virus occurs within the host cell. For phage $T_1$, for example, the time from introduction of the virus to the bursting (lysis) of the cells is about 13 minutes and for phage $T_2$ about 22 minutes.

When the bacterial cells undergo lysis, each bacterium releases one hundred or more mature, infective virus particles. These infect adjacent bacterial cells and a new cycle begins. As the cycles continue, the areas on the culture plate where lysis is going on become cleared of bacteria and are identified as transparent areas or plaques (Fig. 14.7) on an otherwise opaque culture. Plaque characteristics such as shape, size, and marginal outline are controlled by phage genes and are recognized as phage phenotypes.

The invading phage, on first entering the host cell, stops the metabolic activities of the host and takes over the direction of the host-cell processes. In this way, the bacterial cell is parasitized by the phage. Several steps have been recognized in this changeover. When the phage is first adsorbed to the bacterial cell, all bacterial enzymatic activity is blocked and the synthetic processes of the cell are immediately stopped. DNA synthesis, along with other cell activities, stops for a time and is reestablished later under control of the virus

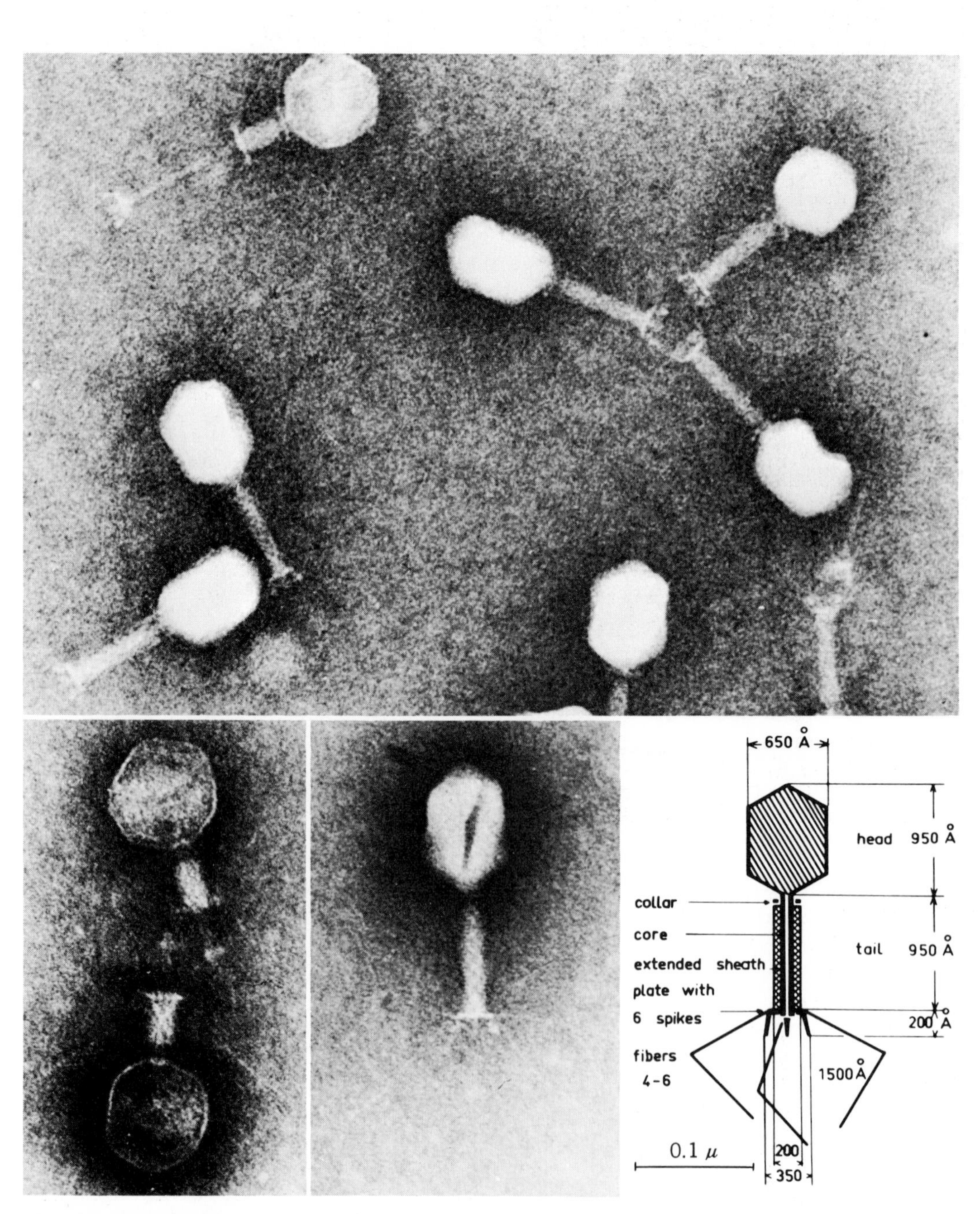


**Fig. 14.4** Bacteriophages $T_4D$. Coloration negative sodium phosphotungstate. (Courtesy of Carl Zeiss Company.)

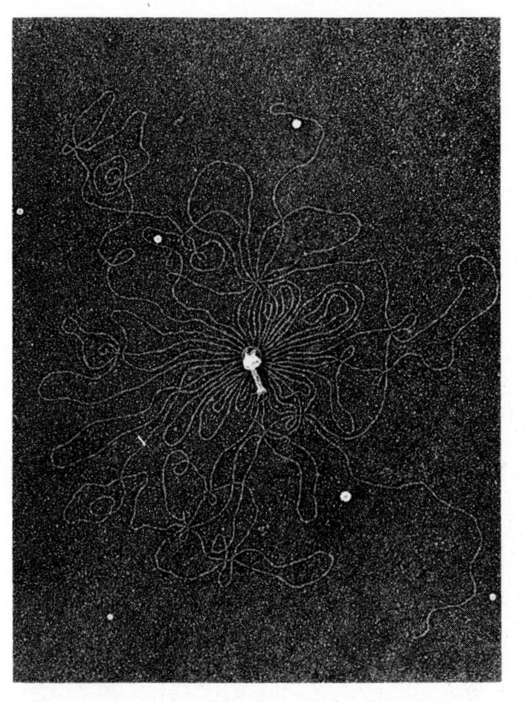

**Fig. 14.5** Bacteriophage $T_2$ with coiled genetic material extruded from head. (Courtesy of Dr. A. K. Kleinschmidt.)

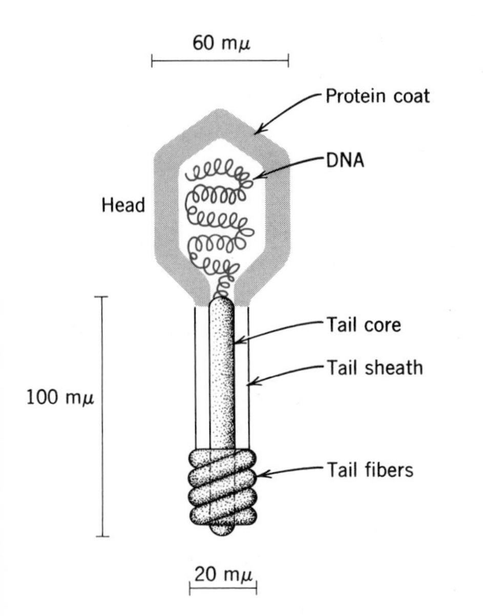


**Fig. 14.6** Diagram illustrating general appearance and structural characteristics of T phage particle.

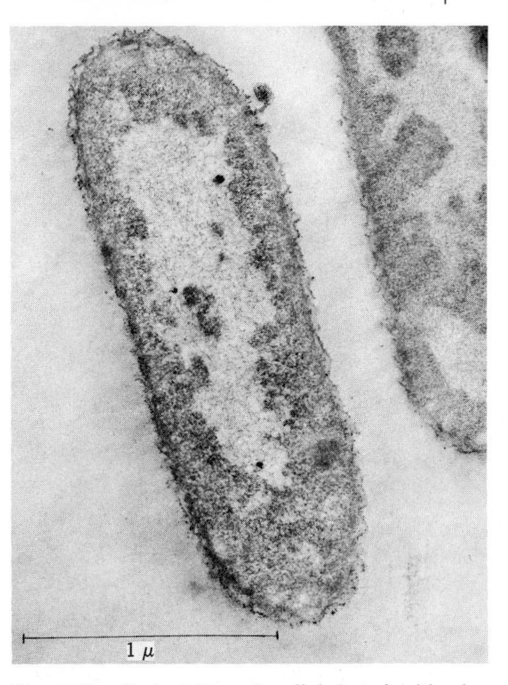


**Fig. 14.7** *Escherichia coli* cell infected with phage $T_2$. Cell is embedded in Vestopal. (Courtesy of Carl Zeiss Company.)

DNA. The DNA of the host is not taken over intact but is broken down and resynthesized according to new specifications from the virus DNA. The metabolic apparatus of the host cell is thus directed toward the production of phages instead of the activities needed by the bacterial cell. One such function is the synthesis of the new protein coats necessary to complete the production of new virus particles. These are synthesized according to the information carried by the virus DNA but with the metabolic apparatus of the bacterial cell.

One of the first demonstrations that indicated recombination in bacteriophages was made by M. Delbrück. He introduced, into the same bacterial culture, a $T_2$ phage carrying the *r* gene, which makes plaques considerably larger than wild-type plaques (Fig. 14.8), and a $T_4$ phage, which produces wild-type plaques ($r^+$). The cross was thus $T_2r \times T_4r^+$. The two phage types were

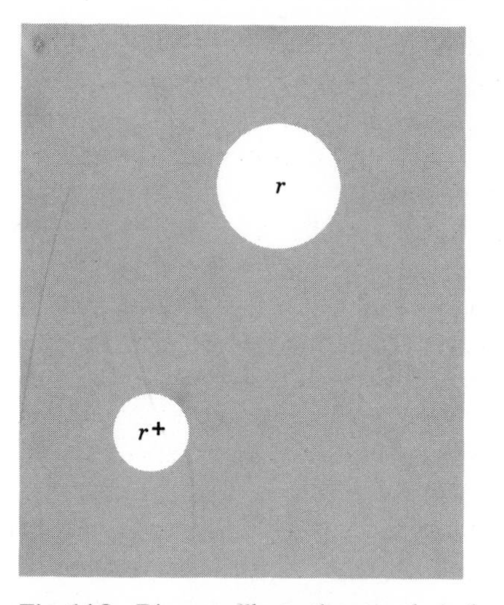


**Fig. 14.8** Diagram illustrating $r$ and $r^+$ plaques on a culture plate of *E. coli* strain B infected with bacteriophage.

recovered along with $T_4r$ and $T_2r^+$ types, which were recombinants. These results showed that two different kinds of phage could reproduce in the same bacterium and that genes for parental traits could recombine and produce new types. Another mutant gene $h$ (which enables the phage to attack the resistant strain $B_2$ of *E. coli*) was then introduced into the $T_2r$ phage. A two-factor cross, $hr \times h^+r^+$, was made between individuals in the same strain. The plaque characteristics and ability to infect strain $B_2$ were readily identifiable in cultures. Recombinations ($h^+r$ and $hr^+$) as well as parental types ($hr$ and $h^+r^+$) were detected.

Studies of this kind giving genetic evidence for recombination in viruses have led to detailed studies of the mechanisms involved. They have also led to the compilation of linkage maps showing the relative positions of many genes in the phage. R. S. Edgar has presented a circular linkage map of phage $T_4$ with 48 cistrons included. The genes are arranged in sequence according to developmental patterns in which they are functional. Some genes function only in assembling the virus; that is, the head and tail are synthesized but they are not joined in the presence of these mutant genes. A single molecule of DNA with a molecular weight of about 130,000,000 is postulated as the physical basis of this linkage group.

### *Recombinations in Virulent Phages*

Observations from electron photomicrographs of viruses have shown that some types are spherical, some rod-shaped, and some are like tadpoles with a head and tail region. The T bacteriophages, which have heads and short tails, have been studied extensively by S. Brenner and his associates. Each measured from 0.1 to 0.2 microns in length or approximately one-tenth the diameter of an *E. coli* cell. Digestion experiments with trypsin demonstrated that the outer part of the head was protein, and labeling experiments with radioactive phosphorus (Chapter 12) showed the inner coils to be DNA. About 300,000 nucleotides make up each strand of the DNA double helix. The tail is cylindrical with an outer sheath of protein and a hollow interior through which the contents of the particles are introduced into the host cell. Protein tail fibers extending from the hexagonal plate at the distal end of the tail hold the virus on the bacterial cell being infected.

Experiments in which the phage DNA was labeled with radioactive phosphorus ($P^{32}$) and its protein was labeled with radioactive sulfur ($S^{35}$) showed that only the $P^{32}$ label was carried to the next generation. These studies established the fact (Chapter 12) that the DNA and not the protein is the carrier of genetic information.

When the results of phage crosses were observed critically, evidence of partial heterozygosis was detected. It was partial in the sense that heterozygosis occurred in only limited regions. Mixed infections of $r$ (for rapid lysis) and $r^+$, for example, usually produced $r$ or $r^+$ plaques, but about 2 percent of resultant plaques were observed to be mottled with some $r$ and some $r^+$. Appropriate testing showed that both $r$ and $r^+$ could be recovered from mottled plaques. The relatively high frequency with which the mottled forms occurred ruled out regular mutations. It was shown further that the $r$ gene was not particularly unstable as expected if an extra high mutation rate occurred. The best explanation was recombination based on the hypothesis that the mottled plaques were heterozygotes.

### *Complementation and Recombination at rII Region*

In bacteriophage $T_4$ and other T-even phages ($T_2$, $T_4$, and $T_6$), a series of mutations has occurred which alters the host range, that is, interferes with the ability of the virus to infect certain strains of bacteria. These mutations are reflected in the shapes and sizes of the plaques on plates of different strains of *E. coli*. In the presence of viruses carrying the wild-type gene ($r^+$), the plaques on strain B are small with rough edges. Each of the $r$ mutants alters in a characteristic way the size and margin of the plaques as they appear on culture plates. The different $r$ mutants have been found to occupy three distinct regions, identified as *r*I, *r*II, and *r*III on the linkage map of the virus. Mutants in all three regions can be detected by large plaques when *E. coli* strain B is used as the host.

When the $r$ mutants are grown on strain K of *E. coli,* however, the *r*II mutants do not form plaques, but the *r*I, *r*III, and $r^+$ do form plaques, just as on strain B. This difference in response to different host strains has provided a technique for studying rates of mutation and genetic recombination. The mutation rate of an *r*II mutant to $r^+$ can be determined by introducing the virus to plates of *E. coli* strain K. Only $r^+$ mutants will form plaques on this host. Experimental studies have demonstrated a mutation rate in the order of one mutant per $10^8$ phages.

Complementation, the ability of two adjacent sections (cistrons) of DNA to supplement each other, was detected by introducing more than one *r*II phage mutant into the same culture. When bacteria were infected by different *r*II mutants, sometimes both viruses together could multiply and lyse the cells. Large plaques were produced on cultures of cells that would not be lysed by either of the *r*II mutants if present alone. Either cistron represented in the experiment by a single *r*II mutant could not, by itself, lyse the cells of strain K. When both subunits were present, however, each represented by a different *r*II mutant, the two complemented each other and the $r^+$ phenotype was produced. An *r*II mutant that was defective in the A cistron, for example, was presumed to make the B product. An *r*II mutant that was defective in the B cistron was presumed to make the A product. A bacterium simultaneously infected with an A and B mutant would have both products. The two defective cistrons thus could complement each other and produce the wild-type ($r^+$) phenotype.

Complementation did not always occur, however, when *E. coli* was infected with different *r*II mutants. If the mutants were both from cistron A or both from cistron B, either A or B would remain defective. Occasionally, a wild type ($r^+$) would appear in such cultures, and the occurrence was sufficiently low to justify its being classed as a spontaneous mutation. When two mutants of the type mentioned above were used to infect a host such as *E. coli,* strain B progeny of two kinds $r$ and $r^+$ were recovered. The recovery of $r^+$ was much higher than could be explained by mutation. The evidence was clear that recombination had occurred within the *r*II region to give the wild-type progeny.

Numerous mutants have now been detected in the *r*II region of the phage linkage map. These have been identified with sites in the cistron. Some phages have been found to be deficient for certain sites. These variants have been cultured and used as tools to map the fine structure of small regions of the linkage map. From the work of S. Benzer and others, several hundred different sites have been detected, each separable by recombination from all other sites. By use of overlapping deficiencies and point mutations as markers to obtain recombination data, it has been possible to arrange these *r*II sites in the A and B cistrons in a linear order (Fig. 14.9). Extensive mapping studies on the *r*II region have indicated that the A and B cistrons contain about 1700 and 1100 nucleotide pairs, respectively. The entire *r*II region of the phage DNA has thus been estimated to have about 2800 nucleotides. With sites numbering in the hundreds detected in a region of this magnitude, the ultimate recombination unit must be very small. One nucleotide or one single-base alteration probably represents the ultimate unit of recombination or recon in phage DNA. Studies on the *r*II region have thus demonstrated the size of the recombination unit in a phage.

### *Recombinations in Temperate Phages*

Temperate phages, which do not destroy host cells, also lend themselves to studies of recombination. They are more prevalent in nature than virulent phages but thus far have not been studied extensively. In contrast to virulent phages, temperate phages do not lyse all host cells but, instead, they lysogenize the host. This means that they establish a degree of tolerance between the invading phage and the host cells so that some phage DNA can live for a time in the host cells. The viral DNA without a protein coat (now called a prophage) becomes inserted in the host genome. When lambda phage, for example, infects sensitive bacteria, plaques are formed with opaque centers. These centers are patches of lysogenized bacteria that have not lysed but have remained intact. In general, when viral DNA prophage is part of the bacterial genome, the cell is immune to infection by homologous phage. Temperate prophages may remain in host cells and divide synchronously with those cells. Several mutants have been associated with the process by which phages become prophages. Three groups of these mutants have been identified in lambda: $C_3$, $C_1$, and $C_2$ (Fig. 14.10). The different groups were given numerical designations before their order in the linkage map was determined, hence the irregular sequence. Mutant phages that have undergone genetic changes in the $C_1$ region are incapable of lysogenation, and those that have mutated in either the $C_3$ or $C_2$ region (or on either side of $C_1$) have considerably reduced lysogenic ability compared with wild-type lambda phage.

When matings (multiple infections in bacterial cells) were made between lambda and some other phages, genetic recombinations were recognized. In each case, recognition of recombination was limited by the number of homologous loci in the two phages identifiable by markers. When

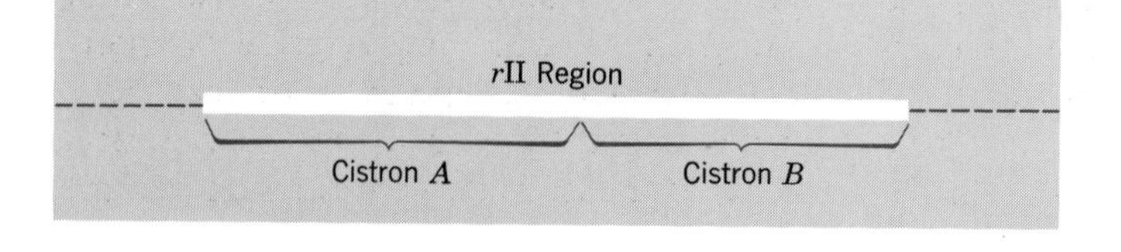


**Fig. 14.9** Diagram illustrating *A* and *B* subregions of the *r*II part in the linkage group for $T_4$ phage.

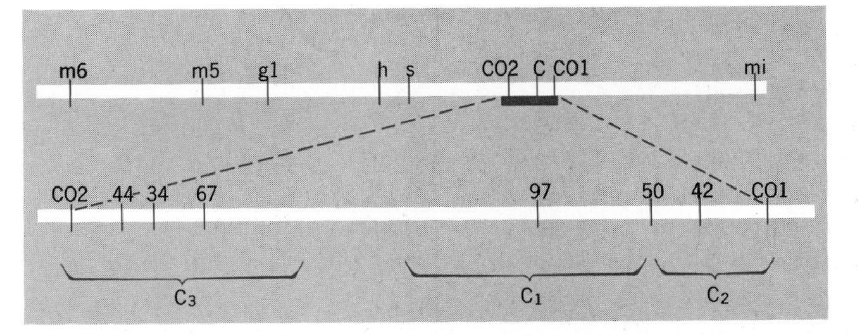


**Fig. 14.10** Diagram illustrating subregions in the C part of the linkage group in lambda phage.

lambda was mated with phage 434, the hybrid phages were found to have completely homologous genotypes except for the $C_1$ (immunity) region. Hybrids between the two phages differed only with respect to this region. It was, therefore, the $C_1$ region that gave these two viruses their differing properties with respect to prophage formation.

## RECOMBINATION IN BACTERIA

Wild-type *E. coli* (prototrophs) can synthesize all the building blocks necessary for the manufacture of their proteins and nucleic acids. They can grow on a minimal medium containing only glucose and inorganic salts. Mutant strains (auxotrophs) lack the ability to synthesize one or more of the building blocks. Auxotrophs, therefore, cannot grow on the minimal medium but must be artificially supplied with whatever essential materials they are unable to synthesize. These characteristics of bacteria and the techniques that allow them to be identified on selective media made possible the discovery of recombinations.

J. Lederberg and E. L. Tatum were the first to demonstrate genetic recombination in bacteria. In their experiments, recombination was detected when a bacterium of one mutant strain conjugated with a bacterium of another mutant strain (Fig. 14.11). During conjugation, one cell of a pair acted as male (donor) and the other as female (recipient). The difference between the donor and recipient mating types was found to be associated with fertility factor (F) which was present only in males. The F factor was a cellular particle that could move freely in the cell or could become attached to the ring-shaped linkage group (Fig. 14.12) of *E. coli*.

### *Episomes*

Genetic bodies such as F factors were named *episomes* (added bodies) by F. Jacob and his collaborators. An episome is a genetic element that can be either chromosomal or cytoplasmic and its effect depends on its location. In individual cells, episomes may be present or absent, and associated with the chromosome or independent of the chromosome. They may be viral structures or larger particles, and they may be pathogenic or nonpathogenic. Most of the evidence for episomes has come from studies of bacteria, but now similar bodies have been described in Drosophila and maize. Other structures that are widespread in nature (for instance, centromeres in chromosomes, centrosomes in the cytoplasm of animal cells, and kinetosomes at the base of cilia and flagella in many animals) may be episomes or may have been derived from episomes. Their central cores (for example, centrioles in centro-

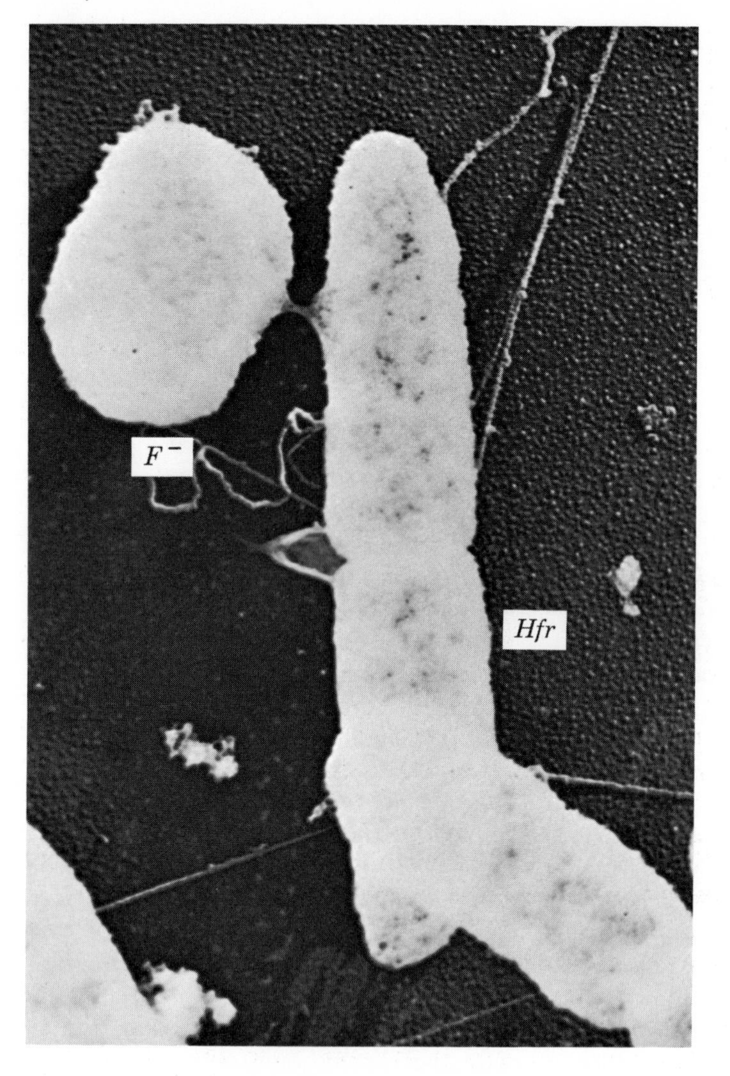


**Fig. 14.11** Conjugation in *Escherichia coli*. ×41,400. Photograph by T. F. Anderson, E. Wollmann, and F. Jacob. (From *Annales Institut Pasteur,* Masson and Cie, Publishers.)

somes) contain DNA, and they have much in common with the episomes of bacteria. The bodies themselves or, in some cases, their primordial structures, are freely movable in the cell.

The F factor in *E. coli* is a classical episome. When it becomes attached to the linkage group of the bacterium, the frequency of recombination is increased. For example, in a mix of the two mating types of *E. coli,* recombination occurs at the rate of about one recombinant per million cells. Donors with a rate of recombination in this order of magnitude are low-frequency recombinants (Lfr). When donors with the F episome incorporated in the linkage group are involved in conjugation, the frequency of recombination is greatly increased. A cell with the F factor attached is called an Hfr (high-frequency recombinant) donor or a metamale. Other male mating types with different rates of recombination have now been detected in *E. coli.* For example, a very high-frequency (Vhf) strain is now known. Only one female mating type has been recognized. The low fre-

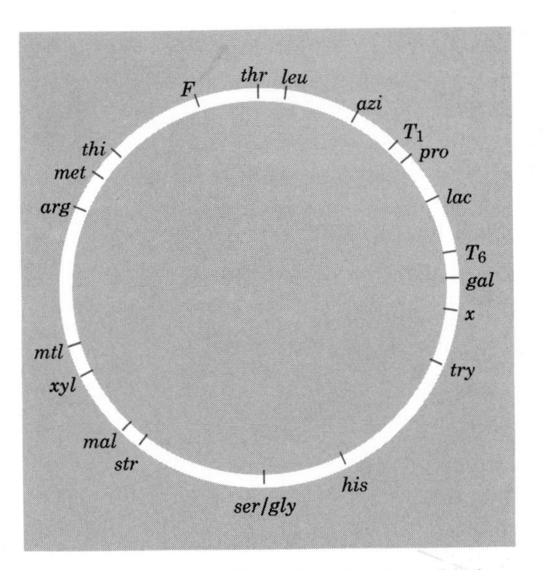


**Fig. 14.12** Diagram illustrating ring-shaped linkage group in *E. coli*.

quency of recombination observed with Lfr is now considered to be the result of rare spontaneous incorporation of the F factor into the bacterial genome.

When the F factor is extrachromosomal, the cell is ineffective as a male in transmission of genetic factors, but the F episome itself may be transmitted during conjugation. Male cells with the F factor not attached to the linkage group but free to move in the cell are called $F^+$ (for fertility) males. When a male cell with $F^+$ comes together with a female ($F^-$) cell in conjugation, the female cell may receive the $F^+$ and be converted into a male cell. To accomplish this transition from female to male cell, the F factor must move across the protoplasmic bridge joining the two cells. The transfer of the extrachromosomal F body occurs rapidly, within only a very few minutes after the beginning of conjugation.

## *Mechanics of Recombination in Bacteria*

In further experiments by Jacob and others, male cells of a Hfr strain were placed in the same culture with female cells, and the two kinds of cells came together in conjugation. While the two cells of each conjugating pair were joined by a temporary protoplasmic bridge, a linear group of genes migrated from the donor cell across the bridge into the recipient cell. This was accomplished as follows: the ring-shaped *E. coli* linkage group opened at the place where the F episome was located. The end opposite the F end entered the protoplasmic bridge and moved across into the recipient cell. About two hours after the beginning of the transfer, the entire linkage group was across the bridge with the F end entering last. The exchange was a one-way process with the genetic material always moving from donor to recipient cell.

When, for example, a cross was made between genetically different Hfr and $F^-$ strains, the sequence of gene exchange during conjugation was demonstrated. Hfr organisms used in the experiment were capable of synthesizing the amino acids threonine ($thr^+$) and leucine ($leu^+$); they were sensitive (*s*) to the metabolic inhibitor sodium azide (*azi-s*), and sensitive to the bacteriophage $T_1$ ($T_1$-*s*); they could ferment lactose ($lac^+$) and galactose ($gal^+$); and they were sensitive to the antibiotic streptomycin (*str-s*). Genotypically, the Hfr organisms were: $thr^+$ $leu^+$ *azi-s* $T_1$-*s* $lac^+$ $gal^+$ *str-s*, and the $F^-$ organisms were $thr^-$ $leu^-$ *azi-r* (*r* for resistant) $T_1$-*r* $lac^-$ $gal^-$ *str-r*. The cross was made by mixing the Hfr and $F^-$ cells and allowing them to remain together in liquid for 25 minutes. At the end of this period, the mixed cells were plated on the first selective medium, a minimal medium containing streptomycin.

On this selective medium, the Hfr parent cells were killed by the streptomycin, and the $F^-$ parent cells were unable to grow because the essential amino acids threonine and leucine, which they could not synthesize, were not supplied. The only cells that

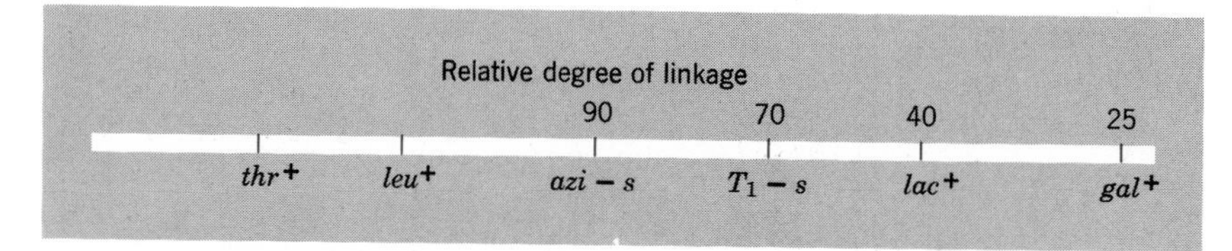


**Fig. 14.13** Linkage map showing some genes of *E. coli* with the relative degree of linkage with *thr*$^+$ and *leu*$^+$. (From experiments of Jacob and Wollman.)

could grow on the medium were those that could synthesize the necessary amino acids and were streptomycin resistant. Since the genes (*thr*$^+$ and *leu*$^+$) for synthesizing these amino acids came from the Hfr parent and streptomycin resistance (*str-r*) came from the F$^-$ parent, the cells that survived were recombinants.

Next, the *thr*$^+$ *leu*$^+$ *str-r* recombinants were replicated or successively plated on minimal media with different additives such as sodium azide and bacteriophage T, and other recombinations were detected. From experiments of this kind, Jacob and Wollman found that 90 percent of the colonies that were *thr*$^+$ *leu*$^+$ *str-r* were also sodium azide sensitive (*azi-s*), 70 percent were $T_1$-*s*, 40 percent were *lac*$^+$, and 25 percent were *gal*$^+$. These percentages represented the linkage strength among the different genes and could be used to develop a linkage map (Fig. 14.13). It should be made clear that these percentages are not equivalent to linkage values discussed earlier, but they do indicate the relative position of genes.

Jacob and Wollman then proceeded with a second method of mapping the genes from the mixed cultures at intervals up to 60 minutes from the time Hfr cells were mixed with the F$^-$ cells. Samples were periodically agitated in a Waring Blendor and the conjugants were thus separated. This separation interrupted the transfer of genetic material from donor to recipient and presumably broke the linkage group. Following separation, the cells were plated and tested for the genes from the donor that had been integrated into the recipient. At 0 minutes from the time of mixing, 0 recombinants had occurred. The *thr*$^+$ gene became integrated in 8 minutes, *leu*$^+$ in 8½, *azi-s* in 9, $T_1$-*s* in 11, *lac*$^+$ in 18, and *gal*$^+$ in 25 minutes (Fig. 14.14).

These studies showed that the transfer from Hfr donors to F$^-$ recipients is not a random process. Rather, the genes move across the protoplasmic bridge in a regular order, as expected if they are tied together in a linkage group (Fig. 14.15). After 50 minutes, almost all the Hfr genes that could be exchanged had been transferred. No genes were transferred after the F episome, indicating that this factor, which is necessary for Hfr, is at the end of the linkage group.

Soon after migration of the linkage group was completed under noninterrupted circumstances, certain portions of the male linkage group could be deduced to be paired with corresponding segments of the female linkage group. While the linkage groups were associated, parts of the male genetic material were exactly substituted

| Minutes | Hfr genes transferred |
|---|---|
| 0 | 0 |
| 8 | *thr*$^+$ |
| 8½ | *thr*$^+$ *leu*$^+$ |
| 9 | *thr*$^+$ *leu*$^+$ *azi-s* |
| 11 | *thr*$^+$ *leu*$^+$ *azi-s* $T_1$-*s* |
| 18 | *thr*$^+$ *leu*$^+$ *azi-s* $T_1$-*s* *lac*$^+$ |
| 25 | *thr*$^+$ *leu*$^+$ *azi-s* $T_1$-*s* *lac*$^+$ *gal*$^+$ |

**Fig. 14.14** Time required for the transfer of different genes from Hfr to F$^-$ as indicated from recombinants obtained by Jacob and Wollman.

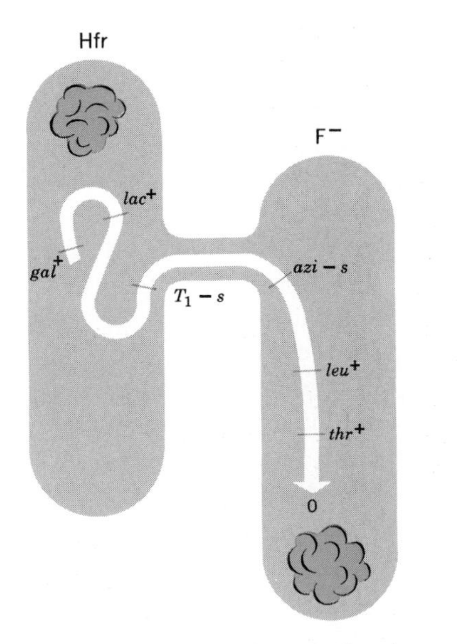


**Fig. 14.15** Diagram representing the transfer of the linkage group from Hfr to $F^-$ in *E. coli.* (Data from T. F. Anderson, Cold Spring Harbor Symposium on Quantitative Biology, Vol. 23, 1958.)

for parts of the female DNA. The occurrence of recombination meant that a new linkage arrangement had been produced which incorporated information from both donor and recipient cells. This new linkage combination was then replicated and transmitted to daughter cells.

## TRANSDUCTION OF BACTERIAL GENES BY VIRUSES

A virus acting as an episome may serve as a natural agent for carrying genetic material from one bacterial host cell to another. When, for example, bacteria ordinarily sensitive to streptomycin were infected with phages carrying streptomycin resistance, the recipient cells became streptomycin resistant. The phages used in the experiment had grown on resistant host cells from which genetic material could be transferred. A very small proportion of the recipient cells that survived the infection received phage genetic material and became streptomycin resistant. Once altered in this way, the cells retained their resistance and could serve as donors for that trait, thus providing further evidence that a genetic change had occurred in the recipient cell. While multiplying in the donor cell, the phage undergoes recombination with the bacterial genome as part of the lysogenization process. When the prophage is induced to begin vegetative growth, part of the bacterial genome may be incorporated in the phage DNA molecule, and this bacterial genetic material may then be incorporated into the bacterium, which is infected by the temperate phage.

The classic investigations of Zinder and Lederberg were conducted on the mouse typhoid organism *Salmonella typhimurium.* Several mutant auxotroph strains were used in the experiments. One auxotroph strain required that methionine ($met^- thr^+$) be supplied, and another required threonine ($met^+ thr^-$). When the two strains were mixed and plated on a medium deficient for methionine and threonine, some wild-types (prototrophs) occurred and gave rise to colonies of prototrophs. The occurrence was too frequent to be attributed to mutation and the prototrophs were judged to be the result of recombination. Transformation (Chapter 12) and conjugation were ruled out as explanations of the mechanism of recombination. A filterable virus was found to be the vehicle of transfer, and transduction was demonstrated to be the means by which this genetic recombination had occurred.

When bacterial strains carrying several markers were used in experiments, it was shown that each individual marker gene could be transduced independently. A temperate phage, for example, was grown on a bacterium that could synthesize methionine, utilize galactose and xylose, and resist streptomycin ($met^+ gal^+ xyl^+$ *str-r*). The phage was later allowed to infect a bacterial strain that could not synthesize methionine, could not utilize galactose or xylose, and was streptomycin sensitive. When representatives of the recipient bacteria were harvested and tested on different selective media, some showed transduction of $met^{+}$, some of $gal^{+}$, others of $xyl^{+}$, and still others of *str-r*. Further studies showed that although most genes were transferred independently, some moved as clusters. These clusters were considered to be closely linked genes. The frequency with which genes were transduced together suggested the relative distance (linkage strength) between them. Based on this information, the genes were mapped.

*S. typhimurium,* like *E. coli,* was found to have a circular linkage map. Many recombinants have been identified in this species. Furthermore, hybrids have been obtained between *S. typhimurium* and *E. coli* in which part of the genetic material has come from each species. When phage particles were raised on different hybrids (that is, hybrids carrying different combinations of markers), all hybrid donors were found to give rise to some transductants. Some hybrids produced many and others small numbers of transductants. From the results of many experiments, it was possible to compare the linkage groups of the two species. Many genes were found to be similar in function, and they were located in corresponding positions in the two linkage groups. Furthermore, the transduction process carried out by the phage was shown to be nonspecific for genetic areas of the host DNA. It is interesting to note that a process similar to transduction occurs with the F factor, which has been mentioned in connection with recombination in bacteria. The F factor can act as an agent to transfer genes in a process called sexduction.

Viruses have thus been shown to have an intimate relation with their host cells. They can take over the genetic mechanism of the host and control its metabolic processes. In their invasion of host cells, they may become intimately associated with the genetic material of the host and act as agents for the transfer of that material to different cells that are subsequently invaded. Knowledge of viruses and their relations with host cells has helped to identify their activities with the diseases they cause. It is now evident that the symptoms of virus diseases in higher organisms are the result of the effects these agents have on enzymatic activity of the host and on their ability to damage and destroy cells of the host.

## VIRUSES, HOST RELATIONS, AND DISEASE

As viruses have become better understood, their chemical nature and relations with their hosts have been found to be more involved than was previously suspected. In some instances, it has been difficult to separate genetic transmission from direct physiological effects.

### *Avian Leukosis Virus and Helper Virus*

W. Stanley and H. Rubin have developed tissue-culture techniques that permit critical investigations of the avian leukosis virus. In this virus, as in TMV (Chapter 12), RNA rather than DNA is the information-carrying agent. The virus is responsible for a leukemialike disease in chickens and is transmitted in nature through the eggs of infected hens to their offspring. Infected roosters do not transmit the disease to their progeny. The strict maternal transmission was the first substantial evidence that the genetic material of this RNA-containing virus was not associated with the chromosomes of the cell. Cytoplasmic inheritance seemed a likely explanation, and it has since been demonstrated that the entire life cycle of the virus occurs in the cytoplasm. Furthermore, this virus has been shown to act in the cell at the physiological rather than the genetic level.

Chickens are also victims of another common virus, Rous sarcoma virus (RSV), which causes a sarcomalike disease of the connective tissue. This virus was discovered in 1911 by Peyton Rous and has been studied for a longer period than any other tumor virus. The discovery of RSV was significant because it demonstrated that a filterable virus was the causative agent for a type of cancer in chickens. The meaning of this situation was not appreciated until a number of other similar facts were discovered. Rous received a Nobel prize in 1966 primarily for his accomplishment in 1911.

RSV has been a favorable tumor virus for study because it reproduces faithfully in tissue culture. Furthermore, it behaves the same way in cultures as in chickens. As a result of these circumstances, much information has been obtained about the interaction between this virus and its host cell. The virus is a large RNA virus quite similar to the avian leukosis virus, but unlike the latter it can induce connective tissue cells to become malignant. The standard RSV is specific for chickens and does not infect other animals (except very young ducks). A variant of RSV has since been found to transmit the disease to other animals including monkeys.

H. Rubin discovered that RSV is defective in protein synthesis and cannot produce the protein coat that is necessary for mature virus. Although RSV can transform a normal chicken cell into a malignant cancer cell, it cannot reproduce infectious virus progeny. This explains why the virus cannot be found for long in the tumors which it has initiated. Apparently the virus merely triggers the malignance in the host cell and then disappears, leaving no progeny. If, however, a "helper" virus is also present, infectious RSV progeny appear. The avian leukosis virus is one of several viruses that can act as a helper for RSV. Unlike RSV, the avian leukosis virus can reproduce itself independently and also provide a factor needed by RSV for the reproduction of new RSV infective particles. RSV is postulated to use an enzyme system of the helper virus protein synthesis when the two kinds of viruses come in contact with each other.

### *Mutations, Viruses, and Cancer*

Cancer is a complex of diseases and different kinds of cancer have different causal relations. A recent classification lists more than 100 kinds of human cancer involving different tissues and behaving in different ways. All varieties, however, have the spreading characteristic, or metastasis, which occurs in the body of the victim. Despite the multiplicity of factors known to indicate cancerous changes in cells, the basic chemical alterations in the cells may be comparable. The many inducing factors may have relevance only at the time of tumor inception.

Two theories based on fundamental biological principles have developed historically to account for the origin of cancer: (1) the somatic mutation theory and (2) the virus theory. These are not mutually exclusive, and both may have genetic and molecular implications. Investigations on bacterial viruses indicate that a virus may act by inducing chromosome changes and may serve as a carrier of genetic material from one cell to another. Viruses have also been shown to influence the process of cell division which is basic to the cancer problem. These two theories may be brought together as the mechanics of the origin of cancer are elucidated.

The basic mutation theory was advanced by deVries in 1901. Suggestions that cancer might be caused by mutations in somatic cells soon followed and the idea has persisted ever since. In 1914, Boveri published a paper entitled "The Origin of Malignant Tumors" in which he related the "chromatin complex" to cancer origin. Very little was then known about carcinogens (cancer-causing substances), and cancer was considered to be a "spontaneous" disease. Boveri postulated that a "wrong" mitosis in a somatic cell could cause chromosomes in the cell progeny to become abnormal or "mutilated." He could not demonstrate chromosome irregularity, but did observe a ring of chromatin around the inside of the nuclear membrane in cancer cells. This characteristic continues to be most useful for microscopic diagnoses of cancer.

In the next 15 years, the somatic mutation theory found only a few adherents. Muller, in 1927, showed that X-rays induce mutations, and in the next year K. H. Bauer suggested that mutagenic agents are also carcinogenic, acting on somatic cells by creating mutation. In 1929, Bauer modified Boveri's theory, rejecting the mutated (or mutilated) number of chromosomes in favor of an "invisible" mutation (point mutation) at the molecular level. Several more recent investigators, particularly C. D. Darlington (1964), have elaborated the somatic mutation theory in explaining the origin of cancer.

It is now evident that neoplastic changes are accompanied by extensive alterations of cellular DNA. Most mutagenic agents are also carcinogens, and the great majority exert an effect on DNA or intercellular materials that are about to be incorporated in DNA. Tumor induction may be the result of gene modifications directly influencing abnormal cell division or the removal of genetic control from the nucleus over the cytoplasm.

Certainly the same materials and the same mechanisms known to control inheritance are also involved in cancer induction. Today the somatic mutation theory is considered by many researchers to be the most plausible explanation for the radical change in the growth pattern of a somatic cell that must precede cancer. The change itself may be initiated by any of several factors such as ionizing radiation, ultraviolet rays, carcinogenic chemicals, or by intervention of a virus or other undefined trigger mechanism.

The virus theory was first proposed in 1903 by a Frenchman, Amadee Borrel, but has become strongly supported only in the past few years. With recently developed techniques and new insights, viruses have been definitely associated with several types of animal tumors. Even so, viruses are probably not the sole agents involved in these cases, and perhaps they are not even the primary agent in many.

The virus origin of some kinds of cancer has been demonstrated in experimental animals and is strongly suspected, if not actually demonstrated at the present time, for one human type (lymphoma) in Africa. Dr. Wendel Stanley, who won the Nobel Prize for his work in crystallization of the tobacco mosaic virus, is an advocate of the virus origin of cancer. Much indirect evidence supports this view. Viruses are ubiquitous in nature and have been found in many places where they might be related to abnormal growth. Known viruses are more hardy than bacteria and can withstand the usual treatment with chlorine in drinking water, freezing, and other common measures that are effective for controlling bacteria.

### *Tumorogenic Viruses*

The polyoma virus is a DNA virus which produces many kinds of tumors. Although this virus has been investigated extensively in mice, it is not specific for mice or any particular animal, but infects most rodents and some other animals and plants in different taxonomic groups. Its DNA will replicate in the bacterium *Bacillus subtilis*. Polyoma tumorogenesis in mice is controlled by a single autosomal gene with incomplete penetrance. If the virus is taken from the skins of mice and injected into new-born susceptible mice, rats, or rabbits, the injected animals may develop one or more of a variety of tumors in the liver, kidneys, or other organs. When the virus is introduced into tissue cultures, the virus particles reproduce. If the virus is washed off the tissue culture cells and injected into rodents, cancer may be induced.

Although the polyoma virus is known to be responsible for the origin of tumor cells, few if any virus particles can be detected in the resultant tumors. Apparently, the genetic material that induces and maintains the tumor is transferred from the virus to the host cell soon after the initial invasion. The virus may have been gone for 20 years before the tumor becomes discernible.

Another virus-caused tumor in animals is the rabbit papilloma identified by Richard Shope in 1933. Papillomas are usually benign epidermal warts that can be transmitted by a DNA virus from one rabbit to another. In the early 1930's it was observed that the cottontails of Iowa had "antlers." Investigation showed that these rabbits had papillomatous growths projecting from their heads. The "antlers" were in reality enlarged warts, some of which resembled small cauliflowers. Most were benign but occasionally one became malignant.

These growths were found to be affected by the chemical content of the cells and tissues. Cell division, through which cell growth occurs, apparently proceeded in regular fashion as long as the keratin in the cell was controlled within normal limits. Papillomas were found to have excessive amounts of arginine, a constituent of keratin, whereas normal rabbit skin has only a small amount of this amino acid. The Shope rabbit papilloma virus has been shown to induce an enzyme (an arginase) which is new to rabbit epithelium. The enzyme controlled by the virus splits arginine and prevents the formation of a histone which might, if present, repress the malignant changes.

A virus similar to the rabbit papilloma virus has now been associated with human warts. This is a DNA virus 45 to 55 millimicrons in diameter. The wart produced by the virus is benign and has no relation to cancer. It does, however, provide a model for the study of other human and animal tumors transmitted by viruses. The virus reproduced successfully in culture and a specific antigen has been developed.

Viruses are now known to induce a variety of tumors in numerous species of animals: chickens, trout, mice, rabbits, dogs, and plants have cancerlike growths called galls. Such tumor viruses are not unique to a given tumor but are comparable with other viruses. Most of them are spherical particles 30 to 250 millimicrons in diameter.

### *Leukemia Viruses*

A virus isolated in 1956 by Charlotte Friend is the causative agent for leukemia in mice. A vaccine has now been developed from killed mouse leukemia virus that will produce immunity against one form of mouse leukemia. Several other viruses have since been found that will produce leukemia in mice and vaccines have been developed against most of them. In addition to the vaccine, a drug, hydroxy urea, has been reported effective against leukemia in mice upon intraperitoneal or oral administration.

### *Aleutian Disease in Mink*

Another interesting virus-host relation has been noted to occur in the Aleutian stock of mink. This type of mink arose from a single recessive mutation and appeared first in 1941 on a ranch near Clatskanie, Oregon. Two female kits in a litter of 7 had bluish or slate-gray fur color. One of these females was mated back to the father, which appeared to be an ordinary standard mink. From this mating, the following year three kits were born, one hybrid female and two pure slate-gray mink, one male and one female. The name "Aleutian" was chosen for this mutant type because the color resembled that of the Aleutian blue fox. Three years later a rather large herd of Aleutian mink had been produced. The new gunmetal color was attractive at the fur market, and Aleutian mink soon became especially valuable. It was noted from the first that Aleutians had a weakness resulting in losses during hot weather. Breeding stocks could not be kept profitably for more than 2 years.

In about 1946, a new presumably virus-transmitted disease became recognized in Aleutian mink. This "Aleutian disease" now threatens the entire mink industry. A virus is postulated to cause the plasma cells (which produce gamma globulin) to multiply at a rate that is out of proportion with that of other cells. This is just a step or two short of leukemia. Aleutian mink were almost exclusively involved at first, but the disease now attacks virtually all strains. Presumably, the mutation in coat color simultaneously made the mink susceptible to a virus, which previously they had resisted. The virus may have gained enough virulence in Aleutian mink to infect all mink.

This case in mink may parallel a case that occurred in a pepper plant some years ago. A single plant in New Jersey apparently underwent a mutation which could be recognized phenotypically, and at the same time the plant become susceptible to TMV. The susceptibility continued in the progeny of the mutant plant.

## SUMMARY

Microorganisms are readily available, can be conveniently cultured in the laboratory, and lend themselves to fractionation techniques which are essential to biochemical investigations. Their relatively simple chemical organization and fundamental position at the base of the phylogenetic tree make them especially useful for genetic studies. Very simple viruses such as the RNA bacterial virus $f_2$ with only about 3000 DNA base pairs may eventually be completely understood in biochemical terms. DNA bacteriophages, 300 times larger than $f_2$ viruses, have been followed through their life cycles in host bacterial cells. Mechanisms resulting in genetic recombination in virulent and temperate phages are associated with the host-parasite relations which have developed in evolution. Recombination has been detected in some strains of bacteria as a result of conjugation. Episomes such as temperate phages and the F factor are also agents of recombination in *E. coli* cells. A virus-episome may serve as a carrier of genetic material from one bacterial cell to another. Viruses are causative agents of some types of cancer as well as of some other abnormal growths. They have been found to affect cell division and thus may have a direct as well as an indirect influence on cell regulation.

## REFERENCES

Axelrod, D., H. Habel, and E. T. Bolton. 1964. "Polyoma virus genetic material in a virus—free polyoma —induced tumor." *Science,* **146,** 1466–1468.

Beckwith, J. 1967. "Regulation of the lac operon." *Science,* **156,** 597–604.

Cairns, J. 1966. "The bacterial chromosome." *Sci. Amer.,* **214,** 36–44.

Cairns, J., G. S. Stent, and J. D. Watson (ed.). 1966. *Phage and the origins of molecular biology.* (Papers by Max Delbrück, K. G. Zimmer, T. F. Anderson, A. H. Doermann, A. Lwoff, N. Visconti, S. Benzer, S. E. Luria, R. D. Hotchkiss, W. Hayes, F. W. Stahl, H. Rubin, and several other specialists on different aspects of phage and bacterial genetics.)

Dalton, A. J., and F. Haguenau. 1962. *Tumors induced by viruses.* Academic Press, New York.

Darlington, C. D. 1964. *Genetics and man*. The Macmillan Co., New York.

Doermann, A. H., and M. B. Hill. 1953. "Genetic structure of bacteriophage $T_4$ as described by recombination studies of factors influencing plaque morphology." *Genetics,* **38,** 79–90.

Dulbecco, R. 1967. "The induction of cancer by viruses." *Sci. Amer.,* **216,** 28–37.

Dulbecco, R. 1963. "Transformation of cells *in vitro* by viruses." *Science,* **142,** 932–936. (Clarification of relations between host cell and virus and experimental approach to the study of virus-induced cancer.)

Edgar, R. S., and R. H. Epstein. 1965. "The genetics of a bacterial virus." *Sci. Amer.,* **212,** 70–78.

Gellhorn, A., and E. Hirschberg (eds.). 1962. *Basic problems in neoplastic disease*. Columbia University Press, New York.

Hayes, W. 1964. *The genetics of bacteria and their viruses*. John Wiley and Sons, New York.

Jacob, F. 1966. "Genetics of the bacterial cell." *Science,* **152,** 1470–1478. (Nobel prize lecture delivered in Stockholm, Sweden, December, 1965.)

Jacob, F., S. Brenner, and F. Cuzin. 1963. "On the regulation of DNA replication in bacteria." *Cold Spring Harbor Symp. on Quant. Biol.,* **28,** 329–348.

Kellenberger, E. 1966. "The genetic control of the shape of a virus." *Sci. Amer.,* **215,** 32–39.

Luria, S. E. 1962. "Bacteriophage genes and bacterial functions." *Science,* **136,** 685–692.

Rubin, H. 1964. "A defective cancer virus." *Sci. Amer.,* **210,** 46–59.

Rubin, H., and R. K. Vogt. 1962. "An avian leukosis virus associated with stocks of Rous sarcoma virus." *Virology,* **17,** 184–194. (Demonstration that RSV is defective and requires a helper virus which may be avian leukosis virus.)

Sager, R., and F. J. Ryan. 1961. *Cell heredity*. John Wiley and Sons, New York. (Chapter 5 deals with recombination in viruses and bacteria.)

Taylor, J. H. 1965. *Selected papers on molecular genetics*. Academic Press, New York. (Reprinted papers by Ingram, Avery et al., Swift, Hershey and Chase, Wilkins, Watson and Crick, and others on aspects of DNA.)

Watson, J. D. 1965. *Molecular biology of the gene*. W. A. Benjamin. New York.

Zinder, N. D. 1965. "RNA phages." *Annual Rev. Microb.,* **19,** 455–472.

# Problems

**14.1** What are the advantages and disadvantages of microorganisms as materials for genetic study? Evaluate the significance of research on microorganisms during the past few years.

**14.2** Why have bacteriophages been used more effectively for studies of DNA replication and mutation than for investigations of protein synthesis?

**14.3** What has been learned thus far and what may be expected from future studies of simple viruses such as the RNA bacterial virus $f_2$?

**14.4** What are the advantages and disadvantages of DNA bacteriophages as compared with RNA viruses, such as $f_2$, for genetic studies?

**14.5** What is the difference between virulent and temperate phages?

**14.6** Outline the life cycle of a virulent type of phage. What is the effect of the phage on the host bacterial cell?

**14.7** How was recombination demonstrated in a virulent phage?

**14.8** How can the different properties of plaques be explained? If no plaques, or only a very few occur in a culture in which *E. coli* cells and phages are both known to be present, what implications might be drawn?

**14.9** How can spontaneous mutations and recombinations be distinguished in the *r*II region of phage $T_4$?

**14.10** How was complementation between cistrons *r*II A and *r*II B detected?

**14.11** How may a virus become a prophage?

**14.12** What is lysogenization and how is it controlled?

**14.13** What is the difference between auxotroph and prototroph bacterial cells?

**14.14** How can female *E. coli* cells be converted into males?

**14.15** How were F factors in *E. coli* identified? Why were they classified as episomes? Where else in living organisms may episomes be found?

**14.16** What form of linkage map is associated with *E. coli?* What is the relation between the F episome and the point of opening of the linkage group of *E. coli?* In what order, with reference to marker genes studied, is the F episome in Hfr cells transmitted to $F^-$ cells?

**14.17** Explain how recombination may occur through transduction. What is the significance of this method of recombination?

**14.18** What are the differences and similarities between the avian leukosis virus and Rous sarcoma virus?

**14.19** Why was the recognition for discovery (in 1911) of Rous sarcoma virus delayed for such a long time (Nobel Prize awarded in 1966)?

**14.20** What techniques may be used to study the interaction between Roux sarcoma virus and its host cells?

**14.21** In what way is Rous sarcoma virus a defective virus? How can the defect be overcome? How does a "helper" virus help a defective virus?

**14.22** How may the somatic mutation theory and the virus theory for the origin of cancer be related? In what ways might viruses be involved in irregular cell division?

**14.23** What is the likelihood that a single cause will eventually be found for all types of cancer?

**14.24** If a virus should be found to be the primary causative agent for common kinds of human cancer, would this discovery be expected to engender hope or despair among medical people and those fearing that they might be cancer victims in future years?

**14.25** If a virus is the primary cause of polyoma tumors, why it it so difficult to associate the virus with an actual tumor?

**14.26** How can the origin and present widespread occurrence of the Aleutian mink virus be explained?

# Genetic Control of Structure and Function | 15

Enzymes, which are proteins synthesized under genetic control, influence metabolic processes and thus alter end products of chemical reactions which may be expressed in the developing of the adult organism. The human abnormality, infantile amaurosis, for example, is the result of a single recessive gene in the homozygous condition which results in the absence of a certain enzyme. This enzyme, which is present in normal people, controls the oxidation of the lipid sphyngomyelin. In its absence, sphyngomyelin accumulates in certain cells and causes ill health. Most obvious symptoms of the disease are blindness, paralysis, and death. The dominant allele of the infantile amaurosis gene controls the enzyme necessary for normal oxidation of sphyngomyelin.

A few other relatively simple examples such as steps in the chemical pathways of pigment production in mice and some plants have been discovered, but the complexity of higher organisms has made it difficult to relate specific enzymes with traits. Because fewer interactions occur in relatively simple forms such as protozoa, molds, yeast, bacteria, and viruses, most investigators are now concentrating on these organisms. Information indicating how genes control differentiation and development in lower organisms is useful in approaching similar but more complex problems in higher forms.

One way to investigate genetic influence on various traits is by comparing genetically different individuals at a particular stage of development. If a hereditary difference between these individuals is known to be caused by a single gene (allele) substitution, it is sometimes possible to relate a gene change or mutation with an altered phenotype. In such a case, the next logical step is to search for an enzyme that is associated with the change that has occurred. At present, only a few specific instances have been proved, and most of these have been associated with a limited number of favorable organisms, such as Neurospora, Drosophila, *E. coli,* and bacteriophage.

## REGULATION OF GENE ACTIVITY

The best understood systems from which data have been obtained are those that govern enzyme production in microorganisms. Studies of these gene-controlled systems have brought investigators nearer the answers to the question: how can the same genes that are present in all cells of the body act specifically in directing particular functions at particular times and places? Inducible enzymes, which are synthesized only when needed, provide in large measure for the regulation of gene activity in living organisms. Inducers are usually the end products or the substrates for the enzymes. These substances control production of enzymes in such a way that the enzymes are available at the time and place needed.

In some instances, the product of an enzymatic reaction may stimulate as well as inhibit the reaction. The amount of the manufactured material on hand thus regulates the rate at which that material is accumulated. This so-called "feedback inhibition" mechanism slows down the process when the product is in surplus but speeds it up when the product is in short supply. When, for example, tryptophan reaches a low threshold level in an *E. coli* cell, the enzyme system for production of this amino acid is accelerated. When, on the other hand, a quantity is available, a key reaction in tryptophan synthesis is inhibited and production slows down.

A more basic mechanism is the regulation of the amount of enzyme itself through the quantity of substrate on which it acts. Many enzymes are adaptive in the sense that they are produced only when the substrate on which they act is present. Beta galactoside (lactose), for example, is the substrate on which the enzymes beta-galactosidase and galactoside permease operate. When lactose is present to be cleaved, the enzymes are produced continuously unless an inhibitor is also present. This is an efficient system because the cell is not burdened with enzyme proteins which would require storage in some inactive form when there is no raw material on which to act. When the proper substrate is available, the necessary enzymes are soon on hand to carry on metabolic processes in which the particular substrate is involved.

### *Operon Model*

Most control systems in the living organism have greater complexity than appears from the above examples in which the regulating substances are either the quantity of the end product or the required substrate. F. Jacob and J. Monod have provided experimental evidence for a specific regulator system in *E. coli* and also a model for more general control mechanisms. Two kinds of genes—structural and regulator genes—were recognized, both of which act through gene-controlled enzymes. Structural genes determine the actual structure of polypeptides by controlling the amino-acid sequence as synthesis occurs. Several structural genes may be located in a cluster or group and may perform sequential functions in a biochemical pathway. Regulator genes control a group of structural genes by switching the entire group on or off. They may function through a third kind of gene, an operator, which has immediate control over a group of structural genes.

The experimental demonstration of regulation by Jacob and Monod on *E. coli* strain K 12 was based on a series of genes controlling enzymes (Fig. 15.1). Four functionally distinct chromosome regions were involved, three closely linked and one located elsewhere in the genome. Two linked structural genes, $y$ and $z$, were each responsible for a separate enzyme (beta-galactosidase and galactoside permease, respectively). The mechanism of this action is explained by conventional molecular biology. Gene $y$, for example, is transcribed in the presence of RNA polymerase giving rise to an appropriate m-RNA. The enzyme is assembled from appropriate amino acids at the ribosomes.

A third gene region adjoining the structural genes was an operator ($O$), which initiated polypeptide synthesis carried out by the structural genes. The operator gene did not produce a particular substance that could be detected in the cell, but functioned only as a control unit in turning on and off the activity of the structural genes. The unit of closely linked structural genes and operator was called an "operon."

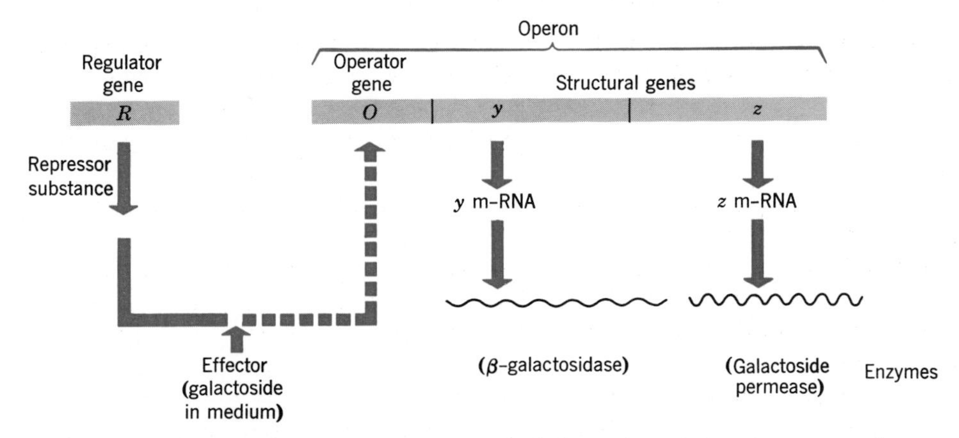


**Fig. 15.1** Model for control of gene action in *E. coli* illustrating relations between regulator, operator, and structural genes. (Data from F. Jacob and J. Monod.)

Control of the operator was accomplished through the regulator located in the fourth chromosome region, which in this example was in a different part of the genome. A single regulator could control many structural genes. In the presence of the product of the regulator, the operator, in the *E. coli,* beta-galactoside example, suppressed the activity of structural genes *y*, by blocking the formation of *y* m-RNA and thus inhibiting the inducible enzyme, beta-galactosidase.

The regulator gene functioned by producing a repressor substance which prevented the operator gene from acting and thus stopped the structural genes which the operator controlled. An effector from the medium removed or inactivated the repressor and thus allowed the operator to turn on the enzyme-making processes controlled by structural genes *y* and *z*. Each structural gene then transmitted its coded information through its particular kind of m-RNA and a particular enzyme was produced. In the presence of the raw material on which the gene acted, the repressor effect of the regulator gene was stopped. Excessive substrate (inducer) inactivated the repressor and released the gene activity. Whatever the actual mechanism, the structural gene functioned to produce enzymes only when the raw material or other inducer was present.

In the model cited (Fig. 15.1), the enzymes beta-galactosidase and galactoside permease represented the products of structural genes. The inducer was beta-galactoside in the medium. When the inducer was not present, the repressor turned off the operator and the structural genes remained inactive. If, on the other hand, the inducer were present, it modified the repressor in such a way that the repressor did not turn off the operator. The information carried by structural genes *y* and *z* was then transcribed in the presence of RNA polymerase on *y* m-RNA and *z* m-RNA and the enzymes beta galactosidase and galactoside permease were produced.

Mutations occurring in structural genes could therefore result in faulty m-RNA and thus altered or nonexistant enzymes. If a mutation should occur in the operator gene rendering it nonfunctional, the adjacent structural genes would no longer be under control and, therefore, always functional. On the other hand, if the operator should mutate in another way and become continuously functional, the adjacent structural genes would never be activated. Mutations of regulator genes could alter the

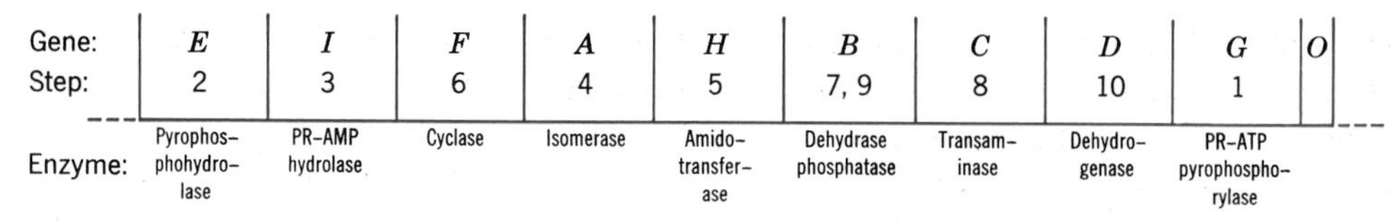


**Fig. 15.2** Operon in *Salmonella typhimurium* composed of a cluster of nine closely linked structural genes (*A* to *I*) and an operator (*O*) gene shown at right. (Data from P. E. Hartman and B. N. Ames.)

production rate, which may be at full capacity or completely inhibited. The mechanism of regulation is that of inhibiting the genes' activity. When the regulator gene is missing or inactive, the protein is produced continuously at the maximum rate.

Operons thus represent groups of linked structural genes that are organized with trigger mechanisms to control their activity. Such systems represent a partial explanation for the mechanism of differentiation which occurs in the development of living things. Although the experiments leading to the operon model were based on microorganisms, and the only operons known in detail are in bacterial systems, they suggest possible mechanisms of regulation of gene action in higher forms as well. Operons have been suggested in maize. In one example, a gene was found to control other genes responsible for anthocyanin synthesis in the maize endosperm. An example from the evening primrose shows that pollen-tube formation is controlled by a structural gene which is, in turn, controlled by another gene. Operons may be widespread among higher organisms as well as bacteria, molds and yeasts, but linkage studies will be required to determine whether genes in the same functional system are in the same location in a chromosome.

The discovery of regulator and structural genes has suggested a more complex level of organization than that implied by the one-gene-one enzyme hypothesis. A single regulator or switch mechanism may control a whole series of chain reactions. This is a new kind of pleiotropism in which one gene locus can control several others. The regulator is not always a special and separate entity located at a distance in the genome from the operator and structural genes which it controls. In some operons, it may be merely the beginning of a region of DNA which controls a series of closely related enzymatic events.

### *Histidine Operon*

In *Salmonella typhimurium,* an operon (Fig. 15.2), composed of a cluster of nine closely linked genes (cistrons), controls a sequence of ten steps in the biosynthesis of the amino acid, histidine. Through the series of ten major steps, ATP and phosphoribosyl pyrophosphate are converted into histidine. Each gene produces a single enzyme and each enzyme except dehydrase phosphatase controls a single step. Dehydrase phosphatase controls two steps (7 and 9) in the sequence. The biochemical steps do not occur in the same order in which the genes are located in the linkage map but they do follow a sequence with each reaction producing the precursor for the step that follows. This cluster includes all the genes involved in histidine synthesis in *S. typhimurium*. No genes not concerned with histidine synthesis are in the cluster. The entire cluster is controlled by a single operator (symbolized *O* at the right in Fig. 15.2) and is an example of an operon.

As in the example of the lactose operon in *E. coli,* feedback inhibition occurs and the enzyme system is inducible; that is, the amount of histidine available to the cell controls the synthetic process. When histidine is accumulated in the surrounding medium, synthesis is discontinued; when the supply is depleted, the synthetic process is activated. Experimentally, the entire operation may be stopped by adding histidine to the medium. The term "coordinate repression" is used to describe such a system in which the entire process is controlled by a single operator gene.

Investigations on the histidine operon by P. E. Hartman, B. N. Ames, and others have established the linkage relations of the cluster of nine structural genes and one operator gene in an area of the circular linkage map of *S. typhimurium*. The histidine operon (termed "histidon" by Ames and Hartman, 1963) includes about 13,000 nucleotides. Apparently, the coded information for the enzymes involved with the steps in the biosynthetic pathway is transcribed on a single long strand of m-RNA. Biosynthesis starts with ATP and purine precursor, phosphoribosyl pyrophosphate. A fragment of the pyrimidine portion of the purine ring of adenine attaches a ribose phosphate group at position 1 to form phosphoribosyl-ATP (PR-ATP). From this beginning, the process proceeds through the steps indicated in Fig. 15.2 to the end product, histidine.

More than 1000 mutants, some of the deletion type, have been identified in the DNA area covered by the histidine operon. All cistrons in this "polycistronic" operon have been involved in the mutations. About half of the point mutations discovered have been shown to have dual effects: (1) activity of one enzyme is lacking and (2) activities of all enzymes higher in the sequence than the mutated gene are decreased. Such mutations are called "polarity" mutations. Most of them are probably single-base changes. Extensive studies of polarity mutants have shown that the m-RNA message begins in one location (at right as shown in Fig. 15.2) and proceeds stepwise through the entire sequence. All steps higher in the sequence may be affected by the mutational change and those lower in the sequence remain unchanged. The message thus starts from the operator end and proceeds linearly to the completion of the synthesis unless interrupted by a mutational alteration which blocks the enzymatic steps.

In wild-type organisms, the amount of each enzyme synthesized is under control of the operator and the ratio of activity of one enzyme to another remains constant. Rate of production of each intermediate substance in the series of reactions thus stays in balance and excessive amounts of any one do not accumulate except in mutants in which the balance is upset by the blocking of one of the enzymatic steps. All of the enzymes in a polarity mutant are under control and are coordinately repressed. However, the steps beyond the mutation are adjusted or "modulated" as compared with those of the wild-type operon. For a given mutant the enzyme ratio remains constant although each polarity mutant shows its own modulation or pattern of enzyme levels.

Data from mutations and other lines of investigation involving the histidine operon have provided a basis for explaining a mechanism of genetic control. When an effector (4-amino-5-insidazole carboxamide ribonucleoside) is present in the medium, derepression of the nine enzymes occurs in a temporal sequence. About 20 minutes is required for the activation of the entire system. The first gene (*G*) is derepressed first and some 20 minutes later the last gene (*D*) is released to produce its enzyme. The entire sequence is required to produce histidine.

In Neurospora, the biosynthesis of histidine follows the same pathway as that in *S. typhimurium*. The *hist-3* cluster of genes in Linkage Group I governs the three reactions in the synthesis. This is an exception, however, because the genes responsible for most other pathways in Neurospora are not linked in clusters but distributed among the chromosomes. Several other operons in bacteria control the synthesis of substances such as leucine and tryptophan, but the groups of genes controlling these pathways in Neurospora are usually distributed in different chromosomes. It has been suggested that operons in bacteria each arise by tandem duplications of a single ancestral gene. In microbial organisms that have only one linkage group and are largely asexual, clusters of genes remain intact. Higher organisms, on the other hand, may have a more elaborate genetic control system which has replaced the operon system. Furthermore, in higher organisms with several chromosomes, unequal crossing over and structural changes such as inversions would tend to disrupt operons.

### *General Repressing Effect of Histones*

Histones are basic proteins which are associated with DNA in the chromatin of the cell. They have been known for a long time to influence gene activity. These proteins do not contain cysteine or tryptophan and they have only small amounts of tyrosine and phenylalanine. They are synthesized in the nucleolus of the metabolic cell and become associated with DNA in chromatin and chromosomes as the chromosomes form in cell division.

Although several histones have been recognized and these may be fractionated into subgroupings with particular characteristics, the same histones are present in all cells of a given organism. Likewise, all organisms thus far studied possess similar histones. Two exceptions to this broad generalization are: (1) sperm cells, which contain little or no histone, and (2) chicken erythrocytes, which have much more histone than other cells of chickens.

The action of histones on DNA seems to be a general one of repressing gene activity. This depends on the quantities of histone present in different cells and organisms in proportion to DNA. The proportion has been defined in terms of the ratio of histone to DNA. Functionally, this is the proportion of the DNA which can be complexed and thus repressed by the quantity of histone present. Chicken erythrocytes, for example, which have an excessive amount of histone, carry genomes that are almost completely repressed and will never be derepressed. Although these cells are nucleated, they are terminal cells which will not undergo cell division. Other cells of the chicken (for instance, liver, spleen, and heart cells) do not have histone in quantity equivalent to DNA.

Chromatin in general does not contain enough histone to complex all the DNA of the particular genome with which it is associated in a cell. About 80 to 90 percent of active cells generally are repressed and only 10 to 20 percent are derepressed at any one time. The same histone must repress different genes at different time periods.

## HORMONAL CONTROL OF m-RNA

Hormones have been recognized by biologists for a long time as agents of differentiation. The control of secondary sex characteristics in animals by estrogens and androgens (Chapter 4) is the best known example. Recently, much progress has been made in explaining the mechanism through which hormones influence development of an organism. In general, they act as effectors by derepressing or releasing genes previously repressed to synthesize m-RNA in tissues and thus increase quantities of enzymes.

Injection of an estrogen into an immature or ovariectomized female rat, for example, causes increased RNA synthesis followed by increased protein synthesis. This basic effect on RNA synthesis is reflected in alterations of the uterine wall and proliferation of the vaginal mucosa. Similarly, introduction of androgens (for example, testosterone) into immature or castrated male rats is followed by increased m-RNA synthesis, and enzyme production in the testes, prostate gland, and seminal vesicles. Sex hormones thus act as effectors, releasing genes which are otherwise repressed for production of m-RNA and enzymes.

If an antibiotic, puromycin, is introduced with the sex hormones, protein synthesis is inhibited. This antibiotic is known to interfere with transfer RNA and thus to block protein synthesis. Actinomycin-D also offsets the effect of sex hormones. It is known to block protein synthesis in bacteria and in animal cells. This antibiotic pairs with guanine in double helical DNA and prevents RNA polymerase molecules from using DNA as a template. It thus prevents RNA synthesis in the sex glands and offsets the induction of enzymes by sex hormones.

When rats and other mammals are treated with cortisone, a hormone from the adrenal cortex, levels of several enzymes in the liver, including glutamictyrosine transaminase, increase. The rate of RNA synthesis in liver cells is increased, more enzymes are produced, and greater enzymatic activity in the liver cells is evidenced. Injected cortisone goes to the liver and causes increased production of particular kinds of m-RNA. It is an effector substance which derepresses particular genes in liver cells and allows them to increase their production of m-RNA. Puromycin and actinomycin-D both inhibit the effect of cortisone and prevent increased enzyme production in liver cells.

Likewise, evidence has been accumulated to show that thyroxine and pituitary hormones (growth, adrenocorticotrophic, and gonadotrophic) increase m-RNA and enzyme production in their target organs. Plant hormones (such as gibberellic acid, which controls dormancy in buds, and indole acetic acid, which controls growth through cell elongation) are effectors increasing synthesis of m-RNA. The increased rate of RNA production caused by each of these hormones is suppressible by actinomycin-D.

Carcinogenic agents such as methylcholanthrene also increase the rate of production of certain enzymes indicating that they derepress genes for m-RNA synthesis. The increase does not occur in the presence of actinomycin-D. This suggests that carcinogens modify genetic repression in much the same way as do hormones. Increase in enzyme protein synthesis induced by carcinogens works to the disadvantage rather than to the advantage of the organism by producing excessive growth in particular body areas in the form of tumors.

### *Hormones Controlling m-RNA in Drosophila Chromosomes*

Giant salivary gland chromosomes of Diptera, which have been used extensively for checking the locations of genes in chromosomes, are now being employed as experimental materials in physiological genetics. When giant chromosomes are used for identifying gene locations, the salivary glands are dissected from uniformly large larvae ready to pupate. Because of the nature of the studies for which these chromosomes have been used, the great majority of preparations represent only one stage in development (Fig. 9.3).

Studies by several investigators have shown that specific areas of these chromosomes change in appearance at successive stages of development (Fig. 15.3). Enlarged

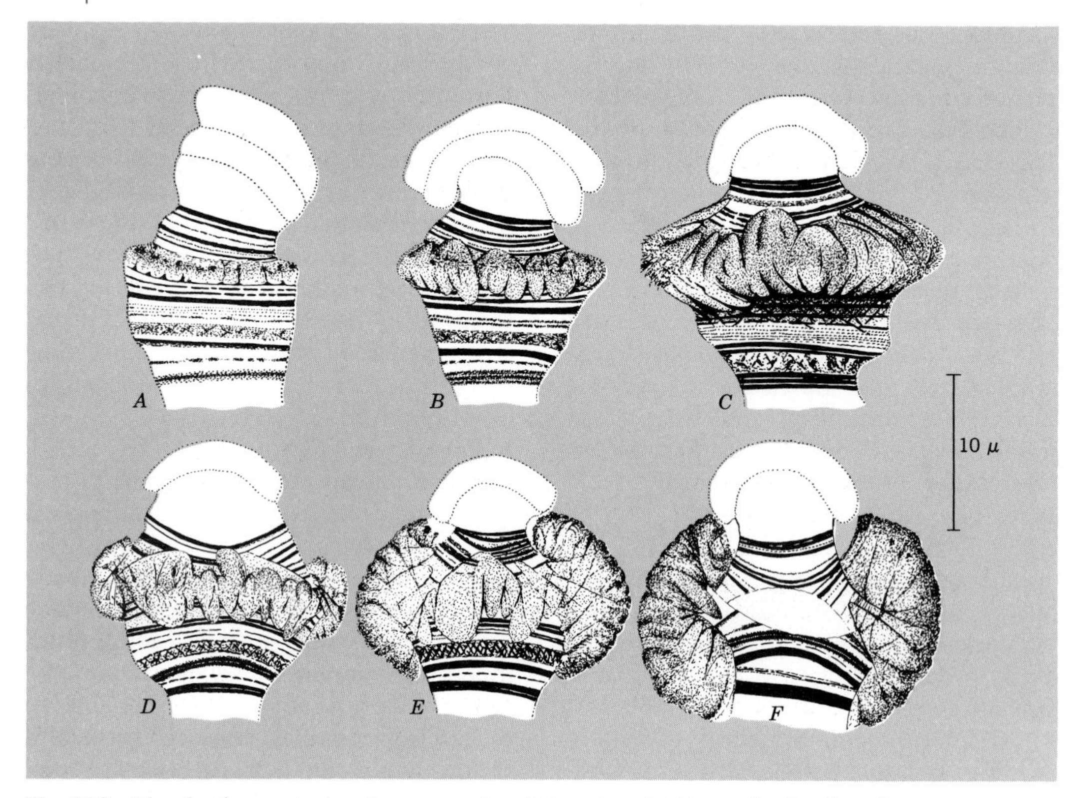


**Fig. 15.3** The development of a chromosomal puff in a larval salivary-gland cell nucleus of *Chironomus tentans.* This reversible phenomenon occurs at a specific developmental stage. Puffs carry an excess of RNA. (Beermann, *Chromosoma,* Vol. 5, 139–198, 1952, Springer-Verlag, Berlin, Heidelberg, New York.)

sections or "puffs" observed in some areas of the chromosomes change position with time as development proceeds, indicating that different parts of the chromosome become active at different time periods. These changes have been related by staining techniques, autoradiographs, and radioactive isotopes to chemical activities of DNA, RNA, and protein synthesis. The succession of observable events in the chromosomes suggests that inducers or regulators are active at particular periods in development. When stains specific for DNA and RNA were introduced together, segments of salivary chromosomes were stained differentially. It was shown that the active areas or puffs carried an excess of RNA. RNA was being synthesized in the chromosome regions that appeared to be active. Further studies showed that different m-RNA's were synthesized in different puffs. Labeled m-RNA, taken from puffs and injected into other specimens, was found to migrate to ribosomes as expected.

Hormonal control of particular puffs has been demonstrated during larval development of the flies. These studies have suggested a relation between hormones and gene action. The insect hormone, ecdysone, obtained from the silkworm (Bombyx) as well as from Drosophila and other Diptera, was found to alter the sequence and change the appearance of the puffs. It has now been established that the salivary chromosome puffs are composed of m-RNA.

Ecdysone has been shown to increase the rate at which $C^{14}$-labeled-leucine is incorporated into protein. These facts have led to the formulation of a hypothesis that some differentiation is brought about by hormonal stimulation of sets of genes which, in turn, produce in an orderly sequence m-RNA's as directed by the DNA, which remains constant in the chromosome.

When hemolymph, the fluid material in the body cavity, from old pupae was injected into the body cavities of young larvae, puffs were induced in particular locations on the chromosomes known to be influenced by ecdysone. Hemolymph from young larvae, on the other hand, would not induce puffs known to be controlled by ecdysone, indicating that the hormone was not present at that time. Particular chromosome regions were followed through their entire larval and pupal cycle. Certain puffs appeared at definite developmental periods and subsided at a later time. This indicated that genes were turned on and off during the cycle of development. Some chromosome areas were concerned with ordinary developmental functions and some with special functions such as molting.

### *Amphibian Lampbrush Chromosomes and m-RNA*

Another giant chromosome that promises to be increasingly useful in relating cytological studies with the chemical steps between genes and traits is the "lampbrush" type of chromosome (Fig. 15.4) found in the oöcytes of newts (amphibians). Chromosomes of this kind are greatly enlarged, some reaching the extraordinary length of 1 mm. They are composed of DNA threads forming the axis and extending laterally as loops on either side of the main axis. Thickened portions of the lateral loops represent accumulations of m-RNA. Similar structures have been observed in other organisms, but none thus far described are as conspicuous as those in newts. This observation is correlated with the fact that amphibian oöcyte chromosomes have an unusually high proportion of DNA. RNA, which may be m-RNA, is produced along the loops of the lampbrush chromosomes in a regular cycle somewhat like the process involving puff formation in the salivary chromosomes of dipterous larvae.

## INFLUENCE OF EXTERNAL ENVIRONMENT ON GENE ACTION

As we saw earlier, each gene may have a particular range of environmental conditions under which it can act. Some genes could have a wide range and produce the same effect in all environments in which the organism can live. The ABO blood groups, for example, are remarkably stable in most environments to which human beings are subjected. Some environmental factors (Chapter 8), however, over long periods of natural selection have apparently influenced the proportions of people with different blood antigens. A few specific selective factors have now been suggested. Carcinoma of the stomach, for example, occurs more frequently among people with A-type blood than among those of other blood types, and peptic ulcer of the duodenum is more common among O-type people than among those of other blood types. Some studies have indicated that small pox occurs more frequently and that its effects are more severe among A- and AB- than among O- and B-type people. In spite of the evidence for natural selection over long time periods, the blood type of an individual remains remarkably constant. Only a very few environmental conditions, such as the disease leukemia (Chapter 8), will alter the blood type of a particular person.

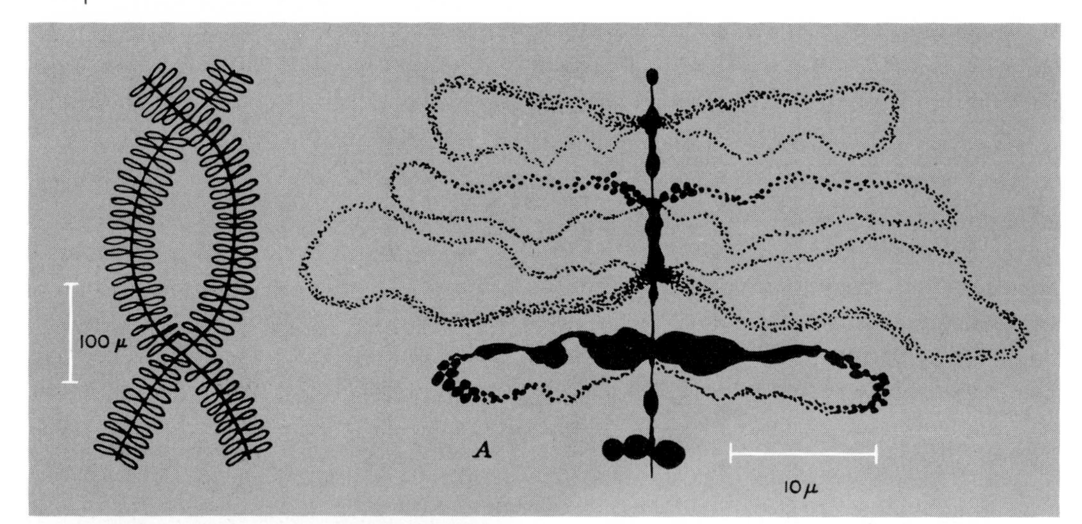


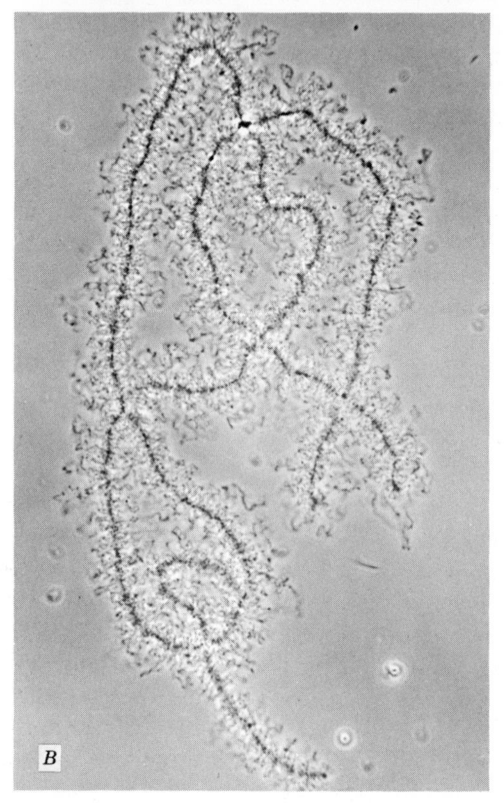


**Fig. 15.4** Lampbrush chromosomes. *A*, (left) highly diagrammatic view of a bivalent with two chiasmata; (right) central axis of a portion of a chromosome with paired lateral loops. (From J. G. Gall, *Mutation, Brookhaven Symposium in Biology;* No. 8, p. 18). *B*, Photograph of lampbrush chromosomes. (Courtesy of J. G. Gall.)

Body weight, on the other hand, has a genetic component but is strongly influenced by the dietary pattern of the individual. Other more delicate mechanisms are involved in the expression of such human traits as polydactyly, where six, or even seven fingers or toes may occur on either hand or either foot. Usually, in people with this abnormality, the number is not the same on both hands or both feet. The condition is controlled by a single dominant gene, but the asymmetry is probably due to fine nongenetic causes occurring in embryology. A basic fact of gene action is that similar genotypes express themselves differently in different environments. This does not imply that the gene itself is changed, but that the reactions controlled by the gene are influenced by the environment. Chemical reactions proceed more rapidly at high than at low temperatures, and it is not surprising that the end products are different at different temperatures.

Many examples could be cited in plants and animals of conspicuous inherited characteristics that are influenced by environmental conditions. The primrose, Primula, has two flower colors, red and white, controlled by a single pair of alleles. Plants with the genotype *AA* produce red flowers at moderate temperatures and white flowers at high temperatures. Those with *aa* have white flowers at all temperatures at which the plant can live. The phenotype thus may not always reflect the genes present, and environmental conditions must be taken into account in describing the relation between genes and characters.

Another environmental agent was found by T. H. Morgan to influence the trait called abnormal abdomen in Drosophila. This phenotype in adult flies was characterized by irregular abdominal segments that reflected earlier developmental abnormalities. A certain gene *A* was required for the expression of the trait, but only those flies that hatched first, while the culture bottles were moist, expressed the trait. Flies that hatched later or those raised in bottles with less moisture did not show the abnormality, even though they carried the gene. When all flies carried the gene, the environment was the determining factor in the expression of the trait.

Sometimes it is possible to determine critical periods in the development of a trait. Bar eye in Drosophila, for example, is influenced by temperature changes during the period from 89.3 to 96.8 hours after fertilization. This period represents only about 5 percent of the larval life of the fly. When flies carrying the genetic composition (treated here as a gene (*B*) but associated with a chromosomal duplication) for bar eye are subjected to a temperature of 30°C during this period, their eyes have about 50 facets. At 25°C, bar eyes have about 150 facets, compared with 700 to 800 for wild type. Changes in temperature at any point throughout larval and pupal stages can effectively change the expression of other traits such as bristle formation. Temperature-effective periods do not necessarily indicate that the gene is acting during that period. The gene may have acted earlier and the period may coincide with an embryological process when the product of the gene is being utilized. Another possibility is that a ground substance, required for the gene to act, is produced during the temperature-sensitive period.

## CONTROL OF PIGMENT PRODUCTION

A classical example of a chain of gene actions which illustrates the research approach and the present status of the problem of chemical genetics is associated with the eye pigments of insects. A. Kühn in Germany, G. W. Beadle, B. Ephrussi, and their associates have provided the framework for the investigation. In the caterpillar of the wild meal moth, *Ephestia kühniella,* the eyes and other organs as well as the entire outer surface are dark brown. Coloring is dependent on certain ommochrome pigments. By spontaneous mutation of a single gene ($v^+$ mutated to $v$), the ability of the caterpillar to form pigment was lost. If aqueous alcoholic extracts of $v^+$ tissue are injected into $v$ caterpillars, these caterpillars regain the ability to form ommochromes, and normal pigmentation occurs. Tissues of the wild-type organisms, therefore, contain an extractable substance which is interposed between the genes and the external phenotype.

By experimental analysis, it was possible to prove that the substance that causes pigment formation under the influence of the gene $v^+$ was kynurenine. This amino acid (*o-amino-benzoyl-alanine*) is an intermediate product of tryptophan metabolism in mammals and is found in the urine of rabbits fed on rice or other food rich in tryptophan. The mammal is thus able to transform tryptophan to kynurenine. Numerous microorganisms have the same ability. Quantitative studies showed that the degree of pigment formation was directly proportional to the amount of kynurenine present. Kynurenine, therefore, does not act as a catalyst in pigment formation, but as a precursor in the synthesis of the ommochrome molecule. This reaction represents one link in the chain leading from tryptophan to the pigment.

The next question is the relation between kynurenine formation and gene $v^+$. In mammals, the transformation of tryptophan to kynurenine is dependent on a specific enzyme, tryptophan-pyrrolase, found in the liver. It may be assumed that a corresponding enzyme is present in $v^+$ but not in the $v$ tissue. The mutation of $v^+$ to $v$ thus deprives the cell of the ability to convert tryptophan to kynurenine and breaks the chain of events required for pigment formation. With the block in the course of tryptophan degradation, this amino acid would be expected to accumulate in $v$ caterpillars. E. Caspari has shown the tryptophan content of $v$ mutants to be greater than that of members of the wild race.

Results paralleling those in the meal moth were found in the fruit fly, *D. melanogaster*. The dark-red eye color of wild-type flies also depends on a $v^+$ gene, and the mutation from $v^+$ to $v$ (vermilion) reduces the pigmentation to orange-red. Kynurenine can fully replace the action of the gene in Drosophila as well as in Ephestia. Another similar effect on the formation of eye pigment in Drosophila is caused by a mutation at another locus. When $cn^+$ mutates to *cn* (cinnabar), the fly is unable to produce ommochrome. Transplantation and extraction experiments have shown that $cn^+$ intervenes at a later stage of the pigment-producing process. Its action requires the presence of $v^+$. The action of $cn^+$ can be replaced by 3-hydroxykynurenine, which evidently represents a further link in the chain between tryptophan and the pigment. Its formation from kynurenine depends on the action of a specific enzyme that acts only in tissue containing $cn^+$ genes. These two links in the chain are illustrated diagrammatically in Fig. 15.5.

A protein carrier is also required in the formation of pigment. In the meal moth, Kühn showed that the formation of protein granules was disturbed by a mutation of a gene $wa^+$ to *wa*, which completely interrupted the pigment formation. Kynurenine and hydroxykynurenine were produced by the *wa* moths but could not be used by the *wa* tissues. This investigation revealed another link in the chain of gene actions involved in pigment formation. Three points have thus been identified at which the chain reaction leading to pigment formation may be broken. The probable actions of the three genes are illustrated in Fig. 15.6.

Pigment production in flowers and other plant parts apparently follows the same principle of gene-controlled pathways as that in insects. Plant pigments include carotenoids (usually confined to plastids), anthocyanins, anthoxanthines, and flavocyanins. Most water-soluble red, blue, and yellow pigments found in flowers are anthocyanins or related compounds. Sev-

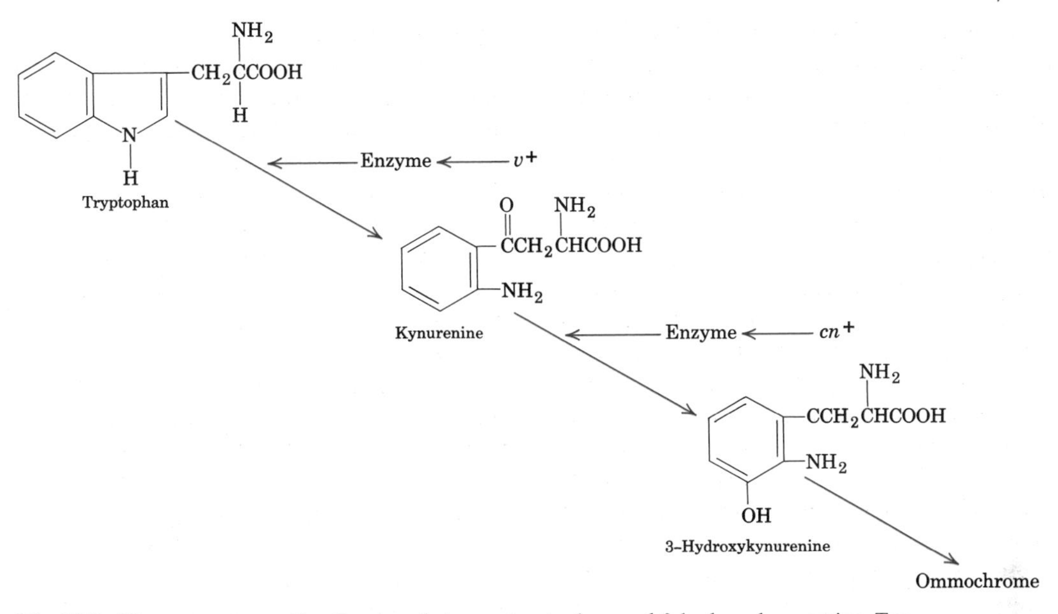


**Fig. 15.5** Diagram representing the steps between tryptophan and 3-hydroxykynurenine. Two genes, $v^+$ and $cn^+$, which control enzymatic action, are postulated for the steps: tryptophan to kynurenine and kynurenine to 3-hydroxykynurenine.

eral pigments falling into the various categories have been synthesized in a test tube, but the mechanisms by which plants make them are largely unknown. Some pigments are closely related chemically and differ only in the number of hydroxyl groups on the benzene rings. In some cases, only *p*H of the substratum controls the color that an indicator substance provided by a gene will produce.

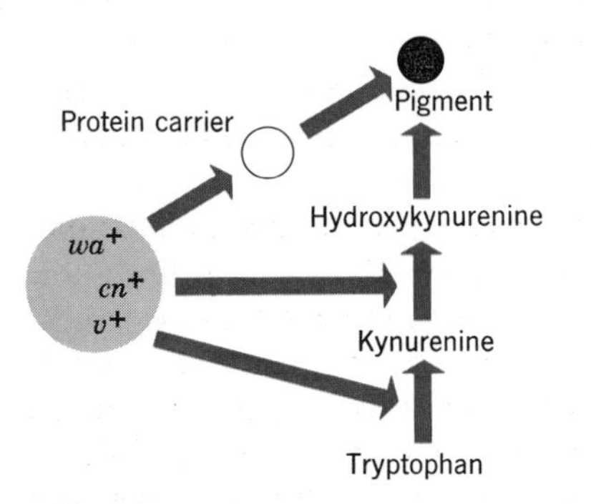


**Fig. 15.6** Diagram representing three steps in a chain reaction leading to pigment formation in the meal moth, *Ephestia kühniella.* (Data from Kühn.)

The pigment that produces the brown, gray, and black coloring in many animals, including man, is melanin. Genes control the quantity of melanin that is reflected in the degree of coloring of the skin (Chapter 17). Negroes have a genotype that provides a relatively large quantity of melanin. On the other hand, Caucasians have a genotype that results in a lesser quantity of the same pigment. Separate genes control the distribution of pigment to the eyes. Within the Caucasian population, various eye colors may be observed that are dependent mainly on the quantity of brown pigment covering the basic blue of the iris. The blue color is not produced by a pigment but is associated with the physical properties of the materials in the eye. When only a thin layer of pigment is present, the eyes appear hazel, gray, or green. When more pigment is present and the blue is completely covered, the eyes appear brown or black.

When pigment production is blocked, the result is albinism. The skin of the

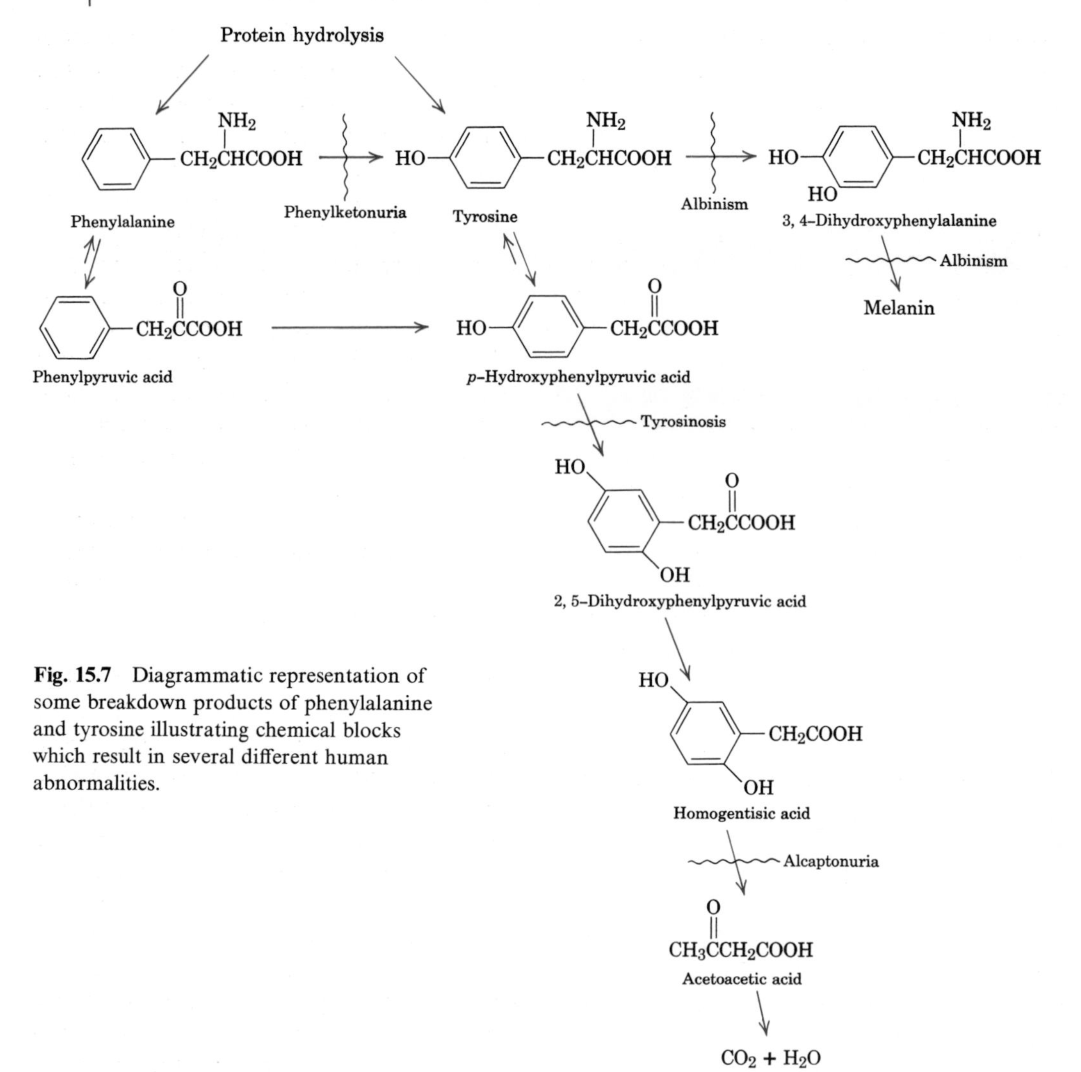


**Fig. 15.7** Diagrammatic representation of some breakdown products of phenylalanine and tyrosine illustrating chemical blocks which result in several different human abnormalities.

albino is extremely light, the hair is white or straw colored, and the eyes may appear light blue, but under strong light they are pink or red. No pigment is present in the iris, and the blood vessels on the inside of the eyeball can be seen through the iris. A single gene ($c$) in homozygous condition ($cc$) blocks pigment production and gives rise to the albino phenotype. The mechanism by which this is accomplished is one of the best-known examples of the relation between gene and character in man. Melanin is produced through a chain of reactions (Fig. 15.7) involving the amino acid phenylalanine (one of the essential amino acids which must be supplied in the human diet) and another amino acid, tyrosine. The enzyme tyrosinase is involved in the oxidation of tyrosine to dihydroxyphenylalanine (dopa) and from dopa to indole-2-carboxylic acid. Further oxidation results in the final product, melanin. An absence of tyrosinase blocks the chain reaction in one or more places.

The lack of tyrosinase results in albinism. When the recessive gene $c$ for albinism is present in homozygous condition, the production of tyrosinase is inhibited. The possibility of artificially supplying an enzyme and thus overcoming albinism has been considered by many investigators. Unfortunately, no method is known by which an enzyme can be introduced and become effective inside a cell except through synthesis in that cell; that is, it must be built up within the cell itself. Therefore, prospects for curing albinism by supplying enzymes artificially are not promising. Previously cited studies in Neurospora, however, indicate that nutritional blocks and color variations created by mutations can be repaired or altered by the addition of appropriate chemicals. Cellular processes in higher organisms may eventually be susceptible to manipulation when more steps in the chain reactions are identified.

## OTHER BLOCKS IN THE METABOLISM OF PHENYLALANINE IN MAN

Another hereditary block in the metabolism of phenylalanine and tyrosine results in the disease alcaptonuria, characterized chiefly by a darkening of the cartilage. In the presence of this abnormality, areas where the cartilage comes close to the surface in the ear, wrist, and elbow show discoloration. A type of arthritis sometimes becomes associated with the cartilage discoloration when the people with the disease reach middle life or old age. A more obvious but superficial symptom is the tendency for the urine of an affected person to turn black when exposed to air or when brought in contact with an alkaline substance. The urine characteristic has been traced to an unusual component, alcapton or homogentisic acid. Normal people have an enzyme—homogentisate oxidase—in their livers which breaks down homogentisic acid to a noncolor-producing substance which eventually is broken down to carbon dioxide and water. Alcaptonurics lack the enzyme because a single autosomal recessive gene is present in homozygous condition (*aa*). When alcaptonurics eat foods containing large amounts of phenylalanine, tyrosine, or p-OH-phenylpyruvic acid, a proportional increase of homogentisic acid is excreted in the urine. Normal people can eat similar foods in reasonable quantity with no such reaction. In alcaptonurics, an intermediate product has thus become an end product because of a hereditary block in the chain reaction.

Another abnormality resulting from a different block in the phenylalanine metabolism is phenylketonuria. This disease is characterized by a serious mental defect and is also associated with the excretion of excessive amounts (about one gram per day) of phenylpyruvic acid in the urine. An increase of phenylalanine in the diet is associated with an increase of the acid in the urine. Again a single recessive gene in homozygous condition (*pp*) is responsible for the metabolic block. People with the normal allele ($p^+$) have parahydroxylase, which changes phenylalanine to tyrosine, and *pp* individuals do not. It has been observed that all phenylketonurics have a light complexion, because the metabolites of phenylalanine interfere with pigment production.

Although albinism, alcaptonuria, and phenylketonuria are very different phenotypically, they are related chemically. Each represents a break in the chain of reactions involved in phenylalanine and tyrosine metabolism. The blocks, however, occur in different places in the sequence. Figure 15.7 illustrates the possible chemical relations among the compounds mentioned in this discussion, and the points at which the known blocks are presumed to occur.

Other alterations may occur through mutation elsewhere in the series of reactions and thus give rise to other abnormalities. Tyrosinosis, characterized by the accumulation of tyrosine in the body, represents another alteration of the normal sequence. This rare human abnormality has been carefully studied only once, and its hereditary nature is unknown, but it is probably the result of a gene mutation leading to a block in the reaction through which *p*-hydroxyphenylpyruvic acid is converted to 2, 5-dihydroxyphenylpyruvic acid. Another block in tyrosine metabolism after dopa, inhibits the production of adrenaline and noradrenaline. Thyroxine deficiency associated with genetic goitrous cretinism is caused by another block in tyrosine metabolism.

## VARIABILITY OF GENE EFFECTS

The phenotypic expression of a given gene depends on its interaction with other genes and environmental factors. When comparing the visible effects of genes, two terms, *penetrance* and *expressivity,* are useful. Penetrance is the percentage of individuals who carry the gene in proper combination to permit expression and who demonstrate the phenotype. If a dominant gene is expressed in only 70 percent of the individuals known to carry it, the penetrance of the gene would be 70 percent. The expressivity is the degree of effect or the extent to which a gene expresses itself in different individuals.

Examples given thus far have involved only genes with complete penetrance and unvarying expressivity. Whenever a gene was identified as a dominant, it was assumed to come to expression and produce a given effect in any individual in which it occurred. Recessives in homozygous condition have been assumed to express themselves in a characteristic manner. In some cases, however, genes known to be present in a proper combination are not expressed in 100 percent of the individuals. Usually the reasons for a variable penetrance and expressivity can be explained on the basis of modifiers that influence the action of a given gene, or of environmental variations. The terms are sometimes used to make ignorance respectable when the reasons for the failure of expression or variation in phenotype are not known.

The penetrance concept is useful in human genetics to account for ratios that do not conform to strict Mendelian patterns. Dominants with reduced penetrance are difficult to distinguish from recessives in family history studies. Statistical methods have been devised to compare the proportion of individuals showing a trait with the proportion of those presumed to carry the gene. Data for statistical analysis of dominants can be obtained by determining the proportion of unaffected parents in whose progeny the trait appears. Further data are obtained by comparing the 1:1 ratio with the total ratio of affected to normal children in all families in which one parent expresses the trait. Such human traits as blue sclerotics, stiff little fingers, and many others, have been described as dependent on incompletely penetrant dominant genes.

The term penetrance in human genetics has been abused to the extent that it is in danger of falling into disrepute. Too often, variable penetrance is used as a catchall to explain presumed genetic patterns that do not follow a common Mendelian ratio. In some cases, the heritability of the trait in question may be doubtful; in others, the expression may depend on more than one gene. Most of the carefully studied human traits have been found to be too complex to be explained by single gene substitutions.

Several investigators have cited the susceptibility to leukemia as a hereditary condition dependent on a dominant gene with incomplete penetrance. If the premise that there is a genetic basis for leukemia is established, and only a single gene is involved, the penetrance would have to be less than 1 percent, since only 1 of every 100 individuals carrying the gene will contract the disease. A statistical investigation by A. G. Steinberg in which more than 200 families were studied indicated that leukemia has no hereditary basis. The incidence among the relatives of leukemia patients was not significantly greater than that among the controls or in the general population.

Expressivity, or the manner in which gene expression occurs, may represent merely an extension of penetrance in the visible range. If genes sometimes fail to come to visible expression, variations would be expected among the phenotypes observed. Therefore, both penetrance and expressivity may be involved in a given expression. Expressivity has significance in human genetics but, like penetrance, has often been abused. In one person, a given gene may produce a slight effect, whereas in another it may result in a marked deviation from the normal. It is not always possible to determine whether genetic or environmental factors are responsible for the difference.

The main difficulty in distinguishing between hereditary and environmental influence in man arises from the fact that no two human beings, except identical twins, are genetically alike. Twins studies thus far have furnished limited but valuable data on problems of expressivity. A single dominant gene is apparently associated with allergy, but the gene may be expressed in many ways in different individuals. Some people carrying the gene may develop hay fever, others asthma, edema, or skin rash. It is not always possible to determine whether a single gene with variable expressivity is responsible for different expressions or whether different genes are involved in the series of phenotypes. The literature includes several examples in which a single basic gene is postulated, and interactions between modifier genes and environmental factors are suggested to account for variation. Sometimes minor and largely unknown factors and interactions must be postulated in order to provide a plausible explanation for variation in expressivity.

## PHENOCOPIES

By altering the environment, it is sometimes possible to induce nonhereditary phenotypic changes (phenocopies) that resemble those caused by mutations. Presumably, environmental agents occasionally influence certain chemical reactions in the same way as do mutations, and thus produce similar end products.

To test the difference between phenocopies and mutations, it is necessary to make appropriate crosses and determine whether a given phenotypic alteration is transmitted in inheritance. Well-established phenocopies have been described in insects, birds, and mammals. Phenocopies have also been described in bacteria, but they have not always been clearly distinguished from mutations. Goldschmidt, who in 1935 coined the term phenocopy, subjected Drosophila pupae to a higher than usual temperature (35°C) for short intervals at different periods of the development cycle. Several phenotypes indistinguishable by visible means from genetic mutants were produced. One group of wing abnormalities (Fig. 15.8) paralleled the expressions of the different alleles of the vestigial (*vg*) series. Temperature alterations were visualized as factors changing the velocity of chemical reactions and, thus, altering the end products. The germ plasm was not affected.

In chickens, two mutations are known that interfere in some fundamental way with development and thus produce a

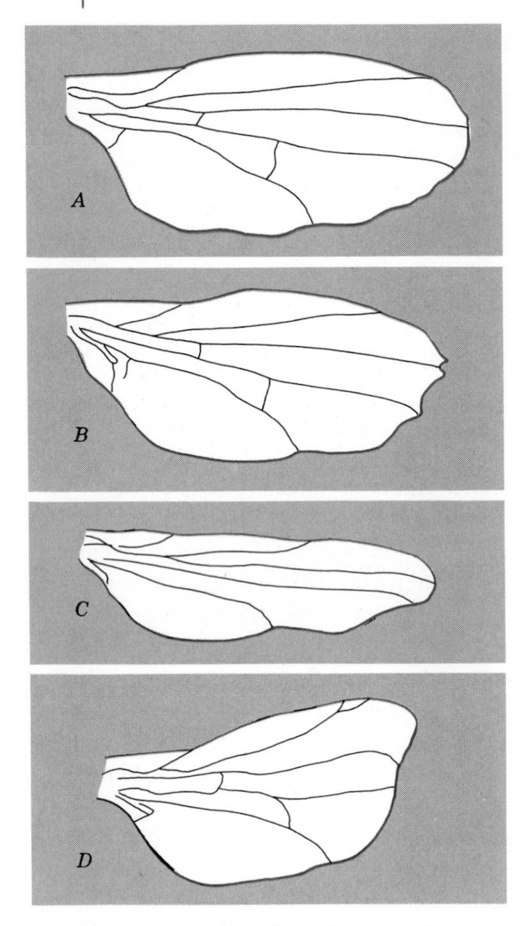


**Fig. 15.8** Drosophila wings showing phenocopies induced by heat. *A*, normal wings; *B*, a phenocopy of a mutant nicked ($vg^{ni}$) (cf. Fig. 8.4*B*); *C*, a phenocopy of the mutant lanceolate; *D*, a phenocopy of the mutant truncate. (After R. B. Goldschmidt.)

phenotype called rumplessness (Fig. 15.9). The abnormality is characterized by the absence of caudal vertebrae and tail structures such as muscles, feathers, and the uropygial or preen gland from which an oily secretion is normally supplied to the feathers. Although the two mutations have the same end product, their other characteristics are different. One is completely dominant whereas the other is recessive with low penetrance. The genes are not alleles and are not closely linked. Furthermore, expressions of the two genes differ in structural details, chemical composition of the bones, and embryonic development.

By mechanically shaking the eggs at a critical period, the rumpless phenotype may be reproduced in chickens carrying the normal alleles of the respective genes. The abnormality sometimes occurs without any treatment, presumably as a result of accidental and unknown external or internal effects on the early embryo. Different breeds of chickens vary in the production of rumpless birds from untreated eggs. About 1.6 percent of the embryos of White Leghorns surviving on the seventeenth day of incubation were rumpless, compared with 0.3 percent for the Jungle Fowl maintained under the same conditions. W. Landauer has induced rumpless phenocopies in chickens with normal genotypes by treating the eggs or embryos with certain chemicals. Embryos treated at 48 hours of age with sodium methyl arsenite, for example, had rump defects and other abnormalities in greater proportion than the untreated controls. Other chemicals, including insulin, were also effective in inducing comparable phenocopies. Further experiments showed that an injection of nicotine amide would counteract the insulin and prevent production of the insulin-induced phenocopies. Nicotine amide apparently acts as a coenzyme in cell respiration and thus affects its counteraction.

The mere fact that nongenetic modifications resemble genetic mutants does not prove similar causation. When the time at which alteration can be induced (the temperature-sensitive period) coincides with the time of gene action (which must occur before visible effects can be detected), however, a similar physiological alteration is suggested. Specific proof of the similarity of the fundamental reaction chains that are affected must be derived in each instance. The physiological mechanism by

**Fig. 15.9** Phenocopy in chickens known as rumplessness. (Left) rumpless chicken; (right) normal chicken.

which the phenocopy is produced may be quite different from that by which the mutant phenotype is produced. Furthermore, adult characters could result from various developmental events which have little in common with each other, for example, dominant and recessive rumplessness.

In human genetics, phenocopies add to the difficulty of distinguishing hereditary traits from those produced by environmental factors. Heart troubles brought on by environmentally conditioned anxiety reactions, for example, are similar to those having a hereditary cause. Similarly, eye defects following measles cannot be distinguished readily from hereditary eye abnormalities. A protozoan infection of mothers during pregnancy, known as toxoplasmosis, sometimes results in abnormalities in the children which resemble hereditary conditions but are not genetically transmitted. Several skeletal and neurological anomalies induced by irradiation have a parallel in genetically produced phenotypes. Use of the tranquilizer, thalidomide, by pregnant women results in deformities in the foetus that bear a resemblance to some hereditary abnormalities. The same basic reactions may be involved in both types of phenotypic changes, but the trigger mechanisms are associated with either a gene or some environmental agent.

## SUMMARY

Genetic material (DNA) acts through m-RNA on enzyme synthesis. Enzymes in turn influence metabolic processes and thus control structural and functional traits of organisms. Hormones and factors in the external environment as well as enzymes regulate gene activity. One model for control of gene action is the operon, which is a complex of genetic units including a regulator, operator and two or more structural genes. Examples of operons are found in *E. coli* and *S. typhimurium.* Although operons are known in detail only in microbial systems, evidence indicates that they occur in higher organisms as well.

Studies on the chain reactions involved in processes such as pigment formation by plants, insects, and mammals (including man) have revealed gene-enzyme controlled steps in biosynthetic pathways. Certain reactions have been blocked by mutational changes and substances ordinarily intermediate have become end products. Variability in gene effects, that is, variable penetrance and expressivity, is explained by delicate interactions between genetic and environmental factors. Phenocopies are expressions similar to mutational or genetic effects but they are responses to altered environment rather than inheritance.

## REFERENCES


Ames, B. N., and P. E. Hartman. 1963. "The histidine operon." *Cold Spring Harbor Symp. on Quant. Biol.,* **28,** 349–356. (Linkage map and description of enzymes associated with operon. Polarity and modulation discussed.)

Beermann, W., and U. Clever. 1964. "Chromosome puffs." *Sci. Amer.,* **210(4),** 50–58. (Enzyme ecdysone related to m-RNA synthesis.)

Bonner, J. 1965. *The molecular biology of development.* Oxford University Press, New York.

Bryson, V., and H. J. Vogel. 1965. *Evolving genes and proteins.* Academic Press, New York.

Callan, H. G. 1963. "The nature of lampbrush chromosomes." *Intern. Rev. Cytol.,* **15,** 1–34.

Changeux, J. P. 1965. "The control of biochemical reactions." *Sci. Amer.,* **212,** 36–45.

Goldsberger, R. F., and M. A. Berberich. 1965. "Sequential repression and derepression of the enzymes for histidine biosynthesis in Salmonella typhimurium." *Proc. Nat'l. Acad. Sci.* (*U. S.*), **54,** 279–286.

Jacob, F., and J. Monod. 1961. "Genetic regulatory mechanisms in synthesis of proteins." *J. Mol. Biol.,* **3,** 318–356.

Jukes, T. H. 1966. *Molecules and evolution.* Columbia University Press, New York.

Sager, R., and F. J. Ryan. 1961. *Cell heredity.* John Wiley and Sons, New York.

Steiner, R. F., and H. Edelhoch. 1965. *Molecules and life.* D. Van Nostrand Co., New York.

Wagner, R. P., and H. K. Mitchell. 1965. *Genetics and metabolism,* 2nd ed. John Wiley and Sons, New York. (Discussions of gene activity and control mechanisms.)


# *Problems*

**15.1** During the past few years, extensive investigation has been centered around the (1) genetic code and (2) the mechanisms of regulation of gene activity. (a) Which of these two studies is most nearly completed? (b) Which will probably receive the most attention in the next few years?

**15.2** From the standpoint of economy of the organism, which method of genetic control would seem to be most efficient: feedback inhibition from finished product or presence of substrata in the medium?

**15.3** In the lactose operon in *E. coli* (a) what is the function of each of the following genes and (b) how does each perform its function: (1) regulator, (2) operator, (3) structural gene $y$, and (4) structural gene $z$?

15.4 What would be the result of inactivation by mutation of the following genes in the *E. coli* lactose operon: (a) regulator, (b) operator, (c) structural gene *y*, and (d) structural gene *z*?

15.5 How could (a) polarity and (b) modulation be demonstrated in the histidine operon? If a polarity mutation should inactivate gene *A* in the histidine operon, how would the ten enzymatic steps indicated in Fig. 15.2 be affected?

15.6 How could the histidine operon in *S. typhimurium* have developed and been maintained in evolution?

15.7 Are operons expected to be more common in bacteria or in higher organisms?

15.8 (a) How could histones regulate gene activity? (b) Where are they synthesized, and (c) how are they related to cell structures in the cell cycle?

15.9 How can (a) estrogens, (b) androgens, (c) cortisone, and (d) gibberellic acid regulate gene activity?

15.10 Why is inhibition by actinomycin-D significant in identifying hormones with the regulation of gene activity?

15.11 How may carcinogens be involved in tumor formation?

15.12 Why are salivary chromosomes in the larvae of Diptera useful in studying hormonal regulation of gene activity?

15.13 What is the probable action of the $v^+$ and $cn^+$ genes in eye color production in Drosophila?

15.14 (a) Why are such organisms as molds, bacteria, and viruses favorable materials for biochemical genetic study? (b) What type of experimental material would be most suitable for a study of (1) operons, (2) repressing effect of histones, (3) hormonal control of m-RNA synthesis, and (4) chromosome puffs?

15.15 (a) Formulate a plausible explanation for variable penetrance and expressivity. (b) How are the terms penetrance and expressivity used and abused in studies of human genetics?

15.16 At birth, rabbits of the Himalayan breed are all white, but as they grow older the extremities (paws, nose, ears, and tail) become black. When the white fur is shaved from a spot on the body of the adult and the rabbit is kept in a cool place, the new hair that grows in the shaved spot is black. The temperature of the body proper is about 33°C, but in the extremities it is about 27°C. (a) How may genetic and environmental factors be involved? (b) Formulate an explanation for the difference in pigmentation.

15.17 Ordinarily, Drosophila eye-disc transplants placed in hosts with different genotype develop according to the genotype of the transplant. For example, transplants from larvae with the genotype for white eye develop white in wild-type hosts and transplants from wild-type larvae develop wild-type red in hosts with genotype for white. Beadle and Ephrussi performed transplantation experiments on larvae with vermilion (*v*) and cinnabar (*cn*) eyes. The phenotypes for these two mutants are similar. They have bright red color because they lack the brown pigment that is a part of the wild-type red. (a) When discs from wild-type larvae were transplanted into vermilion or cinnabar hosts they developed wild type, but when *v* or *cn* transplants were placed in wild-type hosts they also developed wild type. (b) When discs from *cn* larvae were placed in *v* hosts no brown pigment was formed, and the eyes were bright red.

From the reciprocal transplant, that is, *v* in *cn* hosts, brown pigment was produced and the eyes were wild type. Formulate an explanation for these results.

**15.18** The father of two albino children has made widespread inquiries among geneticists and physicians concerning a possible cure for albinism. The steps in pigment production have been elucidated and it seems feasible to him that something might be added to the diet or given by injection which would supply the missing step or steps in melanin production in his children. Evaluate the possibility of such a development on the basis of evidence now available.

**15.19** (a) How could phenocopies be used to study gene action? (b) What values and limitations do they have for investigations of this kind? (c) How can an investigator determine whether an altered phenotype is a mutation or a phenocopy?

**15.20** Develop a plausible explanation for the occurrence of rumplessness in chickens in association with each of the following: (a) without treatment; (b) mechanical shaking; and (c) injection with insulin.

**15.21** What significance may phenocopies have in medical genetics?

# *Developmental and Behavioral Genetics* 16

Genetic mechanisms associated with structurally and numerically classifiable traits have been investigated much more extensively and successfully than those associated with developmental or behavioral characteristics. Development and behavior have been particularly difficult to analyze genetically because they can not be divorced from physiological and environmental factors. Indeed, the effects of inheritance and environment are so tightly interwoven that, on the organismal level, they are virtually inseparable. Component parts are difficult to distinguish, and the mechanisms involved in the development of each are not clearly identified.

Failure to achieve a complete explanation for gene action has not prevented developmental and behavior genetics from moving forward, but progress has necessarily been based on indirect and statistical data rather than on mechanistic associations between genes and traits. Hereditary and environmental interactions, however, certainly should not be considered as merely statistical abstractions. They can be observed and analyzed in experiments with animals in which genetic and environmental factors can be varied and controlled.

The premise for this chapter is that both developmental and behavioral characteristics of an animal develop under the joint influence of heredity and environment. Genetic determiners must provide the guidelines that make it possible for an individual animal to appear and behave generally like other members of its species. Segregating genes and natural selection under environmental fluctuations provide for individual differences.

## GENETICS AND DEVELOPMENT

Three closely interrelated aspects of development—differentiation, organization, and growth regulation—are presumably under general control of the genetic determiners. Precise genetic mechanisms have, for the most part, not been defined for any of the three. The end results of similarities and differences as represented in a given species, however, indicate that genetic specifications are involved.

Abundant evidence indicates that nearly all cells arising from the zygote through mitosis carry identical chromosomes and genes. Numerous observations show that the great majority of somatic cells have the same chromosome number as the zygote, and twice the number carried by the gametes of the particular species. Yet, as development proceeds, the cells in various regions of the embryo become different in appearance and eventually perform diverse functions. This is the process called differentiation. Chemical differentiation must precede the morphological and physiological distinction which can be identified in the developmental process. It is through the chemical reactions that genes may exert much of their influence.

In the usual developmental sequence, single fertilized eggs duplicate themselves by cell division following the duplication of all the hereditary units they contain. The first cleavage results in two cells that usually appear to be similar. Each of these undergoes cell division and a four-celled early embryo is produced. As cleavage continues, a small mass of cells accumulates, resulting in a morula and, later, in a blastula. All the cells in these stages came from the same source, the original fertilized egg. The same process of duplication (cell division) produced each of the cells and all might be expected to be alike. In most developing organisms, the cells do appear alike during the early stages, but as development continues and gastrulation occurs, differences become apparent. In developing vertebrates, some cells take on special characteristics and form the notochord; others give rise to the nervous system; still others to the digestive tract, and so on through the organization of the whole animal. Homogeneous generalized cells are thus transformed into heterogeneous specialized cells.

In order to affect the development of the organism, genes must in some way influence a number of processes. Their activities would have to include: (1) providing for the great variety of forms and functions of cells, (2) directing the proper organization of cells in the formation of parts of the body, and (3) exerting general control over the growth processes that determine the ultimate size and shape of the whole organism as well at its various parts. The gene action, which presumably occurs ultimately through protein synthesis, must be accomplished immediately through numerous chemical reactions accurately timed and properly coordinated throughout development. Several kinds of chemical agents such as enzymes, hormones, antigens, and organizers are known to function directly in developmental processes. The steps between genes and developmental squences are now being established.

### *Early Theories of Differentiation*

Early experiments led to two different hypotheses concerning the mechanism of differentiation. One hypothesis assumed a segregation of nuclear elements during the mitotic divisions intervening between the original zygote and the various cells which gave the cells the properties required for their specialized functions. The other hypothesis assumed a variability within the cytoplasm that provided for interactions or gradients which then initiated differentiation.

The first of the two theories originated in the 1880's when Wilhelm Roux, the founder of experimental embryology, studied frog eggs. In one experiment involving the two-cell stage following the first cleavage, Roux pierced one of the two cells or blastomeres with a hot needle and killed it. The single living blastomere attached to the dead one was allowed to continue development (Fig. 16.1). A half embryo was produced, and Roux concluded that the two halves had already been determined in the two-cell stage. The original zygote was presumed to carry everything necessary for full development, but restrictions were believed to develop by the time of the second division.

August Weismann had shown, from studies on coelenterates, that some cells behaved differently from others in the early cleavage stages. By following the different cells, he thought that he could distinguish between totipotent cells (cells capable of developing into complete embryos) and ordinary somatic cells. Weismann's conclusion fitted well with Roux's idea and led to a more detailed hypothesis for the mechanics of differentiation. To account for differentiation, a type of pre-

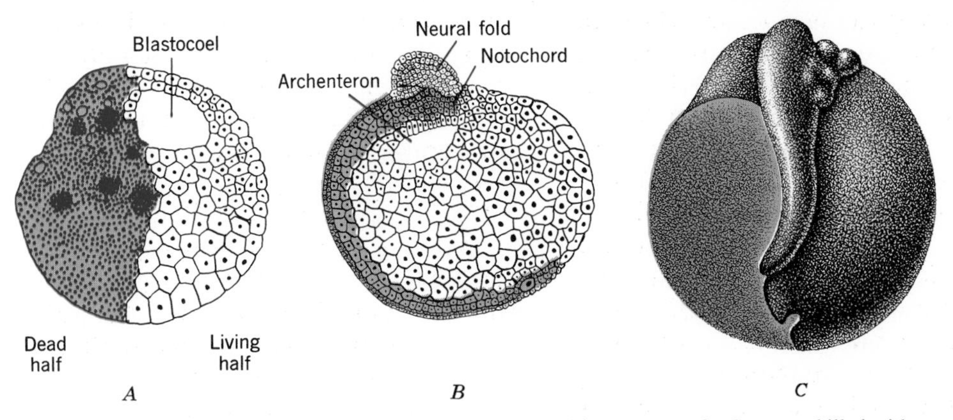


**Fig. 16.1** Roux's experiment in which one of the first two blastomeres of a frog was killed with a hot needle and a half embryo developed. *A*. Dead cell material and living part with a number of cells all derived by cell division from one of the first two blastomeres. *B*. An early neurula in which the dead cell material has been partly cast off but only part of the embryo is developing normally. *C*. Abnormal embryo in later stage of development which Roux described as a "half embryo."

formation was postulated in a more refined form than the preformation theory discussed a century before when miniature organisms were believed to be carried in germ cells. All determiners available to the organism were assumed to be present in the totipotent zygote, but according to the Roux-Weismann theory they segregated to

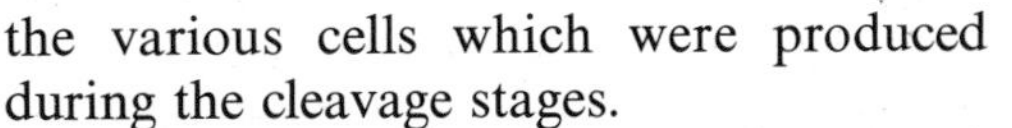

the various cells which were produced during the cleavage stages.

Observations by Theodor Boveri in the same period added further support to the Roux-Weismann theory. Boveri followed the cell lineage (Fig. 16.2) of the round worm, *Ascaris megalocephala* (now *Parascaris equorum*), from the zygote through

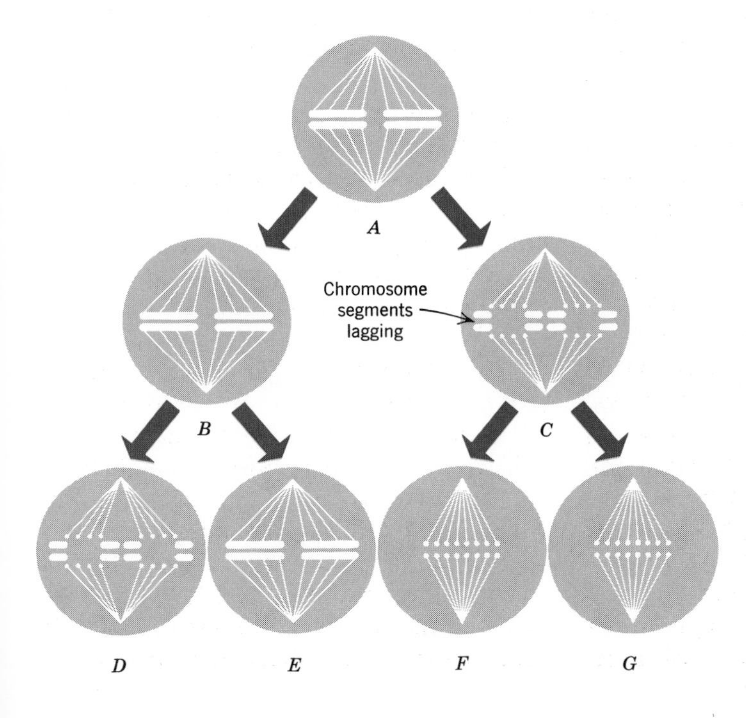


**Fig. 16.2** Diagram of first two cleavage divisions of *Parascaris equorum* (variety univalens), showing chromatin diminution. *A*, zygote; *B*, first stem cell; *C*, cell in second cleavage undergoing diminution; *D*, cell resulting from division of first stem cell, undergoing diminution; *E*, second stem cell; *F, G*, diminished cells dividing to form somatic cells. (All cells are drawn in early anaphase with chromosomes in the same plane. Equatorial plates are actually circular and the divisions occur at right angles to each other. Only 8 small chromosomes are shown in diagrams of the diminished cells. Actually there are many more, e.g., 36 in one variety.) (After Boveri.)

the early cleavage stages. He discovered that when the zygote (*A*) divided, the two long chromosomes each underwent a duplication. The two cells (*B* and *C*) resulting from that division behaved differently in the second cleavage stage. The two long chromosomes formed normal metaphases in the two cells (*B* and *C*) but in one cell (*C*) the long chromosomes became fragmented and only the middle sections of each chromosome were attached to the spindle. At anaphase, the terminal parts were left in the center of the spindle, and the central portion became divided into many small units, each with a spindle fiber attachment. These small chromosomes moved to the two poles and remained independent in further divisions. The cells that had undergone a loss of the terminal ends of the chromosomes (that is, those in which chromatin diminution had occurred) were smaller than the undiminished cells. They continued to divide by mitosis and produced only somatic cells.

In the other cell (*B*) of the two-cell stage, called the stem cell, the long chromosomes divided, but the two daughter cells (*D* and *E*) had different potentialities. Cell *D* underwent chromatin diminution like *C* and gave rise to two somatic cells, which continued to produce somatic cells. The other (*E*) divided like the zygote (*A*) and the first stem cell (*B*), retaining all the chromatin. This process continued through the fifth cleavage, the 32-cell stage. At that time, the stem cell took its place in the interior of the cell mass and continued to divide by ordinary mitotic division, producing other undiminished cells. At the appropriate time in embryonic development, when the gonad was formed, these germ line cells became the reproductive cells of the new individual. The obvious conclusion was that all the chromatin was necessary for germ cells that reproduced the entire organism but not all was necessary for the somatic cells.

These observations constituted a demonstration of the Roux-Weismann theory. Only cells with the original undiminished chromosome arrangement were considered to be totipotent and capable of producing the germ cells and an entire new organism. A systematic sorting of preformed determiners was postulated as providing each cell with the appropriate equipment for the task it was destined to accomplish. The speculation was that most or all cells became different from one another, but the differences were usually not visible. It was ironic that this early observation proved to be an exceptional case. Very few other organisms were found to follow this pattern, but in Ascaris this is a sound observation which can be repeated. The Roux-Weismann hypothesis lost ground when it could not be supported from cell-lineage experiments of this kind on other organisms.

The second early theory about differentiation, also promoted in the second half of the nineteenth century, was based on the theme of epigenesis, another carry-over from an earlier period in the history of biology. According to this view, which is in contrast to the idea of preformation, the organism developed step by step from simple, relatively undifferentiated material originating in the zygote. Although the zygote was more or less organized, and the same genes with the same potential functions were present in all cells, development was visualized as a gradual building process through which complex and accurately timed interactions occurred progressively from the egg to the fully developed animal or plant.

Support for this theory came from observations of regeneration in animals and plants. A small section of the body of a flatworm (for example, Planaria) or a single cell of a carrot will regenerate the whole organism if placed in a suitable environment. Evidently, some entire ani-

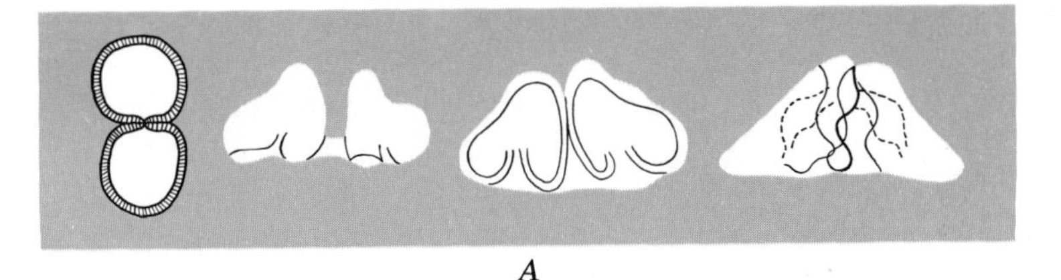

A

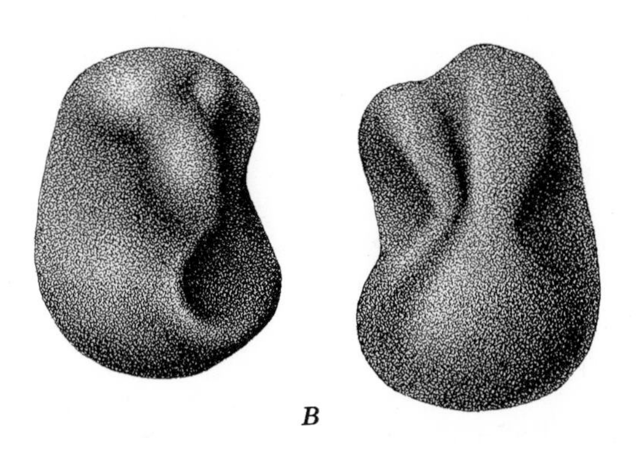

B

**Fig. 16.3** Diagrams of experiments in which the first two blastomeres of sea urchins and frogs, respectively, were separated but not killed. Two whole embryos resulted from each experiment. *A*, Driesch's experiment on sea urchins. *B*, Two whole frog embryos resulting from an experiment similar to the one performed by Roux except that the two blastomeres were carefully separated. Both developed into whole embryos.

mals or plants are totipotent, even in their mature states (however, not all animal and plant tissues can regenerate whole organisms). Continued observations of regeneration fostered more interest in studies of the basic mechanism of differentiation.

Another series of experiments, similar to those of Roux, was carried out on sea urchin embryos by Hans Driesch (Fig. 16.3*A*). Instead of killing one of the blastomeres in the two-cell stage as Roux had done, Driesch separated the two cells with a fine needle. He found that each cell formed a whole embryo and not a half embryo. Therefore, he concluded that all determiners must be present in each cell. Similar results were obtained from cells as late as the fourth division, showing that all determiners were still present.

Driesch next placed a heavy cover glass on sea urchin embryos in the eight-cell stage and forced the cells, which usually divide at right angles to each other, to divide in one plane. This procedure altered the usual pattern of early embryology and, according to the Roux-Weismann theory, should have produced abnormal segregation of determiners in the presumptive ectoderm and endoderm cells. The misplaced cells, however, oriented themselves and formed normal endoderm and ectoderm in spite of the earlier displacement. Similar results were obtained by O. Hertwig, who used frog eggs. These experiments showed that the Roux-Weismann theory did not hold in sea urchin or even in frog development, where it had first been established.

Roux's experiment on the frog egg was later repeated with technical refinements and different results were obtained. Instead of killing one of the two blastomeres and allowing the dead cell to remain intact, the cells were carefully separated with fine needles. This time a whole embryo (Fig. 16.3*B*) was formed from a single blastomere in the frog as in the sea urchin. Apparently, the presence of the dead cell in the earlier experiment had influenced the living cells to produce only half an embryo.

Similar experiments have now been carried out in rabbits. By a delicate tech-

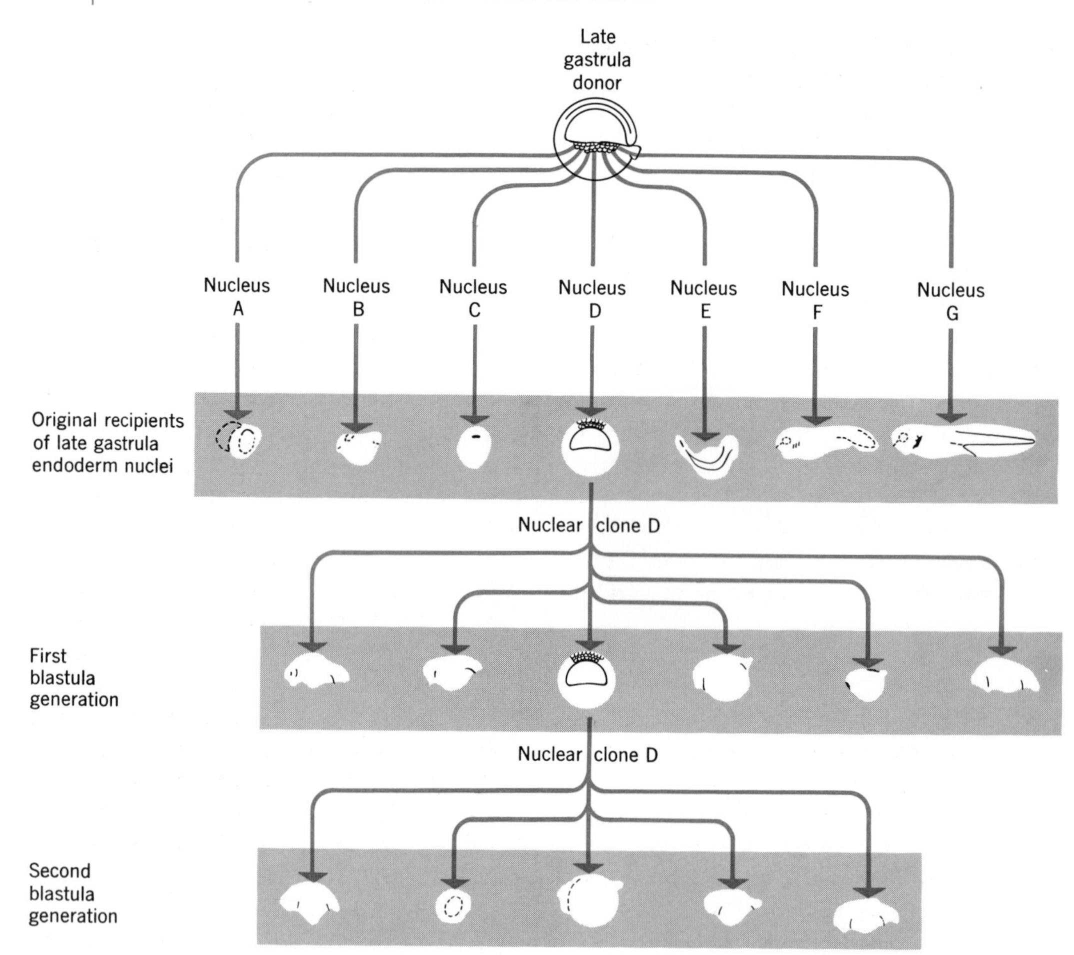


**Fig. 16.4** Diagram illustrating serial transplantation of endoderm nuclei. Donor nuclei were taken from the presumptive anterior midgut region of the late gastrula and transferred to enucleated eggs. They promoted the various types of development shown for the "original recipients" in the diagram. (From T. J. King and R. E. Briggs, *Cold Spring Harbor Symposia* 21: 271, 1956.)

nique, fertilized eggs were recovered from the oviduct of a female rabbit. When two blastomeres were present, following first cleavage, one cell was removed. The remaining cell was transplanted into another properly prepared rabbit and a perfectly normal embryo was developed. Thus, a single blastomere of a mammal as well as of amphibians and echinoderms had the ability to produce a whole embryo.

R. E. Briggs and T. J. King developed a critical technique for demonstrating totipotency of frog cells at different stages of development (Fig. 16.4). They succeeded in removing the nuclei from frog eggs with a micropipette and replacing them with nuclei from cells in blastula and gastrula stages. Studies of the development of the eggs with replaced nuclei showed that the eggs that were nucleated from the cells of the blastula developed into complete embryos. When the nuclei were taken from the gastrula, comparable results were obtained. These experiments showed that the nuclei retained their capacity to direct the development of the whole organism at least through the gastrula stage. The theory that differentiation is the result of early segregation of nuclear contents could not be supported.

Abundant experimental evidence now favors the epigenetic theory as a general explanation of differentiation. New evidence for regulator genes and operons (Chapter 15) has stimulated active investigation of the mechanics of the process. Gene systems have been discovered by which enzymatic activity may be turned on or off by combination effects of operators or repressors of particular cell activities. This gives hope for an eventual firm definition of how genes affect early differentiation.

*Determination*

In studying the interrelationship of development and genetics, it soon becomes evident that all fertilized eggs do not develop in the same way. The fixation of the fate of a part of an embryo, called determination, occurs at different times in different kinds of eggs. In so-called "mosaic" eggs, determination occurs at an early stage but in "regulative" eggs flexibility exists until later stages of development. The distinction between mosaic and regulative eggs and embryos is not hard and fast; all gradations exist between eggs with predetermined regions and those that are indeterminate even in later stages. Some areas of the same embryo may be determined at a time while other areas are still undetermined.

Mosaic eggs of Ascidians, for example, are already separated into organ-forming substances or areas before fertilization. Particular parts of these eggs are destined to give rise to specific organs. Furthermore, the developmental patterns are determined at an early stage in these eggs and cannot be altered experimentally. Mosaic eggs of

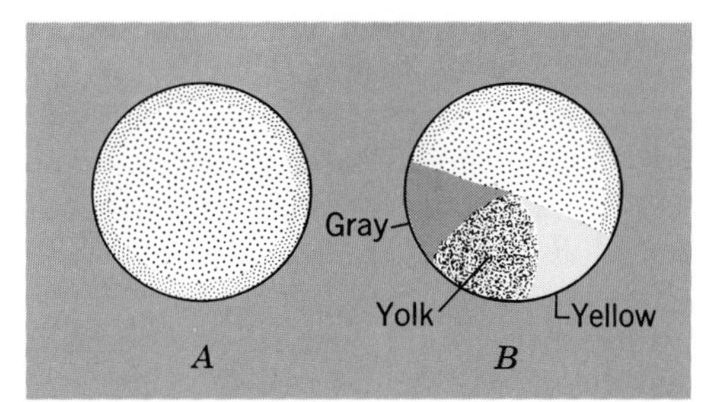


**Fig. 16.5** Diagram of eggs of the tunicate Styela. *A*, unfertilized; *B*, fertilized. The stipling in *A* represents yellow pigment, which is uniformly distributed in the outer cytoplasm of the unfertilized egg. Following fertilization, the yellow pigment becomes concentrated in a crescent-shaped area. A gray crescent and a yolk body are also formed through cytoplasmic streaming. (After E. G. Conklin.)

some organisms have regional differences in the cytoplasm characterized by concentrations of pigment, mitochondria, or yolk. Visible differences enable the investigator to identify the material originating in a given area of the egg as it is distributed in the young embryo during cleavage.

The unfertilized egg of the tunicate Styela, which was investigated by E. G. Conklin, has yellow pigment granules uniformly distributed in the outer layer of cytoplasm. Cytoplasmic streaming occurs after fertilization, and the yellow pigment becomes concentrated in a crescent-shaped area, as shown in Fig. 16.5. This region later gives rise to the posterior surface of the organism and the mesodermal part of the tail is derived from the cells that develop from this material. A gray crescent formed on the opposite side of the yellow crescent becomes the anterior surface of the organism. The notochord and neural plate come from the cells derived from the gray crescent area. The vegetal part of the egg accumulates yolk granules, which later become a part of the endoderm cells. Other parts of the egg that are not included in the yellow crescent, gray crescent, or yolk give rise to the epidermis.

Eggs of the newt, on the other hand, are

regulative or indeterminate at the initial stages, and the embryos become organized only as development proceeds. These embryos can be altered experimentally in the early stages without affecting the end product, but alterations at later stages result in permanent abnormalities. That is, once into the pattern-following stage, groups of cells follow a definite sequence in their development. After determination, the doors are closed and the potential of the cells is restricted.

Hans Spemann, a German experimental embryologist, demonstrated by transplantation experiments on the newt that the fate of most embryonic regions is not determined before a certain stage in gastrulation. When a piece of the gastrula that would ordinarily become a part of the neural tube was removed from one embryo and grafted into another embryo in a region that could form the external gill, the grafted cells turned into gill cells. Therefore, their fate had not been determined when the transplant was made. In the same manner, a piece from the area that ordinarily produced skin was grafted into the presumptive nerve tube of a second embryo and became a part of the spinal cord. Again, the cells were not determined at the time of the transplant. Up to this stage in gastrulation, the cells differentiated along with their neighboring cells according to their location.

The plasticity of most areas of the newt embryo was lost during gastrulation. When Spemann grafted parts of embryos that were past the stage of gastrulation into other embryos, the parts continued to develop as they would have done in their original location and not in harmony with the cells in their new surroundings. Presumptive eye material, for example, formed an eye whether it was in the proper location for an eye or in some other place in the body.

On the basis of these now classical experiments, Spemann developed the organizer theory of determination. This theory, which states that a part of an embryo directs an adjacent part or parts in differentiation, is currently accepted by many experimental biologists. Spemann and Mangold in 1924 provided critical experimental support for this theory from investigations on embryos of two differently colored species of newts. A small piece of tissue was removed from the dorsal lip of the blastopore of the dark-colored donor species and transplanted to another region in a gastrula of the light-colored host species (Fig. 16.6). The donor cells exerted a profound influence in the host. Host cells which ordinarily would have produced epidermis now produced neural folds. A secondary embryo was eventually formed with nerve tube and other structures observed in normal embryos. The dorsal lip region was thus shown to be the organizer which influenced other cells to differentiate and form an embryo.

*Prepatterns and Organization*

C. Stern has investigated differentiation and organization in Drosophila at various stages of development. He used experimentally produced gynandromorphs or sex mosaics to study the patterns of bristle formation and other morphological characters in the flies. A fundamental difference was detected between certain tissues while the bristles in these areas were being formed. Some predisposing factor had already exerted its influence, and the action of specific genes was restricted to local areas of the body. Conspicuous gynandromorphs (such as those cited in Chapter 4) contain large sections of male and female tissue resulting from division irregularities in early cleavage stages. For example, when one X chromosome of a dividing 2X chromosome zygote remained in the center of the spindle in the first cleavage, a gynandromorph was produced, with one half

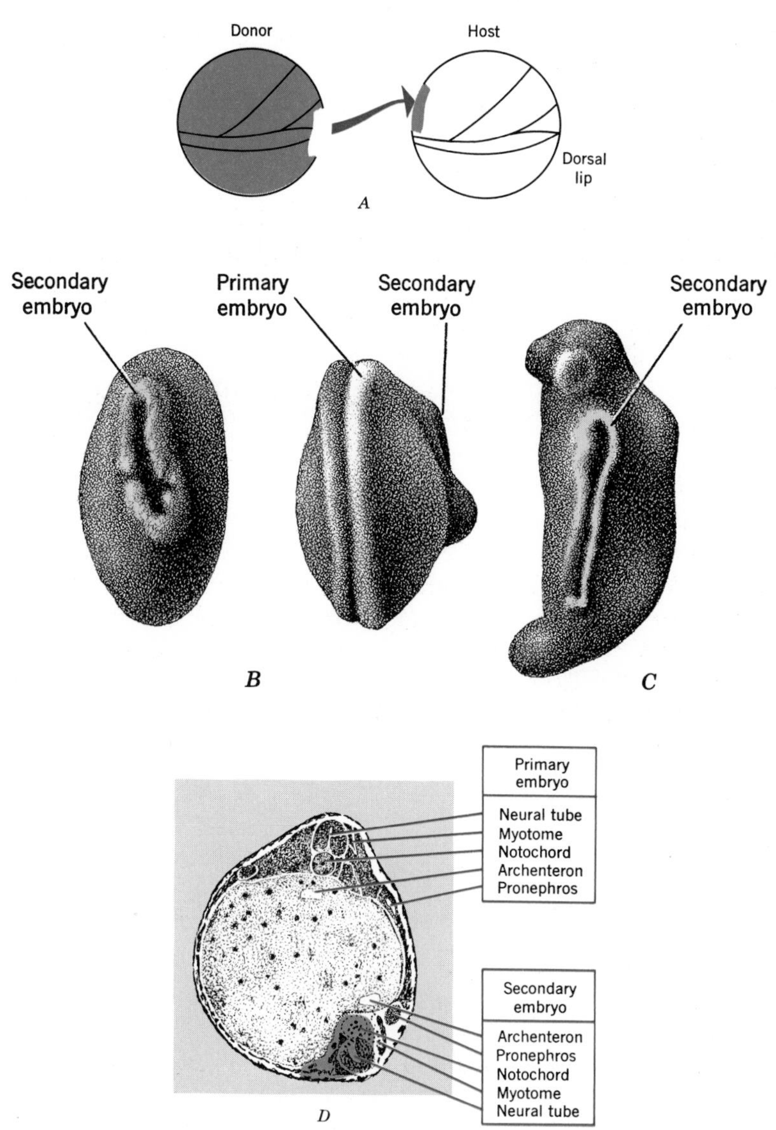


**Fig. 16.6** Experiment of Spemann and Mangold in which a section of the dorsal lip of the blastopore from a frog embryo was transplanted to an embryo of another species. *A*. Diagram of the transplantation. *B*. Two different views of neurula stage showing secondary embryos. *C*. An older stage showing secondary embryo. *D*. Cross section of older stage showing internal structures of primary and secondary embryos. (Data from Spemann and Mangold, 1924.)

composed of male tissue and the other half of female tissue. Similar irregularities in later divisions producd smaller sections of male tissue in an individual predominantly female. When sex-linked recessive genes, such as *y* for yellow body, were made heterozygous, the wild-type allele would sometimes be in the lagging chromosome. Male tissue originating from cells with single *y* genes would express the yellow phenotype and could be readily distinguished from the female parts. Patches of

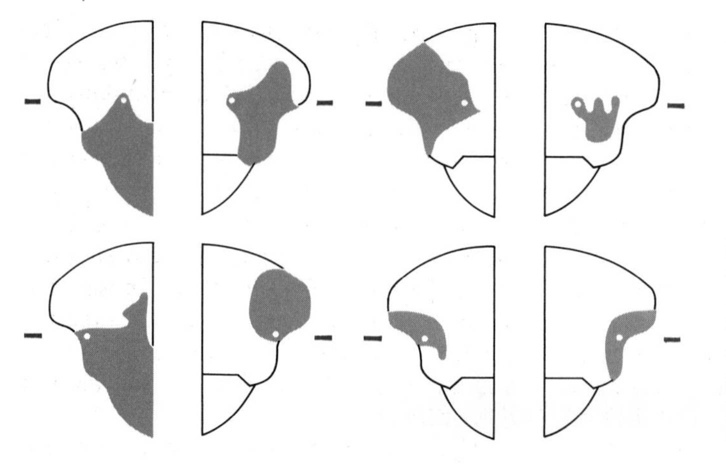

**Fig. 16.7** Half thoraxes of eight different mosaic individuals of *Drosophila.* Black regions, achaete; white regions, nonachaete. — indicates absence of the anterior dorsocentral (*upper row*) or of the posterior supra-alar bristle (*lower row*). (After Stern.)

tissue of one sex could be detected in an individual predominantly of the other sex (Fig. 16.7). Analysis of the patch provided information concerning the events that had occurred during production of the irregularity. If the bristles in the patch were gray, the conclusion would be that genic action responsible for color had occurred early and predetermined the character of the bristle. If, on the other hand, the bristles were yellow, the gene would be assumed to have acted after the $y^+$ chromosome was eliminated. Bristles in the arrangements that were analyzed were yellow, indicating that the $y$ gene was active when the bristle was being formed.

The legs of the flies have characteristic patterns of bristles and other structures. An investigator can distinguish the first, second, and third legs in the two sexes by structure and bristle pattern. One conspicuous sex difference is observed on the first tarsal segment of the front leg (Fig. 16.8). The male (*A*) has a ten-toothed sex comb, but the female (*B*) has no comparable structure. When sex mosaics occur in this part of the leg, the relation between misplaced patches and predetermined regions can be observed. When a male spot was inserted into a female tarsus, a small sex comb was produced in that spot. When a female spot was inserted into a male leg, in the region of the sex comb, a gap occurred in the otherwise normal sex comb. Apparently the inserts were unable to respond to regional differences. It was concluded that some genes respond to one and some to another background or pattern. Regional differences in the tissue thus influence the action and final product of certain genes.

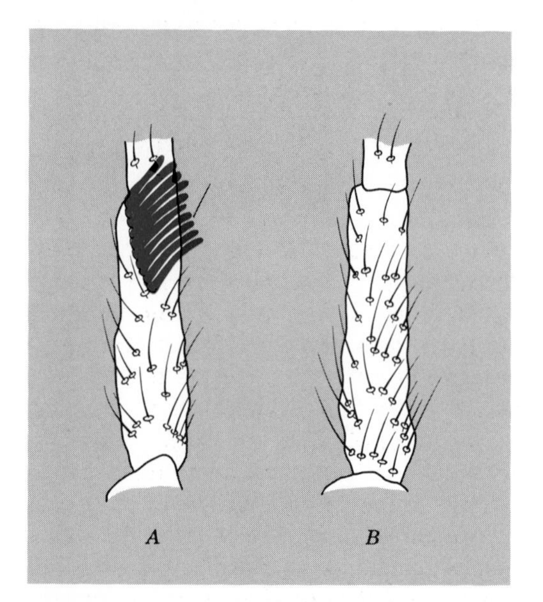


**Fig. 16.8** First tarsal segment of male and female *D. melanogaster. A*, male tarsus showing sex comb; *B*, female tarsus with no sex comb. (After A. Hannah-Alava.)

Extensive analyses by means of gynandric mosaics have shown that the first tarsal segment of males and females possesses a specific region, a prepattern with developmental potencies for formation of a sex comb. The female does not differentiate a comb because the 2X cells do not respond, but the 1X cells of the male respond and produce a comb. Modified combs can be developed in the usual place for the sex comb, and combs can be developed experimentally in other regions and on legs other than the first leg. Other parts of the body also have regional differences. Areas of the thorax show evidence of prepatterns similar to those in the legs. Observed prepatterns help confirm that genes carried in all cells may respond distinctively in restricted regions of the body, or even in particular single cells such as those that produce single bristles. These observations have added significantly to the understanding of genetic influence on differentiation during later stages of development.

If we see the fundamental organization of the individual as a prepattern, we gain an insight into how selective control is imposed on the actions of the genes. A two-way response mechanism commonly exists between prepatterns and genes within specific areas where differentiation occurs. A particular gene may respond only (or uniquely) to a specific regional background. Therefore, all genes may be present in a cell, although only a few are active under existing conditions. On the other hand, many prepatterns may be incorporated in each tissue of an individual, but they remain dormant until certain genes stimulate activity and bring about differentiation.

The concept of prepattern implies that one gene (or its product) responds to one specific regional background and other genes respond to other regional characteristics. Stern, using this concept, has compared the genes that operate in the differentiation process of developing organisms to groups of prospectors working in different regions of a country. The groups would be alike in consisting of men looking for coal, gold, uranium, and so on. In some regions, only the coal prospectors would respond to coal deposits, at other places the gold prospectors would find ore. Each response would depend on the prepattern of geological differentiation. Subsequent man-made differentiation would take the form of specific structures designed by mining engineers to develop the natural prepatterns.

The nature and origin of prepatterns are problems for further experimentation. This concept does not exclude the possibility that genes determine the origin of prepatterns or alter existing prepatterns. In fact, genes are as necessary to indicating the prepattern as they are elsewhere in the developing system. Continuous chains of interactions are assumed to be essential to every aspect of the dynamic developmental process. The genotype is basically responsible for the whole development. Specific genes or their products must activate each consecutive step. Intermediate products between genes and characters eventually may be found to provide a chemical or physical basis for the prepattern and other organizational steps.

### *Probable Genetic Mechanisms*

Although precise genetic mechanisms have not yet been associated with the differentiation, determination, and growth-regulation aspects of embryology, reported experimental results and theoretical models may eventually lead to an understanding of the intricate processes involved. Several hundred different genes have now been found to influence morphogenesis in Drosophila, and it is expected that further studies will show how these or other genes affect patterns of normal development. Specific genes have been identified in *Dro-*

*sophila melanogaster* which control oögenesis. Some of these same genes influence growth rates. Size and shape of organisms and parts of organisms are determined during cell reproduction. When genetic or environmental influences encourage the abnormal growth of cells, tumors and cancer may occur.

The controlling mechanism for normal as well as abnormal cell division has been the object of many investigations over the years. Factors in the cytoplasm have long been considered to influence cell differentiation and other developmental processes. The theory of differentiation promoted by Driesch and Hertwig depended on cytoplasmic determiners. More recently, the puffs recognized in salivary gland chromosomes of Drosophila (Chapter 15) were shown by Beermann and others to be controlled by a hormone, ecdysone, which enters the cell nucleus through the cytoplasm. Cytoplasmic bodies in *Paramecium aurelia* were found by Sonneborn to determine the mating type and other phenotypic characteristics of the organism.

The most provocative suggestion of a mechanism that might explain how genes become active at different times in development is based on the operon model (Chapter 15) formulated by Jacob and Monod from experiments on *Escherichia coli.* So-called effectors are produced in the cell by metabolic activities or overall control mechanisms in the organism. The effectors initiate the activity of an operator gene, which in turn controls one or more structural genes. This model is well established in procaryotes, particularly in bacteria, but it is weak in higher organisms. Nevertheless, it is suggestive of a mechanism that could provide an answer to an important general question about the development process: how can certain genes, which are part of the complement always present in nearly all cells of the organism, become active and produce their end results only at particular times?

## GENETICS AND BEHAVIOR

The behavior of an animal is the sum total of that animal's reactions to its environment. A student of behavior is usually concerned with observable or otherwise detectable alterations in movement or posture. Although invisible processes (such as glandular secretions) may also be factors, the student generally must base his conclusions on reactions of an animal that can be perceived as movements, either of the whole or some part thereof. A deer may elevate its head and prick its ears in response to a strange sound. When a man approaches or another disturbing change occurs in the environment, the deer may jump and run. A bird may erect its feathers, raise its wings, and fly in response to particular stimuli. On the other hand, an animal that has been moving about may become motionless in response to an environmental change. All of these actions are classified as behavior.

Animal-behavior genetics is a young field of biology characterized at present by what seem to be arbitrary interests in a variety of more or less unrelated phenotypes. The one thing in common among these phenotypes is that each is under at least partial genetic control. A theoretical basis or guideline is needed to specify which phenotypes are of fundamental importance and which are not. This basis can well be the relationship of the trait with the environment in which it has developed. An evolutionary significance of the traits is thus implied. Those behavior patterns, for example, that have survived and are now available for observation and analysis are the patterns that have been selected out and refined by the forces of the environment. The genetic mechanism of some behavior traits, like those cited above, may be comparatively simple, depending on a few genes and responding to a limited range of environmental stimuli.

More complex patterns of behavior are associated with communication among members of the same species. All animals communicate to some extent, often relying upon chemical, optical, and mechanical devices. The simplest and most universal type of communication is that associated with mating. Individuals must be able to inform one another that they belong to the same species. They must also indicate the sex to which they belong and when they are ready to mate. Members of highly socialized groups indicate to one another the status they hold in the social hierarchy.

Chemical communication is the most primitive and the most widely used form of information exchange, especially among lower organisms. Behavior studies are now being conducted on the bacterium *Escherichia coli*. Some bacteria will move toward and some away from certain chemicals. Strains can be developed that behave differently. Protozoa and bacteria of opposite sexes or mating types, but of the same species, attract each other through chemical means. Chemical attractants also occur widely among higher animals. Optical communication through bright colors and mating rituals is particularly noted among birds. Sounds are conspicuous parts of the mating ceremony of some birds, insects, spiders, and many other animals. Not only do members of the same species communicate with each other, but members of different species may communicate. Dolphins, for example, communicate with other aquatic mammals.

The genetic aspects of such observable elements of behavior are believed to be determined basically by the same mechanisms as the more tangible physical traits that Mendel and others have described. Genetic bases for behavior patterns in some animals have been indicated by observations and experimental procedures.

### *Communication Among Bees*

The complex social patterns of some Hymenoptera such as honeybees make use of chemical, optical, and sound signals. The effectiveness of the activities of bees in and around a hive as well as in foraging areas depends on the exchange of information among the individual bees. Both inheritance and learning are known to be involved in this case, and indeed these two elements are generally interwoven in the development of behavior patterns. Building of honey combs, for example, is genetically patterned and does not require much, if any, learning or preparatory experience on the part of individual bees. Communication symbols for distance and direction of food-source material, on the other hand, are mostly learned by individuals. Even so, in some groups, this behavior is so stereotyped and well established as to be as usable as morphological characteristics for distinguishing species. Honeybees have developed an elaborate system of communication associated with foraging for food and searching for a new nest.

Bees are among the many organisms provided with built in biological clocks. They fly to the flowers at the time of day when the nectar is flowing and pollen is available. Bees also can recognize the areas where they have been by referring to observable land marks. In the same way that they learn to recognize the location of the hive, they learn to identify feeding areas and will return to the same vicinity day after day as long as the food supply is plentiful. Not only do they know the directions themselves, but individuals recruit other foragers and direct them to the food source that they have found. Information

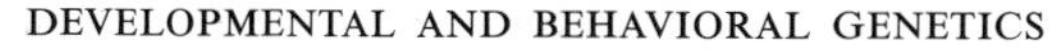

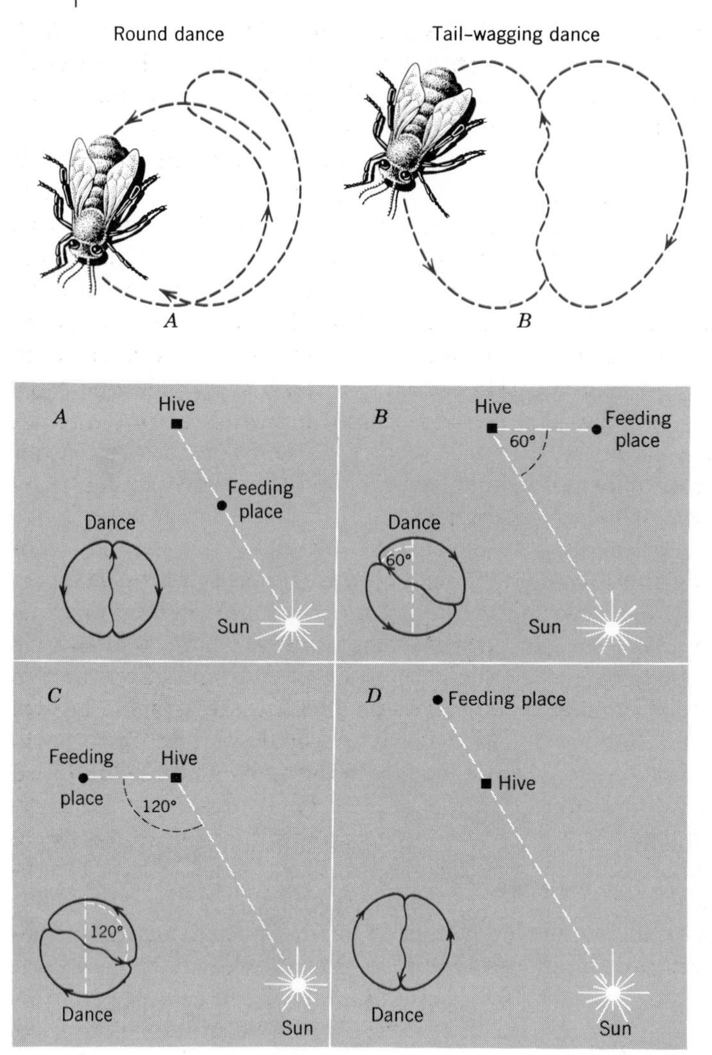


**Fig. 16.9** The dances of honeybees. *A*, the round dance performed when food is within 100 yards from the hive. *B*, the waggle dance performed when food is a greater distance from the hive. In the lower part of the diagram the relation between the angle of the dance and the vertical with the angle between sun and food is illustrated. (Data from Karl von Frisch and Martin Lindauer.)

for foragers, according to the findings of Karl von Frisch and Martin Lindauer, is transmitted through a particular kind of dance which is performed on the vertical face of a honey comb inside the hive.

If the source of food is near the hive, that is, less than 100 yards, the round dance (Fig. 16.9*A*) is performed. This dance simply stimulates other bees to forage in the near vicinity. Information identifying the location is transmitted by odors carried from the flowers on the dancer's body.

If the distance from the hive is greater than about 100 yards, the forager performs a waggle or tail-wagging dance (Fig. 16.9*B*) by which she indicates distance and direction of the food source. This dance takes the form of a figure eight. The number of turns of the dance in a given time indicates the distance of the feeding place. The straight part of the dance shows the direction of the food source with respect to the direction of the sun. As the particular food supply is depleted or if it is low, the vigor of the waggle dance is decreased. Foragers that have found the better food sources will thus attract the attention of more of the foragers in the hive. In other words, the best sources are the most dramatically advertised and subsequently will be visited by the greatest numbers of bees.

On the perpendicular honeycomb inside the hive where the dance is performed, the returned forager cannot see the sun. Von Frisch has shown that the dancer under these conditions relies on the direction of gravity. The straight portion of the dance is oriented at the same angle with reference to the force of gravity as the angle through which the dancer has flown with respect to the sun during the flight from the hive to the feeding place. If a dancer heads directly upward during the straight part of the dance, the feeding place is in the same direction as the sun. If the straight run points down, the feeding place is directly away from the sun. An angle of 60 degrees to the left of the vertical line indicates that the feeding place is 60 degrees to the left of the sun. If the straight run is pointed 120 degrees to the right of the vertical line, the feeding place is 120 degrees to the right of the position of the sun. This elaborate behavior pattern is a species characteristic, but the movements of the dance are learned by each new generation of foragers.

### *Ontogeny, Phylogeny, and Heritability of Behavior Patterns*

Questions that are logically asked about a pattern of behavior are much the same as those likely to be asked about a morphological feature. How does the pattern develop in the individual? How did it evolve in the population? How and to what extent is it inherited and to what extent is it learned by the individual?

In general, behavior traits develop in the individual through the interaction of hereditary and environmental influences and, presumably, through the same basic mechanisms as those associated with morphological traits. The degree to which certain traits depend on heredity or environment varies greatly within and among animal groups.

In the honeybees, some behavior traits such as comb building are immediately dependent on heredity. Other traits, even though they involve structures which are basically inherited, must be learned by each individual. For example, the dance through which information is given about distance and direction to a feeding area requires wings and other body structures that are strongly heritable, but the movements must be learned independently by each dancer.

In the evolution of social bees, communication systems have developed, presumably through natural selection of structural and functional adaptations. Bees have a unique system of communication. No form of communication existing elsewhere in the animal kingdom is comparable to the highly effective and well-developed dance of the highly social bees. It apparently evolved through progressive stages from primitive Hymenoptera to the honeybees (*Apis mellifera*).

Although the basic communication system is the same for all *Apis mellifera* bees, different "dialects" have developed in different races. Members of an Italian race, for example, have slower dancing rhythm than those of an Austrian race. When bees of these two races are mixed they misunderstand each other. An Austrian bee receiving information from an Italian bee about food 100 meters from the nest will fly 120 meters because she interprets the "Italian dialect" on the basis of her Austrian training. Conversely, the Italian bee will fly 80 meters when given the information for 100 meters by the Austrian forager. Each of several geographic races has its own "dialect." Communication systems of three different species of Apis were compared by Lindauer. He observed wider

**Fig. 16.10** Preference of bees for alfalfa pollen. (Courtesy of William P. Nye.)

differences in behavior as well as in structural characteristics between the species than occur between races of the same species.

W. P. Nye and O. Mackensen have shown that preference by honeybees for alfalfa (*Medicago sativa;* Fig. 16.10) pollen depends to a large extent on genetic determiners that respond to selection and breeding. These investigators observed that some colonies of honeybees collected a much higher percentage of alfalfa pollen than did others. Separate inbred lines were developed from colonies showing a high and a low preference for collection of alfalfa pollen. At the end of the fourth generation of inbreeding, the high and low lines had become completely separate, as illustrated in Fig. 16.11. Subsequent hybridization of the bees from the two lines produced bees that were intermediate between the high and low lines. The fact that the preference for alfalfa pollen can be changed markedly by selection, and that this trait follows a predictable pattern based on Mendelian inheritance, indicates that preference for alfalfa pollen has a high hereditary component.

### *Role of Heredity in Behavior in Higher Animals*

Behavior as such is not inherited since behavior includes the complex activity of the whole organism both during development and in the adult stage. All that is biologically transmitted from parents to

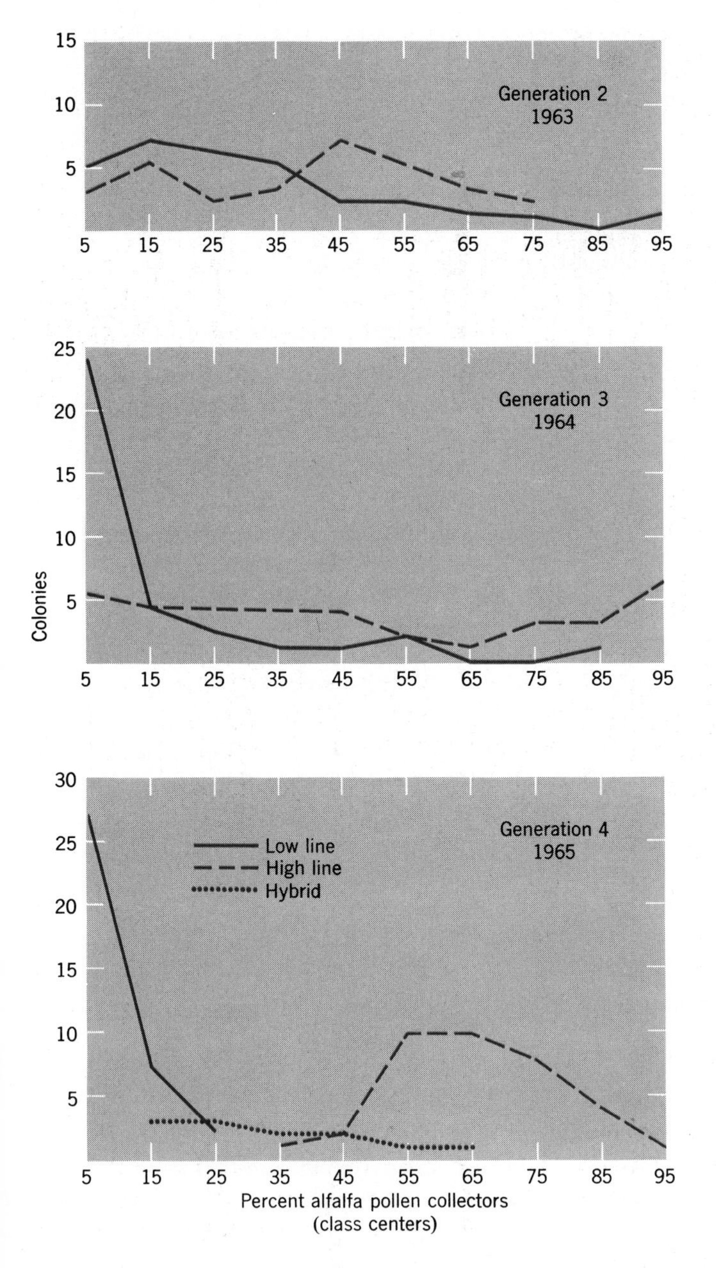


**Fig. 16.11** Distribution of the percentage of alfalfa pollen collectors in honeybee colonies of high and low alfalfa pollen preference lines for 3 generations, and in hybrid colonies. (Courtesy of William P. Nye.)

offspring is the DNA contained in the eggs and sperm. This genetic material controls the synthesis of proteins, and the basic genetic processes are quite different from the end product or the individual that develops from a zygote.

The activities of the animal body, however, are coordinated by the nervous system and the hormonal system. Both of these systems are ultimately dependent on genetic determiners. Structural features of the brain, nerve cord, and nerves, as well as the sensitivity and efficiency of these body parts, are under genetic control. Likewise, the glands that produce hormones for chemical coordination are developed under specifications of genetic material. Since most behavior is influenced by either nervous or hormonal control, most of it is thus at least indirectly dependent on heredity.

In higher animals, hormones are implicated in initiating and sustaining the reproductive drive. Mating behavior is made possible by the presence of hormones at a particular time and place in the animal body. An animal's temperament or mood may be greatly influenced by the particular hormones which are circulating in his blood at a given time. In some animals, reproductive behavior is seasonal. At a particular time of the year, the activity of certain hormones renders the animal sensitive to certain stimuli from the environment. At another time, the same stimuli may occur with no response on the part of the animal.

A fundamental question in the study of the relation between genes and behavior is whether heredity directly affects behavior in any way, or merely sets the stage on which behavioral patterns may be molded by environmental factors. Biologists and psychologists have taken somewhat different views on this issue in past decades, but now both groups recognize that heredity and environment are important factors. The question now can and should be approached by recognizing the sequential levels of organization in the developing animal. We know that environmental factors are interwoven with inheritance mechanisms at every point in the developmental process. The problem now is to disentangle the two and evaluate their relative importance in specific situations.

### *Developmental Interactions in Dogs*

Dogs are like human beings in expressing great genetic variability. Some have club feet, others hemophilia, and many show variations in eye color. Any number of hereditary structural differences can be detected among dogs. The legs of dogs of different breeds vary from the short extremities of the dachshund to the long, graceful limbs of the greyhound. Other quantitative variations are also well recognized. Dogs range in overall size from the Chihuahua, which averages 4 pounds, to the Saint Bernard at 160 pounds, bulldogs have undershot jaws and foreshortened heads whereas borzois have narrow, long heads. Tails may vary from a tight curl to a sickle-shaped structure. Manifold variations are observed in length and texture of hair. The extreme in this respect is the Mexican hairless, which is bald.

Also like human beings, dogs have personality differences. Some are timid and others are confident; some are gentle and others are aggressive. Those that are trained early in life become friendly and understanding companions of man whereas others of the same breed that are not given intimate care while young may become fearful or even hostile toward people.

J. P. Scott and J. L. Fuller have made extensive observations on genetic and environmental factors involved in the building of behavior patterns in dogs. In recent work, daily observations were initiated with newborn puppies of several diverse breeds and were continued until the dogs were 16 weeks of age. Every effort was made to observe the earliest manifestations of hereditary differences and to detect the effects of heredity before they became contaminated by experience. During the first few days after birth, of course, there was very little behavior to observe in the pups.

As soon as recognizable behavior began to be apparent, interaction between hereditary and environmental influences was already present. The puppies changed markedly in reactions from day to day even though the genes in the chromosomes remain essentially constant through the entire life of an animal. Different determiners evidently were becoming active at the different developmental stages. Furthermore, the genes were acting on a very different animal at birth as compared with the same individual a few weeks later.

The results obtained by Scott and Fuller were quite unexpected and scientifically significant. During the very early stages of development there was so little behavior to be observed that genetic differences had few opportunities to be expressed. When behavior patterns did appear, however, the evidence supported the conclusion that genetically determined differences in behavior do not appear all at once early in development, to be modified by later experience. Instead, they are themselves *developed* under the influence of environmental factors. Some behavioral patterns, with genetic bases, may appear in full flower only after the dog has matured and then only if it has been exposed to certain environmental experiences. The Scott and Fuller studies on dogs showed that heredity is an important factor in behavior but that details of specific patterns depend more or less on experience. Furthermore, they demonstrated that genetic differences in behavior can be measured and compared as validly as can hereditary physical differences. A lack of correlation was observed between behavior and "type" within each breed.

Particular breeds of dogs have acquired, through long periods of selection, special characteristics related to the behavioral tasks for which the breed has been developed by man. Very few behavioral traits, however, were found to breed true as would be expected if they were controlled by homozygous pairs of genes. In a few cases, selection has apparently produced traits for which particular breeds are nearly homozygous. Fighting behavior, for example, is almost nonexistent in the hound, but in the terrier this characteristic is well developed. Such instances of near homozygosity are rare.

Dog breeds generally have retained a great deal of genetic flexibility. This was borne out by the studies of Scott and Fuller in which 50 traits were examined in five pure breeds of dogs. Almost all of the traits were significantly different between breeds. Because these traits were selected to represent all important behavioral tests, it is obvious that breed differences in behavior are both real and important. With the great variability available in dogs, it is possible to modify a breed markedly within a few generations of selection. Through cross breeding, entirely new and unique combinations of behavioral traits can be created and studied.

### *Heredity and Human Behavior*

Human beings also show great variation in temperament and behavior as well as in structural features. Attempts to understand the bases for such differences in man have led to much controversy. In the past, a rigid distinction was made between nature and nurture. Some human traits were considered to be hereditary and some acquired. More insight into the mechanisms actually involved has shown that *all* traits *develop* within limits set by genetic material under the influence of the environment. Both heredity and environment are thus involved in the development of any trait, but variations among individuals may depend more on one than on the other factor. The blood type (Chapter 8) expressed by an individual, for example, depends almost entirely on his genetic endowment. His ability to use language, however, depends on structural characteristics of his throat and mouth (developed according to an inheritance pattern), combined with what he has learned through experience in the environment. Other traits, such as body size, are significantly and directly influenced by both genetic and environmental factors.

Many family studies have uncovered unit characters which are related indirectly to psychological patterns. A heritable organic lesion, for example, may result in mental deficiency or psychosis. These phenomena do not indicate the nature of the mechanisms that are functioning, but only show what can occur when the normal processes are altered. By studying a family pedigree, it is sometimes possible to fit a hypothesis of dominant or recessive, single-gene inheritance to the pattern represented in the family. A progressive dementia called Huntington's chorea, for example, follows the pattern of a single dominant autosomal gene. Epilepsy, on the other hand, has been seen in several pedigrees to follow the pattern expected from a single autosomal recessive gene. Certain sensory anomalies, such as defective color vision and taste blindness, have also been studied from family pedigrees.

The pedigree method is useful for conspicuous and rare traits that are determined by single genes. Quantitative traits, however, are influenced by the environment as well as by inheritance. Elaborate statistical methods have been used to control environmental influences in some experiments and thus to determine the degree of heritability of a trait, but these are extremely difficult to impose in human studies. The twin study method has become increasingly popular as a way to control the genetic factor and thus to compare environmental influences. Because members of monozygotic or identical twin pairs have the same genotype, except for rare mutations and chromosome alterations, essentially all variation is environmental. Comparison of intrapair differences in monozygotic and dizygotic twins is a useful basis for evaluating the degree of heritability of a particular trait.

Objectives and methods applicable in human-behavior genetics-oriented studies are quite different from those associated with experimental animals. Animal geneticists can easily use genetics as a tool. Traits and subjects can be selected for experimental convenience. Maze learning in rodents, for example, is not socially or economically significant but is merely a device for the study of learning mechanisms in animals. Any organism that lends itself to experimental attack would be suitable for these studies. Genetic manipulation is then possible with no need to consider moral implications.

Students of human-behavior genetics, on the other hand, are concerned with problems of social importance (such as intelligence and psychoses) but they are restricted in their experimental approach. The mechanisms involved in behavior, as well as applied problems, particularly those concerned with psychological traits, are of considerable interest. Because human psychological traits have not yet been reduced to quantitative mechanisms, however, the scientist must either settle for data from animal studies, or confine his efforts to studies of inheritance of mental dysfunction and determination of heritability of quantitative traits such as intelligence and personality.

## SUMMARY

Genetically transmitted information must guide the developmental sequence of the individual animal in such a way that at each stage of development it appears and behaves generally like other members of the species to which it belongs. Individual variations are superimposed by segregating hereditary determiners and environmental influences on the species patterns. Classical experiments by Roux, Weismann, Boveri, Hertwig, Driesch, Spemann, Conklin, and Stern have elucidated gross and basic aspects of developmental processes. Models, such as the operon, based on cytoplasmic inducers represent the beginning of an explanation for the mechanics of basic developmental processes. Genetic determiners are presumed to be involved in differentiation, determination, organization, and growth regulation in the development of each individual animal. Behavioral characteristics of individuals are controlled at least indirectly by genes and subject to the forces of natural selection. Like other kinds of traits, the behavior of an animal *develops* in response to interactions between his inherited limitations and his environment. Inheritance thus has a quantitatively important effect on behavior.

## REFERENCES

Bonner, J. 1965. *The molecular biology of development.* Oxford University Press, New York.

Briggs, R. E., and T. J. King. 1959. *Nucleocytoplasmic interactions in eggs and embryos.* Academic Press, New York. *The cell,* **1,** 537–617. (Experiments in which nuclei from frog eggs were removed and replaced with nuclei from the blastula or gastrula.)

Edwards, R. G. 1966. "Mammalian eggs in the laboratory." *Sci. Amer.,* **215,** 73–81.

Etkin, W. (ed.) 1964. *Social behavior and organization among vertebrates.* University of Chicago Press, Chicago.

Frisch, K. von. 1950. *Bees: their senses and language.* Cornell University Press, New York.

Fuller, J. L., and W. R. Thompson. 1960. *Behavior genetics.* John Wiley and Sons, New York.

Hadorn, E. 1961. *Developmental genetics and lethal factors.* (Trans. U. Mittwoch) John Wiley and Sons, New York.

Kerr, W. E., and H. H. Laidlaw. 1956. *General genetics of bees.* M. Demerec (ed.). Academic Press, New York. *Advances in Genetics,* Vol., **8,** 109–153.

Lindauer, M. 1961. *Communication among social bees.* Harvard University Press, Cambridge, Mass.

Mackensen, O., and W. P. Nye. 1966. "Selecting and breeding honeybees for collecting alfalfa pollen." *J. Apicultural Research,* **5,** 79–86.

Marler, P. R., and W. J. Hamilton III. 1967. *Mechanisms of animal behavior.* John Wiley and Sons, New York.

Moore, J. A. 1963. *Heredity and development.* Oxford University Press, New York.

Nye, W. P., and O. Mackensen. 1965. "Preliminary report on selection and breeding of honeybees for alfalfa pollen collection." *J. Apicultural Research,* **4,** 43–48.

Scott, J. P., and J. L. Fuller. 1965. *Genetics and social behavior of the dog.* University of Chicago Press, Chicago.

Skinner, B. F. 1966. "The phylogeny and ontogeny of behavior." *Science,* **153,** 1205–1213.

Smith, R. F., Sr. (ed.). 1967. *Annual Review of Entomology.* Vol. 12. (Review of genetics of behavior in bees.)

Spemann, H. 1938. *Embryonic development and induction.* Yale University Press, New Haven.

Stern, C. 1954. "Two or three bristles." *Amer. Sci.,* **42,** 213–247. (Prepatterns and differentiation.)

Tokunaga, C., and C. Stern. 1965. *The developmental autonomy of extra sex combs in Drosophila melanogaster.* Academic Press, New York. *Developmental Biol.,* **11,** 50–81.

Vandenberg, S. G. (ed.). 1965. *Methods and goals in human behavior genetics.* Academic Press, New York. (Symposium on the subject including 17 papers by leaders in the field.)

Waddington, C. H. 1962. *New patterns in genetics and development.* Columbia University Press, New York.

Young, W. C., R. W. Goy and C. H. Phoenix. 1964. "Hormones and sexual behavior." *Science,* **143,** 212–218.

# *Problems*

**16.1** Why did anatomy develop earlier in the history of biology than physiology?

**16.2** Why has behavioral psychology been slow in developing as a field of science?

**16.3** How are differentiation, organization, and growth regulation involved in the development of an animal?

**16.4** (a) How was the Roux-Weismann theory of differentiation developed and supported? (b) What is its present status?

**16.5** What characteristics should be considered in choosing an animal for experimental studies of early development?

**16.6** What techniques are available for investigating determination and the fate of regions of the egg?

**16.7** What differences exist in the eggs and early developmental stages of the tunicate and the newt?

**16.8** How can differences in time of differentiation of different developing organisms be demonstrated?

**16.9** How was the organizer theory of Spemann developed and supported?

**16.10** How was the prepattern theory of Stern developed and supported?

**16.11** How could genes be involved in the establishment of prepatterns?

**16.12** How can the differentiation of cells, all of which came from the same source by the same process, be explained?

**16.13** If the operon theory had been established at the time the two classical hypotheses, (1) segregation of nuclear elements and (2) intervention of cytoplasm, for the mechanics of differentiation were being considered, which hypothesis would have been most acceptable?

**16.14** How could the cytoplasm be involved in differentiation?

**16.15** If all cells in a given organism carry the same genes, how can gene expressions that are localized in time and space be explained?

**16.16** Evaluate the present status of knowledge of the genetics of development.

**16.17** What is animal behavior and how, in general, is it related to genetics?

**16.18** How and to what extent is communication accomplished among (a) protozoans and (b) birds?

**16.19** How do forager bees communicate information concerning (a) a food source near the hive, (b) distance to a food source that is more than 100 yards from the hive, and (c) direction of a distant food source?

**16.20** How and to what extent is genetics involved in the waggle dance of honeybees?

**16.21** How can the differences between the waggle dance itself and the interpretation of information be explained in different geographical races of bees?

**16.22** What evidence suggests a genetic basis for the preference of some bees for alfalfa pollen?

**16.23** (a) How may hormones influence behavior? (b) How and to what extent is hormone production under genetic control? (c) What conclusions may be drawn from the studies of Scott and Fuller on dogs concerning the relative influence of heredity and environment on behavior?

**16.24** Why are dogs highly reactive to selection?

# III

# *Population Genetics and Evolution*

# *Multiple Gene Inheritance* | 17

In 1760, Joseph Kölreuter reported but was unable to explain the results of crosses between tall and dwarf varieties of tobacco, Nicotiana. The $F_1$ plants were intermediate in size between the two parent varieties. The $F_2$ progeny showed a continuous gradation from the size of the dwarf to that of the tall parent. A normal distribution was obtained in the $F_2$, with the midpoint of the curve corresponding roughly with the midpoint of the $F_1$ curve and intermediate between the two original parents (P). Kölreuter was a careful experimenter and a good biologist, but he could not explain these results because the basic principles of genetics had not yet been established.

With the discovery of Mendel's work, more than a hundred years after Kölreuter's experiments were completed, discontinuous variation (falling into distinct classes), based on a particulate mode of inheritance, was demonstrated for certain traits in garden peas. (It should be noted that Mendel also described continuous variation. When he crossed white-flowered and purple-red-flowered beans, an intermediate flower color was obtained in the $F_1$ progeny and a spread from white to red in the $F_2$.) Mendel's results from garden peas were analyzed mathematically, but in terms of simple frequencies that required only simple arithmetic.Bateson supported Mendel and strengthened the case for discontinuous variation. Those who followed were attracted by the ease of classification and simple frequencies associated with the Mendelian pattern. Investigators reported simple ratios from crosses involving many traits in a wide variety of plants and animals. The more elusive and problematical results, which were not readily explained by Mendelian segregation, were pigeonholed or discarded. Several years elapsed after the discovery of Mendel's work before progress was made in the analysis of continuous variation.

The curves presented in Fig. 17.1 diagrammatically compare Mendel's results with those of Kölreuter. When Mendel crossed tall and dwarf varieties of peas, the $F_1$ progeny were all tall. Some of the $F_2$ plants were tall and some were dwarf, in the proportion of about 3 to 1. From these results, pairs of particulate elements were postulated. One member of each pair was shown to be dominant over its allele. Distinct and clear-cut contrasting characters were observed and readily classified under such headings as tall or dwarf, yellow or green, and red or white. Kölreuter's results, on the other hand, showed continuous variation with no distinct class boundaries. The $F_1$ hybrids

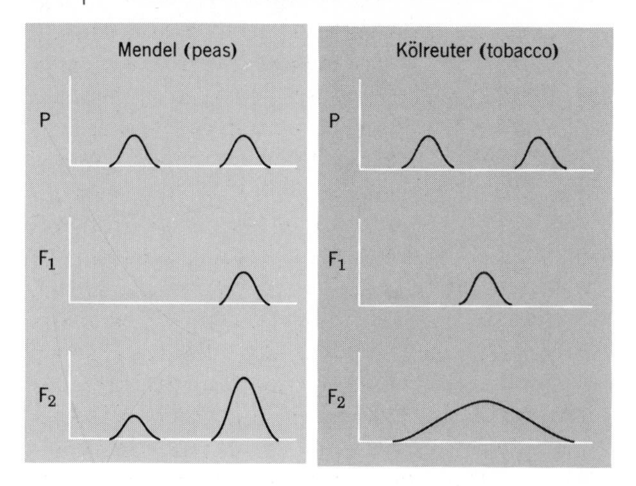


**Fig. 17.1** Curves representing the results of Mendel's experiments compared with those of Kölreuter. (Left) P, $F_1$, and $F_2$ from Mendel's crosses with garden peas; (right) P, $F_1$, and $F_2$ from Kölreuter's crosses on tobacco plants. The ordinate represents the number of plants and the abscissa the range in size.

were intermediate between the parents, and the $F_2$ covered the entire range between the sizes of the parents.

## POLYGENE THEORY

### *Color in Wheat Kernels*

During the period between 1900 and 1910, many geneticists thought continuous variation reflected an entirely different mechanism of inheritance from discontinuous variation. However, when the idea of Mendelian inheritance had become well established, a few keen investigators began to envision a common basis for the results of Mendel and those of Kölreuter. Genes with small but cumulative effects were postulated to behave in a Mendelian fashion. An explanation for continuous variation thus emerged in the form of the multiple-gene hypothesis. Experimental results and interpretations substantiating this hypothesis were obtained from the classical investigations of H. Nilsson-Ehle (1873–1949; Fig. 17.2) in Sweden and E. M. East in the United States during the period 1910 to 1913.

One of these studies was based on crosses between two varieties of wheat producing red and white kernels, respectively (Fig. 17.3). The $F_1$ seeds were intermediate in color between those of the two parents. They were lighter than those of the red parent but distinctly more colored than those of the white-parent variety. When the $F_2$ seeds were classified according to intensity of color, a continuous gradation was observed from red to white, and classes

**Fig. 17.2** H. Nilsson-Ehle, Swedish plant breeder who developed the multiple gene hypothesis to explain the genetic mechanism for quantitative inheritance.

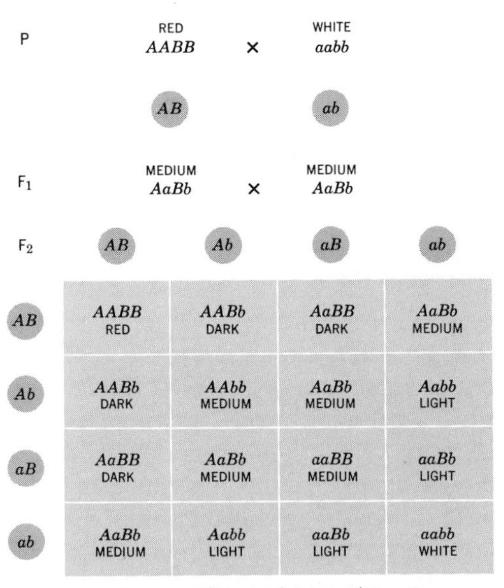


**Fig. 17.3** Diagram of a cross between a wheat variety with red kernels and another variety with white kernels. This cross illustrates quantitative inheritance dependent on multiple genes.

were more or less arbitrary. About 1/16 of the $F_2$ seeds were as red as those of the red parent, and about 1/16 were white, and about 14/16 were intermediate, ranging between the color of the red and the white original parents.

When the 14/16 of the $F_2$ seeds were classified further, on the basis of the color intensity, it was shown that about 4/16 had more color than the $F_1$ intermediates, about 6/16 were intermediate like the $F_1$'s, and about 4/16 were lighter than the $F_1$'s. This result suggested a segregation of two gene pairs and was explained on the basis of duplicate genes acting on the same character and producing a cumulative effect. When the results of this cross were examined critically, they were found to resemble those that Kölreuter had obtained many years before. A second cross between red-kernel and white-kernel varieties of wheat was carried to the $F_2$, and this time about 1/64 of the $F_2$ progeny produced white kernels and about 1/64 produced red kernels. Some 62/64 were intermediate in color, ranging between those of the two parental varieties. Again continuous gradations were recognized between the extremes of the parents. The results of this cross resembled those of a Mendelian trihybrid cross in which three independent pairs of alleles had similar and cumulative effects. Therefore, three independent gene pairs were postulated to explain this result in contrast to the two pairs for the previous cross. Evidently, one pair, which was segregating in the second cross, was homozygous in both parents in the first cross.

The concept of multiple genes for quantitative inheritance is now one of the most important principles of genetics. It has been strengthened greatly by the use of statistical methods devised by R. A. Fisher in England, Sewall Wright in the United States, and others. The explanation, based on the action of many genes (polygenes) usually segregating independently but influencing the same phenotype in a cumulative fashion, has been well established, although the details of the mechanism require further investigation.

Polygenic inheritance differs from the classical Mendelian pattern in that the whole range of variation is covered in a graded series from one parental extreme to the other. Only averages of populations are considered and not values for individuals. Such factors as dominance, epistasis, cytoplasmic influences, interactions among genes and gene products, and interactions with the environment are reflected in the averages. Polygenic inheritance is a statistical concept.

Because most characteristics of domestic plants and animals that have practical significance (including height, weight, time required to reach maturity, and qualities for human nutrition) depend on polygenic inheritance, much attention has centered around this principle. If all of the practical genetic experimental projects that are now in progress at the various experiment stations throughout the world could be listed and classified, the results would probably indicate that some 80 to 90 percent of all practical studies involve quantitative inheritance. Some human characteristics of interest and significance also depend on multiple genes.

### *Skin Color in Man*

C. B. Davenport, one of the first to investigate the inheritance of skin color in man, believed that two pairs of genes accounted for the difference in pigment between Negro and Caucasian people. His most significant studies were conducted among selected groups in Bermuda and Jamaica, where intermarriages between people with different degrees of pigmentation were relatively frequent, and illegitimate births, which could obscure the data, were relatively uncommon. As a part of these studies, an objective classification system was devised to detect different degrees of pigmentation. A rotating disk was prepared by which the skin color of any individual could be matched with a standard. The validity of such a system was increased when it was discovered that the same pigment, that is, melanin, was present in varying degrees in so-called "white" people, those with mixed ancestry, and Negroes. An arbitrary scale was developed in terms of percentage, with albino people designated at 0 and the most heavily pigmented at 100 percent. Average "white" individuals were found to have about 5 percent of the melanin pigment. Objective tests showed considerable variation among whites from only white ancestry. The amount of pigment varied from practically none in the case of light blonds to about 11 percent for some brunettes. The average of individuals sampled from the American Negro population showed about 75 percent of pigment. A range from about 56 to 78 percent of pigment was observed among the American colored people with only Negro ancestry. Other colored people with more pigmentation than that of the average American Negroes were shown to approach the arbitrary 100 percent of pigment.

When samples were taken from the immediate families resulting from intermarriage between colored people with only Negro ancestry and white people with only white ancestry, a range from 27 to 40 percent of pigment was observed. When individuals resulting from intermarriage in previous generations were examined, a color range extending continuously from white to black was encountered. Different classes were arbitrarily distinguished among individuals of mixed ancestry on the basis of intensity of color. The class with 12 to 25 percent of pigment was identified as light; 26 to 40 percent, medium (mulatto); and 41 to 55 percent dark (Table 17.1). These three classes were intermediate between white and black.

In the entire population resulting from intermixture, a continuous gradation was recognized. The first generation hybrids, that is, mulattoes, were found to be intermediate between their black and white parents. When large numbers of individuals known to have come from marriages between first generation hybrids were classified, it was shown that some were as light as the white parent and some were as dark as the original black parent. Most were

**TABLE 17.1 Degree of pigmentation and phenotypic classes in man**

| Percent Melanin Pigment | Phenotype |
|---|---|
| 0–11 | White |
| 12–25 | Light |
| 26–40 | Medium (mulatto) |
| 41–55 | Dark |
| 56–78 | Negro |

| (1) | Black *AABB* | × | White *aabb* | |
|---|---|---|---|---|
| | | *AaBb* | | Mulatto |
| (2) | *AaBb* | × | *AaBb* | |

| Phenotypes | Genotypes | Genotypic Frequency | Phenotypic Ratio |
|---|---|---|---|
| Black | *AABB* | 1 | 1 |
| Dark | *AaBB* | 2 | 4 |
| | *AABb* | 2 | |
| Intermediate | *AaBb* | 4 | 6 |
| | *aaBB* | 1 | |
| | *AAbb* | 1 | |
| Light | *Aabb* | 2 | 4 |
| | *aaBb* | 2 | |
| White | *aabb* | 1 | 1 |

**Fig. 17.4** Diagram of two crosses, (1) and (2), involving colored people (Negroes) and Caucasians, based on the assumption that two pairs of pigment producing genes are involved. (1) Cross between colored and white; (2) cross between mulattos.

somewhere between the extremes of the parents. Davenport's analysis of the data showed a proportion of about 1 black, 4 dark, 6 medium, 4 light, and 1 white. This proportion was based on a model in which two pairs of alleles were involved, each producing about the same amount of pigment. No appreciable dominance existed between the alleles, and the action of the genes was cumulative. By using gene symbols *a* and *b*, the cross based on this hypothesis may be reconstructed as illustrated in Fig. 17.4.

The well-established pattern of quantitative inheritance based on multiple genes is amply demonstrated in the production of gradations of pigmentation. The common belief that dominance favors the pigmented condition over the white is left without a foundation, and the frequently repeated statement that white parents can have black children is unsubstantiated by scientific fact. If one parent is white and genetically homozygous (*aabb*), the children would not be genetically darker than the other parent. If, however, each parent carries one or two of the genes for pigmentation, combinations producing more intense pigment than shown by either parent might occur. One serious difficulty in such phenotypic analyses comes from the influence on pigmentation of environmental factors, both those from natural causes such as the sun and wind and those supplied at the cosmetic counter. It is sometimes difficult, indeed, to distinguish on the basis of color alone between an individual genetically white (*aabb*) but representing a brunette type, and an individual with one gene for pigment (*Aabb* or *aaBb*) but representing the lower range of expression for that genotype.

Comparisons become even more difficult because the amount of pigment increases from birth to maturity and decreases from maturity to old age. Undoubtedly, modifiers of the basic pigment genes are involved. Thus, minor genetic variations may account, in part at least, for the small differences among individuals with similar ancestry and presumably comparable genotypes. Different racial groups with different intensities of pigmentation may be explained on the basis of past mutations that influenced the degree of pigmentation.

Although quantitative inheritance of skin color is well established, questions have arisen concerning the number of gene pairs involved. Davenport's model based on two pairs is too simple to account for the data now available. A more recent model by R. R. Gates is based on three pairs of genes. Curt Stern's mathematical analysis shows that 4, 5, and 6 gene pairs agree better with the observed data than a higher or lower number, but the actual number of genes involved is not known. Various investigators have estimated numbers ranging from 2 to 20 pairs. Variation in the degree of pigmentation exists among colored individuals from only colored ancestry. Likewise, different Caucasian peoples show individual variation. The relatively slight differences that exist among white persons from only white ancestry and colored persons from only colored ancestry may be attributed to minor genetic variation and environmental influence.

### *Ear Length in Maize*

One of the classical studies on quantitative inheritance, which did much to establish the multiple gene hypothesis, was made by R. A. Emerson (1873–1947; Fig. 17.5) and E. M. East on the inheritance of ear length in maize. A cross was made between varieties with small ears and those with large ears, and the $F_2$ results were critically analyzed. The small-eared parent was a variety of popcorn called the Tom Thumb, with ears averaging 6.6 cm in length and ranging from 5 to 8 cm. The other parent was Black Mexican, a sweet corn with ears averaging 16.8 cm and ranging from 13 to 21 cm. The $F_1$ progeny were intermediate in ear length, averaged 12.1 cm, and ranged from 9 to 15 cm.

**Fig. 17.5** R. A. Emerson, pioneer American plant breeder who did basic work on maize genetics.

The $F_2$ represented a wider spread of variation than the $F_1$, with some of the ears extending into the range of both parents. This is a characteristic pattern for the results of crosses involving traits dependent on only a few genes. When many genes are involved, the extremes represented by the parents occur infrequently in the $F_2$. The histograms (Fig. 17.6) represent the maize data and illustrate graphically the characteristic pattern of multiple gene inheritance. Since the parental lines were inbred and relatively homozygous, the variation within these lines and that shown for the $F_1$ were mostly environmental or a result of sequential development in time. The $F_1$ represented the fully heterozygous condition between the genotypes of the two original parents. The results of genetic segregation involving the genes from the two parents were illustrated by the wider variation in the $F_2$.

As in other examples involving quantitative inheritance, the environmental influence is the most confusing factor in analysis, and it must be considered and as adequately controlled as possible. The environment can produce results similar to those of the genes with respect to size differences between large and small varieties. Plants raised in unfavorable environments—that is, without sufficient water, sunlight, or soil nutrients—will be smaller than others of the same genotype that enjoy a more satisfactory environment. On the other hand, under ideal environmental conditions, organisms with inferior genotypes may develop phenotypes equivalent or superior to those with better genotypes but inferior environments. Even minor environmental variations affect the expression of quantitative traits. The environmental influence must be controlled as completely as possible with experimental design.

If, in the maize example, two gene pairs are active, the variation is all hereditary, and each gene produces an equal effect on

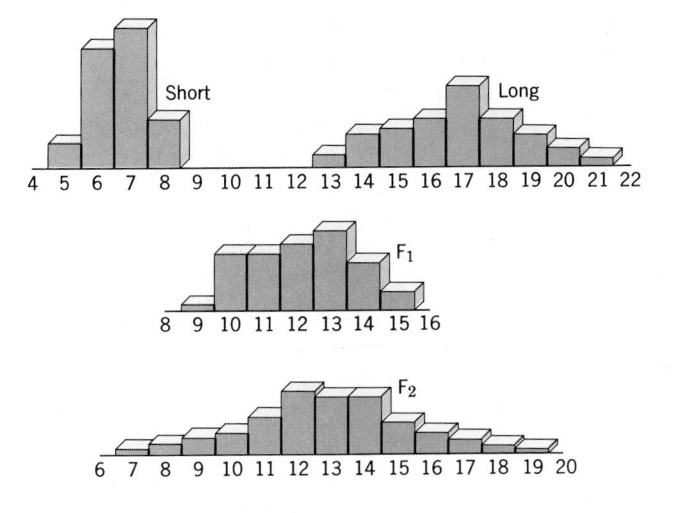


**Fig. 17.6** Histograms illustrating maize data from cross involving multiple gene inheritance. (Modified from Sturtevant and Beadle, *An Introduction to Genetics,* published by W. B. Saunders Co. Based on data from Emerson and East.)

the size of the ear above the size dependent on the residual genotype (6.6 cm), the individual contributions would be

$$\frac{16.8 - 6.6}{4} = 2.55 \text{ cm per gene}$$

Each active allele thus would produce 2.55 cm in addition to the 6.6 made possible by the residual genotype for the small variety. When the $F_2$ plants were classified according to phenotype, a ratio of 1:4:6:4:1 was obtained. This is a modification of the 1:2:1:2:4:2:1:2:1 ratio, which may be changed to 9:3:3:1 by dominance. The diagram in Fig. 17.7 represents a model for these data based on the multiple gene hypothesis.

## *Size in Rabbits and Corolla Length in Tobacco*

Another example of multiple gene or polygenic inheritance may be taken from the work of W. E. Castle on the inheritance of weight of rabbits. Rabbits from the large Flemish Giant breed, which, when fully mature, averaged about 13 pounds, were crossed with those from a small Polish variety averaging about 3 pounds. The $F_1$ hybrids were intermediate between the two parents, averaging 7 to 8 pounds, and the $F_2$ progeny ranged from a size nearly as small as the Polish breed to a size approaching that of a Flemish Giant. Several litters of $F_2$ progeny were obtained, but no rabbits reached the extremes of the parental strains, presumably because a

Individual contribution of genes:
(*A* or *B*) 2.55 cm
Size produced by residual genotype: 6.6 cm
Genotypes of parents:

| Black Mexican | | Tom Thumb |
|---|---|---|
| *AABB* | × | *aabb* |

$F_1$ *AaBb* (12.1 cm)

| $F_2$ | Genotype | Frequency | Phenotype (cm) | Phenotypic Ratio |
|---|---|---|---|---|
| | *AABB* | 1 | 16.8 | 1 |
| | *AaBB* | 2 | 14.2 | 4 |
| | *AABb* | 2 | 14.2 | |
| | *AaBb* | 4 | 11.7 | 6 |
| | *aaBB* | 1 | 11.7 | |
| | *AAbb* | 1 | 11.7 | |
| | *aaBb* | 2 | 9.1 | 4 |
| | *Aabb* | 2 | 9.1 | |
| | *aabb* | 1 | 6.6 | 1 |

**Fig. 17.7** Diagrammatic analysis of Emerson's maize data based on the multiple gene hypothesis with two pairs of active alleles, each contributing equally to the phenotype.

large number of gene pairs were acting in the cross. If enough $F_2$ individuals were raised, the parental extremes would be expected to occur eventually. On the other hand, the extremes of the parents might never be obtained, even with large numbers of hybrids, because further work of Castle showed that the effects of the genes were not proportional. Modifiers and maternal size effects were involved along with the effects of polygenes.

In examples that involved several thousand $F_2$ progeny from plant crosses, none even approached the parental phenotypes and many gene pairs were presumed to be involved. As many as 200 pairs of alleles were postulated to be active in some traits that have been reported. E. M. East studied the corolla length in a cross between two varieties of tobacco, *Nicotiana longiflora,* and found none of the several hundred $F_2$ plants to resemble the parents (P). Many gene pairs were therefore postulated.

**TABLE 17.2 Probability of occurrence of $F_2$ individuals as extreme as either parent**

| Pairs of Segregating Alleles | Fraction of $F_2$ as Extreme as Either Parent |
|---|---|
| 1 | 1/4 |
| 2 | 1/16 |
| 3 | 1/64 |
| 4 | 1/256 |
| 5 | 1/1024 |

### *Estimating The Number of Gene Differences*

The contributions of individual genes to a quantitative character can be evaluated roughly from the results of some of the foregoing detailed crosses. In the maize data, for example, each extreme of the parents occurred in the proportion of about 1 in 16 in the $F_2$. Two pairs of alleles, then, might be assumed to be operating. Determining the number of genes involved in a given cross is usually more difficult, however, mainly because environmental as well as genetic variations are represented by the same measurements. In nature, the genes may not all influence the phenotype in the same way or to the same extent. Models devised to estimate the number of genes are oversimplified if based on the assumption of equal effects.

One of the problems confronting the geneticist when he begins to study a trait known or suspected to depend on quantitative inheritance is the estimation of the number of genes involved. In some organisms, a rough estimate has been made by determining the frequency of occurrence in the $F_2$ population of the extremes representing the parental phenotypes (Table 17.2). If the extremes occur with a frequency of 1 in 4, one pair of genes may be assumed to be operating. If the phenotype of each parent occurs in about 1 in 16, two pairs are involved; 1 in 64, three pairs; 1 in 256, four pairs; and 1 in 1024, five pairs. Obviously, this is an inadequate approximation of the number of active genes, but the method is useful for preliminary genetic analysis. More complicated mathematical procedures are employed when sufficient $F_1$ and $F_2$ data are available. This method is based on the assumption that all genes produce comparable effect on the phenotype and that random assortment occurs among gene pairs. Gene combinations and interactions may become complex, and simple conclusions are not always possible.

### *Transgressive Variation*

Extremes have been obtained from some $F_2$ results which exceeded the corresponding values in the parents (P). This pattern, in which the extremes of the $F_2$ exceed those of the parents, is called transgressive variation. The explanation for extra large or exceedingly small individuals resulting from crosses is based on the hypothesis that the parents did not represent the extremes possible from the combined genotypes. If some genes for large size were lacking in the genotype of the large parent but were present in the genotype of the small parent, an $F_2$ individual might receive a combination of genes producing a larger or smaller size than that represented by either parent. For example, in a cross between a large Hamburgh chicken and a small Sebright Bantam, Punnett found that the $F_1$ chickens were intermediate between the two parents. The $F_2$ progeny included some birds larger and some smaller than the parental varieties. Most of the $F_2$, however, were intermediate between the original parents. Punnett explained the result on the basis of a 4-factor difference between the two parents. The Hamburghs were postulated to have the genotype $a^+a^+b^+b^+c^+c^+dd$ and the bantams $aabbccd^+d^+$. The $F_1$ birds would be uniformly heterozygous $a^+ab^+bc^+cd^+d$, accounting for the intermediate weight. Some $F_2$ individuals might have the genotype $a^+a^+b^+b^+c^+c^+d^+d^+$ and be heavier than the original Hamburgh parent, whereas others could have the genotype *aabbccdd* and be smaller than the bantam parent.

Genes responsible for transgressive variation and other patterns of quantitative inheritance are considered to behave in the typical Mendelian fashion. It is only the phenotypic results of crosses that differ from the familiar ratios. Thus a 9:3:3:1 ratio expected from a dihybrid cross involving complete dominance is modified to a 1:4:6:4:1 ratio with continuous variation and no dominance (that is, $AAbb = AaBb$ phenotypically). If three pairs of independent alleles were involved in a cross, the ratio of 1:6:15:20:15:6:1 would replace the familiar 27:9:9:9:3:3:3:1 ratio based on discontinuous variation and complete dominance.

## *The Mechanism of Quantitative Inheritance*

The mechanism of quantitative inheritance is not as well established as it might seem from the examples and explanatory models introduced in the early part of this chapter. The multiple-gene hypothesis was effectively illustrated by the kernel color of wheat experiment in which six genes with cumulative effects were postulated. Common bread wheat is a polyploid (a hexaploid, see Chapter 10) and has six chromosomes of a particular kind, each presumably carrying a gene for color. Segregation of the six genes postulated for kernel color might be attributable to multiple chromosome sets. Thus, the mode of inheritance would be more properly described on the basis of duplicate genes with cumulative effect than by polygenes. The Capsella example cited in Chapter 4 may also be explained on the basis of polyploidy. Capsella has four sets of chromosomes. The two pairs of duplicate genes, on which the explanation for triangular and top-shaped capsules was based, may be explained by the presence of two sets of chromosomes in the gametes. In animals, however, polyploidy is relatively nonexistent, but quantitative inheritance is very common. Polyploidy is limited also as an explanation for plants, because the possible number of similar genes would depend on the number of chromosome sets that a plant could carry. The high numbers of genes postulated for some plants, therefore, could not be explained on this basis. *Crepis capillaris* ($n = 3$), for example, is not a polyploid but is reported to have a high proportion of duplicate gene or polygene inheritance.

Multiple genes might also arise through mutations in different chromosome areas producing similar effects, but it is difficult to visualize how numerous mutations affecting the same trait could occur. Duplicated segments of chromosomes (discussed in Chapter 9) or tandem duplications of genes might account in part for this occurrence. Duplicate genes do exist and examples have been cited to indicate that they are involved in quantitative inheritance, but the duplicate-gene concept cannot be used to interpret all cumulative effects of genes.

Modifier genes are also known to influence size differences in animals and plants, but they do not always follow a uniform pattern. Some act as enhancers and some as inhibitors of a particular effect, and the end result is an average of the varying effects of a number of genes. Certain genes may serve a dual capacity by influencing both qualitative and quantitative traits. Furthermore, the effect of a particular gene substitution may vary with different genetic backgrounds.

The same phenotype may be produced by different genetic systems. Size in animals and plants, for example, is generally controlled by a polygenic system, but a single major gene may produce a dwarf animal such as a calf (Chapter 19) or a dwarf plant such as Mendel's peas (Chapter 1), thus accomplishing the same end result as that produced by a balance of polygenic effects. In cases where only one or a few genes are involved, it is possible to develop homozygous, pure-breeding types in a few generations of inbreeding. This is not possible in systems of polygenes where many genes are involved; the genes cannot be individually recognized, and techniques ordinarily applied to Mendelian inheritance are inadequate for analysis. A. S. Fraser and others have applied new techniques making use of the digital computer to test various models based on different hypothetical patterns. It has been possible to demonstrate results comparable with those of natural systems of polygenes on the model of Mendelian segregation. These studies support the basic premise that polygenic inheritance is Mendelian.

Kenneth Mather, an English authority on biometrical genetics who coined the word "polygene," has postulated that such genes are located in the heterochromatin. According to Mather's interpretation, polygenes would be expected to behave in Mendelian fashion, with many genes influencing the same trait and supplementing the effect of each other. R. D. Milkman has studied a series of genes, which he considers to be polygenes, that controls the crossvein-making ability in the Drosophila wing. Some of these genes have been located by linkage studies in the three major chromosomes of *Drosophila melanogaster* and are thought to occupy the euchromatin. Whether these identifiable genes are properly called polygenes, as defined by Mather, is questionable. The problem of what polygenes are chemically will undoubtedly be resolved along with the other aspects of gene chemistry now under investigation.

Although there are many unresolved problems concerning the nature and action of genes or polygenes associated with quantitative traits, the multiple-gene concept is a good working hypothesis. Polygenic systems must be considered in statistical terms. It is impossible at this time to identify particular polygenes or to obtain a detailed knowledge of their properties. From statistical studies, however, comprehensive averages may be obtained in terms of quantitative values. In natural selection, the balance of the operative polygenic system is more important than the effect of individual genes. Polygenic inheritance fits the Darwinian pattern of gradual and continuous changes directed by natural environments.

### *Statistical Methods*

Statistical tools are widely applicable in investigations of quantitative inheritance. Data are usually numerous and complex, requiring analysis and organization before their significance can be fully appreciated. Large numbers of individuals are usually included in populations to be studied and compared; therefore, sampling methods are used to facilitate comparison. One requirement that must be rigidly observed when sampling techniques are employed is that of randomness. A sufficiently large sample, taken at random without bias or favoritism, may adequately represent a complete population which could not be measured in its entirety. Most biological populations are so large that they are assumed to be infinite. In some cases they do not actually exist, but are only theoretical. Some examples illustrating different kinds of populations will clarify the difference between total population and sample.

A study was made of the weight of deer presently living in the western part of the United States. Four hundred deer picked at random were weighed. The population consisted of all the deer living in the area and could be represented by the weight measurement of all the deer. The sample consisted of 400 measurements actually obtained. An ornithologist measured the wing length of 55 birds of a particular species. The population concept in this instance consisted of the wing length of all the birds of that species. The sample consisted of the 55 measurements that were made. An animal nutritionist fed a special diet to 100 mice and then measured their increase in weight over a certain length of time. The sample consisted of the 100 mice from which the measurements were obtained. The population did not actually exist. It consisted of an infinite number of measurements which theoretically could be obtained if an infinite number of mice had been fed the diet. Finally, a coin was tossed 100 times and the number of heads and tails was recorded. The sample consisted of the 100 tosses, but the population consisted of an infinite number of tosses theoretically possible.

It is important to distinguish clearly between estimates based on samples and actual values that would be obtained if it were possible to measure the entire population. Estimates are called *statistics,* and true values based on entire populations are called *parameters.* In biological investigations, parameters are seldom known. If they were known, direct comparisons could be made between populations. Species A, for example, could be compared directly with species B in terms of the actual mean or degree of variability. When parameters are not known, statistics based on samples are used for comparisons. Measurements especially useful to the geneticist are the mean and the variance. The square root of the variance is the more familiar statistic called the standard deviation.

Unfortunately, there is no uniformity among statisticians in the choice of symbols to represent statistical terms. The use of different symbols by various authors to represent the same type of measurement can lead to considerable confusion. Statisticians generally tend to use Arabic letters for estimates or statistics, and Greek letters for the values of which estimates are being made, or parameters. In this discussion, the mean of the population (a parameter), will be represented by the Greek letter *mu* ($\mu$), and the mean of the sample by $\bar{x}$. The variance of the population will be represented by sigma squared ($\sigma^2$) and the standard deviation by sigma ($\sigma$). Estimates of $\sigma^2$ and $\sigma$, calculated from samples, will be symbolized $s^2$ and $s$, respectively. The number of individuals in the sample will be symbolized by $n$ and those of the entire population will be $N$.

A major reason for using statistical techniques is to estimate the properties of populations for which parameters are unknown. The first step in applying these techniques is the selection of appropriate estimating functions or estimators. A good estimator is a function of the sample values which will provide a unbiased estimate of a certain parameter. The estimator is said to be unbiased if the mean of the sampling distribution is equal to the parameter. An unbiased statistic is as likely to be too low as too high, but it is expected to approach the parameter more closely as sample size is increased.

The first statistic to be considered here is the mean, which is an estimate of magnitude. It is an average in terms of weight, height, or any other feature measured. The common method of obtaining the mean of a sample is merely to add the individual measurements and divide by the total number of individuals. This is illustrated by the following formula: $\bar{x} = \frac{\Sigma X}{n}$ where $\bar{x}$ is the sample mean, $X$ the individual measurements, $\Sigma$ the summation and $n$ the number of individuals in the sample. This statistic is an unbiased estimate of the population mean $\mu$, which is given by $\mu = \frac{\Sigma X}{N}$, where $X$ represents the individual measurements and $N$ the total individuals in the entire population.

Data obtained from measuring the height of 122 guayule rubber plants, which constituted a random sample of a population, may be used as an illustration. The following measurements in inches were taken from plants growing in the field 107 days after planting (rounded off to the nearest whole number):

| | | | | | | | | |
|---|---|---|---|---|---|---|---|---|
| 12 | 12 | 11 | 11 | 12 | 15 | 12 | 11 | 10 |
| 13 | 14 | 12 | 13 | 13 | 10 | 13 | 14 | 13 |
| 11 | 12 | 12 | 10 | 15 | 16 | 13 | 11 | 9 |
| 12 | 13 | 11 | 13 | 14 | 11 | 13 | 8 | 10 |
| 11 | 13 | 14 | 13 | 12 | 14 | 13 | 10 | 10 |
| 11 | 11 | 10 | 12 | 10 | 12 | 11 | 12 | 11 |
| 12 | 11 | 13 | 12 | 9 | 10 | 14 | 11 | 13 |
| 13 | 11 | 12 | 11 | 11 | 13 | 11 | 12 | 13 |
| 10 | 10 | 11 | 11 | 12 | 16 | 16 | 12 | 12 |
| 14 | 12 | 13 | 10 | 9 | 12 | 13 | 12 | 12 |
| 17 | 13 | 13 | 10 | 11 | 10 | 13 | 12 | 11 |
| 14 | 11 | 11 | 11 | 10 | 11 | 14 | 11 | 14 |
| 8 | 10 | 10 | 11 | 13 | 10 | 11 | 12 | 12 |
| 13 | 12 | 15 | 15 | 15 | | | | |

The mean is obtained by summing ($\Sigma$), that is, by adding all the values $X$ and dividing by the total number $n$.

$$\bar{x} = \frac{\Sigma X}{n} = \frac{1458}{122} = 11.95$$

In analyses involving numerous measurements it is advantageous to begin by classifying or grouping the data.

In the example of 122 guayule plants, the interval between classes was 1 and the range was from 8 to 17 inches. To classify the data, intervals must be continuous and equal. Suppose that one plant measuring 19 inches was added to the sample. To keep the intervals equal it would be necessary to add another group for 18-inch plants (with frequency $f = 0$) and a group for 19-inch plants with $f = 1$.

If the range had been wider, for example, from 2 to 36 inches, an interval of 2 might have been chosen for ease of computation and presentation. Under the plan, all measurements falling between 2 and 4 could arbitrarily be given the value of 3, which would be the class center. Other class centers would be 5, 7, 9, 11, 13, . . . 35. What if the range covered a much wider area, for example, from 1 to 100, and continuous variation was represented throughout the sample? Perhaps intervals of 10 would then be chosen. Class centers of 5, 15, 25, and so on, would be used for grouping the data. If the measurements covered a smaller range and were more precise, for example, presented in terms of one or two decimal places, appropriate class centers, such as 70.5 to represent observations falling between 70 and 71, might be chosen. When the data are grouped, the mean is represented by the following formula:

$$\bar{x} = \frac{\Sigma fX}{n}$$

where $f$ is the frequency of individuals having the value of $X$, and $n$ the total number of individuals in the sample. In the example presented, the data are not extensive, ranging from 8 to 17, and may be arranged as shown in Table 17.3. The first two columns in the table show the

**TABLE 17.3 Chart illustrating the steps in a statistical problem involving the height in inches of 122 guayule seedlings representing a random sample of plants 107 days after planting**

| $X$ | $f$ | $fX$ | $X - \bar{x}$ | $(X - \bar{x})^2$ | $f(X - \bar{x})^2$ |
|---|---|---|---|---|---|
| 8 | 2 | 16 | −3.95 | 15.60 | 31.20 |
| 9 | 3 | 27 | −2.95 | 8.70 | 26.10 |
| 10 | 18 | 180 | −1.95 | 3.80 | 68.40 |
| 11 | 29 | 319 | − .95 | .90 | 26.10 |
| 12 | 27 | 324 | .05 | .00 | .00 |
| 13 | 24 | 312 | 1.05 | 1.10 | 26.40 |
| 14 | 10 | 140 | 2.05 | 4.20 | 42.00 |
| 15 | 5 | 75 | 3.05 | 9.30 | 46.50 |
| 16 | 3 | 48 | 4.05 | 16.40 | 49.20 |
| 17 | 1 | 17 | 5.05 | 25.50 | 25.50 |
| | 122 | 1458 | | | 341.40 |

various values of $X$ and the frequency of measurements having these values, respectively. The classified data obtained from measurements of the sample may now be substituted into the formula and the calculations may be made as follows:

$$\bar{x} = \frac{\Sigma fX}{n} = \frac{1458}{122} = 11.95$$

The mean of 11.95 inches represents the average from the sample and an estimate of the population mean.

The mean is useful as an estimate of magnitude, but it does not provide all the information that may be desired from the sample. For example, in a certain experiment, one cross resulted in a sample of plants averaging 70 inches in height. Another cross produced plants of approximately the same average. From the mean alone, the two samples seemed to be similar, but further analysis showed that the range of one was from 40 to 100, whereas that of the other was from 69 to 71. A measure of the variation in addition to the average had significance for the geneticist who was conducting the experiment.

One measure of variation is called the variance. The population variance $\sigma^2$ is represented by the following formula:

$$\sigma^2 = \frac{\Sigma(X - \mu)^2}{N}$$

where $X$ represents the individual measurements in the population, $\mu$ the actual but usually unknown population mean (parameter), and $N$ the total number of individuals in the population. This is the ideal value because it is the actual population variance, but it is unrealistic because the true population mean $\mu$ is seldom known. The way to avoid this difficulty is to substitute the sample mean ($\bar{x}$) for the parameter $\mu$ and the sample size $n$ for the population size $N$. This statistic is biased, however because it tends to underestimate the true value of the population variance $\sigma^2$. On the average, the estimates would be too small. When $\bar{x}$ is used in place of $\mu$ in the formula, the number of independent measurements becomes one less than $n$. To use the sample mean $\bar{x}$ in the formula, a correction factor $n/(n - 1)$ is introduced to overcome the bias. This modification results in the standard formula for the variance $s^2$, which is derived by multiplying the biased statistic

$$\frac{\Sigma(X - \bar{x})^2}{n}$$

by the correction factor $n/(n - 1)$ as follows:

$$\frac{\Sigma(X - \bar{x})^2}{n} \times \frac{n}{n - 1} = \frac{(X - \bar{x})^2}{n - 1} = s^2$$

When this is done, $s^2$ becomes an unbiased estimate of the population variance $\sigma^2$. If the sample size is large, the difference between $n$ an $n - 1$ is small or negligible, but even for large samples the correct divisor for an unbiased estimate of the population parameter $\sigma^2$ is $n - 1$.

When the data are grouped, as in Table 17.3, the formula for the sample variance is modified as follows:

$$s^2 = \frac{\Sigma f(X - \bar{x})^2}{n - 1}$$

The data from the sample of 122 guayule plants may now be substituted into the formula and the variance calculated as follows:

$$s^2 = \frac{\Sigma f(X - \bar{x})^2}{n - 1} = \frac{341}{121} = 2.82$$

The variance $s^2 = 2.82$ is an unbiased estimate of the population variance $\sigma^2$. The accuracy of the estimate may be increased by enlarging the size of the sample or by taking the average of several sample variances from samples of similar size.

The difficulty with the variance as a measure of variation is that it is given in terms of the square of the units of measurement. Extracting the square root of the variance converts it to the same units in which the measurements were taken. The statistic thus obtained is called the standard deviation $s$. Curiously, even though the sample variance $s^2$ is an unbiased estimate of the population variance $\sigma^2$ the sample standard deviation $s$ is not an unbiased estimate of the population standard deviation $\sigma$. The bias is introduced by extracting the square root. This can be demonstrated by a simple model. The mean of the numbers 4, 9, and 16 = 9.67. The square roots of the numbers are 2, 3, and 4, respectively. The mean of the square roots is 3, which is not the square root of 9.67. When, however, the data are to be plotted on a curve and certain types of tests of significance are to be carried out, it is necessary to express the estimate of variance in the original units, for example, inches in the example from the guayule seedlings, rather than squared units. For such purposes, the standard deviation is employed despite its bias. From the sample of guayule seedlings the standard deviation $s$ would be: $s = \sqrt{2.82} = 1.68$ inches.

The symmetrical bell-shaped curve presented in Fig. 17.8 represents a normal distribution of individuals. If one standard deviation is plotted on either side of the mean, the arc would include about two-thirds (68.26 percent) of the population represented. The shape of the curve is determined by the amount of variation, as indicated by the standard deviation. If the same area is maintained, a small $s$ is associated with a high curve and a large $s$ with a flat curve. Furthermore, if $s$ is small and the curve is high, most of the observations are clustered around the mean. On the other hand, if $s$ is large and the curve is flat, the observations are spread away from the mean.

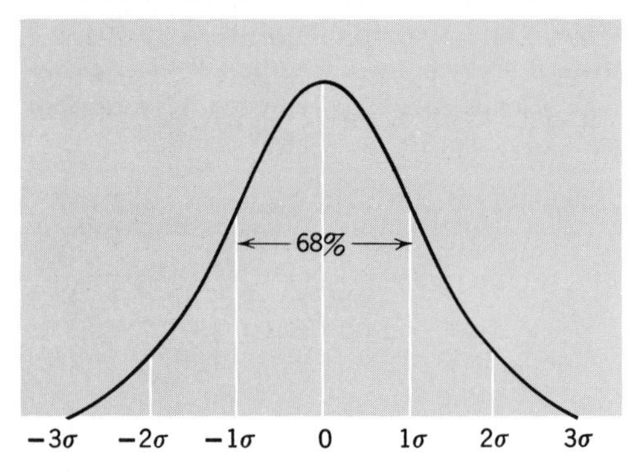


**Fig. 17.8** A symmetrical bell-shaped curve showing a normal distribution of individuals in a population.

Another useful statistical measurement is the standard deviation of means or the standard error of the mean. This is a measure of the reliability of the sample mean $\bar{x}$ as an estimate of the population mean. As suggested by the name, the standard error is an estimate of the standard deviation of means of samples drawn from a single population. Means represent central values for groups of individuals and therefore are expected to vary less than individuals drawn at random from the population. It is not necessary to actually go through the process of taking several samples from the same population, since it can be shown that the standard error is inversely proportional to the square root of the sample size $n$.

Two factors are involved in an evaluation of reliability based on a sample: the size of the sample, and the amount of variation in the population sampled. If great variation is present, a large sample will be required to represent the population adequately. If individuals are fairly uniform, a smaller sample may be satisfactory. These two factors are taken into consideration in the following formula for the standard error $\sigma_{\bar{x}}$ of the population mean:

$$\sigma_{\bar{x}} = \sqrt{\frac{\sigma^2}{n}} = \frac{\sigma}{\sqrt{n}}$$

Since the variation $\sigma^2$ of the population is usually unknown, it must be estimated from the sample variance $s^2$. With this alteration, the formula for the standard error of the mean $s_x$ becomes:

$$s_{\bar{x}} = \sqrt{\frac{s^2}{n}} = \frac{s}{\sqrt{n}}$$

Substituting the data from the guayule sample we have:

$$s_{\bar{x}} = \frac{s}{\sqrt{n}} = \frac{1.68}{11.05} = 0.15$$

This value indicates whether the estimated mean $\bar{x}$ is near the population mean $\mu$ or likely to be far removed from it. The mean may now be written $11.95 \pm 0.15$. This standard error was based on one standard deviation which, plotted on the normal curve in a + and − position from the mean $\bar{x}$, includes about 68 percent of the population. Therefore, the investigator is about two-thirds or 68 percent confident that the true mean $\mu$ lies within the limits of + one standard error and − one standard error from the sample mean $\bar{x}$. Such areas or proportions of the population are called confidence intervals. The true mean $\mu$ is constant and does not possess a probability distribution. It either does or does not fall between established limits with reference to a given sample. If several samples are to be taken, and statements are made concerning each as to whether the population mean lies inside or outside the limits, two-thirds of these statements will be correct.

Other confidence intervals with probabilities different from 0.68 may also be chosen to evaluate the reliability of a given estimate. Suppose the investigator wishes to be 0.95 or 95 percent confident, that is, to be able to say that the probability that $\mu$ will fall within certain limits on either side of $\bar{x}$ is 0.95. For this purpose, he may make use of the $t$-distribution concept. The $t$ is defined as the difference between the sample mean and the true mean divided by $s_x$, as shown by the formula

$$t = \frac{(\bar{x} - \mu)}{s_{\bar{x}}}$$

To solve for $\mu$ the equation may be transposed as follows:

$$\mu = \bar{x} \pm ts_{\bar{x}}$$

The confidence interval may be obtained from the formula at a particular confidence level. One limit is on the + side of the mean and the other is on the − side. Table 17.4 has been devised to show the distribution of $t$. At the left the degrees of freedom or $n - 1$ are listed. The $t$ values are given in the body of the table, and the probabilities of as large as or larger $t$ values are given at the top. To use this device an appropriate $t$ value from the table is substituted in the formula along with the sample mean $\bar{x}$ and the standard error $s_{\bar{x}}$. The equation is then solved for $\mu$. At the 0.95 confidence level, the probability of being misled by sampling is 0.05. Lower ($L_1$) and upper ($L_2$) limits of the confidence interval may be established at this level as follows:

$$L_1 = \bar{x} - t\,0.05 s_{\bar{x}}$$
$$L_2 = \bar{x} + t\,0.05 s_{\bar{x}}$$

These limits are random variables. If they are superimposed on the bell curve (Fig. 17.8) they will include the population

**TABLE 17.4 Probability (P) for values of t (vertical columns) and various degrees of freedom (d.f.)**[a]

The degrees of freedom are one less than the number of classes.

| d.f. \ P | 0.5 | 0.4 | 0.3 | 0.2 | 0.1 | 0.05 | 0.01 |
|---|---|---|---|---|---|---|---|
| 1 | 1.000 | 1.376 | 1.963 | 3.078 | 6.314 | 12.706 | 63.657 |
| 2 | 0.816 | 1.061 | 1.386 | 1.886 | 2.920 | 4.303 | 9.925 |
| 3 | 0.765 | 0.978 | 1.250 | 1.638 | 2.353 | 3.182 | 5.841 |
| 4 | 0.741 | 0.941 | 1.190 | 1.533 | 2.132 | 2.776 | 4.604 |
| 5 | 0.727 | 0.920 | 1.156 | 1.476 | 2.015 | 2.571 | 4.032 |
| 6 | 0.718 | 0.906 | 1.134 | 1.440 | 1.943 | 2.447 | 3.707 |
| 7 | 0.711 | 0.896 | 1.119 | 1.415 | 1.895 | 2.365 | 3.499 |
| 8 | 0.706 | 0.889 | 1.108 | 1.397 | 1.860 | 2.306 | 3.355 |
| 9 | 0.703 | 0.883 | 1.100 | 1.383 | 1.833 | 2.262 | 3.250 |
| 10 | 0.700 | 0.879 | 1.093 | 1.372 | 1.812 | 2.228 | 3.169 |
| 15 | 0.691 | 0.866 | 1.074 | 1.341 | 1.753 | 2.131 | 2.947 |
| 20 | 0.687 | 0.860 | 1.064 | 1.325 | 1.725 | 2.086 | 2.845 |
| 25 | 0.684 | 0.856 | 1.058 | 1.316 | 1.708 | 2.060 | 2.787 |
| 30 | 0.683 | 0.854 | 1.055 | 1.310 | 1.697 | 2.042 | 2.750 |
| 50 | 0.680 | 0.849 | 1.047 | 1.299 | 1.676 | 2.008 | 2.678 |
| 100 | 0.677 | 0.846 | 1.042 | 1.290 | 1.661 | 1.984 | 2.626 |
| ∞ | 0.674 | 0.842 | 1.036 | 1.282 | 1.645 | 1.960 | 2.576 |

[a] Abridged from Table 4 of Fisher: *Statistical Methods for Research Workers,* published by Oliver and Boyd, Ltd., Edinburgh, by permission of the author and publishers.

mean $\mu$ in 95 percent of repetitions of the same experiment.

Now reading $t = 1.984$ from the table and 100 degrees of freedom, which is nearest to $n - 1$ or 121, and substituting the values $\bar{x} = 11.95$ and $s_{\bar{x}} = 0.15$ for the guayule sample, we have:

$$L_1 = 11.95 - 1.984\,(0.15) = 11.65$$
$$L_2 = 11.95 + 1.984\,(0.15) = 12.25$$

These are the confidence limits. If statements based on samples are made repeatedly to the effect that the true mean $\mu$ falls within these limits, 95 percent of them will be correct.

Consequently, the standard error of the mean is an indication of the reliability with which the sample mean $\bar{x}$ estimates the population mean $\mu$. The smaller the standard error, the more reliable is the estimate. It can be seen from the formula that, as the sample size $n$ increases, the value of the standard error tends to decrease, and vice versa. This relation illustrates the advantage of large samples for obtaining the best possible estimates of parameters.

### *Statistics Applied to Genetic Problems*

Indirect contributions that have come from the application of statistical treatments to genetics are perhaps more significant than those that are direct. Statistical requirements have made it necessary for the geneticist to carefully design each experiment before he undertakes the actual investigation. He has thus developed a more critical attitude concerning methods and interpretations of experimental results. Objective procedures have helped the modern geneticist to avoid the loose thinking characteristic of many early speculations in genetics. A number of variations formerly attributed to genetic mechanisms have now been explained on the basis of sampling errors. Some genetic patterns were not recognized in the past or were confused with the effects of environmental factors. The modern geneticist controls all aspects of his study that can be controlled and allows for the element of chance in sampling. The development of effective statistical methods has helped foster this trend. The mean, variance, and standard error of the mean have been presented as basic statistical tools. Their value can be demonstrated by applying them directly to a problem. In cereal crops, the time required for the plants to mature is dependent to some extent on inheritance. Since environmental factors such as temperature are also involved, the plants to be compared must be grown in a single environment and adequate checks for uncontrollable environmental factors must be provided.

In a particular experiment, seeds representing each of four types of wheat were planted in randomized field plots. This is a device for distributing the types in the field so that genetic and environmental effects can be distinguished. The following types were included: two inbred parent varieties (PA and PB) and $F_1$ and $F_2$ from the cross between PA and PB. The seedlings were all raised in the same season and the randomized plots were designed to control minor environmental variations in soil, moisture, and other factors. The time required for maturing was recorded in units of days from the time of planting to the time when the heads were fully formed. It would be impossible to record and analyze the data for plants composing the entire populations. Each population consists of a theoretically infinite number of plants grown under similar environmental conditions. A sample of 40 plants was taken at random from each population. The data representing the four samples of 40 individuals each are given as follows:

PA

| | | | | | | | |
|---|---|---|---|---|---|---|---|
| 75 | 74 | 72 | 72 | 73 | 71 | 72 | 71 |
| 76 | 73 | 72 | 72 | 72 | 70 | 71 | 72 |
| 71 | 73 | 74 | 73 | 73 | 72 | 71 | 72 |
| 72 | 74 | 73 | 72 | 71 | 72 | 73 | 72 |
| 74 | 71 | 72 | 73 | 75 | 70 | 72 | 76 |

PB

| | | | | | | | |
|---|---|---|---|---|---|---|---|
| 58 | 55 | 56 | 56 | 53 | 55 | 55 | 57 |
| 54 | 55 | 56 | 55 | 58 | 57 | 55 | 56 |
| 55 | 57 | 55 | 57 | 56 | 57 | 55 | 55 |
| 56 | 57 | 55 | 54 | 59 | 57 | 55 | 55 |
| 58 | 56 | 57 | 54 | 53 | 56 | 58 | 56 |

$F_1$PA × PB

| | | | | | | | |
|---|---|---|---|---|---|---|---|
| 60 | 65 | 63 | 61 | 65 | 60 | 62 | 63 |
| 61 | 60 | 63 | 64 | 64 | 61 | 62 | 63 |
| 65 | 62 | 64 | 62 | 60 | 59 | 61 | 62 |
| 61 | 60 | 63 | 62 | 60 | 63 | 60 | 65 |
| 64 | 61 | 62 | 64 | 64 | 61 | 62 | 64 |

$F_2$PA × PB

| | | | | | | | |
|---|---|---|---|---|---|---|---|
| 69 | 66 | 62 | 60 | 63 | 67 | 72 | 64 |
| 61 | 63 | 62 | 63 | 60 | 59 | 64 | 63 |
| 56 | 62 | 62 | 65 | 64 | 73 | 60 | 65 |
| 57 | 64 | 63 | 70 | 68 | 62 | 71 | 63 |
| 65 | 66 | 64 | 58 | 61 | 65 | 62 | 64 |

The data from each sample were classified and are summarized in Table 17.5. The means, variances, standard deviations, and standard errors of the means are also included in the table. Several facts can be derived from the data and calculations. In the first place, the two parents represent different populations in regard to the length of time required for maturity. One population (PA) had a mean ($\bar{x}_A$) of 72.47 and the other (PB) had a mean ($\bar{x}_B$) of 55.85.

The conclusion here that the two parents came from separate populations seems evident from inspection of the data. When the discontinuity is not so obvious, however, it is necessary to devise tests to determine whether differences between means indicate different populations sampled or merely chance differences in two different samples from the same population. The

**TABLE 17.5 Data and calculations from samples of the two parents, $F_1$ and $F_2$, of wheat populations classified according to time in days required for maturity; forty plants are included in each sample.**

| Days | 53 | 54 | 55 | 56 | 57 | 58 | 59 | 60 | 61 | 62 | 63 | 64 | 65 | 66 | 67 | 68 | 69 | 70 | 71 | 72 | 73 | 74 | 75 | 76 | $\bar{x}$ | $s_{\bar{x}}$ | $s^2$ | $s$ |
|---|---|---|---|---|---|---|---|---|---|---|---|---|---|---|---|---|---|---|---|---|---|---|---|---|---|---|---|---|
| PA | | | | | | | | | | | | | | | | | | 2 | 7 | 15 | 8 | 4 | 2 | 2 | 72.47± | 0.23 | 2.05 | 1.43 |
| PB | 2 | 3 | 13 | 9 | 8 | 4 | 1 | | | | | | | | | | | | | | | | | | 55.85± | 0.22 | 1.92 | 1.39 |
| $F_1$ | | | | | | | 1 | 7 | 7 | 8 | 6 | 7 | 4 | | | | | | | | | | | | 62.20± | 0.27 | 2.88 | 1.70 |
| $F_2$ | | | | 1 | 1 | 1 | 1 | 3 | 2 | 5 | 7 | 6 | 4 | 2 | 1 | 1 | 1 | 1 | 1 | 1 | 1 | | | | 63.72± | 0.60 | 14.26 | 3.78 |

standard error of a difference ($S_D$) may be used for such a test. $S_D$ is the square root of the sum of squares of the two standard errors calculated from the samples being compared, or

$$S_D = \sqrt{(S_{\bar{x}1})^2 + (S_{\bar{x}2})^2}$$

where $S_{\bar{x}1}$ represents the standard error of one sample and $S_{\bar{x}2}$ the standard error of the other. Substituting the standard errors calculated for the two parents in the wheat we have:

$$S_D = \sqrt{(S_{\bar{x}1})^2 + (S_{\bar{x}2})^2} = \sqrt{(0.23)^2 + (0.22)^2} = 0.318$$

The significance of the $S_D$ of 0.318 can be appreciated by comparison with the actual difference between the means of the two parents. This comparison can be shown by calculating $t$ as follows:

$$t = \frac{\bar{x}_A - \bar{x}_B}{S_D} = \frac{72.47 - 55.85}{0.318} = 52.3$$

where $t$ is the difference between the two means $\bar{x}_A - \bar{x}_B$ divided by the standard error of the difference $S_D$. Arbitrarily, if the actual difference is more than twice the standard error, it is considered to be significant. More values of $t$ in terms of probability are given in Table 17.4. The value of $t = 52.3$ with 78 degrees of freedom is off the table. Suffice it to say here that the probability that these two samples represent the same population is extremely low.

The next interpretation from the data and calculations concerns the mode of inheritance. The $F_1$ plants were intermediate between the two parents, and the $F_2$ were also generally intermediate but represented a wider range than the $F_1$. This result suggested the quantitative pattern of inheritance.

The variation measured by the variance and standard deviation was fairly comparable for the two inbred parents and the $F_1$, as expected in the results of crosses between parents that were homozygous. If we assume that the parents were completely homozygous, the variation would be entirely environmental. The $F_1$ plants from such crosses would be uniformly heterozygous; again all variation would be environmental. Segregation would be expected in the $F_2$, providing for genetic variation in addition to that directly associated with the environment.

The standard error of the $F_2$ mean (used as a measure of reliability) was larger than those of the parents and $F_1$ because of the increased variation in the $F_2$ and the comparable sample size. A larger sample would provide a better estimate of the parameter (mean). For a sample of 80 with $s = 3.78$, the $s_{\bar{x}}$ would be 0.425. A sample of 200 with the same $s$ would give $s_{\bar{x}} = 0.267$.

The number of gene pairs operating in the cross may now be roughly estimated from the classified $F_2$ data. In the wheat crosses under consideration, 4 of the 40 $F_2$ plants, or about 1 in 10, occurred within the range of each parent. One representative of the parental type in every 16 would be theoretically expected if two independent gene pairs were segregating. This method of determining the numbers of active genes is too simplified to be of much value, however. If polygenes with small cumulative effects are involved in the quantitative traits being considered, it would take thousands of $F_2$ plants to obtain even a rough estimate of the number of genes present. Furthermore, the method just cited for estimating the number of active genes implies that all are additive and contribute equally to the end product.

Alternatively, an estimate of the number of active genes may be obtained mathematically by comparing the variances of the $F_1$ and $F_2$. Assuming that all variations being considered were hereditary, that only independent genes with cumulative effects were involved, and that the $F_1$ plants were fully heterozygous, the difference between the variance of the $F_1$ and $F_2$ should provide a minimum estimate of the number of genes acting. The larger the difference between the $F_1$ and $F_2$ variances, the fewer the number. Since the requirements for use of this method are seldom realized in ordinary genetic research, and standards are necessary to form a basis for comparison, the method will be left to the specialists. Although the simplified procedure detailed earlier (which depends on the frequency with which the parental (P) phenotypes occur in the $F_2$) has definite limitations, it will be used here for the purpose of estimating the number of segregating genes.

The premise of Nilsson-Ehle (which was later developed by Fisher, Wright, Mather, and others), that polygenes behave in Mendelian fashion, is accepted as generally correct. Furthermore, the effect of the individual genes in the polygenic systems is known to be cumulative and may operate in a plus or minus direction. The cumulative effect often seems to be geometrical rather than arithmetical. A logarithmic scale provides a more uniform pattern of the results of crosses than the true scale developed in the units of actual measurement. So many factors are involved and so many assumptions are required that it is doubtful whether the number of genes operating in any but the exceptionally simple cases can be estimated realistically by any method.

## SUMMARY

Polygenic inheritance is a statistical concept which emphasizes not the individual but population aggregates. Many genes are associated with metric traits. A continuous rather than a discontinuous scale of measurement must therefore be used. Nevertheless, the Mendelian foundation forms the basis for the genetic mechanisms of populations as well as of individuals. If only a few genes are active in the production of a trait, a discontinuous genotype may be reflected in a continuous phenotype. When large numbers of interchangeable genes (multiple genes or polygenes) are involved, both the genotype and phenotype may appear to be continuous. Seven features of polygenic inheritance are now listed.

1. Segregation occurs at an indefinitely large number of loci.
2. The effects of allelic substitutions at each locus are trivial.
3. Phenotypic effects of gene substitutions are interchangeable; that is, genes may have different biochemical functions but similar phenotypic effects.
4. Phenotypic expression is subject to modification by differences in the intangible environment to which each member of the population is exposed. Even when the environment is as controlled as possible, environmentally produced variations occur.
5. Natural populations carry great reserves of genetic variability. Several cross-fertilizing, diploid populations have been studied in nature, and all are found to have variation in every quantitative character studied.

6. Blocks of genes are bound together by inversions and transmitted as units from inversion heterozygotes to their progeny, but such blocks are broken up by crossing over in inversion homozygotes.

7. Polygenes have pleiotropic effects; that is, one gene may modify or suppress more than one trait. A single allele may do only one thing chemically but may ultimately affect many characters. Pleiotropy is more manifest in polygenic inheritance than in single-gene inheritance.

## REFERENCES

Dunn, L. C., and D. R. Charles. 1937. "Studies on spotting patterns." *Genetics,* **22,** 14–42. (Analysis of quantitative variations in the pied spotting of the house mouse.)

East, E. M. 1910. "A Mendelian interpretation of variation that is apparently continuous." *Amer. Nat.,* **44,** 65–82.

East, E. M. 1916. "Studies on size inheritance in Nicotiana." *Genetics,* **1,** 164–176. (Early application of multiple gene hypothesis to tobacco plants.)

Emerson, R. A., and E. M. East. 1913. "The inheritance of quantitative characters in maize." *Nebraska Agric. Exp. Res. Bull.* (Early applications of multiple-gene inheritance in maize.)

Fisher, R. A. 1947. *Statistical methods for research workers,* 10th ed. Oliver and Boyd, Edinburgh.

Fraser, A. S. 1957. "Stimulation of genetic systems by automatic digital computers I." *Austral. J. Biol. Sci.,* **10,** 484–491. (New techniques used to demonstrate that polygenic inheritance is Mendelian.)

Kempthorne, O. 1957. *An introduction to genetic statistics.* John Wiley and Sons, New York.

Mather, K. 1949. *Biometrical genetics.* Dover Publications, New York.

Mather, K. 1954. "The genetical units of continuous variation." *Proc. IX Intern. Cong. Genet.,* Part I: 106–123. (Interpretation of the relation between genes and quantitative inheritance by the man who coined the word "polygene" and who has done much to develop the polygene concept.)

Milkman, R. D. 1960. "The genetic basis of natural variation, I. Crossveins in *Drosophila melanogaster.*" *Genetics,* **45,** 35–48, II. "Analysis of a polygenic system in *Drosophila melanogaster.*" *Genetics,* **45,** 377–391.

Stern, C. 1960. *Principles of human genetics,* 2nd ed. W. H. Freeman and Co., San Francisco. (Chapter 8 deals with polygenic inheritance and includes a discussion of skin-color inheritance.)

Stern, C. 1953. "Model estimates of the frequency of white and near-white segregants in the American Negro." *Acta Genetica et Statistics Medica,* **4,** 281–298. (Analysis of available data on the basis of 2, 3, 4, 5, 6, 7, 10, and 20 additive gene pairs. Models of 4, 5, and 6 gene pairs agree best with observed data.)

# *Problems*

**17.1** Using the forked-line method, diagram the cross between a wheat variety with red kernels (*AABB*) and a variety with white kernels (*aabb*) in which the two pairs of genes have a cumulative effect. Classify the $F_2$ progeny under the headings, red, dark, medium, light, and white, and summarize the expected results.

**17.2** From another cross between red and white kernel varieties, $\frac{1}{64}$ of the $F_2$ plants had kernels as deeply colored as the red parent and $\frac{1}{64}$ had white kernels. About $\frac{62}{64}$ were between the extremes of the parents. How can the difference in $F_2$ results in Problems 17.1 and 17.2 be explained?

**17.3** Different $F_2$ plants from the foregoing cross were crossed with the white parent (*aabbcc*). Give the genotypes of the individual plants from which the following backcross results could have been obtained: (a) 1 colored, 1 white; (b) 3 colored, 1 white; and (c) 7 colored, 1 white.

**17.4** Different $F_2$ plants from the cross in Problem 17.2 were selfed. Give the genotypes of the parents that could have produced the following results: (a) all white; (b) all colored; (c) 3 colored, 1 white; (d) 15 colored, 1 white; and (e) 63 colored, 1 white.

**17.5** Different $F_2$ plants from the cross in Problem 17.2, all producing kernels with some red color, were crossed with each other. Give the genotypes of parents which could have produced the following results: (a) 7 colored, 1 white; (b) 31 colored, 1 white; and (c) 63 colored, 1 white.

**17.6** Assume that two pairs of genes are involved in the inheritance of skin pigmentation. For the purpose of this problem, the genotype of the Negro may be symbolized *AABB* and that of the Caucasian *aabb*. What color might be expected in the $F_1$ from crosses between Negro and Caucasian people?

**17.7** If mulattoes (*AaBb*) mated with other mulattoes of the same genotype, what results might be expected with reference to the intensity of skin pigmentation?

**17.8** (a) If people with various degrees of skin pigmentation married only people known to have the genotype *aabb*, could they have "black" babies? Explain. (b) Could a "white" couple with Negro ancestry have a "black" baby? Explain.

**17.9** If the number of gene pairs involved in skin pigmentation should actually be 4, 5, or 6, as indicated by Stern's model, (a) how would the expected results of crosses between white and Negroes differ from those considered in the above problem? (b) What criteria and data would be necessary to determine the number of genes actually involved?

**17.10** Two pairs of genes (*AABB*) with equal and additive effects are postulated to influence the size of corn in certain varieties. A tall variety averaging 6 feet was crossed with a dwarf averaging 2 feet. (a) If the size of the dwarf is attributed to the residual genotype (*aabb*), what is the effect of each gene that increases the size above 2 feet? (b) Diagram a cross between a large and small variety and classify the expected $F_2$ phenotypes.

**17.11** The size of rabbits is presumably determined by genes with an equal and additive effect. From a total of 2012 $F_2$ progeny from crosses between large and small varieties, 8 were as small as the average of the small parent variety and about 8 were as large as the large parent variety. How many gene pairs were operating?

**17.12** A sample of 20 plants from a certain population was measured in inches as follows: 18, 21, 20, 23, 20, 21, 20, 22, 19, 20, 17, 21, 20, 22, 20, 21, 20, 22, 19, and 23. Calculate (a) the mean; (b) the standard deviation; and (c) the standard error of the mean.

**17.13** What is measured by (a) the mean? (b) the standard deviation? and (c) the standard error of the mean?

**17.14** If the population sampled in Problem 17.12 was an $F_2$ involving parents from varieties averaging 7 inches and 33 inches, respectively, would you conclude that few or many gene pairs were involved? Why?

**17.15** A sample of 20 plants from a certain population was measured in inches as follows: 7, 10, 12, 9, 10, 12, 10, 9, 10, 11, 8, 12, 10, 10, 9, 11, 10, 9, 10, and 11. Calculate (a) the mean; (b) the standard deviation; (c) the standard error of the mean; and (d) apply the *t* test at the 0.99 confidence level.

**17.16** If the population sampled in Problem 7.15 was an $F_2$ from parents averaging 7 inches and 12 inches, respectively, would you conclude that few or many gene pairs were involved? Why?

**17.17** The width or spread of 122 guayule plants representing a random sample were measured 107 days after planting in inches as follows:

13 12 11 13 13 13 12 11 13 11 12 11 12 12 13 12 13
13 13 12 11 11 12 12 12 13 10 11 11 11 11 12 10 12
11 10 9 10 10 10 14 12 11 11 9 11 12 13 11 11 12
11 12 12 14 13 14 13 16 13 13 11 14 12 13 15 12 11
10 11 11 11 10 11 12 13 12 12 12 12 13 12 10 13 10
10 10 10 13 11 10 13 14 12 9 10 10 11 11 14 11 9
12 10 10 13 11 11 13 10 12 12 10 9 14 12 10 11 10
12 14 11

Calculate (a) the mean; (b) the standard deviation; (c) the standard error of the mean; and (d) apply the *t* test at the 0.95 confidence level.

**17.18** Seed from four different types of wheat were planted and samples of each type were measured as to the time required for maturity. This is the number of days elapsing from the time of planting the seed until the heads of the grain appear. The following statistics were computed from the samples of different sizes:

| | Mean | Standard Deviation | Standard error of the mean |
|---|---|---|---|
| Strain A | 72.37 | 1.31 | 0.221 |
| Strain B | 55.85 | 0.93 | 0.179 |
| $F_1$ (A × B) | 61.40 | 1.35 | 0.350 |
| $F_2$ (A × B) | 63.84 | 3.45 | 0.277 |

Several of the $F_2$ plants were selfed. The $F_3$ seeds were planted in randomized plots and raised in the same season. The progeny thus produced were classified according to the time required for maturity. A sample of 24 plants from the seed of a single $F_2$ were recorded as follows:

56 55 54 56 57 56
55 56 57 56 57 56
55 57 56 55 56 58
56 55 57 56 59 58

Compute the following: (a) the mean, (b) the standard deviation; (c) the standard error of the mean and (d) apply the *t* test at the 0.95 confidence level.

**17.19** (a) Discuss briefly the biometrical significance of the sample in Problem 17.18. (b) From which part of the $F_2$ population was the $F_2$ parent likely obtained? (c) What suggestions can be made concerning the genotype of the $F_2$ parent?

**17.20** Make a similar analysis of the following samples, each of which represents a random sample from the $F_3$ obtained from the seed of a single $F_2$ plant:

(a)
73 72 70 74 76 71
72 74 74 74 71 76
73 72 77 73 78 75
76 70 74 70 71 70

| | | | | | | |
|---|---|---|---|---|---|---|
| (b) | 67 | 65 | 64 | 66 | 65 | 66 |
| | 68 | 64 | 65 | 66 | 69 | 71 |
| | 70 | 63 | 62 | 61 | 60 | 64 |
| | 63 | 65 | 64 | 63 | 68 | 67 |
| (c) | 65 | 64 | 66 | 67 | 65 | 64 |
| | 64 | 68 | 65 | 64 | 63 | 65 |
| | 65 | 64 | 66 | 65 | 67 | 66 |
| | 65 | 68 | 65 | 64 | 66 | 65 |

**17.21** How can the number of gene differences between two varieties be estimated with reference to a particular quantitative trait? What limitations are associated with such estimates?

**17.22** Evaluate the practical and theoretical significance of multiple-gene inheritance.

# Population Genetics

# 18

In 1908, an English mathematician, G. H. Hardy, and a German physician, W. Weinberg (1862–1939; Fig. 18.1), independently discovered a principle concerned with the frequency of genes (alleles) in a population that has since formed the basis for population genetics. Before 1908 Mendelian genetics had been amply demonstrated by W. Bateson and others. Simple 3:1 and 1:1 ratios had been obtained from controlled pair matings involving many different kinds of plants and animals. The observed proportions of different phenotypes in natural populations, however, suggested different gene frequencies than those characteristic of laboratory experiments. Hardy and Weinberg showed that an equilibrium is established between the frequencies of alleles in a population. The relative frequency of occurrence of each allele tended to remain constant, generation after generation. A mathematical relation now called the Hardy-Weinberg theorem was developed to describe the equilibrium between alleles.

Mendelian segregation may be represented mathematically by the expansion of a binomial $(a + b)^n$. The familiar ratio of 1:2:1, representing the segregation of a single pair of alleles ($Aa$), in a cross between heterozygous parents, may be represented by the simplest expansion of $(A + a)^2$, which is $1AA + 2Aa + 1aa$. To express the relation in more general terms which will apply to any pair of alleles, the symbols $p$ and $q$ will be introduced. Let $p$ represent the frequency for allele $A$, and $q$, that for allele $a$. The probability of homozygous $A(AA)$ occurring through random mating would be $p^2$, that for the heterozygous combination ($Aa$) would be $pq + qp$ or $2pq$, and that for homozygous $a(aa)$ would be $q^2$. A frequency is the ratio of the actual number of individuals falling in a single class to the total number of individuals and a probability is a function that represents the likelihood of occurrence of any particular form of an event. Possible combinations of sperm and eggs from heterozygous individuals are depicted in Fig. 18.2 illustrating the allele frequency relations which form the basis for the Hardy-Weinberg equilibrium.

The zygotic combinations predicted in a randomly mating population may be represented by $p^2 : 2pq : q^2$, where $p^2$ represents the $AA$ genotype, $2pq$ the $Aa$, and $q^2$ the $aa$ genotype; or, in the form of an equation, $p^2 + 2pq + q^2 = 1$. When only two alleles are involved, and therefore $p$ and $q$ represent the frequencies of all of the alleles concerned, $p + q = 1$. Since $p + q = 1$, $p = 1 - q$. Now, if $1 - q$ is substituted for $p$, all the relations in the formula can be represented in terms of $q$ as follows: $(1 - q)^2 + 2q(1 - q) + q^2 = 1$.

The frequency of alleles in a population is represented by the relative proportion of

Fig. 18.1 Wilhelm Weinberg, German physician who pioneered in the field of population genetics.

all the segregating alleles. If allele $A$ has a frequency of $1 - q$ and allele $a$ a frequency of $q$, the expected distribution of these alleles under conditions of random mating in succeeding generations may be calculated. The formula may be applied to any pair of alleles and the gene frequencies calculated, if the frequency of one member of the pair of alleles in the population can be determined.

|  |  | Sperm |  |
|---|---|---|---|
|  |  | $A(p)$ | $a(q)$ |
| Eggs | $A(p)$ | $AA(p^2)$ | $Aa(pq)$ |
|  | $a(q)$ | $Aa(pq)$ | $aa(q^2)$ |

Summary: $p^2(AA) + 2pq(Aa) + q^2(aa)$

Fig. 18.2 Combinations of sperm and eggs from heterozygous individuals illustrating the allele frequency relations which form the basis for the Hardy-Weinberg equilibrium.

The significance of the Hardy-Weinberg equilibrium was not immediately appreciated. A rebirth of biometrical genetics was later brought about with the classical papers of R. A. Fisher (1890–1962; Fig. 18.3), beginning in 1918 and those of Sewall Wright, beginning in 1920. Under the leadership of these mathematicians, emphasis was placed on the population rather than on the individual or family group, which had previously occupied the attention of most Mendelian geneticists. In about 1935, T. Dobzhansky and others began to interpret and to popularize the mathematical approach for studies of genetics and evolution. Questions concerning the behavior of genes in populations and the mechanics of evolution took on new significance. Animal breeders dealing with expensive material and long periods between generations, began to

Fig. 18.3 Sir Ronald A. Fisher, British statistician who did much to lay the mathematical foundation for population genetics.

apply statistical methods in their breeding programs. Interest developed in the application of mathematics to human populations. Geneticists now dealing with population problems are analyzing and interpreting population dynamics in terms of gene frequencies.

## GENETIC EQUILIBRIUM

As shown by Hardy and Weinberg, alleles segregating in a population tend to establish an equilibrium with reference to each other. For example, if two alleles should occur in equal proportion in a large, isolated, breeding population and neither had a selective or mutational advantage over the other, they would be expected to remain in equal proportion generation after generation. This would be a special case because alleles in natural populations seldom if ever occur in equal frequency. They may, however, be expected to maintain their relative frequency, whatever it is, subject only to such factors as natural selection, differential mutation rates, migration, meiotic drive, and chance, all of which alter the level of the gene frequencies. An equilibrium is maintained through random mating.

### *Calculation of Gene Frequencies for Intermediate Inheritance*

The M and N blood antigens (Chapter 8) provide a model for the segregation of a single pair of alleles with intermediate inheritance in human populations. To be consistent with symbols for alleles, the same letter should be used to represent the different genes at the same locus; that is, the letter M or N with appropriate forms or superscripts, should be used for both alleles. Because the symbols M and N were used by the original investigators and have become widely dispersed in the literature, however, they will be used in this discussion despite the inconsistency. These alleles are especially well adapted for a beginning study of gene frequency because dominance is not expressed. The M, N, and MN phenotypes are detectable by serological tests. Table 18.1 shows the relations between genotypes and phenotypes with the specific reactions of the blood cells to anti-M and anti-N sera.

**TABLE 18.1**

| Phenotype | Genotype | Anti-M | Anti-N |
|---|---|---|---|
| M | *MM* | + | O |
| MN | *MN* | + | + |
| N | *NN* | O | + |

The heterozygous combination (*MN*) is distinguishable phenotypically from the two homozygotes (*MM* and *NN*). Since no significant selective value is associated with these blood characters, most people do not know and do not care whether they have M, N, or MN blood. Several investigators have suggested recently, however, that a type of immunization is possible which may give these antigens significance in selection. Numerous samples of blood representing different populations have been tested. The frequency of *M* and *N* alleles in these populations may be calculated from the data obtained. Following are the proportions of the different phenotypes based on a sample of 6129 Caucasian people in the United States:

| M | MN | N |
|---|---|---|
| 1787 | 3039 | 1303 |

If the data are interpreted in terms of the frequency of genes ($MM + MN + NN$) rather than the proportions of individuals with the different phenotypes in the population sampled, the relations shown in Table 18.2 based on the total number of genes are obtained.

The same result may be obtained by calculating $q$ or $(1 - q)$ from the relations in the Hardy-Weinberg formula and determining the frequency of the two genes *M* and *N*. For example, the frequency of

**TABLE 18.2**

| Allele | Proportion | Gene Frequency |
|---|---|---|
| $M = 2 \times 1787 + 3039 = 6613$ | 6,613/12,258 | 0.54 |
| $N = 2 \times 1303 + 3039 = 5645$ | 5,645/12,258 | 0.46 |

N people $= q^2 =$ (from the sample) $1303/6129 = 0.21$; $q = \sqrt{0.21} = 0.46$ and $1 - q = 0.54$. In the population sampled, about 0.54 or 54 percent of the chromosomes of the pair carrying these alleles would be expected to have M, and about 0.46 or 46 percent would have *N*. This is the relative frequency of the two alleles in the population sampled.

When gene frequencies are represented in decimal fractions, as in this example, they can be used directly as functions or probabilities. Thus, the probability is 0.54 that a member of the particular pair of chromosomes will carry *M* and the probability is 0.46 that a member of the pair will carry *N*. From such information, predictions can be made concerning the various combinations of the alleles in the population.

### *Calculation of Gene Frequency When Dominance is Involved*

Dominance and recessiveness of genes do not directly influence gene frequency; that is, dominance alone does not make an allele occur more frequently in the population than recessiveness. The same type of equilibrium is maintained for alleles showing dominance or recessiveness as is maintained for those with intermediate inheritance, such as the *M* and *N* alleles just described. It is true that dominant genes express themselves in heterozygous combination and therefore more frequently than recessives. If one phenotype has a selective advantage over another, dominance could indirectly influence gene frequency.

An interesting pair of contrasting traits, which has been detected in human populations and has no known selective value, is the ability or inability to taste phenylthiocarbamide (PTC). The difference in the ability of different people to taste this chemical was discovered accidently by investigators in a university laboratory. One laboratory worker found it bitter whereas another could not taste it. When more people were tested, about 70 percent could taste the chemical and 30 percent reported no sensation or at least they experienced no disagreeable taste. A hereditary difference in the mechanism was postulated to account for tasters and nontasters. Inability to taste the chemical was found to be dependent on a single recessive gene.

From a group of 228 university students who were invited to taste the chemical, the following results were obtained: 160 tasters and 68 nontasters. What are the relative gene frequencies of *T* and *t* in the population? Since *T* is dominant over *t*, the 160 tasters include the genotypes *TT* and *Tt*. The 68 nontasters must have the genotype *tt*. The best approach to the Hardy-Weinberg formula is through the nontasters, all of whom can be assumed to have the same genotype. The 68 $tt(q^2)$ individuals represent 0.30 of the population. $q = \sqrt{0.30} = 0.55$. Thus, the frequency of *T* in the sample was 0.45 and the frequency of *t* was 0.55. These gene frequencies are comparable with those obtained from larger samples of the Caucasian population in the United States. Predicted genotypes based on random mating in the population are:

$$TT = 0.45 \times 0.45 = 0.20$$
$$Tt = 0.45 \times 0.55 = 0.25$$
$$tT = 0.55 \times 0.45 = 0.25$$
$$tt = 0.55 \times 0.55 = 0.30$$

Substituting these figures into the Hardy-Weinberg formula we have:

$$p^2 = 0.20,\ 2pq = 0.50,\ q^2 = 0.30.$$

**TABLE 18.3 Phenotypes, probabilities, and genotypes represented by a sample of 173 genetics students.**

| Phenotypes | Probabilities Based on Sample of Students | Genotypes | Genotypic Frequency | Sum of Frequencies of Genotypes with Similar Phenotypes |
|---|---|---|---|---|
| O | 0.4509 | $aa$ | $r^2$ | $r^2$ |
| A | 0.4104 | $AA$<br>$Aa$ | $p^2$<br>$2pr$ | $p^2 + 2pr$ |
| B | 0.0983 | $A^BA^B$<br>$A^Ba$ | $q^2$<br>$2qr$ | $q^2 + 2qr$ |
| AB | 0.0405 | $AA^B$ | $2pq$ | $2pq$ |

When the gene frequencies are known, it is possible to predict the likelihood of occurrence of certain genes and expressions of corresponding traits in populations. A method is thus provided by which the probability of an expression of a trait dependent on a recessive gene may be calculated, even in family groups or other populations where no previous expression has occurred and no evidence is available to indicate which individuals carry the recessive genes in question.

### *Equilibrium and Multiple Alleles*

The equation $p + q = 1$, applies when only two alleles occur at a given locus. If more alleles are known, more symbols must be added to the equation. The four human blood types, for example, are controlled by three alleles, $A$, $A^B$, and $a$. Both $A$ and $A^B$ are dominant over $a$ but neither is dominant over the other, that is, both anti-A and anti-B sera will coagulate the cells from an individual with $AA^B$ genotype. For substitution into the formula, the frequencies may be symbolized, $p$, $q$, and $r$, respectively. Since all three are alleles and these represent all of the alleles involved, it follows that $p + q + r = 1$. Multiple alleles establish an equilibrium in the same way as the single pairs of alleles previously described.

The blood type was determined for members of a group of 173 students in genetics laboratory classes. The following proportions were observed for the four blood groups (that is, phenotypes): O, 78; A, 71; B, 17; and AB, 7. Genotypes and probabilities in the population samples are summarized in Table 18.3.

From these data, the gene frequency of the various alleles may be calculated. The gene pool includes all of the alleles in this sample as well as all others in the population. Since $r^2$ (O) $= 0.45, r = \sqrt{0.45}$ or 0.67. The Hardy-Weinberg formula may now be applied to two of the three alleles. The proportion of the A ($p$) and O ($r$) individuals in the population is represented by the equation $\text{O} + \text{A} = r^2 + 2pr + p^2$, which equals $(r + p)^2$. Therefore, $r + p = \sqrt{\text{O} + \text{A}}$ or $\sqrt{0.45 + 0.41}$, which equals $\sqrt{0.86}$ or 0.93. Therefore, $p = 0.93 - 0.67 = 0.26$. The frequencies of $p$ and $r$ have now been obtained and the next step is to calculate the frequency of $q$. Since $p + q + r = 1$, $0.26 + 0.67 = 1 - q$, or $q = 1 - (0.67 + 0.26) = 0.07$. Now summing up the gene frequencies calculated from the sample of 173 students, we have $0.26\,(p) + 0.07\,(q) + 0.67\,(r) = 1$. The value of 1 represents all the alleles considered in this example. Allele distribution in the gene pool differs from the distribution of phenotypes caused by the alleles. Results from this small sample of 173 students are comparable with those from larger samples in the general population.

## FACTORS INFLUENCING GENE FREQUENCY

The Hardy and Weinberg explanation of equilibrium in the gene frequency pattern of a population required three assumptions: (1) individuals with each genotype must be as reproductively fit as those of any other genotype in the population; (2) the population must consist of a large number of individuals; and (3) random mating must occur throughout the population. The Hardy-Weinberg theorem with its assumptions does not account for any change in gene frequency within populations. That is just what Hardy and Weinberg intended, because their formula described the statics of a Mendelian population. Something more was required to formulate a mathematical explanation of change or dynamics in terms of gene frequencies. This need was filled by Fisher, Wright, and J. B. S. Haldane, who conceived additional theoretical models and superimposed the mechanisms for change in gene frequencies upon the Hardy-Weinberg equilibrium. Population statics was thus extended to become population dynamics.

Now that mathematical tools have been established, the dynamic relations that exist between individuals representing particular genotypes and the environment can be determined. Population genetics seeks an explanation for the genetic architectures of different populations. This discipline is necessarily concerned with the origins of adaptive norms or arrays of genotypes as they are consonant with the demands of the environments. The genetic architecture of a population is the manner in which the genetic material is arranged and the frequency with which each unit is used. In ascertaining the genetic architecture of a population, questions must be answered concerning gene frequency, the frequency of chromosome structural changes such as inversions and translocations, and chromosome numbers. Changes in gene frequency depend on selection, mutation, chance (genetic drift), meiotic drive, and differential migration.

### *Selection*

The gene frequencies established between alleles in a population at equilibrium are dynamic and subject to change. If, for example, gene *A* makes the organism more efficient in reproduction than *a*, *A* is expected to increase generation after generation at the expense of *a*. Continued selection of this kind would tend to decrease the proportion of *a* in favor of *A*.

Observations made in natural populations, such as the one involving moths in England, have provided examples of selection occurring in nature. In 1850, surveys indicated that most of the moths in various nonindustrialized communities were light in color, whereas a very few, less than 1 percent, were dark. As these cities became industrialized and factory smoke darkened the buildings and countryside, a parallel change occurred among the moths. Later surveys showed that 80 to 90 percent of the moths in certain industrial areas were dark. L. Doncaster, R. Goldschmidt, A. Kühn, and E. B. Ford showed, from experimental breeding, that the dark color was inherited and controlled by one or two dominant genes. Presumably, those moths which matched their environment best, lived, reproduced, and transmitted their genes for dark color to their progeny, whereas more conspicuous light-colored moths on a dark background were caught by predators. The alternative explanation, that in some way the direct influence of the environment changed the genetic color-producing mechanism, was considered but not substantiated. Observations have now borne out the explanation that the change is based on selection favoring moths that most closely blend with their surroundings.

In a particular study conducted by H. B. D. Kettlewell, 447 black moths, *Biston betularia,* were collected elsewhere and released in smoky Birmingham. At the same time 137 white moths of a type not already present in the vicinity were also released. After a period of time, moths in the area were trapped and classified. Only 18 (13 percent) of the original 137 white moths and 123 (27.5 percent) of the blacks could be found. The collections were extensive and it was presumed that virtually all of the released moths that were still alive were captured. The blacks were favored 2:1 over the whites in survival. In Dorset, which is not industrialized, 398 black and 376 white moths were released and retrapped in a similar way. This time 14.6 percent of the whites survived and only 4.7 percent of the blacks. The moths that fit their surroundings best were concealed from predators and therefore survived, whereas the conspicuous moths were more readily seen and devoured by predators, birds in particular.

The implication in the theory of natural selection is that certain genotypes in a species endow their carriers with advantages in survival and reproduction. In dealing with "fitness" traits, that are less conspicuous than such traits as color in moths, it is difficult to evaluate the effects of individual genes on survival and reproduction because it is whole organisms with their full complements of genes which survive or fail to survive. Usually only slight differences in survival and reproductive efficiency characterize different genotypes. Nevertheless, single gene pairs in particular environments contribute to total fitness and it is appropriate to approach a complex problem through a consideration of its component parts.

For illustrating the process of change in gene frequency through selection, a large, random-mating population with a single pair of alleles, *A* and *a*, segregating will be considered as a model. Let $1-q$ represent the frequency of *A*, which in this example is completely dominant, and $q$ the frequency of the recessive allele *a*. A constant selective advantage is assumed for one phenotype over the others. Reproductive rates for genotypes *AA*, *Aa*, and *aa* would be $1:1:1-s$, respectively. The selection coefficient $s$ is a measure of the advantage or disadvantage of an organism with reference to a particular genotype under selection. It has a positive value if selection favors *A*- over *aa*. If selection is complete and in favor of *A*- (that is, if *aa* is lethal), $s = 1$. Change per generation in gene frequency can be determined when $q$ and $s$ are known.

For example, in a population with three fourth (0.75) of the individuals expressing the phenotype of *A*- (dominant allele) and one fourth (0.25) the phenotype of *aa*, the relations may be summarized as follows: The *AA* parents would contribute proportionally $(1-q)/1-sq^2$ *A* gametes to the gene pool, and the *Aa* parents would contribute $[q(1-q)]/1-sq^2$ *A*. The *aa* individuals would contribute only *a* gametes but the *Aa* would also contribute *a* gametes. Therefore, the frequency of *a* would be

| Genotype | *AA* | *Aa* | *aa* | *Total* |
|---|---|---|---|---|
| Relative proportion before selection | $(1-q)^2$ | $2q(1-q)$ | $q^2$ | $= 1$ |
| Genotypic frequencies | 0.25 | 0.50 | 0.25 | $= 1$ |
| Selective value | 1 | 1 | $1-s$ | |
| Relative proportion after selection | $(1-q)^2$ | $2q(1-q)$ | $q^2(1-s)$ | $= 1-sq^2$ |

$q(1 - q) + q^2(1 - s)$ or $[q - sq^2]/1 - sq^2$ which $= q_1 =$ frequency of $a$ in $F_1$.

The change ($\Delta$) in frequency of $a$ ($q$) from the parental (P) to the filial ($F_1$) generation would be:

$$\Delta q = q_1 - q \quad \text{or} \quad \frac{q - sq^2}{1 - sq^2}\, q$$

$$\text{which} = \frac{-q^2 s(1 - q)}{1 - sq^2}$$

This measures the amount of change in $q$ per generation of selection.

Different values of $s$ would indicate different trends in the population. Under conditions of complete selection ($s = 1$) against *aa* (homozygous lethal or completely sterile) in a particular environment parents for producing the next generation would be reduced to two genotypes: *AA* and *Aa*. If the initial gene frequencies before the selection factor was introduced were $q = 1 - q = 0.5$ the proportion of genotypes after selection would be 0.25 $(1 - q)^2$ *AA* to 0.50 $2q(1 - q)$ *Aa*. In the breeding population, they would represent 0.25/(0.25 + 0.50) = 0.33 *AA* and 0.50/(0.25 + 0.50) = 0.66 *Aa*. If the *AA* and *Aa* individuals mate at random and become the parents of the next generation, the following progeny would be expected:

| Type of Mating | Frequency | Progeny *AA* | *Aa* | *aa* |
|---|---|---|---|---|
| *AA* × *AA* | $(0.33)^2 = 0.11$ | 0.11 | | |
| *AA* × *Aa* | 2(33)(66) = 0.44 | 0.22 | 0.22 | |
| *Aa* × *Aa* | $(0.66)^2 = 0.44$ | 0.11 | 0.22 | 0.11 |

The genotypes would again be at equilibrium but the genotypic and phenotypic frequencies would have changed considerably under the condition of complete selection against one genotype (*aa*).

If in the same situation of complete dominance of allele *A* and complete selection against *AA* and *Aa* genotypes (*A*- phenotype) in a particular environment, *A* could be completely eliminated in one generation. This allele would be lost from the population and would be restored only by new mutation.

Examples such as the two above involving complete dominance and complete selection against *aa* and *A*- phenotypes, respectively, are dramatic but they probably do not occur very often in nature. When they do occur, the gene selected against soon becomes so infrequent that it is lost completely from the population. In natural situations, gradations occur in the effectiveness of selection. Under one set of conditions selection may be strong, producing significant changes in gene frequency within only a few generations. Under other conditions selection might be weak, resulting in only slight changes over long periods of time. Apparently, the most common situation in nature is characterized by one genotype that is only slightly less efficient than another. It is difficult to detect such a force and more difficult to obtain a realistic measure of selection pressure.

### *Mutation*

Recurrent mutations that change one allele to another, such as *A* to *a* would tend to alter the relative frequency of members of pairs of alleles by increasing the proportion of *a* at the expense of *A*. If mutations occur only in one direction, that is, *A* to *a*, eventually only *a* alleles would be expected in the population. Because mutation rates for particular genes are low, long periods of time would be required for appreciable change in the relative frequency of alleles. In fact, mutation rates for most genes in higher organisms are so low that it is doubtful that mutation alone is an important factor for gene frequency changes. In addition to the direct effect of mutations in changing the relative proportion of alleles, mutations have a more general indirect influence on gene frequency changes in populations. They represent an original source for variation providing alternative genes and corresponding traits which are necessary for the operation of other processes such as segregation, recombination and selection.

Mutations may be reversible as well as recurrent. If reverse mutations should occur from $a$ to $A$, the proportion of $A$ would increase and the relative rates of the two kinds of mutations would determine the proportion of alleles at any given time. When the proportions become established, the population will be stabilized with respect to the two alleles under pressures of recurrent and reverse mutations. Usually the two kinds of mutations are not equally frequent in occurrence and a mutational trend is established in one direction. If mutations $A$ to $a$ occur at rate $u$ and $a$ to $A$ mutations occur at rate $v$, the forward and reverse mutations may be represented according to the following scheme:

$$A \underset{v}{\overset{u}{\rightleftarrows}} a$$

The frequency of $A$ and $a$ will be influenced by the relative rates $u$ and $v$. If $1 - q$ represents the frequency of $A$, and $q$ represents that of $a$, the population will be stable with reference to these alleles when $(1 - q)u = qv$.

### *Mutation and Selection Operating Together*

The influence of a recurring mutation in altering the frequency of a particular gene in a population of organisms is called *mutation pressure*. A parallel term, *selection pressure*, is used to identify the influence of selection in altering the frequency of a gene in a population. When mutation pressure and selection pressure can be estimated, corollaries to the Hardy-Weinberg formula may be introduced to describe mathematically the trend in the population.

Change in gene frequency because of mutation pressure would be:

$$\Delta q_{\mathrm{m}} = (1 - q)u(\text{gain}) - qv(\text{loss})$$

If we assume that $a$ is a deleterious allele, that is, $q$ is approximately 0 and $1 - q$ is approximately 1 and the values of $q$ and $1 - q$ are related according to the expression $\Delta q = [-q^2s(1 - q)]/(1 - q^2s)$

$$\Delta q_{\mathrm{m}} \approx u \quad \Delta q_{\mathrm{s}} \approx -sq^2$$
$$\text{then } \Delta q = \Delta q_{\mathrm{s}} + \Delta q_{\mathrm{m}}$$
$$\text{or } \Delta q = -sq^2 + u$$
$$\text{at equilibrium } \Delta q = 0$$
$$\therefore u - sq^2 = 0$$
$$sq^2 = u$$
$$q = \sqrt{u/s}$$

If $u$ is 0.00001 and $s$ is 0.001, the numerical values of $q$ and $1 - q$ at equilibrium will be:

$$q = \sqrt{u/s} = \sqrt{\frac{0.00001}{0.001}} = \sqrt{0.01} = 0.1$$
$$1 - q = 0.9$$

Thus, we have the frequency of $q = a = 0.1$ and the frequency of $1 - q = A = 0.9$ at equilibrium.

Unfavorable recessive mutations will accumulate in the population to a much greater extent than equally disadvantageous dominants because recessives must be homozygous to come to expression and as heterozygotes they are hidden from selection.

Observations in nature indicate that both mutation and selection are operating in natural populations, and both must be recognized in defining population trends. In an unchanged environment, mutant organisms usually are at a disadvantage when compared with unmutated forms. A few changes might be inconsequential or neutral, but the chance of making an already well-adjusted organism better able to meet the conditions of an environment by random change is remote indeed. How often would the engine in an automobile, or any other well-adjusted machine, be improved by random changes? The random origin of newness in higher organisms will not alone explain population changes, but it is a significant factor when combined with natural selection and reproductive isolation.

In organisms such as fungi and bacteria, which reproduce primarily by rapid, asexual means, mutations associated with selection may abruptly change the trend in the population. If, for example, a single bacterium *Escherichia coli,* in an environment where penicillin is present, should undergo a spontaneous mutation and become resistant to penicillin, it might give rise to an entire population of penicillin-resistant bacteria in a short period of time. In this example, penicillin is not a mutagen but a selective agent. Animals as far up the phylogenetic ladder as scale insects have been found to undergo chance mutations that happened to make them more fit for the particular environment in which they were located. These mutants may rapidly give rise to whole populations of individuals favored in that environment. Organisms becoming resistant to the insecticide DDT, for example, would be favored in an orchard sprayed with DDT. They and their descendants could take immediate advantage of the man-made environment in which competing insects would have been killed. In the citrus groves of California, for example, whole populations of resistant scale insects have developed within a single season. Again, the DDT is not a mutagen but a selective agent.

Pathogenic microorganisms associated with epidemic diseases of man and animals probably respond in the same way. Through chance mutation in a particular environment, virulent mutant forms spread rapidly in susceptible host populations.

Mutations occur as frequently in higher, sexually reproducing organisms as in microorganisms, but the numbers are too few to allow many mutations to become established even in long periods of geologic time. In higher organisms, mutation pressure alone is not a major factor in evolution. This is mainly because the individuals in the population are too few in number. A mutation with a frequency of one per 100 million ($10^8$) cells might occur a few times in the population of human beings on the earth. A virus population of this size may occur in a single plate culture. The $f_2$ virus, for example, may produce 20,000 to 40,000 particles in a single bacterial cell.

Under most circumstances of recurrent mutation and selection, an equilibrium is reached with regard to gene frequencies. In higher organisms, recombination of genes already present in a population provides a more effective source of variation than mutation. Recombination, which was unrecognized before the twentieth century, also occurs through crossing over, with the rate depending on strength of linkage. In sexually reproducing organisms where random matings occur in the population, the genotype of each individual incorporates genetic contributions from many preexisting members of the species. As time goes on, mutant genes thus become widely dispersed through the entire population.

### *Random Genetic Drift*

Random fluctuation in gene frequencies, called genetic drift, also occurs in breeding populations. The effect of genetic drift is negligible in large populations, but in small breeding populations all the limited numbers of progeny might be of the same type with respect to certain gene pairs because of chance alone. Should this happen, fixation or homozygosity will have occurred at the locus concerned. Fixation is defined as gene frequency reaching $p = 1.00$ or $q = 1.00$. Chance fluctuations may or may not lead to fixation.

If a pair of alleles *Aa* should be present in all members of a small breeding population, normally one-fourth of the progeny would be $AA$, one-half $Aa$ and one-fourth $aa$. If it should happen by chance that all progeny are $AA$ or that all progeny are $aa$, fixation would have occurred. No further genetic fluctuation would be expected at that locus unless mutation occurred. In small breeding populations, genetic drift will act on all other loci represented by two or more alleles, but the direction and magnitude of the effect will be different at each locus. This chance factor could account for an appreciable amount of variation in small populations of cross-mating organisms.

Gene frequencies are subject to fluctuation about their mean, from generation to generation. If a population is large, the numerical fluctuations are small and have little or no effect. On the other hand, if the population is small, random fluctuations could lead to complete fixation of one allele or another, as illustrated in Fig. 18.4. An allele, even though it might have high adaptive value, could be completely lost from a small breeding population by chance alone, and an allele with little or no adaptive value could become established or fixed by chance in a small population.

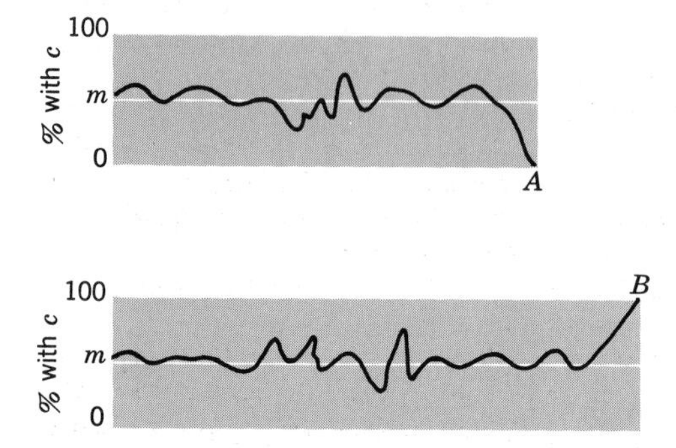


**Fig. 18.4** Schematic drawings to illustrate random fluctuation of an allele ($c$) about the mean ($m$) in small breeding populations. At point $A$, no members of the population would have $c$, that is, all would have $c^+$; at $B$, all members would have $c$ and none would have $c^+$. If the population were large, the numerical fluctuations would be small and would have little or no effect.

### *Meiotic Drive*

Another factor that may alter allele frequencies in a population is an irregularity in the mechanics of the meiotic divisions, called meiotic drive. Ordinarily, heterozygous $Aa$ individuals produce $A$ and $a$ gametes in equal proportions and these gametes have equal probabilities of fertilization and development. For many years, cases of preferential segregation have been reported but most of these have been sporadic occurrences which were not hereditary. Now examples of systematic deviations from Mendelian ratios, which have a genetic basis, are on record.

The *SD* (segregation distorter) locus in chromosome II of Drosophila, for example, has two known alleles, one wild type and one a distorter of the wild-type allele. In the presence of the homozygous wild-type allele, normal segregation of the chromosomes occurs. Heterozygous males carrying the mutant allele, under certain environmental conditions, show a marked departure from the 1:1 ratio. The mutant allele apparently interacts with its wild-type homologue causing it to fragment and behave irregularly during spermatogenesis. As a result, only a few sperm contain the normal allele. Duplication of whole chromosomes or parts of chromosomes may occur in meiosis resulting in irregularities in the gametes.

Likewise in Drosophila, females heterozygous for structurally different chromosomes may have preferential segregation. One member of the pair may be systematically retained in the egg and the other segregated to the nonfunctional polar body. If the two homologues are of unequal length, the shorter one is usually included in the egg nucleus. Chromosomes that have undergone structural changes are often extruded. Any persistent factor disrupting a particular chromosome would result in preferential rather than random segregation.

Sex ratio is expected to be altered by irregularities in the segregation of X and Y chromosomes. Examples have been reported in certain races of *Drosophila pseudoobscura* where abnormal spermatogenesis results in failure of the X and Y chromosomes to pair. The Y degenerates and the X undergoes an extra division. As a result, X chromosomes are segregated to all sperm. When these males, which carry only X chromosomes in their sperm, are mated, excessive numbers of females are produced in their progeny. In other examples, all X chromosomes have systematically degenerated and a preponderance of males has been observed in the next generation.

Meiotic drive could be a significant factor in evolution. Even the most favorable genes would not be perpetuated if the chromosomes in which they were carried were systematically excluded from gametes. The importance of meiotic drive in nature must depend on the extent and persistence of preferential segregation at meiosis.

### *Migration*

Another factor which may influence relative frequency of alleles is differential migration. In local units of a species, gene frequencies may be altered by an exchange of genes with other breeding units. This exchange is effective in changing gene frequencies if the breeding populations have been partially or completely separated for enough time to have developed markedly different frequencies for the same genes. The significance of migration in changing gene frequencies thus depends on the degree of isolation of the subpopulations involved and will be considered further in connection with race and species formation.

## SUMMARY

The Hardy-Weinberg theorem describes mathematically the equilibrium that is established among alleles in a population. An equilibrium is maintained through random mating but the relative frequencies of the genes involved may change. Factors influencing relative gene *frequency* are selection, mutation, random genetic drift, meiotic drive, and migration. Change in gene frequencies is the basis for evolution.

## REFERENCES

Boyd, W. C. 1950. *Genetics and the races of man.* D. C. Heath and Co., Boston. (Extensive data on human blood groups.)

Dobzhansky, T. 1951. *Genetics and the origin of species,* 3rd ed. Columbia University Press, New York. (Data and interpretation of mechanics of evolution.)

Dobzhansky, T., and O. Pavlovsky. 1957. "An experimental study of interaction between genetic drift and natural selection." *Evolution,* **11,** 311–319.

Fisher, R. A. 1918. "The correlation between relatives on supposition of Mendelian inheritance." *Trans. Roy. Soc. Edinburgh,* **52,** 399–433. (This paper deals in involved mathematics but it is a classic of great value in population genetics.)

Greenberg, R., and J. F. Crow. 1960. "Comparison of the effect of lethal and detrimental chromosomes from Drosophila populations." *Genetics,* **45,** 1153–1168.

Haldane, J. B. S. 1961. "Natural selection in man." In *Progress in medical genetics,* Vol. 1, Chapter 2. A. G. Steinberg (ed.) Grune and Stratton, New York.

Hardy, G. 1908. "Mendelian proportions in a mixed population." *Science,* **28,** 49–50. (Original paper by Hardy establishing the Hardy-Weinberg formula for genetic equilibrium.)

Kempthorne, O. 1957. *An introduction to genetic statistics.* John Wiley and Sons, New York. (Statistical concepts and methods used in genetics.)

Lerner, I. M. 1958. *The genetic basis of selection.* John Wiley and Sons, New York.

Li, C. C. 1955. *Population genetics.* University of Chicago Press, Chicago.

Spiess, E. B. (Selector of articles) 1962. *Papers on animal population genetics.* Little, Brown and Co., Boston. (Selection of thirty-seven papers by leaders in the field.)

Stern, C. 1962. "Wilhelm Weinberg." *Genetics,* **47,** 1–5. (Biography and contributions of one of the men who pioneered in population genetics.)

Wallace, B. 1956. "Studies on irradiation populations of *Drosophila melanogaster.*" *J. Genet.,* **54,** 280–293. (Evidence for alleles which are deleterious in homozygous state but favorable as heterozygotes.)

Wallace, B., and T. Dobzhansky. 1962. "Experimental proof of balanced genetic loads in Drosophila." *Genetics,* **47,** 1027–1042.

Warren, K. B. (ed.) 1955. "Population genetics: the nature and causes of genetic variability in populations." *Cold Spring Harbor Symp. Quant. Biol.* Vol. 20. (Thirty-one papers by specialists in the field.)

Weinberg, W. 1908. "Uber Vererbungsgesetze beim Menschen." *L. indukt. abstramm-u vererbelehre,* **1,** 377–392. (Original paper by Weinberg establishing the Hardy-Weinberg formula for genetic equilibrium.)

Wright, S. 1931. "Evolution in Mendelian populations." *Genetics,* **16,** 97–159. (Basic theory of population genetics.)

## *Problems*

**18.1** How did the work of (a) Hardy and Weinberg, (b) Fisher and Wright, and (c) Dobzhansky aid in bringing together the biometricians and Mendelian geneticists?

**18.2** (a) Do dominant genes spread more readily in a population than recessives? (b) What factors influence the relative frequency of genes in a population? (c) When the relative frequency of alleles in a population is altered, how can equilibrium be maintained?

**18.3** The frequency of children homozygous for a recessive lethal gene is about 1 in 25,000. What is the proportion of carriers (heterozygotes)?

**18.4** The following M-N blood types were obtained from a sample of 205 American Negroes: M 123, MN 72, and N 10. Calculate the gene frequency of $M$ and $N$.

**18.5** From a sample of 278 American Indians, the following M-N blood types were obtained: M 78, MN 139, and N 61. Calculate the gene frequency of $M$ and $N$.

**18.6** Among 86 Indians from Central America, the frequencies of the $M$ and $N$ genes were 0.78 and 0.22, respectively. Calculate the percentage of individuals with M, MN, and N type blood.

**18.7** From a sample of several hundred people, 29 percent were M, 50 percent were MN, and 21 percent were N. Does the gene frequency fit the hypothesis of random mating in a population?

**18.8** A group of 212 college students were invited to taste PTC. There were 149 tasters and 63 nontasters. Calculate the gene frequency of $T$ and $t$.

**18.9** Among 798 students, 70.2 percent were tasters. (a) What proportion of the students were $TT$, $Tt$, and $tt$? (b) What proportion of the tasters who marry nontasters might expect only taster children in their families? (c) What proportion might expect some nontaster children?

**18.10** Among 11,335 people, the following blood types were obtained: 5150 O, 4791 A, 1032 B, and 362 AB. Calculate the gene frequencies of the three alleles $A$, $A^B$, and $a$.

**18.11** Among 237 Indians, the gene frequencies of $a$, $A$, and $A^B$ blood alleles were 0.96, 0.03, and 0.01, respectively. Calculate the percentage of individuals with O, A, B, and AB type blood.

**18.12** Blood samples from 999 (883 male and 116 female) students were typed as follows:

| | O | A | B | AB |
|---|---|---|---|---|
| Male | 419 | 371 | 68 | 25 |
| Female | 68 | 38 | 7 | 3 |

(a) Calculate the gene frequency for males and females separately. (b) Determine the proportion of heterozygotes ($Aa$, $A^Ba$, and $AA^B$) and the proportion of homozygotes ($aa$, $AA$, $A^BA^B$) for males and females in the sample. (c) Give the genotypic frequencies ($r^2$, $p^2$, $2pr$, $q^2$, $2qr$ and $2pq$) for the entire sample (males and females combined).

**18.13** When the blood samples from 999 students were tested with anti-Rh serum, 74.9 percent were positive and 25.1 percent were negative. Assuming a single pair of alleles $R$ and $r$ (for this problem only) what proportion of the students would be expected to be $RR$, $Rr$, and $rr$?

**18.14** In laboratory experiments, *D. pseudoobscura* representatives from two different natural populations were raised together in population cages. The weaker competitor was not eliminated, but rather an equilibrium was established between the weaker and stronger competitor. Formulate a plausible explanation.

**18.15** Distinguish between hereditary variation and environmental modification and evaluate the significance of each in natural selection.

**18.16** In a large population of random-mating animals, 0.84 of the individuals express the phenotype of the dominant allele ($A$-) and 0.16 express the phenotype of the recessive ($aa$). Calculate the proportion of $AA$, $Aa$ ($aa$ is lethal and not present in the adult stage when $s = 1$.) individuals in the present generation and the proportion expected in the next generation of random mating under the following levels of selection against the $aa$ phenotype: (a) $s = 1$, and (b) $s = 0$.

**18.17** In a large population of random-mating animals, 0.84 of the individuals express the phenotype of the dominant allele ($A$-) and 0.16 express the phenotype of the recessive ($aa$). Calculate the amount of change in gene frequency in the first generation under 0.05 selection against the $aa$ phenotype.

**18.18** In a large population of random-mating animals, 0.84 of the individuals express the phenotype of the dominant allele ($A$-) and 0.16 express the phenotype of the recessive ($aa$). Under complete selection ($s = 1$) against the $A$- phenotype, what proportions of $AA$, $Aa$, and $aa$ would be expected in the next generation?

**18.19** In a large random-mating population in which $A$ is completely dominant, the gene frequency of $A$ $(1 - q) = 0.7$ and $a$ $(q) = 0.3$. Calculate the rate of change per generation if selection is against $aa$ with $s = 0.005$.

**18.20** In a large random-mating population, if the mutation rate of $A$ to $a$ is 0.00001 and the reverse mutation rate $a$ to $A$ is 0.000001 and neither $A$ nor $a$ has a selective advantage, at what gene frequency level would $A$ and $a$ be at equilibrium?

**18.21** In a large random-mating population, if an unfavorable recessive recurrent mutation $A$ to $a$ should occur at a net rate ($u$) of 0.000001 and selection against the phenotype $aa$ is $s = 0.01$, what would be the frequency of $a$ at equilibrium?

**18.22** In a large random-mating population, an unfavorable recessive, recurrent mutation $A$ to $a$ occurs at a rate of $u = 0.000001$ and $s = 0.01$. What will be the frequency of $A$ at equilibrium?

**18.23** How do mutations and recombinations compare as factors responsible for observed variation in (a) bacteria and (b) higher animals and plants?

**18.24** (a) How is meiotic drive related to the frequency with which genes occur in a population? (b) How can meiotic drive be detected? (c) Evaluate the possible significance of meiotic drive in evolution.

# *Genetics of Race and Species Formation* | 19

Alterations in gene frequency represent the basis for change in the genetic structure of natural populations. In essence this is evolution. More is required, however, to establish changes in gene frequencies in population units over periods of time and thus to account for race and species formation.

## CHANGE IN NATURAL POPULATIONS

Extensive investigations designed to analyze the behavior of genes in natural populations are those of Dobzhansky and his associates, involving the various species of Drosophila. *D. pseudoobscura* is especially well adapted to such studies. This species is widely distributed in nature. Flies representing different populations can be collected readily in the field, reared in population cages in the laboratory, and mated with those from other populations. Numerous distinct traits, which are well understood genetically, are available for study and comparison in different populations. Chromosomes from flies representing the various populations can be compared from salivary gland preparations. This cytological process provides a more direct index of genetic variation than any tool available for use in other organisms. Several structural variations of the third chromosome that were associated with different gene arrangements in natural populations of *D. pseudoobscura* formed the basis for the study. Appropriate comparisons showed chromosome inversions (Chapter 9) to be mainly responsible for the different chromosome types. The standard (ST) chromosome type, for example, differed from a type symbolized CH on the basis of certain areas of the third chromosome of ST that were inverted with respect to CH. Chromosomes carrying inversions behaved essentially like other chromosomes in the population. Some individual flies were found to be homozygous and others heterozygous for a given inversion.

Natural populations were usually not distinguishable by the universal presence or absence of a particular chromosome type. Quantitative, rather than qualitative, differences were found to be characteristic of different geographical populations of *D. pseudoobscura.* The relative frequency of different genes or of particular chromosome arrangements formed the main criterion for distinguishing one population from another. Homologous chromosomes, distributed through random mating, tended to establish an equilibrium in the same way as do the alleles described by the Hardy-Weinberg theorem. Wide differences were observed for the relative frequencies of different chromosome types in geographic races of *D. pseudoobscura* in California, Arizona, and New Mexico. Seasonal variations were also detected by comparing the frequencies of chromosome types at different times of the year. Sampling at Piñon Flats on Mount San Jacinto in Southern California in March of one season, for example, showed that 53 percent of the chromosomes had ST and 23 percent had CH. In June of the same season, 28 percent were ST and 40 percent were CH. When certain laboratory conditions (environments) were established to compare different populations, it became evident that at particular seasons of the year more flies carrying some chromosome types survived than those carrying others.

Flies with certain chromosome types were better fitted to particular temperature and nutritional conditions than to others and thus were favored in certain areas and during particular seasons of the year. The effectiveness of selection was indicated by the relative frequencies of chromosome types which varied from population to population and from season to season within a given population. Results of field observations were further tested in the laboratory by subjecting mixed populations of flies to different temperatures. Flies from a given warm locality were favored in the laboratory at a warm temperature, and those from a colder region were adapted to a lower temperature. A laboratory model was thus created to illustrate one mechanism by which natural selection influences chromosome and gene frequencies in populations.

In some laboratory experiments, the weaker competitors were not eliminated completely, but instead an equilibrium was established between the frequencies of the more favorable and less favorable chromosome types. Dobzhansky explained the failure of the weaker to be eliminated on the basis of the superiority of the heterozygous combination, that is, heterosis. The heterozygous arrangement, which in itself was considered to be favored, contained both competing chromosome types and thus perpetuated the weaker competitor, which would otherwise have been eliminated. The term *balanced polymorphism* was used to describe a stable mixture of different genotypes in a population. Other Drosophila populations are now known to be polymorphic with respect to the gene arrangement in their chromosomes.

### *Darwin's Contribution, Natural Selection*

The concept of natural selection as a directing force in evolution was crystalized by Charles Darwin (1809–1882; Fig. 19.1) and A. R. Wallace in 1858. In his *Origin of Species* (1859), Darwin presented a detailed argument in support of evolution by natural selection. He had been led to his interpretation largely by his own observations and reflections on the natural distribution of animals and plants. His theory began to take form in 1838 when he read an essay on human population, which had been written by T. R. Malthus in 1798. Applying to all animals and plants the principles

**Fig. 19.1** Charles Darwin, English biologist who explained speciation by natural selection.

suggested by Malthus, Darwin developed a theory based on three facts and two deductions. The facts were: (1) populations increase geometrically and tend to overproduce, that is, progeny outnumber parents; (2) in spite of overproduction, the numbers in a given population or species remain fairly constant because space and resources are limited; and (3) inherent variation exists in all populations. The first deduction was called the "struggle for existence." Those individuals having slight variations which better fit them to the environment will survive, but those having unfavorable variations will be eliminated. The second deduction, "survival of the fit," implies that individuals best fitted to their environment will reproduce their genotypes in their progeny and thus perpetuate genotypes favorable to their particular environment.

Darwin's work supported the concept of evolution, but it left unclarified many points concerning the mechanics of the process. The completion of numerous later experiments has served to modify and refine Darwinism, but the basic theory is firmly established. Investigations of population genetics have laid the foundation for an explanation of race and species formation.

## RACE FORMATION

The terms "subspecies" and "race" are used to describe natural subgroups within a species. These groups represent breeding populations usually separated from other breeding populations by physical or geographical barriers, but composed of individuals that are enough like members of other groups to mate with them if the opportunity existed. White-footed mice, *Peromyscus maniculatus,* for example, are widely distributed in North America. About 25 races within the species are recognizable, each adapted to a different habitat. *Pontentilla glandulosa* (herbs of the Rosaceae family) have been classified into at least 11 subspecies.

Other kinds of restrictions to random mating besides those that are strictly geographical also occur in nature. Any factor that separates segments of breeding units for long periods of geological time may be significant in race and species formation. Ecological factors involving differences in habitat requirements may be as effective as geographical barriers. Small groups within a species might become adapted to a particular restricted food supply or local soil condition and remain separated from other units of the same species. The monkey flower, of the genus Mimulus, for example, has separated into distinct types on the basis of ecological preference. *M. cardinales* occurs from sea level to about 5000 feet elevation. Another type that taxonomists have given species rank, *M. Lewisii,* is found between elevations of 7000 to 9000 feet above sea level. R. K. Vickery made crosses between the two types and observed a wide array of variation in the progeny. Altitudinal separation keeps them apart in nature, but the two types are not yet reproductively isolated. In this example not mere spatial isolation but specific ecological preference is involved.

Breeding seasons of some organisms are sufficiently different from those of other organisms to make interbreeding impossible or at least improbable, even though the individuals concerned are otherwise capable of intermating. Many examples have been found in the plant world where pollen of closely related populations is produced at different times of the year. The pollen of one population is not available for fertilization at the time the egg of the other population is ready to be fertilized. Pine trees of related species that occur throughout the coast range of central

California, for example, are much alike; but trees representing the northern species (*Pinus radiata*) do not interbreed with those of the southern species (*P. attenuata*), even though the populations overlap in a wide area. The Monterey pine (*P. radiata*) is adapted to the mild, moist coastal plain and good soil of the area north of Pescadero, California, while *P. attenuata* is adapted to the poor soil and the hot, dry conditions that occur at higher elevations south of Pescadero. Above Pescadero, the two varieties of pine overlap but do not intercross. Observations have shown that the pollen of the one variety is not produced at the proper time to fertilize the ovules of the other variety. Slightly different timing in the reproductive cycle thus provides a sufficient barrier to keep the different types separated, even though they overlap geographically.

In the animal world, delicate patterns of mating behavior provide the same kind of isolation. In birds, insects, and some other animals, for example, elaborate courtship patterns involving scents, songs, and recognition marks are associated with the mating process. Slightly different courtship patterns restrict mating between racial groups. Ordinarily, *Drosophila pseudoobscura* females will not mate with males of another species, *D. persimilis*. When females are partly etherized, however, they do not discriminate between males of their own species and those of *D. persimilis*.

### *Human Blood-Group Polymorphism*

The ABO blood alleles are present in different frequencies in populations originating in different geographical areas of the world. Frequencies of genes such as those associated with the blood groups indicate something of the ancestral history of presently living human populations. When the hereditary antigens which help define the different blood profiles are studied individually in various populations, it is seen that their distribution varies among different races. Thus, these characters, which have a known mode of inheritance, allow us to determine how the frequency of the given allele in a given population compares with the frequency of that allele in another population. This objective approach to racial classification offers a number of advantages over morphological characters, which are much more difficult to analyze genetically.

The exact mechanisms of inheritance that have been worked out for blood have been studied mainly through biochemical processes, ordinarily observed in the laboratory (Chapter 8). Certain blood-group antigens are easily detected by appropriate reagents, and at the present time these factors are most useful in studying relationships of ancient and modern peoples—their migrations and possible origins.

What are some of the facts and premises that recommend the use of the blood groups to explore racial formation?

1. The blood-group antigens are genetically determined at conception and remain fixed for life.
2. There is a direct relationship between the blood-group antigens and the genes.
3. Certain blood-group antigens are determined by individual genes. These groups can be sharply differentiated from one another by a simple objective serological test. Such a test is less subject to personal judgment and error than are most other anthropological criteria, and thus they provide a more reliable indicator of genotypes.
4. Blood groups appear to be affected very slightly, if at all, by the external environment.
5. The frequencies of the single blood-group genes that determine each different blood-group antigen often vary to a statistically significant degree from one population to another.

## *World Distribution of ABO Genes In Man*

More data are available on the world distribution of genes for the ABO system than for any other blood system and for any other set of human traits. Comprehensive reports of data on the ABO blood groups have been published independently by W. C. Boyd, A. E. Mourant, and other investigators. Native populations of aborigines have been studied extensively.

Among American Indians, the Utes from Utah and the Navahos from New Mexico (Table 19.1) and most other tribes in North, Central, and South America have

**TABLE 19.1 Frequencies of blood groups O, A, B, and AB in samples of world populations.**[a]

| Population | Place | Number Tested | Percent of Phenotypes | | | | Gene Frequency | | |
|---|---|---|---|---|---|---|---|---|---|
| | | | O | A | B | AB | $r$ | $p$ | $q$ |
| American Indians (Utes)[b] | Utah | 138 | 97.4 | 2.6 | 0.0 | 0.0 | 0.987 | 0.013 | 0.000 |
| American Indians (Blackfeet)[b] | Montana | 115 | 23.5 | 76.5 | 0.0 | 0.0 | 0.485 | 0.515 | 0.000 |
| American Indians (Navahos) | Northern Mexico | 359 | 77.7 | 22.5 | 0.0 | 0.0 | 0.875 | 0.125 | 0.000 |
| Caucasians[b] | Montana | 291 | 42.3 | 44.7 | 10.3 | 2.7 | 0.650 | 0.257 | 0.053 |
| Polynesians | Hawaii | 413 | 36.5 | 60.8 | 2.2 | 0.5 | 0.604 | 0.382 | 0.018 |
| Australian Aborigines | South Australia | 54 | 42.6 | 57.4 | 0.0 | 0.0 | 0.654 | 0.346 | 0.000 |
| Basques | San Sebastián | 91 | 57.2 | 41.7 | 1.1 | 0.0 | 0.756 | 0.239 | 0.008 |
| Eskimos | Cape Farewell | 484 | 41.1 | 53.8 | 3.5 | 1.4 | 0.642 | 0.333 | 0.027 |
| Buriats | Siberia | 1320 | 32.4 | 20.2 | 39.2 | 8.2 | 0.570 | 0.156 | 0.277 |
| Chinese | Peking | 1000 | 30.7 | 25.1 | 34.2 | 10.0 | 0.554 | 0.193 | 0.250 |
| Pygmies | Belgian Congo | 132 | 30.6 | 30.3 | 29.1 | 10.0 | 0.554 | 0.227 | 0.219 |
| Asiatic Indians | Southwest India | 400 | 29.2 | 26.8 | 34.0 | 10.0 | 0.540 | 0.208 | 0.254 |
| Asiatic Indians | Bengal | 160 | 32.5 | 20.0 | 39.4 | 8.1 | 0.571 | 0.154 | 0.278 |
| Siamese | Bangkok | 213 | 37.1 | 17.8 | 35.2 | 9.9 | 0.595 | 0.148 | 0.257 |
| Japanese | Tokyo | 29,799 | 30.1 | 38.4 | 21.9 | 9.7 | 0.549 | 0.279 | 0.172 |
| English | London | 422 | 47.9 | 42.4 | 8.3 | 1.4 | 0.692 | 0.250 | 0.050 |
| Germans | Berlin | 39,174 | 36.5 | 42.5 | 14.5 | 6.5 | 0.604 | 0.285 | 0.110 |

[a] Boyd, W. C., *Genetics and the Races of Man.* Boston, D. C. Heath and Company, pp. 223–225.

[b] Matson, G. A., "Hereditary Blood factors Among American Indians." *Fifth Intn'l. Congress of Blood Trans. Reports and Comm.,* 274–283.

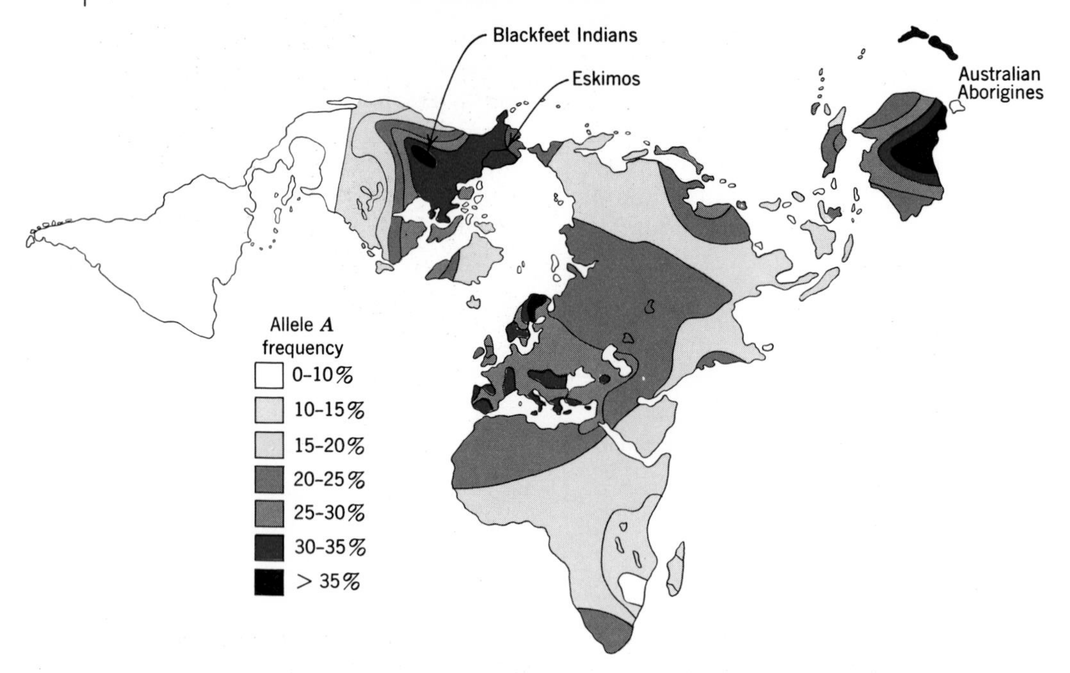


**Fig. 19.2** World map showing percentage frequencies of blood-group allele *A*. High frequencies occur among the Blackfeet Indians and Australian aborigines as also shown in Table 19.1. (Data from Mourant, Kopeć, Domaniewska-Sobczak, Boyd, and Matson.)

a high incidence of O, comparatively little A, and no B or AB. On the other hand, Blackfeet Indians (Fig. 19.2), of Montana, have less O and a high proportion of A (76.5 percent in the sample listed). Polynesians represented by the sample cited have 60.8 percent A and very little B and AB. Australian aborigines have a high A (57.4 percent in the sample cited) and no B or AB. Basques, who are believed to be similar to the ancestors of many present day populations, have a high incidence of A, little B, and virtually no AB. Siamese and Japanese, on the other hand have a high proportion of A and B (Fig. 19.3). Western European peoples and Caucasians of the United States have a fairly high proportion of A and some B and AB. The sample from London, for example, showed 42.4 percent A and 8.3 percent B and the one from Berlin showed 42.5 percent A and 14.5 percent B. In none of the extensive samples, however, was the frequency of A as high as among the Blackfeet and related tribes of Indians.

The highest incidence of B-type blood occurs in central Asia (Fig. 19.3). From this high point of more than 25 percent of the $A^B$ allele, a somewhat lower frequency extends quite uniformly through most of Africa. A similar frequency is found in Japan and other islands farther east. The percentage frequency of the $A^B$ allele declines in western Europe.

G. A. Matson has traveled extensively in Mexico, Central, and South America and has studied the blood types of different peoples. He has made several visits to Mayan Indian groups, which are remnants of the historic Mayan kingdom in the rain forests of Mexico and in Guatemala. In samples from isolated peoples of Central and South American jungles (Table 19.2), Matson and his associates found nearly 100 percent O-type blood. So high was the incidence of O among various tribes that

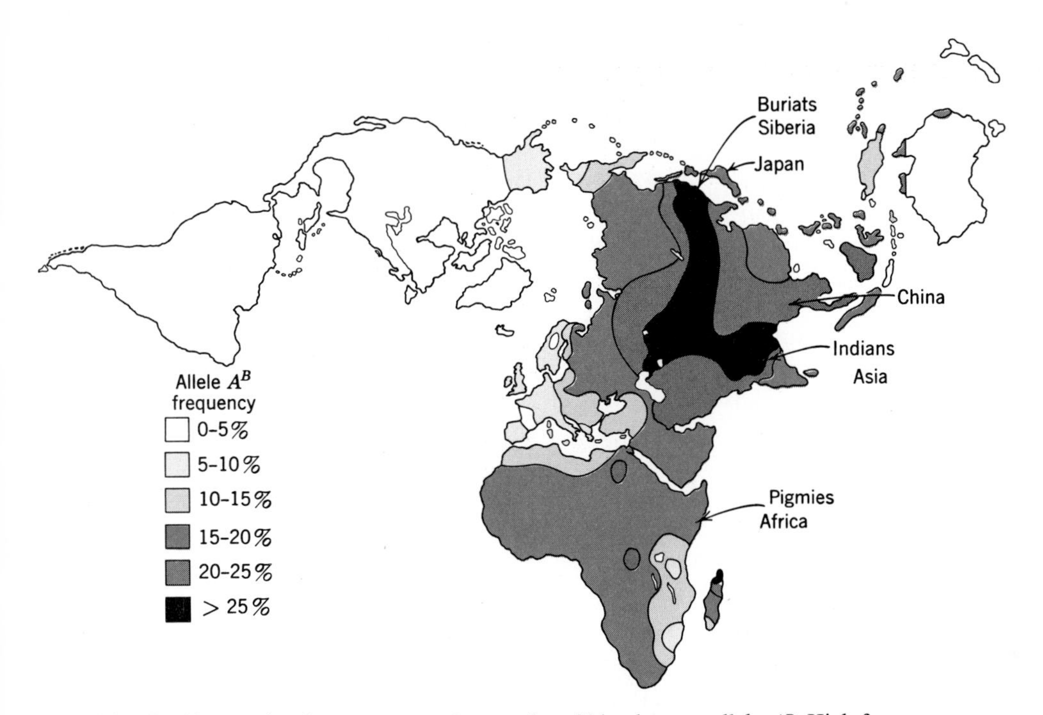


**Fig. 19.3** World map showing percentage frequencies of blood-group allele $A^B$. High frequencies occur in Siberia and India, and somewhat lower frequencies in Japan and other parts of Asia and Africa. (Data from Mourant, Kopeć, Domaniewska-Sobczak, Boyd, and Matson.)

**TABLE 19.2 Frequencies of blood groups O, A, B, and AB in the Indians of Central and South America.**[a]

| Population | Place | Number Tested | Percent of Phenotypes | | | | Gene Frequency | | |
|---|---|---|---|---|---|---|---|---|---|
| | | | O | A | B | AB | $r$ | $p$ | $q$ |
| Maya Indians | Mexico and Guatemala | 1089 | 95.35 | 3.44 | 0.9 | 0.09 | 0.9746 | 0.0190 | 0.0064 |
| Jicaque | Honduras | 194 | 64.95 | 18.04 | 13.40 | 3.61 | 0.7971 | 0.1143 | 0.0886 |
| Lenca | Honduras | 152 | 90.79 | 6.58 | 2.63 | 0.00 | 0.9533 | 0.0335 | 0.0132 |
| Kekchi | British Honduras | 162 | 95.06 | 3.09 | 1.23 | 0.62 | 0.9659 | 0.0117 | 0.0124 |
| Guaymí | Panama | 240 | 100.00 | 0.00 | 0.00 | 0.00 | 1.0000 | 0.0000 | 0.0000 |
| San Blas | Panama | 388 | 100.00 | 0.00 | 0.00 | 0.00 | 1.0000 | 0.0000 | 0.0000 |
| Miskito | Nicaragua | 150 | 90.00 | 8.67 | 1.33 | 0.00 | 0.9490 | 0.0443 | 0.0067 |
| Sumo | Nicaragua | 103 | 100.00 | 0.00 | 0.00 | 0.00 | 1.0000 | 0.0000 | 0.0000 |
| Indians of Ecuador | Ecuador | 9167 | 95.37 | 3.35 | 1.05 | 0.23 | 0.977 | 0.015 | 0.007 |
| Shipibo | Peru | 142 | 93.30 | 0.00 | 0.07 | 0.00 | 0.997 | 0.000 | 0.003 |
| Aguaruna | Peru | 151 | 100.00 | 0.00 | 0.00 | 0.00 | 1.0000 | 0.0000 | 0.0000 |
| Ticuna | Peru | 122 | 100.00 | 0.00 | 0.00 | 0.00 | 1.0000 | 0.0000 | 0.0000 |

[a] Matson, G. A. et. al., *Am. J. Phy. Anthro.*, **24,** 325–349, 1966. (Earlier publications from which data were taken are cited in this publication.)

some investigators have suggested that American Indians at one time constituted a pure race of O-type people and that whenever A or B appeared in supposedly full-blooded Indians, it indicated racial crossing. Observations among Blackfeet and Blood Indians of Montana and Alberta, however, have made these suggestions untenable. Among these Indians, A type was found to be as predominant as O type among some other Indian populations. From another sample, larger than that cited in Table 19.1 from Boyd, Matson found an A-type incidence of 83 percent among the Blood Indians of Montana who are related to the Blackfeet, and 79.07 percent of a total of 688 of the Blackfeet were A type.

When a study was made of the distribution of the ABO blood groups among putatively full-blooded Indians of neighboring tribes not related to the Blackfeet (such as the Flatheads, Crees, Sioux, and Utes), it was observed that these tribes are similar to the larger body of Indians in being predominantly of group O. Whereas the Indians of Montana are mostly O, the Montana Caucasians are 42 percent O, 45 percent A, 10 percent B, and 2.7 percent AB. There is more A among Montana Caucasians than among Caucasians in other areas of the United States. Actually the A and O types are just reversed with reference to the general Caucasian populations in America. This is probably because of the heavy infiltration of Scandinavians among Minnesotans. In Sweden, the frequency of A type is higher than that among other groups of western Europeans.

Although the ABO system is not the most useful one, anthropologically, the fact that blood-antigen A can be divided serologically into subgroups, $A_1$ and $A_2$, greatly increases the value of the system. All full-blooded group-A Blackfeet Indians belong to subgroup $A_1$. In Caucasians the occurrence is about 84 percent, and in Negroes, about 55 percent. The $A_2$ gene is absent in peoples of eastern Asia, in the Pacific, as well as among American Indians. It is found only in peoples of Europe, Africa, and the Middle East. The proportion of $A_2$ to $A_1$ is higher in Africa than in Europe, whereas the Middle East has a distribution intermediate between Europe and eastern Asia. In native Hawaiians, for whom the distribution of the four blood groups resembles in a general way that of the Blackfeet Indians, 60.8 percent were group A and all of these were $A_1$. In Caucasian populations, generally, as many as one fourth of the A or AB may be $A_2$. Incidence of $A_2$ is higher among Negroes than has thus far been reported in any other race.

The remaining populations of the world differ mainly in the frequency of the B antigen. Gene frequencies range from about 0.04 to 0.05 in western Europe and the Caucasus, to nearly 0.30 in parts of central Asia (Fig. 19.4). Basques, long thought to be an isolated remnant of an early European people, are moderate in B. Absence of group B among American Indians is well known. Mourant has suggested that American Indians and Polynesians received many genes from a common gene pool. The gene pool is the sum total of all different kinds of genes in the population. The gene pool which gave rise to American Indians and Polynesians apparently did not contribute the $A^B$ gene to either population. This poses the question as to whether $A^B$ was actually present in the progenitors of these peoples. Present inhabitants of Mongoloid Asia exhibit some of the highest known incidences of group B. American Indians may have descended from earlier inhabitants of Mongoloid Asia who did not carry the $A^B$ gene in high frequency. P. B. Candella presents serological and histological data which indicate that the $A^B$ gene was introduced into Europe through Mongolian invasians which occurred between the 5th and the 15th centuries A.D. He contends

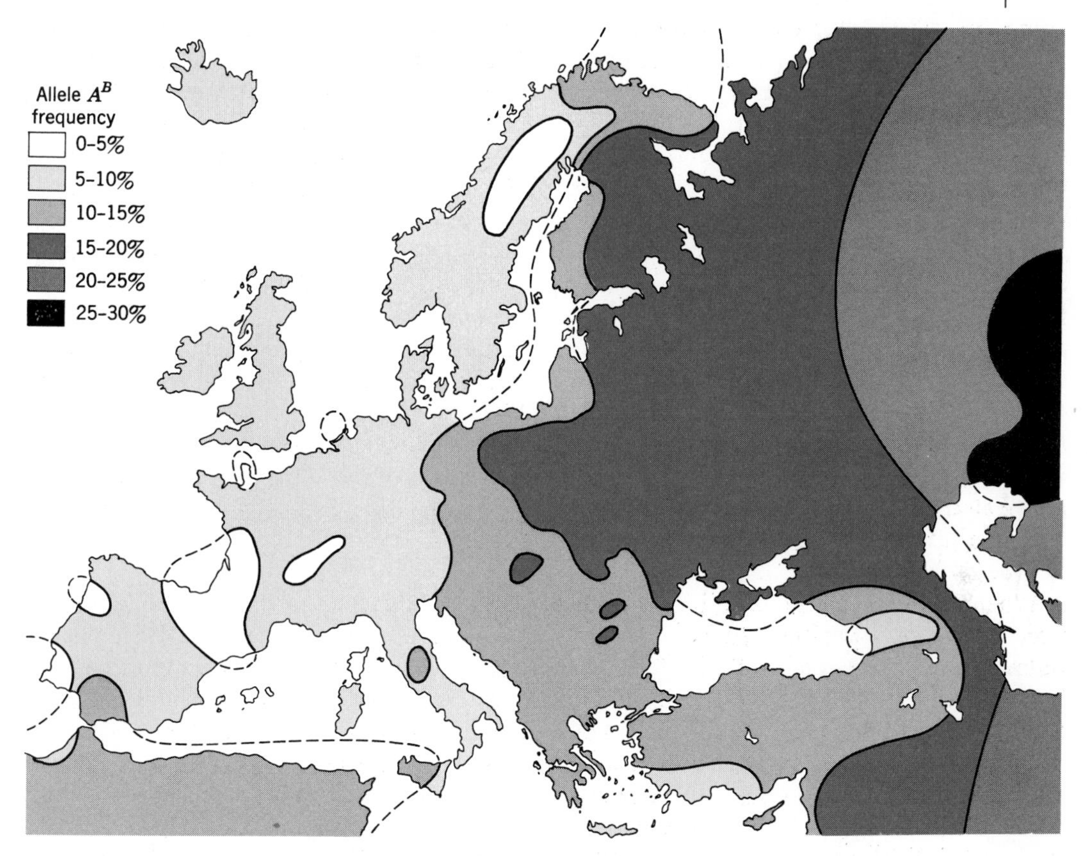


**Fig. 19.4** Map of central Asia (on right) extending to western Europe (on left) showing percentage frequency of $A^B$ allele. From the high point of more than 25 percent in central Asia the frequency declines to 0–5 percent in western Europe. (From A. E. Mourant, A. C. Kopeć and K. Domaniewska-Sobczak, *The ABO Blood Groups,* by permission of Blackwell Scientific Publications Ltd., Oxford.)

that the $A^B$ gene in Europe was derived from central Asiatic Mongolians.

## *M and N Blood Systems*

Frequencies for the *M*, *N* genes show less geographical variation than do those for the ABO group. American Indians and Australian aborigines, however, differ widely in this respect. Groups M and MN are higher than N among American Indians (Table 19.3), but M and MN are low among the Australian aborigines on the other side of the world. Peoples of western Europe have a more even distribution of the MN phenotypes. The highest frequency for *N* and the lowest for *M* are found among the Papuans in New Guinea, whereas the highest *M* and lowest *N* occur among the American Indians.

The value of the M and N antigens has been greatly increased with the discovery of a pair of antigens, S and s, which are closely associated with the M and N groups. It is now possible to postulate four gene combinations: *MS*, *Ms*, *NS*, and *Ns*. To illustrate the usefulness of S and s, we can distinguish sharply between the peoples of New Guinea and the Australian aborigines on these factors alone because the antigen S is present in New Guinea and absent in native peoples of Australia.

**TABLE 19.3 Frequencies of blood groups M, N, and MN in the Indians of Central and South America and other populations for comparison.**[a]

| Population | Place | Number Tested | Percent of Phenotypes | | | Gene Frequency | |
|---|---|---|---|---|---|---|---|
| | | | M | MN | N | M | N |
| Quiché | Guatemala | 203 | 55.17 | 36.46 | 8.37 | 0.7340 | 0.2659 |
| Jicaque | Honduras | 194 | 43.29 | 44.32 | 12.37 | 0.6546 | 0.3454 |
| Lenca | Honduras | 152 | 57.90 | 36.84 | 5.27 | 0.7632 | 0.2368 |
| Kekchi | British Honduras | 162 | 44.45 | 46.29 | 9.26 | 0.6759 | 0.3241 |
| Guaymí | Panama | 240 | 48.33 | 42.92 | 8.75 | 0.6979 | 0.3021 |
| San Blas | Panama | 388 | 50.77 | 42.01 | 7.22 | 0.7178 | 0.2822 |
| Miskito | Nicaragua | 150 | 58.00 | 38.00 | 4.00 | 0.7700 | 0.2300 |
| Sumo | Nicaragua | 103 | 80.58 | 18.43 | 0.99 | 0.8981 | 0.1019 |
| Quechua | Ecuador | 372 | 62.90 | 32.53 | 4.57 | 0.792 | 0.208 |
| Shipibo | Peru | 142 | 47.89 | 44.37 | 7.74 | 0.701 | 0.299 |
| Aguaruna | Peru | 151 | 40.40 | 45.70 | 13.90 | 0.632 | 0.368 |
| Ticuna | Peru | 122 | 67.21 | 27.87 | 4.92 | 0.811 | 0.189 |
| Blackfeet | Montana | 95 | 54.7 | 40.0 | 5.3 | 0.74 | 0.23 |
| Navaho[b] | New Mexico | 361 | 84.5 | 14.4 | 1.1 | 0.917 | 0.083 |
| Aborigines[b] | Australia | 372 | 02.4 | 30.4 | 67.2 | 0.176 | 0.824 |
| Papuan[b] | New Guinea | 355 | 01.1 | 15.5 | 83.4 | 0.088 | 0.911 |

[a] Matson, G. A. et. al., *Am. J. Phy. Anthro.*, **24,** 325–349, 1966. (Earlier publications from which data were taken are cited.)

[b] Boyd, W. C., *Genetics and the Races of Man.* Boston, D. C. Heath and Co., pp. 234, 1950.

Since the original report of the M, N blood antigens and their corresponding genes by Landsteiner and Levine in 1927, other genetically determined antigens which belong to this system have been discovered (Table 8.1). Besides the S and s, the Hunter (Hu), Henshaw (He), Miltonberger ($Mi^a$), and Verwyest (Vw) belong to this system. Several antigens produced by alleles of $M$ and $N$ have been discovered: $M_1$, $M_2$, $N_2$, and $M^g$. Other antigens belonging to the system but apparently not dependent on $M$, $N$ alleles are Mu, Vr, $Mt^a$, $Ri^a$, $St^a$, and $M^c$. The Hunter and Henshaw antigens are much more common in Africa than elsewhere in the world.

## *Rh System*

Undoubtedly the Rh system (Chapter 8) is the most useful of the blood-group systems employed in population studies. The phenotype distinguishable with the usual sera depends upon the action of at least 8 genes, the frequencies of which vary significantly in different parts of the world. Thirty-six different genotypes result from various combinations of these 8 genes. Most population surveys have been carried out with 4 anti-sera called anti-C, anti-D, anti-E, and anti-c, plus certain special sera for detecting the variants of the antigen. If the rare anti-d and anti-e antisera were included, 27 different phenotypes could be distinguished. With only the 4 common sera, however, 12 phenotypes can be distinguished. Particular frequencies of genes in the Rh system have been associated with geographical areas and populations. The blood group known as V or $ce^s$, for example, has a frequency among American Negroes of about 27 percent and in West Africa Negroes of about 40 percent. Very little V occurs among American Indians. From 444 blood samples taken from New York Caucasians, only two were V-positive and these were from Puerto Ricans. Only four Puerto Ricans were included in the sample of 444.

### *Other Blood Systems*

Some other blood-group systems have been useful in population studies. The $P^1$ blood group is more prevalent among Negroes than among Caucasians. It is infrequent among Chinese. The Diego factor ($Di^a$) is prevalent among Eskimos, Chinese, Japanese, and Koreans. The Duffy blood-group system, determined by genes $Fy^a$ and $Fy^b$, and by the rare allele $Fy^x$ (Chapter 8), is found in different frequency in Caucasian and Negro populations. In England the gene $Fy^a$ is present in about 0.4 percent of the people, but in Lapland and Asia it is more frequent. One or both Duffy factors can be found in the blood of all Caucasians. Only Negroes are likely to lack both $Fy^a$ and $Fy^b$, and this is true of 68 percent of the New York Negroes samples and in nearly 90 percent of the West African Negro samples.

When the serum of a Caucasian male patient previously transfused with Negro blood was studied, an antibody was discovered which reacted to a blood group apparently present only in Negroes. This blood group is called Kell ($JS^a$). The antibody reagent failed to react with any specimen of blood from 500 Caucasian donors, but it did react strongly with 20 percent of random blood specimens from American Negroes. A total of about 77 percent of blood samples from American Negroes can be unmistakably identified as such by V and Duffy blood grouping alone. In West Africa, over 90 percent of all random samples would so label themselves. Twenty of the remaining 23 percent of blood samples from American Negroes could be identified as being Negro blood by using anti-$JS^a$ reagent. If, therefore, we had available anti-V, anti-$JS^a$, anti-$Fy^a$ and anti-$Fy^b$, we should have about an 81 percent chance of correctly identifying blood from a Negro. Hunter, Henshaw, and $S^u$ would also be indicative of Negro blood. Other genetic factors of anthropologic importance are the secretor gene, the haptoglobins, the gammaglobulin groups, and the hemoglobin types.

### *Random Genetic Drift or Natural Selection?*

Matson found that many of the populations of natives in Central and South America were small and isolated. Chance or random genetic drift coupled with small original groups (founder principle), which probably formed the basis for isolated populations, could explain the distinctive gene frequencies found in these populations. Chance fixation or elimination of genes in the past could account for the situations observed in present populations.

The situation in Central and South America may be similar to established cases in England and on the Continent of Europe. An Irish colony in Liverpool, for example, which originated from a few founders, was observed to have a different frequency for blood-group alleles than the Irish in Ireland. Again, some small Swiss isolates have a high proportion of A and others a high proportion of O-type blood; yet all these populations came from the same ancestry. Chance fluctuations in gene frequency presumably caused these changes.

R. Singer recently reported a survey of blood groups of large populations of Hottentots in southwest Africa. He found that A and B types of blood increased as he sampled populations down the west coast of Africa. A high frequency of B is distinctive of Hottentots generally. Bushman natives in Africa likewise have distinctive blood-group gene frequencies as well as other characteristics that distinguish them from other populations of Africans. This example is more difficult to explain by chance and would seem to require an explanation involving adaptiveness and natural selection.

Haldane (1961) has presented evidence to indicate that most human populations tend to be at or near equilibrium. When natural selection changes genotype frequencies, investigators seek to determine why the population is not at equilibrium. It may be because:

1. Relative fitness values of genotypes have recently altered. The great changes in the human environment during the past 25,000 years, since upper paleolithic, would be expected to bring about genotypic change.
2. Mutation rates have been altered by mutagenic agents.
3. Migration resulted in the movement of people to locations where they were not well adapted. Lightly pigmented people moving to tropical parts of India or Africa, for example, have a higher death rate from skin cancer than well-pigmented people who are native to these areas. Negro people in the United States have more tuberculosis than others in this country. Immediate environmental conditions, such as infection and poor living situations, may be a factor especially with reference to tuberculosis, but the implication is that recent migrants to India have not had time to build up pigmentation by natural selection as a protection against skin cancer. Likewise, comparatively recent migrants from Africa to the United States have not developed a degree of immunity to tuberculosis comparable with those whose ancestors have lived in an area where the disease has been prevalent.
4. Recent mutations are favored in selection and, therefore, their frequency is increasing.
5. Mating systems have been altered. Inbreeding has been common in some primitive rural communities but it is less common in present-day urban societies.

Data from relatively large and extensive populations have provided several examples that suggest that certain selective mechanisms may possibly be associated with the blood groups. Carcinoma of the stomach, for example, occurs more frequently among people with A-type blood than among those of other types. The reason is not known and, at present, this represents only a statistical difference. Because carcinoma of the stomach is a fatal disease that occurs in high proportions of various human populations and manifests some heritability, a selection factor against people with A-type blood is suggested. Pernicious anemia (acute leukemia) also seems to occur more frequently in people with A-type blood. Recent studies, in Scotland and in New York City, have indicated that A-type people are also relatively susceptible to salivary and some other types of tumors.

People of blood-group O suffer more from peptic ulcers of the stomach and duodenum than do people of other blood types. Since carcinoma of the stomach and duodenal ulcer are mainly diseases of older people beyond the reproductive period, the selective force would be at a minimum even if there were a strong relation between the disease and the blood type.

A basis for speculation, at least, has

been established concerning the relation between the ABO blood groups and environmental selective agencies such as infectious disease. Some anthropologists have suggested that present gene frequencies in human populations may reflect an infectious disease-related selection in the ancestral history of particular groups of people. One study of mummies representing presumed ancestors of American Indians who now have O blood appears to show that B-type blood was present in earlier periods of history. In this study, 4 of 205 American Indian mummies from Mexico seemed to show B-type antigen. Dating with carbon-14 showed these mummies to be about 8000 years old. A reason for the change (if it actually occurred), from some B to virtually all O would be most interesting and significant to an understanding of the mechanics of evolution. Typing of mummy tissue has many technical pitfalls. Matson could demonstrate no A or B antigen in the tissue of 16 Peruvian mummies.

Much has been done to control postnatal death rates but prenatal mortality probably remains a major factor in selection for some human genes. Patterns of embryonic deaths have not changed in recent years. The total embryonic death rate in man is unknown because there is no way to accurately measure the number of conceptions. In domestic animals, however, some 30 to 40 percent of the individuals conceived die in embryo. One factor is maternal-fetal incompatibility. An embryo of blood-group A or B which is carried in a mother of group O is approximately 10 percent more likely to die as an embryo from antigen-antibody reactions between embryo and mother than is an embryo with another blood combination. In cases where no incompatibilities have existed, the numbers of presumably homozygous blood types produced are less than expected and, therefore, some must have died as embryos. It has been estimated that about 6 percent of all fertilized eggs die before birth owing to the effect of this single ABO gene locus. The ABO alleles represent the largest known single cause of genetic mortality. If other blood-group factors have a comparable effect, a few genes may account for the majority of embryonic deaths.

Random genetic drift may account for changes in gene frequency in small populations. Natural selection would be expected to be a major mechanism in large populations. Several possible selective factors have been suggested but no adequate explanation has yet been presented to account for the different frequencies of blood-trait genes. Pleiotropism, linkage, and other mechanisms that carry genes along passively with other favorable variants in particular environments may account for some changes in blood groups. A few years ago, only genetic drift was being considered as an explanation for differences in gene frequency. Now a basis for natural selection has been indicated.

### *Equilibrium of Genes Associated with Blood Diseases*

Polymorphism has been found in connection with the gene $Si^S$ for a human blood trait, sickle-cell anemia, and its allele $Si^A$ for normal blood. A relation between sickle-cell anemia and one form of malaria has also been established. The sickle-cell condition is characterized by a deficiency in hemoglobin resulting in misshaped red corpuscles, inability of the blood to carry oxygen (resulting in anemia), and in many secondary ill effects. A single pair of alleles is involved in the highly fatal sickle-cell disease. In the heterozygous condition ($Si^S/Si^A$), the red corpuscles are normal in appearance, the hemoglobin is slightly abnormal (insoluble), and the disease symptoms are slight but usually sufficient to make possible the recognition of heterozygous individuals. A simple blood test is available to verify carriers. Sickle-cell anemia is common in parts of Africa. About 40 percent of the people in some Negro tribes carry the gene. Between 7 and 13 percent of the Negroes in the United States are carriers. The gene is virtually nonexistant in other racial groups.

Malaria is common in the same areas where sickle-cell anemia is prevalent, but the greatest death rate from malaria occurs among natives with normal hemoglobin in their red corpuscles. Those with sickle cells are resistant to the malarial protozoan. Heterozygous people ($Si^S/Si^A$) are thus favored in an area where malaria is prevalent. Their blood is resistant to the malarial parasite and the anemia is not severe. Those homozygous for the sickle-cell trait ($Si^S/Si^S$) usually die early from anemia, those homozygous for normal blood hemoglobin ($Si^A/Si^A$) suffer from malaria, and those heterozygous ($Si^S/Si^A$) live reasonably healthy lives, but perpetuate the disadvantageous gene in their progeny.

Enough is known about the sickle-cell gene and its behavior in populations to predict changes in frequency which are presumably associated with conditions under which people live and changes in prevalence of malaria. Selective forces in a malarian environment and among people with an agricultural mode of life which favors exposure to the malaria-bearing mosquito have apparently resulted in this polymorphism. Investigators believe that the combination has occurred recently in man's history and that the gene has not yet reached equilibrium.

If malaria should be controlled, the polymorphism would disappear and the population would become essentially homozygous for $Si^A$ except for rare mutations from $Si^A$ to $Si^S$. By effective control of mosquitoes and other public health measures malaria is being controlled in many parts of the world.

Another hemoglobin disease somewhat similar to sickle-cell anemia is thalassemia (or Cooley's anemia) which occurs mostly in children and is nearly 100 percent fatal. The disease is controlled by a single gene *c* which, in homozygous condition (*cc*), produces the severe Cooley's anemia or thalassemia major. The same gene in heterozygous condition results in a mild form of the disease called thalassemia minor or microcythemia. People with the heterozygous combination may have no outward symptoms, but they can be identified with blood tests. The importance of the disease from a public-health standpoint and the ease with which carriers can be detected have led to many gene frequency surveys in areas where the disease is prevalent.

The thalassemia gene is widespread, mostly in equatorial areas around the earth (as shown in Fig. 19.5). In the United States, the gene is rare, but a few cases of Cooley's anemia occur. The gene is especially frequent in the Mediterranean region, particularly in Italy, Greece and Syria. About 5 percent of the people in parts of Italy carry the gene. Local areas may have as many as 10 percent carriers. The frequency of the gene in different parts of Italy is illustrated in Fig. 19.6. In areas where carriers are as frequent as one in 20, the chance of the severe form (which requires the homozygous condition) occurring by random mating is about one in every 400. Since the homozygous form is lethal and heterozygotes can be identified early in life, the gene frequency could be greatly reduced or even removed from the population if heterozygotes would not mate with each other.

Studies of gene frequencies in man have demonstrated that variations exist in different populations. These variations reflect

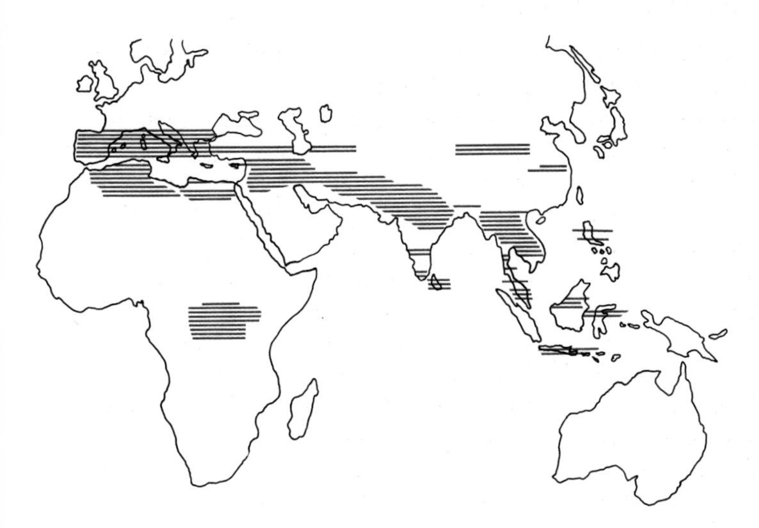

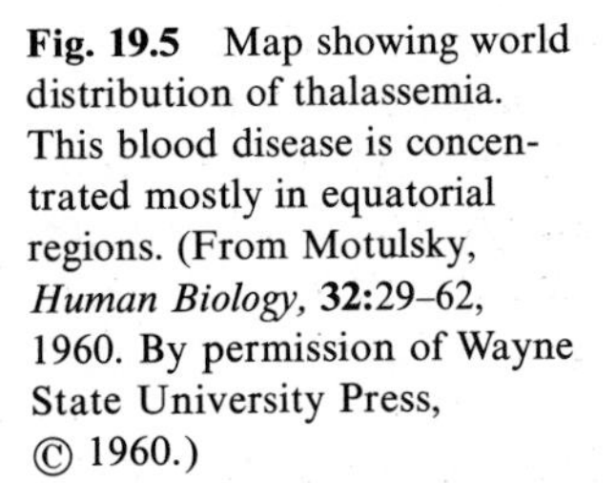

**Fig. 19.5** Map showing world distribution of thalassemia. This blood disease is concentrated mostly in equatorial regions. (From Motulsky, *Human Biology,* **32:**29–62, 1960. By permission of Wayne State University Press, © 1960.)

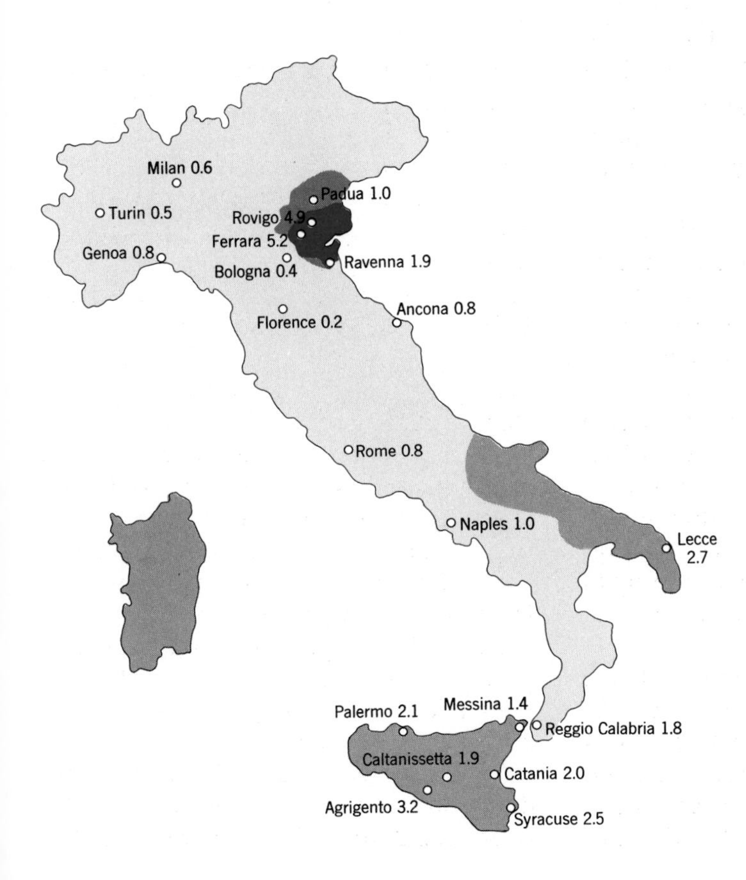



**Fig. 19.6** Map of Italy and Sicily illustrating the distribution of the gene for thalassemia. Percentage frequencies of allele *c* are given for several cities where samples have been taken. (After Bianco, Montalenti, Silvestroni and Siniscalco, *Annals of Eugenics* 16:299–315, 1952.)

mechanisms that have caused gene-frequency changes in the past history of these populations. Blood-group variations are the best known among all human traits and they have been most useful in identifying populations and suggesting ancestral connections and mechanisms involved in race formation. Several distinct races (Fig. 19.7) have developed. Had the geographical isolation (which was present in the past) continued, the different populations might have become more unlike and eventually reached the point where separate species might have been formed. As it is, all populations of man now present on the earth can intermix and all belong to the same species *Homo sapiens.*

## SPECIES FORMATION

Although the species is a well-established natural biological unit, the term is difficult to define precisely, because there are many different kinds of species with different modes of origin (beyond the scope of this book but discussed in references at the end of the chapter). For the present purpose, however, we need be concerned only with "new" species. Three criteria will suffice to distinguish new species. (1) They must be new, which means that members of the group must be different from those of other groups. (2) The points of difference must be fairly constant, that is, genetically determined. (3) Members of the group must be reproductively isolated from members of related groups. This third criterion is ordinarily accepted by Neo-Darwinians as quite adequate to delimit species in sexually reproducing, outcrossing organisms. The criteria of newness and constancy of differences are met through the operation of original mutations, recombinations, selection, meiotic drive, and random genetic drift, all of which have been discussed.

Self-fertilizing plants (for instance, barley) tend to develop pure lines and thus to restrict the variation in the gene pool, whereas cross-fertilizing organisms maintain a constant reserve of heterozygotes. If, for example, there should be 1000 loci in a particular type of organism and each should be capable of forming 10 alleles, there would be $10^{1000}$ possible combinations. The scope of such a vast number of possibilities is virtually incomprehensible, but the figures serve to at least suggest the great variation made possible in a population through heterozygosity.

A gene pool is restricted to a particular breeding population called a "Mendelian population," in which genes can be exchanged among the members of the group. Reproductive isolation with reference to other breeding populations is implied, and it follows that such a group represents a beginning in the direction of speciation. The concept of the common gene pool was developed to explain how individual members are related to the group. These populations must become reproductively isolated if they are to maintain their integrity. Members of other groups that are maintained separately participate in their own gene pools. Morphological differences, which eventually build up to distinguish one species from another, are the signposts along the way, but they are not necessarily fundamental to the mechanics of speciation. Indeed, some species (sibling species) are so nearly alike morphologically that members of one species are sometimes indistinguishable from those of another species by ordinary examination.

### *Problems for Further Thought*

Mutation in the broadest sense, genetic recombination, variation in the external environment as it influences selection, effects of chance in small breeding populations, and reproductive isolation have been suggested as major factors responsible for

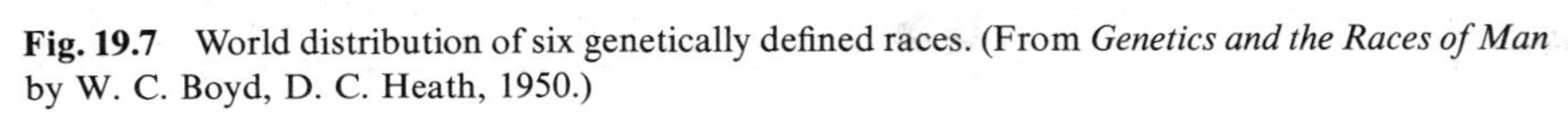

**Fig. 19.7** World distribution of six genetically defined races. (From *Genetics and the Races of Man* by W. C. Boyd, D. C. Heath, 1950.)

organic evolution. Mutation and recombination are the sources of variation for the organism. Natural selection is the main directing force of the evolutionary process. Geographic isolation is a mechanism that separates off segments of breeding populations and makes reproductive isolation and species formation possible.

Many seemingly paradoxical aspects of evolution must also be recognized. The great majority of observed mutations are disadvantageous, at least when they first occur. Genetic change therefore usually makes organisms less well adapted to their environment. Selection is a conservative factor in the sense that it maintains the most highly adaptive types. It tends to reject change and to eliminate newness rather than to perpetuate it, but if more highly adaptive types can be produced, selection will maintain them. The intriguing problem is: how can evolution, which is the result of inherent variation and selection, be a creative process? Two factors contributing to the apparent enigma are offered for further thought.

1. Recombination magnifies variation. The tremendous number of possible gene combinations in a given organism ($10^{1000}$ was suggested earlier in this chapter) might give some hope that a few new combinations would be neutral or even good for the organism. If only one per million ($10^6$) should be of this type, over long periods of time some advantageous new combinations would almost certainly occur.

2. The adaptive value of new traits in changing environments. Environments are not static; they are constantly subject to change. Given enough time, they may produce new selective forces. If a change in the organism should coincide with and complement an environmental change, many new adjustments might result. When one species changes, others are indirectly affected and more changes occur. Every change constitutes a new challenge. Occasionally, mutational or recombinational accidents may be instantly advantageous for the organism.

## APPLICATIONS OF GENE-FREQUENCY INFORMATION IN HUMAN GENETICS

Studies of gene frequencies in populations have provided an approach to some of the most elusive problems in human genetics. One of these is concerned with the prediction of the whereabouts and expected expressions of recessive genes in a population. Many recessive genes with detrimental effects are known to be segregating freely in the human population. This "genetic load" has developed over long periods of time through the accumulation of recessive genes that arose ultimately from gene mutation and chromosome changes. Two categories of genetic load have been distinguished: (1) segregational load: the amount of fitness or the number of offspring left by individuals in a population, as compared with that expected if there were no change through Mendelian segregation; and (2) mutational load: the amount of fitness in a population as compared with that which would be expected if no mutations occurred.

Ordinarily, it is not known who carries rare recessive genes that would be disadvantageous in homozygous condition. They express themselves infrequently and they are difficult to trace, even after an expression occurs in a family group. Carriers sometimes can be detected by appropriate clinical tests, but usually there is no means of knowing who carries the undesirable gene. By resorting to probability formulas, it is possible to calculate the likelihood of an expression of these genes on the basis of their frequency in the general population. Since only those people who are homozygous for a recessive gene express the trait, it is possible to estimate the frequency of such genes in a population on the basis of the proportion of individuals showing the trait. For example, albinism is known to be dependent, in most cases at least, on the homozygous state of a recessive gene. The proportion of albinos varies in different human populations, but in general this abnormality occurs infrequently. An estimate from a sample of one population placed the occurrence at 1 in 40,000. Converting this proportion to a decimal fraction we have: 0.000025, which represents the $q^2$ in the Hardy-Weinberg formula. Solving for $q$ we have $q = \sqrt{0.000025} = 0.005$.

This information may be used to determine the proportion of carriers of the recessive gene, which is equal to $2pq$. Substituting the values of $p$ and $q$, we have $2pq = 2 \times 0.995 \times 0.005$, which equals 0.009950 or approximately 0.01. This indicates that about 1 out of every 100 individuals in the population sampled carries the gene for albinism. The chance, then, for a child born to two unrelated people in the general populations to be an albino is $\frac{1}{100} \times \frac{1}{100} \times \frac{1}{4} = \frac{1}{40,000}$. If the people concerned should be relatives, with a common ancestor somewhere in their history, the chance would be greater than 1 in 40,000. The likelihood would be dependent on the degree of relationship between them.

The behavior of genes in a population is often difficult to determine, but it is an important consideration because it represents the basis for the biological principle of evolution. With experimental animals it is possible to develop models of natural populations from which experimental data may be obtained. In human populations, it is sometimes possible to examine enough pedigrees to detect particular types of matings and to observe the results of these matings with reference to particular traits. Another approach is through the analysis of gene frequencies on the assumption that the population is at equilibrium according to the Hardy-Weinberg theorem.

## SUMMARY

When a breeding population is isolated for a prolonged period of time, its gene pool becomes distinctive in terms of gene frequencies as compared with that of other isolated populations. Subunits may thus be formed within breeding populations. If these separations persist, subspecies or races may develop. Members of these groups may intermate and thus exchange genes with those of other groups if the barriers separating the subpopulations are removed. Eventually, when genetic isolation has occurred as well as geographical separation, isolated populations may become so different from other such populations that their members are unable to intermate. When this stage is reached, populations are well on the way toward the formation of separate species.

## REFERENCES

Caspari, E. 1963. "Selective forces in the evolution of man." *Amer. Nat.*, **47,** 5–14.

Crow, J. F. 1961. "Mechanisms and trends in human evolution." *Daedalus,* **90,** 416–431.

Darwin, C. 1951. *The origin of species by means of natural selection, or the preservation of favoured races in the struggle for life.* Philosophical Library, New York. Reprint of first edition, published November 24, 1859. Classic on the origin of species by natural selection.)

Dobzhansky, T. 1964. *Heredity and the nature of man.* Harcourt, Brace and World, New York.

Fisher, R. A. 1930. *The genetical theory of natural selection.* Clarendon Press, Oxford. (Reprint, Dover Publ., 1960. Interpretations of natural selection.)

Ford, E. B. 1956. "A discussion of the dynamics of natural populations." *Proc. Roy. Soc. London,* **145,** 291–364. (Report on symposium under auspices of the Royal Society of London.)

Kettlewell, H. B. D. 1959. "Darwin's missing evidence." *Sci. Amer.*, **200(3),** 48–53. (Industrial melanism in moths from studies in England.)

Matson, G. A., H. E. Sutton, J. Swanson, A. R. Robinson, and A. Santiana. 1966. "Distribution of heredity blood groups among Indians in South America." *Amer. J. Phys. Anthro.*, **24,** 51–70. (Earlier publications by this group cited in this paper.)

Mayr, E. 1963. *Animal species and evolution.* Harvard University Press, Cambridge.

Mourant, A. E. 1954. *The distribution of the human blood groups.* Blackwell Scientific Publications, Oxford.

Osborne, R. H., and F. V. DeGeorge. 1963. "The ABO blood groups in neoplastic disease of the ovary." *Amer. J. Human genet.*, **15,** 380–388.

Wallace, B. 1966. *Chromosomes, giant molecules, and evolution.* W. W. Norton and Co., New York.

Wright, S. 1956. "Modes of selection." *Amer. Nat.*, **90,** 5–24. (Wright's views on selection at all levels from genes to species.)

## *Problems*

**19.1** (a) List the facts and deductions through which Darwin arrived at the theory of the origin of species through natural selection. (b) Evaluate Darwinism in modern terms. (c) What effect has genetics had on Darwinism?

**19.2** How are new races formed in natural populations of animals and plants?

**19.3** On the basis of studies of blood groups in man (a) what can be said in general about race formation within the species *Homo sapiens?* (b) What can be said about the present trend with reference to race formation? (c) What can be predicted with reference to the future trend in race formation among mankind?

**19.4** A blood stain associated with questionable circumstances in a race riot was tested for blood antigens and the results were recorded as follows: $A_2$, MN, Hu, He, $P^1$, $V^{su}$, $JS^a$, and Duffy negative. Does this information give a clue that could be useful in an investigation?

**19.5** A letter sealed with blood was known to have originated either in a remote area of New Guinea or a remote area of Australia. Antigens A, N, and S were detected in the blood sample. Does this give a clue that might help in tracing its origin?

**19.6** The label was accidentally removed from a blood sample in a blood bank which had originated from a particular hospital ward. At the time the blood samples were taken the ward was occupied by three men of different ancestry, (1) Caucasian, (2) Japanese and (3) Australian aborigine. The blood was $A_1B$, MS, $Di^a$, and $Fy^a$. (a) Would this information help in identifying the patient? (b) Which patient was most likely the donor of the blood?

**19.7** Compare the method of species formation described in Chapter 10, that is, hybridization and chromosome doubling (allopolyploidy), with the Darwinian method outlined in this chapter, that is, mutation and recombination, natural selection, and geographic isolation, under the following headings: (a) the group in which each might be expected to occur; (b) the time required for a new species to be formed; and (c) the extent to which each might be controlled by man.

**19.8** What circumstances would favor (a) random genetic drift and (b) selection as mechanisms for changes in gene frequency?

**19.9** On the oceanic island of St. Helena in the South Atlantic, where winds are strong and nearly constant, a number of species of wingless insects have become established. (a) How might the wingless insects have developed? Teissier carried out the following experiment with Drosophila in a windy part of the Mediterranean region: equal numbers of flies with normal wings and those with vestigial wings were placed in open but protected dishes well supplied with food on the roof of a building. At the end of several generations most of the flies in the dishes had vestigial wings. (b) How could the change in proportion of long-winged and vestigial-winged flies be explained?

**19.10** (a) What is a gene pool? (b) How is a gene pool related to race and species formation? (c) What is the difference between race and species formation?

**19.11** How are the processes of mutation, recombination, natural selection, and geographic isolation involved in the origin of species?

# Systems of Mating

# 20

The Hardy-Weinberg equilibrium and population changes, discussed in previous chapters, were based on random mating. Other systems of mating encountered in nature and in man-controlled populations are divided under two main headings: inbreeding and outbreeding. Inbreeding is the production of offspring by closely related parents, and outbreeding is the production of offspring by unrelated parents. The distinction between the main categories is not hard and fast; gradations occur. It is often helpful to think in terms of degree of inbreeding. Self-fertilizing plants typify extreme inbreeding whereas cross-fertilizing plants and animals evidence varying degrees depending on such factors as compatibility, motility, and proximity. What effects do different systems of mating have on the frequency of genes in a population?

To illustrate the effects of a particular mating system on gene frequency, a model will be developed from a very small population of mice consisting of two families. In family I, one parent is white (*cc*) and the other parent is black (*CC*). Eight progeny, four females and four males, are all black and heterozygous (*Cc*). In family II, both parents and all eight (four females and four males) progeny are black (*CC*). In the total population (parents and progeny), there are 10 *c* and 30 *C* genes. If only the $F_1$ of the two families make up the population, there are 8 *c* and 24 *C*.

Two brother-sister matings ($Cc \times Cc$) are made from family I and two similar matings ($CC \times CC$) are made from family II. Two females from I are mated with males from II ($Cc \times CC$) and the two remaining males from I are mated with the two females from II. If each mating resulted in four progeny, the expected distribution for the two types of mating (inbreeding and outbreeding) could be calculated, as shown in Table 20.1. From inbreeding, 8 *c* and 24 *C* genes result, and from outbreeding 8 *c* and 24 *C*. When the entire population is considered, the same proportion of *c* and *C* genes is maintained whether inbreeding or outbreeding is practiced. The system of mating in itself does not influence the proportion of alleles. A population with a frequency of 0.9 for allele *A* and 0.1 for *a* will maintain these frequencies, whether close relatives or unrelated individuals are mated, unless some other factor changes the proportions.

One difference between inbreeding and outbreeding is that more recessive genes express themselves when the mating is between related individuals. Although the total gene frequency remained the same in the model, the proportion of phenotypes was different. Two of the sixteen progeny resulting from inbreeding expressed the

**TABLE 20.1 Expected distribution of genes in families of mice from inbreeding when the initial proportion of genes is the same in the parent and all progenies are equal in size (4)**

| Family | Cross | Progeny |
|---|---|---|
| | *Inbreeding* | |
| I | *Cc* × *Cc* | 1*CC* 2*Cc* 1*cc* |
| I | *Cc* × *Cc* | 1*CC* 2*Cc* 1*cc* |
| II | *CC* × *CC* | 4*CC* |
| II | *CC* × *CC* | 4*CC* |
| Total genes | | 20*C* 4*C*, 4*c* 4*c* = 24*C*, 8*c* |
| | *Outbreeding* | |
| I × II | *Cc* × *CC* | 2*CC* 2*Cc* |
| I × II | *Cc* × *CC* | 2*CC* 2*Cc* |
| II × I | *CC* × *Cc* | 2*CC* 2*Cc* |
| II × I | *CC* × *Cc* | 2*CC* 2*Cc* |
| Total genes | | 16*C* 8*C*, 8*c* = 24*C*, 8*c* |

trait (white) controlled by the recessive gene, but none of those resulting from outbreeding were white. There were also more homozygous blacks (*CC*) resulting from inbreeding. If the environment should be less favorable to whites than blacks and if the population were large, some change in gene frequency might arise through selection over a period of time. If the population should be very small, random genetic drift might influence the trend in gene frequency, but the type of mating alone has no effect.

Continued mating among close relatives tends to eliminate the heterozygotes and produce homozygotes or distinct (pure) types within the population. Although the total proportion of different alleles in the entire population remains the same, a number of subgroups of more or less pure lines may develop. Again, if a certain trait or type is better adapted than another in nature, or operates for man's advantage in domesticated animals or plants, inbreeding is a method for getting the necessary genes in homozygous condition. If, on the other hand, a certain uncommon recessive gene is disadvantageous, outbreeding is a method for hiding it by heterozygosity from the forces of selection.

## INBREEDING

Extreme inbreeding occurs naturally in self-fertilizing plants such as peas and beans. This was a real advantage to Mendel in his studies. It meant pure lines of peas were available to hybridize, and it also facilitated his experimental procedure. He could emasculate the plants he was crossing and thus prevent self-fertilization. They did not become contaminated with foreign pollen to any great extent by natural agents, such as wind or insects, because the construction of the flower favored self-fertilization, yet the hybridizer could transfer pollen readily from one plant to another. In 1903 Johannsen recognized the uniformity that characterized self-fertilizing plants grown in the same environment. On this basis he postulated pure lines: populations that breed true without appreciable genetic variation.

**TABLE 20.2 Expected progeny in generations following self-fertilization of an annual plant with genotype Dd, for progenies of equal size (4). (After Gregor Mendel)**

| Generation | Progeny Representing Different Genotypes Based on Families of 4 | | | Percent of Each Genotype | | |
|---|---|---|---|---|---|---|
| | *DD* | *Dd* | *dd* | *DD* | *Dd* | *dd* |
| I | 1 | 2 | 1 | 25 | 50 | 25 |
| II | 6 | 4 | 6 | 37.50 | 25 | 37.50 |
| III | 28 | 8 | 28 | 43.75 | 12.50 | 43.75 |
| IV | 120 | 16 | 120 | 46.875 | 6.25 | 46.875 |
| V | 496 | 32 | 496 | 48.4375 | 3.125 | 48.4375 |

Johannsen considered the pure lines resulting from inbreeding to depend on the similarity of genes in the various individuals making up the group. Completely pure lines, in which all gene pairs are homozygous, would represent the ultimate result of inbreeding. It is doubtful that complete homozygosity ever actually occurs because of new mutations and the inherent tendency to maintain a few heterozygotes in the system, but for all practical purposes lines subjected to inbreeding over long periods of time are pure.

### *Development of Pure Lines in Plants*

How do pure lines develop in nature? If tall heterozygous (*Dd*) garden peas and their descendants were allowed to self-fertilize over a period of time and neither tall nor dwarf was favored by selection, what would be expected in five or ten generations? In the first generation, the proportion would be 1 *DD*:2 *Dd*:1 *dd*. In terms of fractions of the total population, the proportion would be ¼ *DD*:½ *Dd*:¼ *dd*. The hybrids now represent only 50 percent of the population instead of 100 percent as in the beginning. If, for simplicity, the population at this point is considered to consist of 4 and each plant should produce 4 progeny in the next generation, the *DD* would produce 4 *DD* and the *dd* would produce 4 *dd*, but the 2 *Dd* plants would each produce 4 distributed as 1 *DD*:2 *Dd*:1 *dd*. The total would be 6 *DD*:4 *Dd*:6 *dd*. Now only 25 percent are hybrids and 37.5 percent represent each of the two homozygotes. This trend would go on generation after generation, as illustrated in Table 20.2. In the fifth generation the proportion in whole numbers would be about 48 percent *DD*, 4 percent *Dd*, and 48 percent *dd*. In the tenth generation, only about one in a thousand would be heterozygous. Most of the plants would eventually be *DD* or *dd* with a smaller and smaller proportion of hybrids remaining. The population of peas would eventually consist of two types, tall and dwarf, in essentially equal proportion. In contrast, if the plants had been cross-fertilized and mated at random, the proportion of 1 *DD*:2 *Dd*:1 *dd* would have continued generation after generation.

Mendel worked this out with a model including 1600 plants. He asked what would be the proportion of the three genotypes in five or ten generations if the original population consisted of 1600 heterozygous (*Dd*) plants and each produced only one offspring. In the first generation, the proportion would be 1 *DD*:2 *Dd*:1 *dd*, or 400 *DD*:800 *Dd*:400 *dd*. In the second generation, there would be 600 *DD*:400 *Dd*:600 *dd*, and so on. The heterozygotes would be decreased by half in each generation.

Now suppose that the hybrid peas had been heterozygous for flower color (*Rr*) as well as plant height in the beginning. About half the plants over a period of time would be tall and half dwarf. They would be expected to occur in the following (about equal) proportions: *DDRR*, *DDrr*, *ddRR*, and *ddrr*. Four "pure" phenotypic lines: tall, red; tall, white; dwarf, red; and dwarf, white would have developed. When other genes were included they would behave in the same way, and a greater variety of pure lines would be expected. The entire population would eventually be made up of distinct types or races. This has actually occurred in many self-fertilizing plants in nature.

Self-fertilizing plants have undergone inbreeding and selection for long periods of time and have virtually eliminated undesirable recessive genes from their breeding populations. Further improvements, possible by selection alone, are limited because of the small amount of genetic variation. However, the usual deleterious effects of inbreeding are negligible. Pure lines may therefore be developed and tested under different environmental conditions. Hybridization may be used to bring together desirable traits, and new combinations may be established as pure lines. It is thus possible to select desirable varieties and provide lines that have practical advantages and from which further breeding experiments can be conducted.

### *Development of Homozygosity Under Different Degrees of Inbreeding*

Self-fertilization occurs only among a limited group of plants and is nonexistent among the higher animals. In experimental animals such as mice, the system by which homozygosis can be approached most rapidly and conveniently is that of brother and sister matings. Backcrosses between progeny and one parent are efficient, especially when sex-linked genes are involved, but technical factors, such as the age difference between parents and progeny, make this system less practical than matings between litter mates. Another simple method of inbreeding in mice involves double first cousins, that is, progeny of parents that are brothers or sisters of each other. The fathers may be brothers and the mothers may be sisters. Sewall Wright has contributed significantly to the theoretical aspects of the problem with his studies on the effect of inbreeding in guinea pigs. His series of papers on *Systems of Mating* (see the references at the end of this chapter) represents a landmark in the field of population genetics.

Wright's coefficient of inbreeding (F) measures the proportion by which inbreeding has reduced heterozygosity. It is the probability that two allelic genes in an individual are both descended from the same gene, which was present in a common ancestor. If frequencies of two alleles $a_1$ and $a_2$ are in the proportions $p$ and $q$, the probability that two uniting gametes will contain identical genes from the same ancestor is F. Thus an individual has probability F of being homozygous for such a gene as $a_1$ or $a_2$. Since $p$ and $q$ represent the relative frequencies of the two alleles, he has a probability $p$F of being $a_1/a_1$ and $q$F of being $a_2/a_2$. He also has a probability $1 - F$ that the two alleles did not come from the same gene in a common ancestor. In this case the chance would be that of any alleles in a randomly mating population, that is, $p^2$ for $a_1/a_1$ and $q^2$ for $a_2/a_2$. Table 20.3 shows the frequencies of the three genotypes that would occur in a population under random mating as compared with those of a population with a coefficient of inbreeding equal to F.

When $F = 0$ no inbreeding is occurring

**TABLE 20.3 Frequencies of three genotypes represented by one pair of alleles under random mating and inbreeding with coefficient of inbreeding equal to F.**

| Genotype | Frequency | |
|---|---|---|
| | Random Mating | Inbreeding |
| $a_1/a_1$ | $p^2$ | $p^2(1 - F) + pF$ |
| $a_1/a_2$ | $2pq$ | $2pq(1 - F)$ |
| $a_2/a_2$ | $q^2$ | $q^2(1 - F) + qF$ |

and the values for gene frequencies are those of the Hardy-Weinberg formula. When F = 1 the population is completely homozygous. By inbreeding, the proportion of heterozygotes is reduced from $2pq$ to $2pq(1 - F)$. In a population of inbreeding coefficient F, the proportion of heterozygous loci is reduced by a factor F compared with what it would be if mating had been random. The problem is to determine the value of F in a given situation.

F values may be determined from pedigree studies. In the pedigree shown in Fig. 20.1, for example, representing a marriage between first cousins, the probability that any gene (for example, $a_1$ or $a_2$) carried by either of the common ancestors would be present in both parents of the child would be the product of the probabilities that this particular allele was transmitted through each step in the pathway. The probability for an allele such as $a_2$ to have come from a common ancestor to the father and also to the mother of the child would be ½ (for father) × ½ (for the father's mother) × ½ (for the father's grandmother) and so on for the next two steps in one pathway. A similar pathway of five steps would represent the probability that the same gene came to both parents from the grandmother. The chance that both father and mother would carry the same gene (such as $a_2$) from either common ancestor would be the sum of the probabilities for the two pathways from the two common ancestors and would represent the coefficient of inbreeding F.

$$F = (1/2)^5 + (1/2)^5 = 1/16$$

If in the general population, a particular trait such as albinism dependent on a recessive gene ($a_2$) in homozygous condition occurs in about one person in 40,000. How much is the probability of expression enhanced if the parents are cousins?

$$q^2 = 1/40{,}000,\ q = \sqrt{1/40{,}000} = 1/200$$

Proportion of homozygous recessives in the population when F = 1/16 would be:

$$q^2 \text{ (after inbreeding with F} = 1/16)$$
$$= q^2(1 - F) + qF = 1/40{,}000 \times 15/16 + 1/200 \times 1/16 = 13.4/40{,}000.$$

The probability of an expression of this trait would be about 13.4 times higher if the parents were cousins than if the parents were unrelated.

Percentages of homozygosis compared with the original degree of heterozygosis have been calculated by Wright and others

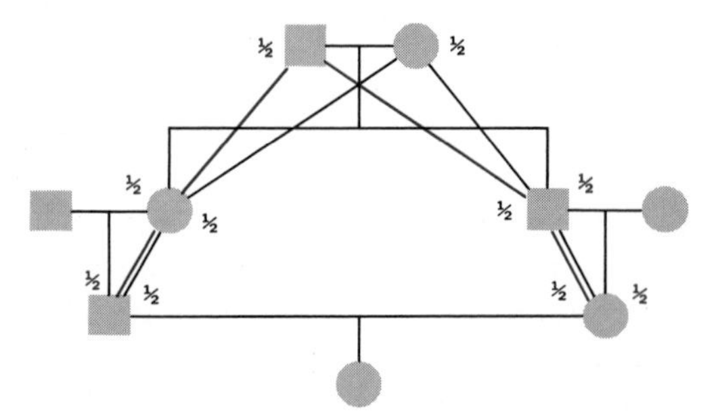


**Fig. 20.1** Pedigree of a man (square symbol at lower left) and woman (round symbol at lower right) from common ancestry illustrating a first cousin marriage. The probability that any gene carried by either the common grandfather or common grandmother to both the man and the woman would be the sum of the probabilities that the man and the woman would receive this gene from each grandparent. The probability for each parent of the child (round symbol at lower center) would be the product of the separate probabilities (each one half) that the particular allele and not the alternative allele would be transmitted through each of the five steps in the pathway.

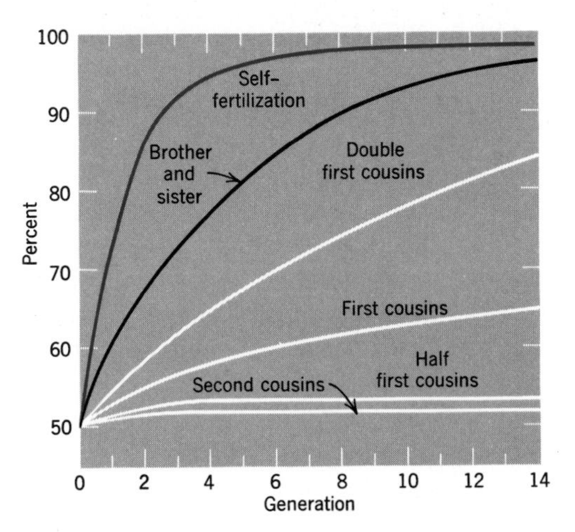


**Fig. 20.2** Graph representing percentage of homozygotes in successive generations under different systems of inbreeding. (After Sewall Wright.)

for successive generations under different systems of inbreeding. Results for simple combinations are shown graphically in Fig. 20.2. As shown in the graph, self-fertilization produces homozygosis most rapidly. The 90 percent mark is passed in the third generation and 95 percent in the fourth. After eight generations, nearly all the genes that were heterozygous before inbreeding began would theoretically be homozygous. Brother and sister matings are somewhat less efficient in producing homozygosis. Under this system, 95 percent of the genes which were originally heterozygous would become homozygous in eleven generations of inbreeding, and 5 percent would remain heterozygous. Following continued brother and sister matings, homozygosity is closely approached in twenty generations. The proportion of homozygous pairs would continue to increase and approach 100 percent of the genes involved in a few more generations of brother and sister matings. Double first cousins would yield about 65 percent homozygosity in the fourteenth generation. It might be expected, on the basis of superficial observations, that any system of inbreeding followed consistently would lead to complete homozygosis of all the originally heterozygous pairs. This is not true for matings between individuals in a large population who are more remotely related than first cousins. Continued matings between half first cousins result in a rise from 50 to 52 percent after an infinite number of generations. The continued mating of second cousins would cause a rise in homozygosis only from 50 to 51 percent.

Other factors such as linkage, the common procedure of selecting the more vigorous animals for mating, and spontaneous mutations interfere with the development of completely homozygous strains. Genes located near each other in the same chromosome pair, cross over infrequently and the investigator must often wait a long time for appropriate crossovers to occur and thus to make possible a high degree of homozygosity. Selection of the more vigorous animals for mating tends to delay homozygosity because vigor is associated with heterozygosity. Spontaneous mutations may occur at any time and decrease the homozygosity of the strain. To obtain and maintain homozygous strains, it is necessary, therefore, in higher animals, to continue the inbreeding over long periods of time and to constantly watch for new variations in the inbred stocks, even after homozygosity has become well established.

Such calculations have established a background for theoretical as well as practical aspects of inbreeding. They have been employed extensively in the breeding of domesticated animals. Wright contributed further to this aspect of genetics through his later studies on polydactyly and otocephaly in guinea pigs. These traits were found to follow the pattern of multiple-gene inheritance. The mathematics was somewhat more complicated but the polygenes responsible for these traits were also shown to become homozygous through inbreeding.

### Inbred Mice and Cancer Studies

In the early part of this century, C. C. Little recognized a practical application of inbreeding in connection with studies on the genetics of cancer. He and others had been studying the inheritance of tumors in ordinary laboratory mice, with little success. The possibilities of greater success with homozygous strains led to an extensive inbreeding program which lasted several years. After many generations of inbreeding and selection, strains highly susceptible to specific types of cancer were produced. The inbred lines have lived up to expectations and have proved to be a most valuable material for investigating the genetics of different kinds of tumors as well as other aspects of genetics. Some inbred mouse strains were developed which had a high incidence of mammary tumors, others were high in lung tumors or leukemia, and still others were relatively free from all types of tumors. A summary of the incidence in some well-known inbred strains is given in Table 20.4. Little started the well-known dba strain in 1909 by selecting a stock he was then using for a coat-color experiment. He selected three recessive coat color genes, *d* for dilute, *b* for brown, and *a* for nonagouti, from which the strain (dba) obtained its name. The original progenitors presumably carried genes favorable for mammary gland tumors which were eventually fixed in the stock by inbreeding.

Mouse studies have shown that tumors do not usually follow a simple Mendelian pattern in inheritance. Apparently, either combinations of interacting genes or polygenes with cumulative effects are involved in the hereditary mechanism. Furthermore, the different types of cancer affecting different sites are tissue specific and genetically independent. W. E. Heston has suggested further uses of inbred strains of mice for studies of heart disease, dental caries, and physiological characters which occur in mice as well as men. Besides their contribution to the genetics of cancer and their potential value for studies of other diseases, inbred strains of mice have contributed much background knowledge concerning the nature and effect of the inbreeding process itself such as the relation between the time required for homozygosity to develop, and the system of inbreeding.

### Practical Applications of Inbreeding in Domestic Animals

By controlling the matings of the animals within the herd or flock and by selecting desirable traits, the breeder has at his disposal a powerful method for developing a desirable genotype in the group. He can

**TABLE 20.4 Incidence of mammary tumors, lung tumors, and leukemia in several inbred strains of mice. (After W. E. Heston)**

| Strain | Mammary Tumor (Percent) | Lung Tumor (Percent) | Leukemia (Percent) |
|---|---|---|---|
| dba | 55–75 | low | 30–40 |
| A | 70–85 | 80–90 | low |
| C3H | 75–100 | 5–10 | low |
| C57 black | low | low | 20 |
| C57 brown | low | low | Most common neoplasm in strain |
| C57 leaden | low | low | low |
| C58 | low | low | 90 |
| Ak | low | low | 60–80 |

**Fig. 20.3** Result of breeding merino sheep. Left, modern merino ram; right, direct descendant of the original strain from which the present-day merino was developed. (Australian News and Information Bureau.)

restrict the matings to a small circle of animals through inbreeding and thus prevent the introduction of genes from outsiders. This process tends to decrease variation within the group and to stabilize the type. Registered breeds are obtained in this way. By limiting the size of the breeding unit, the effects of random sampling or genetic drift may also be realized and directed toward the goal of the breeder.

Inbreeding combined with selection over periods of time has resulted in many valuable breeds of domestic animals. Merino sheep for example, which are widely known as fine wool producers, are the result of about 170 years of breeding. This strain was being developed in Spain in the 17th century by stock raisers. They observed that the ancestors of the present day merino sheep had two coats of wool, one composed of long, coarse fibers arising from primary follicles, and a second coat composed of short, fine wool arising from clusters of secondary follicles. Intensive selection was maintained for animals with more uniform production of fine wool and a lesser amount of coarse wool. For a time, Spain had a monopoly on the valuable merino sheep. When France invaded Spain, merino sheep were removed to France where they were maintained and eventually distributed to other parts of the world. Merino sheep were taken to South Africa and in 1796 they were introduced into Australia, which has since become the world's largest producer of fine wool. A modern merino is shown in Fig. 20.3 along with a descendant of the original unselected strain from which the present-day merino was developed. Rambouillet sheep were developed in France from the Merino breed. Thomas Jefferson, through the United States ambassador to France, brought merino sheep to the United States.

Intense inbreeding has led to an unfortunate situation in certain breeds of cattle. Recessive genes for undesirable characteristics have become concentrated in the descendants of certain common ancestors. Expressions of the undesirable traits have occurred with increasing frequency in some beef breeds of cattle as inbreeding and selection for type have become more intense. Dwarf calves, for example, have demoralized some otherwise enthusiastic breeders of a particular beef cattle breed. Five of a total of 36 calves in the recent spring crop of one herd were dwarfs. One bull and several cows in the herd were found to carry a recessive gene for dwarfism.

Hereford beef cattle, for example, have been inbred for type over a period of many generations. Along with the desirable traits, which have made the Hereford strain the best range variety for the western United States, expressions of insidious recessives have crept in with increasing frequency. Records indicate that only a few sires have produced most of the present population. It is likely that the gene has been present for a long time but, until recently, it has nearly always been hidden by the dominant allele.

A dwarf ten months old is shown with a normal animal of the same age in Fig. 20.4. From the side view, the characteristic head and body features of the dwarf can be compared with those of the normal animal. This type of dwarf is called brachycephalic dwarf; the name was suggested by the characteristic short, broad head. The lower jaw is extra long, the forehead is bulging, the abdomen is out of proportion and the legs are short. More critical observations of the separate bones have shown other anatomical differences. Breeding data indicate that a basic recessive gene is necessary for dwarfing, but additional modifiers have been postulated to account for the different types of dwarfs. Those encountered in the Angus and Shorthorn breeds may depend on the same basic gene but different modifiers which have developed in the different breeds. Dwarfs in any breed are of little economic value and are avoided whenever carriers of the recessive gene can be detected.

Line breeding is the mating of animals in such a way that their descendants will be kept closely related to an unusually desirable individual. All matings may be made to a sire with particularly valuable qualities. The objective of line breeding is to perpetuate a certain type represented by an individual. It is a time-honored form of inbreeding used for maintaining a definite type and has yielded good results in quarter horses and other breeds. Since it is a form in inbreeding, the limitations mentioned previously must be considered. As the individuals involved become more homozygous, their progeny are more likely to suffer from the expression of undesirable recessives. This has caused many breeders to be fearful of continued line breeding as well as other forms of close inbreeding.

Unfortunately, the ill effects of inbreeding have been overemphasized by some practical breeders. Some ranchers have been overly cautious and have avoided line breeding when it might have been used to good advantage to fix a type. It is the only method by which an unusually good stock may be maintained. Good combinations of genes have too often been lost by outcrossing when some form of inbreeding might have maintained them intact. A certain sheep rancher was advertising for a new ram and also had a ram for sale. While visiting the ranch, another sheep man, observing the excellent quality of the "sale ram" and the uniformity in the

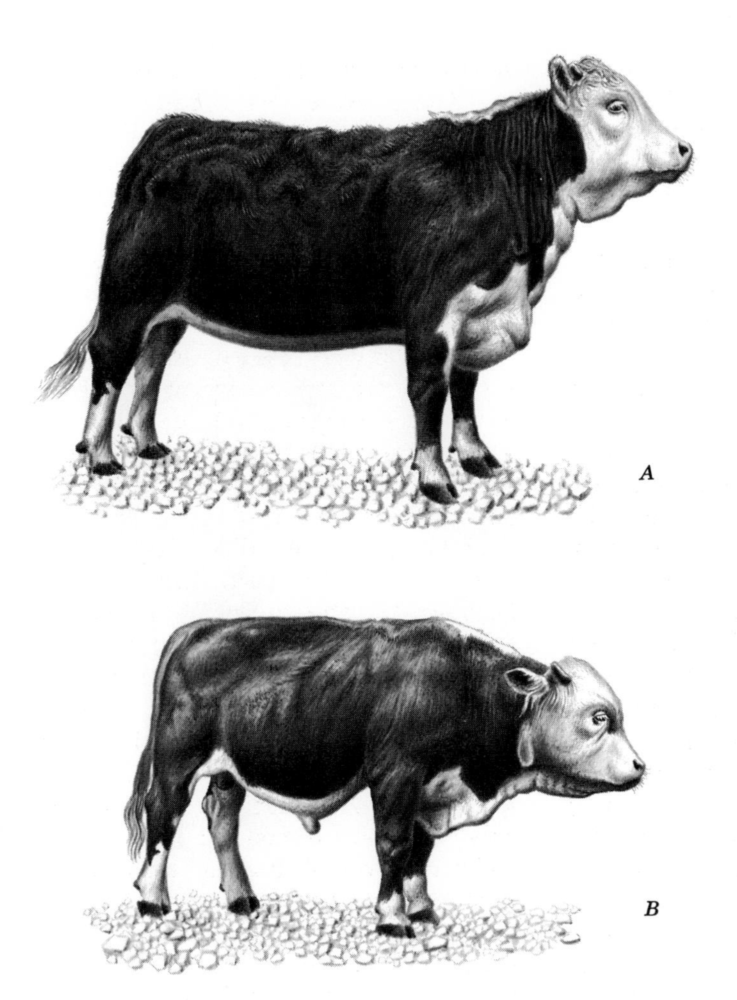


Fig. 20.4 Side view of *A*, normal and *B*, dwarf Hereford calves both of the same age. The dwarf shows characteristic head and body features of brachycephalic dwarfism.

rancher's stock asked, "Why don't you use the one you have up for sale?" "Well, he is all right, but we raised him," was the answer. No ill effects had been observed in the flock and the rancher was persuaded to use his own ram, even at the risk of hidden ill effects which might come from the expression of undesirable recessives carried by the related sheep. Remarkable results followed the experiment. A stock of uniform, high-quality sheep was maintained. The rancher said it was the best lamb crop he had ever had. The advantages of perpetuating something exceptional must not be lost because of the risk of having to cull animals with unfortunate gene combinations. It is true that undesirable genes could be perpetuated and expressed in the flock if this method were continued.

Over a long period of time, even the culling might be an advantage. After all, only by allowing recessives to come to expression can they be identified and removed by selection. Rewards for ruthless culling over a prolonged period of time are often great. Breeders of quarter horses (Fig. 20.5) for example, have accomplished remarkable results through line breeding and culling.

Animal breeders speak frequently of a quality that they call "prepotency," the ability of animals to perpetuate characteristics in their offspring. Obviously, if the progeny perpetuate the characteristics of

**Fig. 20.5** Quarter horse, example of a breed of useful horses developed by line breeding and culling over a period of about 200 years.

an ancestor, they will be uniform among themselves. Homozygosity and dominance provide the main underlying genetic bases for prepotency. A breeder interested in greater prepotency must develop greater homozygosity in his breeding stock.

## OUTBREEDING

The most valuable result of outbreeding is the increased vigor of the hybrids as compared with inbreds. Heterosis has not been exploited in animals to the same extent as in plants. There is good reason to expect that heterosis will provide for greater efficiency in the production of meat, milk, and eggs when it is better understood and fully utilized. Poultry raised for meat responds remarkably well to outcrossing. Rabbits also show marked increases in birth weight and slaughter weight following outbreeding.

A type of outbreeding practiced among Hereford cattle, of which one animal is illustrated in Fig. 20.6, has resulted in distinct advantages over the usual practice of inbreeding. When inbred bulls were crossed with unrelated cows which were sired by other inbred bulls, significant improvement was demonstrated. Hybrids from a large experiment averaged about 12 percent greater weight at weaning than did inbreds. An even more impressive advantage in favor of the hybrids was noted after the feeding period. In final weight, the hybrids averaged 65 pounds more than the inbreds, which were maintained under the same conditions. An investigation on rabbits has also demonstrated the value of outbreeding. The weight at birth and the weight at 180 days of 915 rabbits of four inbred strains and their $F_1$, $F_2$, and backcross generations provided evidence for heterosis. The crossbreds were all significantly heavier than the inbred rabbits. The birth weight and the weight at 180 days of the $F_1$ crossbreds had the smallest variability, whereas those in the $F_2$ generation had the largest variability. All the crossbreds showed significant heterosis in weight at 180 days.

Outbreeding has been employed effectively in the development of improved strains of sheep. Hybrid sheep have been bred successfully for meat and also for increased wool production. Crosses were conducted at the Western Sheep Breeding Laboratory at Dubois, Idaho, between the Rambouillet, a gregarious range animal with fine, short wool, and the Lincoln, a solitary animal with good meat quality but long, coarse (braid) wool. The result was the Columbia breed of sheep which has intermediate wool that is considerably longer than that of the Rambouillet. Columbias also have good characteristics for the range and good meat quality.

Hybrids between black-faced Hampshire sheep and Rambouillets have yielded smutty-faced lambs of excellent meat quality. Since sheep breeders are interested in maintaining the registers of the standard types, they usually dispose of the hybrids early as lambs and maintain only standard breeds for mating purposes.

### *Crossbreeding*

Mating of individuals from entirely different races or even different species is called crossbreeding. This represents the most extreme form of outbreeding that is possible among animals. The extent to which this pattern of mating can be carried out is limited by the ability of distantly related individuals to mate and produce fertile hybrids. Successful interspecific crosses are rare in domestic animals. Numerous breeds and races of different animals have been intercrossed with good

**Fig. 20.6** Beef animal of Hereford type resulting from outcrossing among individual animals from closely inbred lines.

**Fig. 20.7** Ringneck dove, baldhead tumbler pigeon, and sterile hybrid resulting from interspecific hybridization.

results, but members of only a few different species have mated and produced fertile hybrids. The ringneck dove and tumbler pigeon can mate and produce progeny (Fig. 20.7), but the hybrids are all sterile.

The mule is the result of a successful cross between two different species, the horse and the donkey. In many ways the mule is superior to either parent. It is a larger, swifter, and stronger animal than the donkey, and more hardy, more resistant to disease, and more capable of prolonged work with short food rations than the horse. Mules have been produced commercially for a long time. They have served and continue to serve as valuable beasts of burden in many parts of the world. The qualities that made the mule valuable are attributed partly to heterosis. The mule is usually sterile. A few fertile mules have been reported, but the number is too small to have significance in practical breeding. Each new generation must be produced from new crosses between donkeys and horses. Breeders of mules would no doubt be inclined to perpetuate the mule directly from mules if this were possible, but it is impossible because of hybrid sterility.

The zebu, representing a geographical race of cattle native to India, has been crossed successfully with domestic cattle of European origin. Wide phenotypic differences separate these two races. They differ in type of horns, skull shape, dewlap, voice, size of digestive tract, behavioral traits, and resistance to disease. One type of zebu, called "Brahman" (Fig. 20.8), has thus far been more successfully used for outcrossing than any other breed. The characteristics of economic importance, such as adaptability, meat production, and milk production, are the qualities that the breeder would like to develop in the hybrid.

Some crossbred cattle show remarkable adaptability to warm, humid climates. Their rates of gain under these conditions are above those of either parent, and the quality of the meat is comparable with that of ordinary range cattle. Milk production increased above that of either parent line has also been reported for some crossbreds. However, the figure representing this increase is subject to modification when better production records become available for the zebu. A year's production record for one crossbred animal was 348 pounds of butterfat. This may be compared with 500 pounds for a good quality Holstein. Large numbers of crossbreds have now been produced by artificial in-

**Fig. 20.8** Zebu or Brahman bull. Although members of this geographic race differ markedly in phenotype from domestic cattle of European origin, successful crosses have been made and useful qualities have been developed in the hybrids.

semination. Heterosis is apparently an important factor in the increased value of these crossbreeds as beasts of burden as well as for milk and meat production.

Other wide crosses in cattle include: bison × domestic cattle, domestic cattle × yak, gayal × domestic cattle. Greater incompatibility and hybrid sterility have been encountered in most of these crosses and none has shown the promise of the zebu × domestic cattle cross. Other attempts are being made to exploit heterosis by crossing more closely related animals represented by established breeds. The blue-gray cattle in Britain, for example, have resulted from a cross between white shorthorns and Aberdeen Angus. This has proved to be a favorable combination.

**Fig. 20.9** George H. Shull, American plant geneticist who made early and significant contributions in maize (corn) breeding.

### *Heterosis in Plants*

In the second half of the last century it was shown by W. J. Beal and others that the products of varietal crosses were superior to the products of inbred varieties of maize (corn). G. H. Shull (1874–1954; Fig. 20.9) working at Cold Spring Harbor (1908), E. M. East at the Connecticut Agricultural Experiment Station (1908), and later D. F. Jones, H. K. Hayes, and others continued the investigation and found that hybrid corn had more vigor than the inbred lines or the open pollinated varieties then in use. This observation has been elaborated and tremendous increases in production have been obtained. The acreage in the United States has decreased from slightly over 100 million acres in 1929 to less than 80 million in 1968 but the yield has increased by one third. In 1929 practically none of the acreage was hybrid; ten years later (1939) about 23 percent was planted to hybrid seed. The increased proportion has continued to the present (1968) with 99 percent of the field-corn acreage planted with hybrid seed. The monetary value of the increase in corn production for a single year has been estimated as more than the total cost of federal research of plant improvement since 1900. Hybrid corn is the most practical attainment of genetics thus far, but paradoxically, the early contributors were not located in the corn belt and apparently had no thought of making a practical contribution.

Both inbreeding and outbreeding are involved in the production of hybrid corn. Hybrid seed is produced by crossing inbred strains which are developed by controlled pollination. This is done on a small scale by placing paper bags over the ears and tassels of the corn plants when these parts first develop. Pollination is accomplished by transferring the pollen from the tassel to the silk of the same plant and protecting the silk from foreign pollen.

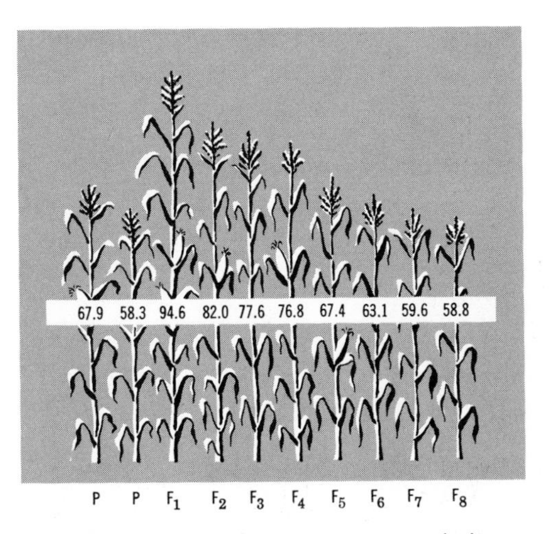


**Fig. 20.10** Diagram illustrating heterosis in corn. The figures in the center represent the average height in inches for the different generations identified at the bottom. (Data from D. F. Jones.)

Only the most desirable lines are kept during the several generations of inbreeding. The inbred strains are then crossed to produce hybrid seed. To make the cross, a few rows of one type of inbred corn are planted near a few rows of another inbred variety in the direction of the prevailing wind. The tassels are removed from the seed parent plants and the silks are fertilized by the wind-borne pollen of the other inbred line (pollen parent). $F_1$ plants are larger and more productive than those from further generations of selfing, as illustrated diagrammatically in Fig. 20.10. Experimental results for the different generations are illustrated by sketches drawn to scale. Commercial seed for hybrid corn is produced on a large scale in places where facilities are suitable.

Vigorous hybrids between two properly matched $F_1$ plants will produce seed more efficiently and economically than weak inbred plants which would be used in the single cross. Therefore, the double cross (Fig. 20.11) has been developed for hybrid seed production of field corn. This is accomplished by developing four inbred varieties, making parallel crosses between two pairs in the same season, and, in the next season, crossing the hybrids. Inbred strains A and B, for example, are crossed together, and other inbred strains, C and D, are crossed with each other. $F_1$ plants from AB are then crossed with $F_1$ plants from CD. Seed from this cross is sold to the farmer. Double crosses do not actually improve the hybrid vigor above that of the single cross; they are employed mainly to provide large uniform vigorous plants for seed production and thus to reduce the cost of commercial seed. The uniformity of the crop in height, yield, and ear characteristics can also be improved with seed production. Plant size and vigor, and particularly the size of the cob, determine the amount of seed that can be produced. A weak inbred plant must be the cob producer for $F_1$ and therefore the amount of seed is limited. On the other hand, if an $F_1$ plant can be used as a seed parent, a much larger cob and greater plant vigor are available.

The biological basis for heterosis is unknown, but several hypotheses have been presented. Shull was one of the first to attempt an explanation for heterosis in corn. His "physiologic stimulation hypothesis" described the phenomenon as resulting from the stimulating effect of heterozygous pairs of genes on the organism. Heterozygosity itself was thus considered to be the controlling factor.

Another theory postulates dominant genes for increased vigor and assumes that these genes tend to accumulate in inbred lines by random mutations and selection. Vigor depends on a large and efficient root system, well-developed leaves with a good supply of chlorophyll, firm supporting tissue, and other properties. Genes for vigor are brought together in hybrids and, because of their dominance, produce maximum expression in the $F_1$. When we consider all the many avenues through

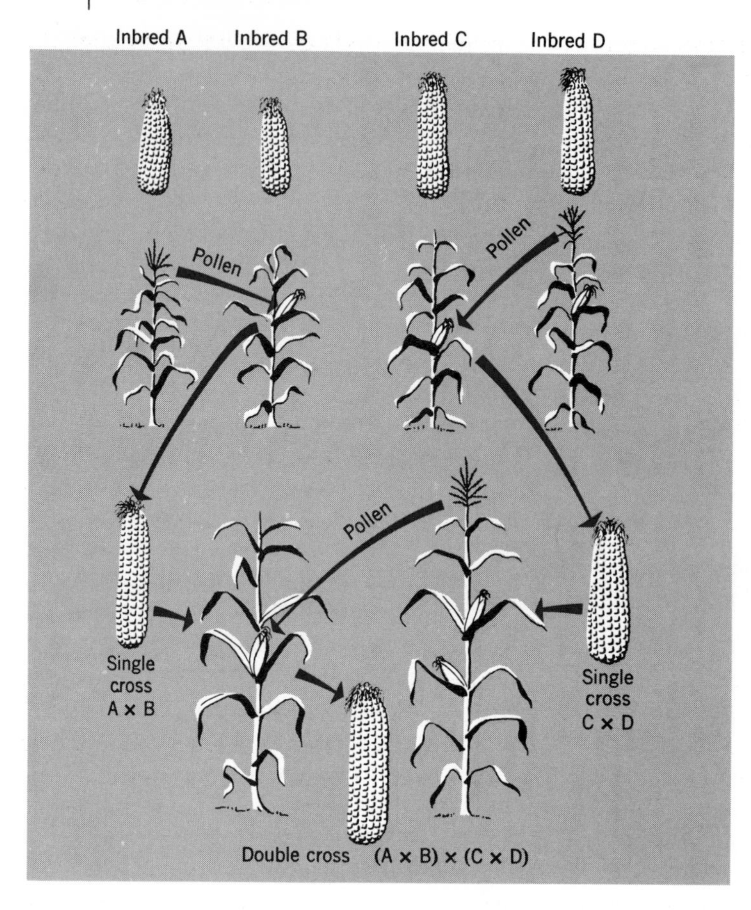


**Fig. 20.11** Diagram of double cross method for producing hybrid corn. (From Dobzhansky, *Evolution, Genetics, and Man,* John Wiley and Sons, New York, 1955.)

which plants could become better fitted to their environment, we might expect different inbred lines to accumulate many different genes for increased vigor. Dominant genes postulated in this theory would become homozygous through continued inbreeding. Crosses between inbred lines would result in the heterozygous $F_1$ plants expressing the good characteristics from both inbred lines, which are controlled by the dominant genes. Under this system, the maximum expression of vigor would be expected to occur in individuals having the maximum number of loci with dominant favorable alleles.

Let us consider a simple model with only two pairs of genes involved; one inbred line will be considered to have become better able to meet the conditions of the environment through an improved root system controlled by gene $A$. Another inbred line is also improved because it has a better chlorophyll system controlled by gene $B$. Through inbreeding, each line has become homozygous for its dominant gene, that is $\frac{Ab}{Ab}$ and $\frac{aB}{aB}$ respectively. A cross between these inbred lines brings the good qualities from both together in the hybrid $\frac{Ab}{aB}$. The weak genes $a$ and $b$ are also present in the hybrid, but they are recessive and do not influence the efficiency of the hybrid. If it should happen that the inbred parents are $\frac{AB}{AB}$ and $\frac{ab}{ab}$, the hybrid would be no better than the more vigorous parent. Complete homozygosity would be a rare occurrence if many genes were involved. The theory is dependent on dominant genes controlling in separate ways the vigor of progeny. Assuming that such genes for vigor are distributed between the two inbred parents, the hybrids should be better than either parent.

What happens when hybrids with a high level of vigor are inbred? If the hybrids illustrated in the oversimplified model presented above were self-fertilized, that is, $\frac{Ab}{aB} \times \frac{Ab}{aB}$, nine combinations would be expected, but only those with $A$ and $B$ (that is, $AABB$, $AABb$, $AaBB$, and $AaBb$) would be as vigorous as the $F_1$. Continued inbreeding over many generations would result in more or less pure lines that were crossed to produce the hybrids. If fully homozygous plants with the dominants could be distinguished from the others, these should be as vigorous, but no more so, than the hybrid. The population as a whole would decrease in vigor and the plants would lose the uniformity that was conspicuous in the original hybrids. By the eighth generation, when the lines would be relatively pure, further inbreeding would have little effect.

On the basis of this explanation, it would seem to be possible eventually to develop inbred lines carrying the genes for increased vigor. This has been attempted many times without success. A possible explanation is that dominant genes for vigor are linked with recessives for undesirable characteristics, which also accumulate through inbreeding and become homozygous. The deleterious recessives, which on this assumption come together in later generations, more than counteract the good effects observed in the $F_1$. The genetic basis of heterosis is probably more complex than that expressed in any single explanation offered thus far. Such genetic principles as (1) complementary gene action, (2) epistasis masking deleterious recessives, and (3) effects of multiple alleles may be involved in the process. It now seems evident that only certain genes produce heterosis when they are in heterozygous condition. Favorable chemical combinations controlled by particular alleles may be responsible for the increased vigor.

Several plant species other than maize have been found to display hybrid vigor. Hybrid sorghums now seem to offer as much promise as hybrid corn. $F_1$ plants obtained by Mendel from his cross between tall and dwarf garden peas were larger than the tall parents and thus may represent an example of heterosis. East and Hayes, two of the foremost investigators on heterosis in maize, crossed two strains of tobacco 31 and 54 inches in average height, respectively, and obtained hybrids averaging 67 inches high under the same environmental conditions. $F_1$ tomato hybrids are widely grown in home gardens. Other garden varieties such as cucumbers, squash, and sweet corn have proved to respond to outcrossing. Pine trees are known to respond to appropriate methods of cross-pollination and display hybrid vigor. This principle is also being utilized with millet, Sudan grass, Bermuda grass, and several other grasses.

In onions, as in sugar beets, the procedure for producing hybrids has been improved remarkably through the discovery of male sterile lines. Better varieties of many vegetables and flowers have been made possible through the development of the sterile-pollen method of producing hybrid seed. Male sterility has now been introduced into three varieties of onions—the crystal wax, the yellow Bermuda, and the sweet Spanish. With male sterile plants it is possible to make crosses without the laborious task of emasculating each individual flower. Discovery of male sterility has therefore greatly facilitated the production of hybrid onion seeds. A hybrid white sweet Spanish onion is now in production. It should be pointed out that factors other than yield are important in hybrid plants. Ability to stand up in wind or rain, resistance to pests, uniformity of maturity, and high-quality seed are also of practical concern.

## GENERAL EFFECTS OF INBREEDING AND OUTBREEDING

In general, inbreeding in organisms capable of crossbreeding tends to stabilize the type and to weaken the individuals. The explanation for this weakening is based on the accumulation of deleterious recessive genes in homozygous condition. Following random mating, rare recessives ordinarily remain heterozygous and seldom come together to make possible the expression of their phenotypes. Inbreeding increases the chance that recessives will come to expression because some genes in the related individuals mated will have come from the common ancestry. These genes that express themselves in natural populations are subjected to natural selection. Inefficient or defective individuals are weeded out, and if inbreeding is continued over a long period of time in the same environment, the strain may be improved by the expression and elimination of recessive genes. In a changing environment mutations that were initially deleterious may become advantageous and contribute to the adaptation and evolution of the species. Recombinations involving such mutations may also alter their adaptive significance.

Populations of cross-fertilizing organisms that are subjected to inbreeding in a more or less constant environment tend to retain some carriers of recessive genes. The chance of completely removing undesirable recessive genes in such a population is remote, even if the inbreeding is very close and consistent over a long period of time. In self-fertilizing plants, on the other hand, relatively pure lines would have already developed in nature. Most defective genes would have already been eliminated and only a few random gene changes would be constantly recurring through mutation. Inbreeding may be continued under these conditions without further ill effects.

In contrast to inbreeding, outbreeding decreases the constancy of the type, but augments, temporarily at least, the vigor of the individuals. This type of mating tends to keep gene pairs heterozygous and thus protects recessives from the forces of natural selection. Outbreeding is important in providing heterozygosity and greater variation for natural selection to work on. It has practical application in hybrid vigor or heterosis as developed extensively in maize.

In breeding programs practiced with domesticated animals and plants, the breeder may direct the mating pattern toward a particular goal. Control of the system of mating is one of the main tools the breeder has at his disposal. Inbreeding is commonly used among naturally self-fertilizing plants; outbreeding generally is used among plants that cross-fertilize in nature. There are degrees of inbreeding above the level of self-fertilization which the plant breeder may employ. He may combine the two systems, that is, inbreeding and outbreeding, and obtain advantages from both. In plants which can be either self- or cross-fertilized, the good qualities can be maintained by inbreeding, but new genes can be introduced to establish desired combinations through outbreeding.

Self-fertilization does not occur in the higher animals. In some breeding populations of domestic animals all individuals are related in some degree. All members of a herd of dairy cows, for example, may have come from the same foundation stock. The same sire is frequently used over a period of time. Inbreeding is defined by animal breeders as the mating of individuals more closely related than the average of the group, whereas outbreeding refers to the mating of individuals more distantly related than the average of the group. As shown earlier in this chapter, precise calculations can be made in terms of degree of inbreeding.

## INBREEDING AND OUTBREEDING IN MAN

The present trend in human populations is in the direction of outbreeding. Improved transportation and communication have resulted in greater and greater mixing of peoples. Recent studies show that inbreeding is now at a low level in most parts of the world. During periods in past history inbreeding was much higher, especially in isolated rural areas. In the more remote periods of human history, a good deal of inbreeding undoubtedly occurred.

From the standpoint of the human species as a whole it would be desirable for individuals likely to carry defective genes not to have children. Improving the human race is a tremendous task and seemingly hopeless for individuals or single families to undertake. Populations, however, are composed of individuals. Research, education and mass interest will undoubtedly lead to improvement in the genetic quality of mankind.

From the personal and immediate aspect of the problem, it may seem desirable to keep seriously defective genes hidden and postpone the effort to improve the race. Man is extremely heterozygous. Defective genes are widespread and most recessives are hidden by dominant alleles. Family histories are usually not complete and reliable enough to make known the presence of defective genes even when they have been expressed in the family. The trend in the past has been to keep deleterious genes hidden and thus to avoid the personal sacrifice among parents and children which is inevitable when such genes come to expression. Most genes in this category are infrequent, and homozygous combinations are rare when matings are made at random. It should be remembered that not just the defective genes but all recessives tend to come to expression through inbreeding. If the makeup of the genotype could be known, judgment in these matters would be greatly improved.

## SUMMARY

Inbreeding itself does not change gene frequency in the population. The proportion of alleles in the total population remains the same, regardless of whether inbreeding or outbreeding is practiced. Inbreeding brings recessive genes to homozygous condition and thus gives selection, either natural or man-controlled, phenotypic variation on which to work. Dominant as well as recessive genes tend to become homozygous through inbreeding, but the result is usually not spectacular because dominants presumably express themselves in the same or nearly the same way when heterozygous as when homozygous. Outbreeding mixes genotypes and keeps infrequent recessives hidden by their dominant alleles. It provides for new combinations which may eventually be tried out in selection.

## REFERENCES

Burton, G. W., and G. F. Sprague. 1961. "Uses of hybrid vigor in plant improvement." In *Germ plasm resources*. R. E. Hodgson (ed.) p. 191–203. Amer. Assoc. Adv. Sci. Publ., 66, 1961.

Dobzhansky, T. 1951. *Genetics and the origin of species,* 3rd ed. Columbia University Press, New York. (Population studies relating genetics and evolution.)

East, E. M. 1936. "Heterosis." *Genetics,* **21,** 375–397. (Discussion of heterosis in maize by one of the original investigators.)

East, E. M., and D. F. Jones. 1919. *Inbreeding and outbreeding*. Lippincott Co., Philadelphia.

Gowen, J. W. (ed.) 1952. *Heterosis*. Iowa State College Press, Ames. (Symposium volume.)

Hayes, H. K. 1963. *A professor's study of hybrid corn*. Burgess Publishing Co., Minneapolis.

Heston, W. E. 1949. *Development of inbred strains in the mouse and their use in cancer research*. Roscoe B. Jackson Memorial Laboratory, Twentieth Commemoration. Maine, Bar Harbor.

Lerner, I. M. 1958. *The genetic basis of selection*. John Wiley and Sons, New York.

Li, C. C. 1955. *Population genetics*. University of Chicago Press, Chicago.

Mather, K. (discussion leader). 1955. "A discussion on hybrid vigour." *Royal Soc. London, Proc. Ser. B.*, **144,** 143–221. (Thirteen papers by leading geneticists treating different aspects of heterosis.)

Richey, F. D. 1946. "Hybrid vigor and corn breeding." *J. Amer. Soc. Agron.*, **38,** 833–841. (Review of theories of heterosis.)

Spiess, E. B. (selector of articles). 1962. *Papers on animal population genetics*. Little, Brown and Co., Boston. (Compilation of thirty-seven papers by investigators in the field of population genetics.)

Wallace, B. 1963. "Modes of reproduction and their genetic consequences." *Stat. Genet. and Plant Breeding. NAS-NRC,* **982,** 3–20.

Wright, S. 1921. "Systems of mating, I, II, III, IV, V." *Genetics,* **6,** 111–178. (Mathematical analysis of the results of different mating patterns based on breeding experiments on guinea pigs.)

Wright, S. 1932. "The roles of mutation, inbreeding, cross breeding, and selection in evolution." *Proc. VI Int. Cong. Genet.,* Part 1, p. 356–366.

Wright, S. 1934. "On the genetics of subnormal development of the head (Otocephaly) in the guinea pig, an analysis of variability in number of digits in an inbred strain of guinea pigs, the results of crosses between inbred strains of guinea pigs, differing in number of digits." *Genetics,* **19,** 471–551.

## *Problems*

**20.1** How does inbreeding affect (a) gene frequency? (b) heterozygosity?

**20.2** What are the general effects of inbreeding and outbreeding among plants or animals which are ordinarily cross-fertilized?

**20.3** Why do self-fertilizing plants such as peas and beans not lose vigor through continued inbreeding?

**20.4** If it was known that self-fertilization resulted in decreased vigor in a certain type of plant but the natural method of breeding was not known, what speculation might be drawn as to the natural system of mating?

**20.5** How are inbreeding and outbreeding related to (a) natural selection? (b) methods of plant and animal breeding?

**20.6** Why are pure lines valuable for (a) hybridization experiments? (b) experiments designed to compare genetic and environmental variation?

**20.7** Garden peas heterozygous for three genes, *g* for seed color (yellow or green); *y* for pod color (green or yellow); and *c* for pod shape (inflated or constricted), are allowed to self-fertilize and their descendants are self-fertilized for many generations. What phenotypic pure lines would be expected to develop?

**20.8** When pure lines are obtained, would the self-fertilizing individuals be expected to produce anything but homozygous progeny? Explain.

**20.9** If 1600 garden peas heterozygous (*Dd*) for height were inbred for ten generations, about how many plants would be expected to be heterozygous? (Assume no differential adaptive value and that each parent produced one offspring so that 1600 plants will be present in each generation.)

**20.10** A large number of fruit flies, all heterozygous for a gene *a* were allowed to mate at random and their descendants also mated at random for ten generations in a population cage. What proportion of $AA$, $Aa$, and $aa$ would be expected assuming no differential adaptive value?

**20.11** Evaluate the following systems of mating with reference to their relative efficiency in producing homozygosis: self-fertilization, brother and sister mating, double first cousins, first cousins, second cousins, and random mating.

**20.12** In some herds of beef cattle, dwarf calves occur. A recessive gene is responsible for the abnormality. (a) How could this condition have developed? (b) What measures might be taken to avoid the financial losses which come from the production of dwarfs?

**20.13** If genes $A$, $B$, $C$, and $D$, produce vigor in maize, evaluate the efficiency with which superior hybrid seed could be produced from the following crosses and give reasons for evaluation: (a) $\frac{abCD}{abCD} \times \frac{ABcd}{ABcd}$, (b) $F_1 \times F_1$, and (c) $F_1$ from $\frac{aBCD}{aBCD} \times \frac{AbCD}{AbCD} \times F_1$ from $\frac{ABcD}{ABcD} \times \frac{ABCd}{ABCd}$.

**20.14** In certain breeding stocks of maize, assume that gene $A$ for increased vigor is closely linked with a recessive gene $w$ which makes the plant weak, and that gene $B$ for another quality also resulting in increased vigor is closely linked with a recessive gene $l$ for low viability. (a) What combination would be most efficient for production of vigor? (b) What kind of mating would produce the desired combination? (c) What would be the likelihood of obtaining a pure breeding strain with superior vigor?

**20.15** To what extent does heterosis have practical significance in animals? Based on the studies of rabbits, mules, and sheep, what are the prospects for the future in exploiting heterosis in animals?

**20.16** Describe the practical usefulness of inbred strains: (a) mice in cancer research; (b) cattle breeding; and (c) production of hybrid seed maize.

**20.17** How can the high concentration of certain tumors in certain inbred strains of mice be explained?

**20.18** What effects might be expected from (a) inbreeding, and (b) outbreeding in the present human population?

**20.19** A trait dependent on a recessive gene ($aa$) occurs in the general population at the rate of one in 10,000 people. In the following pedigree, (a) what would be the chance of it occurring in A's child if he married at random and if the trait was not known to occur in his family?

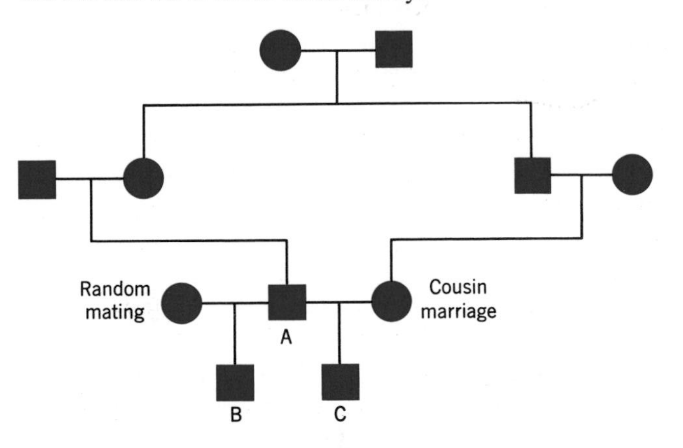

(b) What is the inbreeding coefficient for C? (c) What is the chance that C will express the trait? (d) If A's grandmother was known from family history to be a carrier for *a* and A's grandfather was known not to carry the gene, what is the chance that C will express the trait? (e) If A's grandmother was known to have expressed the trait and his grandfather was known not to carry the gene, what is the chance that C will express the trait?

**20.20** What would be the inbreeding coefficient of a child whose parents were (a) second cousins (that is, the children of first cousins)? (b) uncle and niece? (c) double first cousins?

# 21 Practical Applications of Genetic Principles

The emphasis in the preceding chapters has been on the *principles* of genetics, on the premise that applications can be made as occasion requires when the principles are well understood. In a rapidly changing world, specific applications of any science become obsolete with appalling rapidity. Nevertheless, some illustrations from areas to which genetic principles have been fruitfully applied may be useful and provocative.

## ANIMAL BREEDING

Animal breeding is as old as civilization. Before the time of the written record, animal breeders, or at least good husbandmen, were at work. As evidence of their accomplishments, virtually all animals that have proved capable of domestication were domesticated and used by man. Many animal breeders in more recent times have contributed to the improvement of animals for man's purposes.

A few domesticated animals, including cattle, sheep, pigs, goats, and fowls, are the major producers of animal food for man. Bees may be added to the list as animals of secondary importance. Horses and rabbits constitute fringe sources of meat. Rabbits have been used increasingly, but they still represent a minor source of human food. Wild animals such as fish, game birds, and big game furnish a small part of the human food supply, but these are at present not of interest to the animal breeder. Animals are not only bred for their value as food but also to serve man as wool, fur, and leather producers, and as beasts of burden. Mechanized equipment has largely replaced draft animals in the United States and other well-developed countries, but horses, cows, oxen, camels, elephants, and water buffalos still do much of the work in the world.

Current efforts to improve animals that serve man in so many diverse ways are often concentrated in developing types to fit local needs. One project in central Italy is developing the Chianina breed of cattle to make available to Italian farmers improved animals that are especially adapted for meat production and agricultural work in hot climates. Large size, rapid growth, sturdy build, and meat quality are the main characteristics considered in the selection program. These animals have been distributed widely among peasant farmers in central Italy. The sire of about eighty choice animals in the Arezzo area is shown in Fig. 21.1.

Breeding for improvement of domesticated animals is time-consuming because

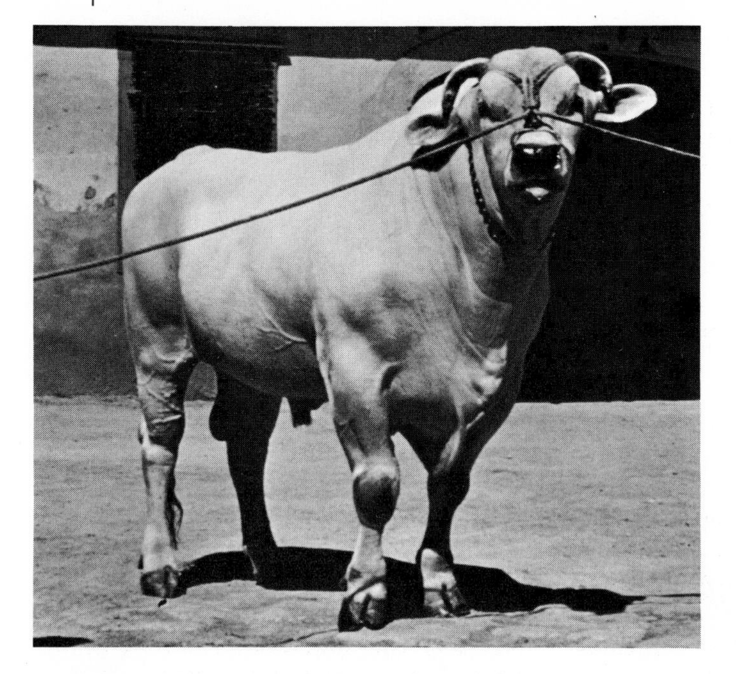

**Fig. 21.1** The sire of about 80 choice animals of the Chianina breed in the Arezzo area of Italy.

of the slow rates of reproduction and the complexity of genetic mechanisms in higher animals. The long life span makes it impossible for the geneticist to observe many generations. Low heritability of most traits with practical value presents further difficulties. Virtually all of the animal characteristics of interest to the practical breeder are quantitative, depending on cumulative effects of multiple and interacting genes interconnected with environmental factors. In very few cases have single gene substitutions been found to control such practical properties as size and quality of domestic animals or their products.

Selection and controlled mating are the main methods available to the animal breeder. Types of controlled mating include inbreeding and crossing. The most widely used procedure for breeding better animals is the selection of certain choice individuals to perpetuate the stock. The problem is distinguishing those that are of high genetic quality. In fact, the ability of the breeder to pick the right individuals is fundamental to his success. Two criteria are available for his guidance in estimating the breeding value of an animal. The first is the phenotype or individual performance of the animal itself; the second depends on the phenotypes of the ancestors, collateral relatives, and progeny of the individual in question. Genetic values are determined as well as possible from objective estimates of all available sources, including performance, pedigree, relatives, and progeny. Each characteristic requires skillful evaluation according to the aims of the breeder. Obviously, the objectives must be clearly and fully defined. On the basis of realistic objectives supported by persistence and judgment, the breeder may direct the selection of animals toward improved germ plasm and increased production.

### *Economic Consideration*

The objectives of most animal breeders are influenced by economic conditions and trade relations among and within nations. By affecting world and local markets, these factors determine what can be produced profitably. For example, large-scale importation of furs from wild animals at low cost has made American fur farmers consider critically their investment in improved fur-bearing animals. Competition, both immediate and potential, between wool, fur, and leather, and synthetic or man-made materials also makes it difficult for the breeder interested in these products to clarify and persist in long-term objectives. Animals must produce efficiently if they are to remain in direct competition with other sources of food and fiber. Sheep have not met the demands of the modern markets and have decreased in number because of lagging profits. The task of making sheep profitable is a real challenge to the sheep breeder. The unpredictable whims of human beings are constantly reflected in the markets and economic conditions that animal breeders must consider. A few years ago the dairy breeder was mainly concerned with improving butterfat production, but then plant fats entered the market, and after a short period of uncertainty and hesitation many consumers in the United States prefer the less expensive oleomargarine. Changed demands of the American people have also modified the objectives of the swine breeder. A few years ago, for example, lard was considered a major contribution of the pig, and round, fat animals with a high proportion of lard were bred. As lard was replaced on the market by vegetable oils, bacon became a more important product from the pig. Now narrow lean pigs with high bacon and low fat production are desirable. Conformation has also become a major consideration in beef animals because of its correlation with the production of certain cuts of meat.

Foods of animal origin are also in competition, potentially if not presently, with synthetic foods. In spite of the prospects for synthetic foods, however, people probably will continue to have appetites for real animal products. Turkeys, such as those shown in Fig. 21.2, represent an important source of man's food, and the breeder may take pride in his present accomplishment. Eggs and milk are difficult to replace in the diet of the better-fed populations of the world, but production efficiency is always a challenge. If eco-

**Fig. 21.2** Beltsville small white turkeys, eight months old. Male: 21 lbs; female: 10½ to 12 lbs. (U.S.D.A. photograph.)

nomic demands are not met, even these animal products will decrease in importance.

### *Disease Resistance*

Disease resistance is more strikingly heritable, especially in poultry, than most other characteristics of economic significance in domesticated animals. Resistance to avian diphtheria is apparently determined by a single gene which behaves as a simple dominant. Resistance to fowl paralysis also depends on a single gene. White Leghorn chickens are more resistant to *Salmonella pullorum* than other breeds. Furthermore, resistance to this pathogen can be improved by selection. One study showed that in 3 years of selection mortality was decreased from 73 percent to 24 percent with the same dosage of the pathogen and under carefully controlled experimental conditions. Resistance to *Salmonella gallinarum* in chickens can also be increased rapidly through selection. In the same way, resistance to leukosis has been built up appreciably in strains of White Leghorns. In mammals such as dairy cattle, no cases have been reported in which the resistance to a particular disease is determined by a single gene. Nevertheless, the resistance to at least six important diseases in dairy cattle is in some degree inherited.

## PLANT BREEDING

The basic objective of the plant breeder is to develop plants that will serve man better. As a scientist he is interested in the plants themselves, and in their ability to survive in environments likely to be provided for them. From an economic viewpoint, however, he is concerned more specifically with the hardiness of the plant, its resistance to disease and insects, the size and numbers of individual plants, and their productivity. He endeavors constantly to manipulate gene frequencies and develop new genotypes that will produce more efficiently under existing or potential environmental conditions. General or long-time objectives are requisites, but the plant breeder also must be flexible enough to adopt new aims as these are indicated by modern discoveries and conditions.

Modern methods of harvesting, preparing, and preserving food require different plant characteristics. Qualities that make fruits and vegetables suitable for commercial canning and quick freezing have been added to the list of desirable characteristics. In agricultural areas where certain crops such as maize, wheat, and peas are produced in quantity on a commercial scale, it has become necessary to develop plants that mature at the same time and have properties that make them suitable for machine harvest. One of the great advantages of new varieties of hybrid field maize is their uniformity in time of maturity and in ear position on the stalks, making mechanical harvest possible.

Many plant breeders have made notable contributions, but for the purpose of this brief discussion only N. I. Vavilov (1887–1942; Fig. 21.3), will be cited as an example. After graduating from a Russian agricultural academy, Vavilov entered Cambridge in England and became a student of William Bateson. His first research was on the genetic basis for immunity in plants, which he explained in Mendelian terms. He returned to Russia at the beginning of World War I and initiated investigations on the origin of cultivated plants. His great classic, *The Centers of Cultivated Plants,* was published in 1926. The whole subject was reviewed, and theories concerning principal centers of origin of cultivated plants were presented. His practical objective was to search out new genes to be tested and used in hybridization experiments designed for the improvement of domestic plants.

Fig. 21.3 N. I. Vavilov, Russian plant breeder.

*Methods and Accomplishments*

The selection of individuals with desirable characteristics to produce seed for perpetuating the crop has been used since ancient times as a way to improve the crop. The object of selection is to concentrate the genes for desirable characteristics in a single variety. Success in selection depends on the hereditary variation already present in the species. It is important to remember that phenotypes and not genes are used as the basis for selection, and that the whole plants and not the genes represent the units for selection. These particular principles also apply to animals.

The plant breeder using selection to develop better varieties of domesticated plants must design his experiments carefully in order to determine the most efficient method of selection. Two general methods, mass selection and pedigree or individual plant selection, can be used. Each method has characteristics that make it particularly useful with certain crops. Mass selection is accomplished by planting a mixture of seed taken from a number of desirable plants and rooting out (roguing) or otherwise removing the least desirable plants. The better plants are allowed to interbreed freely and to produce seed, and the seed from these plants is mixed. This type of selection represents the average of the most desirable plants in the field or plot. Little or nothing is known of the genetic background of the individual plants from which the seed is taken, and selection is made only on the basis of conspicuous phenotypic variations. A disadvantage in mass selection comes from the difficulty of distinguishing between hereditary and environmental variations. These are often similar and easily confused, making it impossible to determine in advance whether selection will be effective. On the other hand, mass selection keeps the selection on the group or variety level and avoids close inbreeding. Mass selection makes it possible to secure the advantage of heterosis or hybrid vigor along with those benefits arising directly from selection.

In contrast to mass selection, pedigree selection centers on individual plants and their progeny. This method is favored with self-pollinated crops where it is possible to select for desirable qualities within a closely related group for which the genotypes are, to some extent, known. Individual plant selection also affords a basis for comparison between lines, and provides for controls to distinguish between genetic properties and strictly environmental modifications of the plant. The undesirable effects of inbreeding in cross-pollinated species, which often result in individual weakness or lack of vigor, represent the most serious disadvantage of pedigree selection. Mass selection is used more extensively than individual plant selection for cross-pollinated plants such as the forage crops.

An example illustrating the accomplishment of plant breeders is the new and improved alfalfa (*Medicago sativa*) variety called Vernal. Compared with many of the older varieties, Vernal has a slightly higher forage-yielding capacity, improved winter hardiness, and increased resistance to bacterial wilt (a serious soil-borne disease that is widely prevalent in the alfalfa-growing areas of the United States). About 20 years of intensive research at the University of Wisconsin were required to develop Vernal alfalfa. The steps included: (1) critical evaluation of component materials; (2) widespread selection and testing for seed and forage production in different areas; (3) appropriate crossing and production of foundation seed stocks; and (4) production of certified seed under conditions that insure the preservation of the distinctive varietal characteristics.

The plant breeder uses controlled hybridization as a way to build desirable genotypes. He makes previously designed crosses under controlled conditions and evaluates the results through progeny tests and statistical analyses. Hybridization and selection methods have been combined effectively by many breeders of cereal crops. An example may be taken from the work of plant breeders in the United States Department of Agriculture, who, over a period of years, have developed many improved strains of barley. The major steps in the development are illustrated in Fig. 21.4. The particular project under consideration began with a cross between Colorado 3063 with white kernels, smooth awns, medium yield, and stiff straw, and Winter Club, a variety with rough awns, stiff straw, and high yield. From this cross, a number of segregants were obtained. Seven years were required to produce pure lines of plants carrying the more desirable characteristics. In the course of selection, both spring and winter types were obtained. One of the spring selections had especially desirable qualities and was subjected to field testing during 8 years, after which it was released under the name "Bonneville."

Certain limitations are associated with hybridization. First, it is usually impossible to make crosses and utilize the variability between plants that are not closely related. The delicate meiotic sequence obstructs the reproduction of hybrids that do not have similar chromosome arrangements. A good deal of variation usually occurs within a species, however, and this can be manipulated through hybridization and selection.

Another major limitation of hybridization methods is inherent in random assortment. Valuable gene combinations may be lost from desirable strains through outcrossing. Combinations, once broken up, may be difficult to recover. The process obviously is not a simple mechanism by which new genes may be added to a variety without loss or risk to valuable genotypes already established. The likelihood of losing the good qualities already accumulated must be weighed against the possibility of adding new desirable characteristics.

It is sometimes possible, through well-chosen crosses, to avoid some of the hazards of outcrossing and to introduce new genes without losing the combinations already established. The backcross method is especially useful for this purpose. In this method, individuals that have certain desirable qualities are crossed with the standard or the commercial variety to which a new trait is to be added. Hybrids are then backcrossed repeatedly to the (desired) parent. The gene contribution from the nonrecurrent parent is cut in half in each backcross generation. A series of backcrosses therefore sometimes permits essentially complete reestablishment of the original genotype of the recurrent parent along with introduction of the desirable quality from another strain. Linkage may alter the speed and completeness of the synthesis.

Backcrosses have been widely used in

**Fig. 21.4** Barley heads representing steps in development of Bonneville barley. *A*, from strain known as Colorado 3063, one parent in the original cross; *B*, Winter Club, the other parent; *C*, $F_1$ from cross; *D*, three heads from $F_2$ showing different combinations of traits from original parents; *E*, Bonneville variety developed after many years of selection from $F_2$ segregants.

vegetable crop breeding. Investigators of the United States Department of Agriculture have succeeded in introducing resistance to Verticillium wilt into the valuable Moscow variety of tomatoes through a series of backcrosses. Moscow was first crossed with "Peru wild," a resistant variety with red, cherry-size fruit, which was entirely undesirable as a commercial tomato. Through a series of five backcrosses to the recurrent parent (Moscow), it was possible to combine essentially all of the good qualities of the commercial variety with resistance to Verticillium wilt. The results of appropriate crosses between resistant and the nonresistant varieties demonstrated that resistance to Verticillium wilt depends on a single gene which behaves as a dominant with respect to its allele for nonresistance.

## METHODS AND ACCOMPLISHMENTS IN HUMAN GENETICS

The Greek philosophers were keen in their discernment of similarities among related people. Hippocrates (460–370 B.C.), the father of medicine, called attention to the recurrence of human traits such as crossed eyes and bald-headedness in certain family groups. He also observed that certain disorders such as epilepsy and a particular eye disease causing blindness in older people occurred in some families and not in others. Disease syndromes were recognizd by the Greeks, and the idea of a physical constitution providing immunity or susceptibility for disease became well established.

These concepts of the Greeks were lost in the middle ages and were not restored until modern times. Pierre Maupertuis, an eighteenth century biologist, was one of the first to revive an interest in human genetics. He collected pedigrees of families in which polydactyly and albinism occurred and analyzed the results by statistical means with application of the theory of probability. The scientific background had not been established and the significance of these studies was not appreciated at the time. In the nineteenth century, Sir Francis Galton applied more sophisticated statistical tools to human problems and directed attention to the social implications of human genetics. In spite of the early beginnings and inherent interest in the subject, human genetics has developed slowly.

Following the discovery of Mendelian inheritance, it soon became apparent that Mendel's principles were applicable to man. During the first decade of the present century, considerable interest was shown in human genetics. Many traits were known to be more prevalent in certain families than in the general population. Some were explained in simple Mendelian terms. Feeblemindedness, for example, was considered to be a single entity and was interpreted on the basis of a single gene substitution. Several types of feeblemindedness can now be considered to depend on single gene substitutions whereas other types are genetically and environmentally complex. Critical analysis has since indicated that most early explanations for most human traits were oversimplified. With the experimental method being readily applicable in animal and plant genetics, and giving promise of the objective and definite results in a short time, human studies were allowed to lapse as too imprecise. Controlled matings among experimental organisms took precedence over the more uncertain human studies as the way to establish basic genetic principles. Fortunately, the experiments with organisms that were more amenable to the experimental approach demonstrated the universal application of the basic principles of genetics and indirectly strengthened human genetics.

### *Complicating Factors*

Many types of experiments simply cannot be performed on man and objective data are difficult to obtain. Ideally, genetic investigations are performed using standardized individuals maintained in a controlled environment. Man is far from standardized genotypically, and to a large extent he regulates his own environment. Home, school, nutrition, and numerous other factors influence the growth of a child. It is difficult, therefore, to find anything in human society that is comparable with the material required by the experimental geneticist. Identical twins and other multiple births provide the only human groups that approach a genotype standard. They occur infrequently and usually the members of pairs or groups are raised in the same home and essentially the same overall environment. When identical twins are separated early in life and subjected to different environmental situations, it is possible to compare the effects of different environments on similar genotypes.

The problem of human genetics has been further complicated by the long period (on the average, about 30 years) between generations. The life span of the investigator is no greater than that of his material for study. Methods are now available, however, for securing significant data from one or two generations. Furthermore, large families are desirable for genetic studies, and even the largest human families fall short of the size necessary to establish genetic ratios and pursue orthodox statistical analyses. New statistical tools, however, now permit analysis of data from small families.

Incomplete knowledge of human cytology also has been a limiting factor in the past. Although the human chromosomes were observed several years ago and the sex chromosomes were identified, little other basic cytological knowledge was available until recently (Chapter 10). The present interest in the number of human chromosomes, and the increased availability of human material for cytological studies have greatly stimulated chromosome studies in man. At present the human chromosomes in cultures, at metaphase in mitosis are probably better understood than those of any other mammal. Human cytogenetics is now an active and progressive field of research.

Further difficulties encountered in the past by the human geneticist are associated with the genetic mechanism itself. The emphasis has been centered around phenotypes rather than genotypes. Obviously, a true genetic picture must be obtained before the gene behavior can be properly analyzed and evaluated. Hereditary deafness, for example, may result from any one of several abnormalities in the ear, nerve tracts, or brain, each of which is controlled by a different combination of genes. On the other hand, different manifestations of the same gene may result in strikingly different phenotypes. These difficulties are being overcome by more precise information concerning gene action.

Many human traits result from the cumulative action of polygenes, which undergo segregation and crossing over but cannot be identified or localized individually. They are similar to the usual Mendelian genes in transmission but dissimilar in action. Their individual effects are slight but cumulative. They play an important part in selection mainly because of their relatively small effect on viability. Much of the great variation known to occur in man is probably based on numerous polygene differences which cannot be studied individually.

Nevertheless, the classical approach to human genetics through analysis of single gene effects is still valid and useful. McKusick (1966) in his catalogue of human traits has listed 837 phenotypes controlled by single dominant genes, 531 by recessives and 119 by X-linked genes. With 1487 traits now known to be controlled by single genes, conventional methods of pedigree analysis are by no means obsolete. Modern computerized experiments may now be designed for determining genetic mechanisms from family history data.

Statistical approaches and refinements of twin studies are perhaps the best methods for the immediate future. The application of statistical methods to human genetics in the last century made this discipline a quantitative science. Although statistical approaches are more comprehensive than Mendelian analyses and cover the whole variation of the character, the individual units cannot be considered separately and are therefore lost in the analyses. The average effect of all acting genes in the group can be demonstrated by such methods, but not the effect of single genes.

### *Medical Genetics*

Members of the medical profession are largely entrusted with the physical and mental welfare of mankind. This task is particularly complex because the health of man is influenced by hereditary as well as environmental factors. A large number of human structural and functional diseases are more or less hereditary. The susceptibility to many more, including several common infectious diseases, is based on inheritance. Hereditary diseases are incurable in the sense that the genes cannot be changed. Symptoms of many may be alleviated or suppressed but the diseases are not cured. Progress has been made recently in the understanding of several so-called "hereditary diseases" of man.

Phenylketonuria, for example, is transmitted by an autosomal recessive gene. In the presence of this gene in homozygous condition (*pp*), phenylalanine accumulates in the blood because of a deficiency or defect in the enzyme phenylalanine hydroxylase. The high serum phenylalanine level and the accumulation of associated metabolic products such as phenylpyruvic acid result in severe brain damage. Babies who have inherited the genotype for this disease are usually normal at birth but suffer irreversible brain damage within a few months unless treatment is initiated. The treatment consists mainly of a diet that maintains a low serum phenylalanine level in the blood.

Infants with excessive serum phenylalanine who may have phenylketonuria can be detected more or less successfully by screening tests. The simplest of these is a diaper test that can be performed by placing a few drops of 10 percent ferric chloride on the urine-wet diapers of newborn babies in hospital nurseries and checking for a characteristic color change if excessive phenylalanine is present. Unfortunately, this simple test is not entirely foolproof. Some false positives have been obtained. Phenylketonuria has been estimated to occur in about one in 10,000 births in the general population.

Most cases that are detected and placed on treatment within the first month after birth do not express any mental retardation symptoms. Attempts to treat brain damage due to phenylketonuria usually fail if the afflicted person is more than three or four years of age. Besides being mentally retarded, however, phenylketonurics are irritable, hyperactive, and exhibit unpredictable erratic behavior. And although the mental retardation is not usually influenced to any great extent in older people by treatment, emotional stability may be improved. With low-phenylalanine diets and good therapy, phenylketonurics can make remarkable progress towards satisfactory environmental adjustment. In other words, the genotype (*pp*) for phenylketonuria can be at least partially and sometimes totally offset by manipulating the environment.

Other hereditary diseases have been cured symptomatically by replacing a missing hormone. The metabolic disorder galactosemia, for example, can be treated by supplying a hormone, cortisol, and thus correcting a metabolic block. In galactosemia, a genetic defect in the synthesis of a hydroxylating enzyme (hydroxylase) in the adrenal cortex causes a deficiency of cortisol. Without this hormone, galactose is not metabolized properly and can be detected in the blood serum. Replacement of the hormone in the diet removes the metabolic block and the symptoms.

Cystic fibrosis is a hereditary disease transmitted by an autosomal recessive gene that has been known for many years as a fatal disease of childhood. It is a complicated disease involving abnormal functioning of several exocrine glands, including the pancreas, liver, and sweat glands. Nevertheless, early diagnosis and intensive and persistant treatment now make it possible for its victims to live fairly normal and active lives. Unlike phenylketonuria, however, this disease cannot be treated with a single package treatment. Each symptom resulting from the malfunction of a particular gland must be treated separately.

The most conspicuous glandular defect associated with cystic fibrosis involves abnormally high concentrations of sodium and chloride in the sweat. Individuals with the disease may sweat profusely over long periods of time and lose enough salt to upset the salt balance in the body. If the normal intake of salt is not supplemented, heat prostration may result. The cure for this particular symptom therefore is salt supplementation, which may be accomplished by salt tablets taken orally.

More severe physiological problems occur when the mucus glands function abnormally. The mucus of a cystic fibrosis patient may be too viscous to flow properly in the small tubules of the lungs. It becomes mixed with bacteria, serum fluids, and debris and creates an unhealthy situation. Bronchial walls become infected and chronic bronchitis results. Infection of the respiratory tract is the most common cause of death among young cystic fibrosis victims. Treatment with antibiotics, sulfonamides, and pulmonary therapy designed to liquify the mucus and remove infected secretions has improved the health and extended the life expectancy of many cystic fibrosis patients.

The more severe glandular defects which threaten the life of the patient are associated with malfunctions of pancreas, liver, and intestines. These challenges can still be only partially resolved. Cystic fibrosis affects the pancreas by destroying the secreting tissue and causing a deficiency or absence of pancreatic enzymes. These enzymes can be supplied in the diet but the treatment must be constant. Some patients develop cirrhosis of the liver, which leads to an absence of bile-emulsifying factors. As a treatment for this symptom, bile salts may be supplied in the diet. Along with the special treatments, a diet well balanced with fats, proteins, and carbohydrates and supplemented with fat-soluble vitamins is prescribed for the cystic fibrosis patient. Much remains to be done before the symptoms of this disease will be conquered, but the effects of the genotype can be overcome to a considerable extent.

Diabetes mellitus is more common among close relatives than among individuals chosen at random in the populations; this suggests a familial pattern. Studies of twins have indicated a significant hereditary predisposition. When concordance in identical twins in one study was compared with that in fraternal twins, 65 percent of the identical twins both had diabetes compared with 18 percent of the fraternal twins. Diabetes of one type occurs in young people, while another form is fairly common among people in advanced years. The twin studies included twin pairs of different ages and therefore gave only general evidence for a hereditary component.

Symptoms of diabetes can be controlled by administration of insulin, either orally or intravenously, depending on the severity of the case. Dietary modifications are also necessary, particularly for women during pregnancy. Diet may even be a factor in preventing the onset of the symptoms. Obesity in older people has been shown to precede the onset of diabetes in some 85 percent of the cases. A carefully controlled diet, therefore, may help prevent as well as cure the symptoms of diabetes.

Coronary heart disease depends to some extent on hereditary predisposition, but management of environmental factors provides some control. An elevated serum cholesterol level in the blood and high blood pressure are associated with coronary disease. These conditions can be controlled to some extent through the diet and other environmental factors. Other diseases such as intestinal polyposis, pyloric stenosis, congenital dislocation of the hip, rheumatic fever, and tuberculosis, which are influenced by hereditary predisposition or susceptibility, are being successfully prevented or cured by environmental means. A particular pattern of management may include surgery, diet, drugs, and a goodly portion of just common sense in dealing with the environmental factors associated with healthful living.

The physicians of today and tomorrow will undoubtedly make increasingly greater use of genetics than their predecessors, who practiced medicine earlier in the present century. This is partly because of the greater awareness of the role that inheritance plays in human health and illness. Most medical students now include courses in human genetics in their program and some medical colleges have their own departments of human genetics. Furthermore, a progressive change is occurring in the type of services a physician is called upon to perform. Infections of childhood and adult diseases, in which heredity is relatively unimportant, occupied much of the time of a physician of a few decades ago. Now these diseases are effectively controlled. More people now reach advanced ages where degenerative diseases are the main problem. In these diseases, heredity is a factor of major importance. Challenges that face the medical researcher and the physician now and which will undoubtedly continue in the future are cancer, heart disease, arthritis, and other degenerative diseases which require keen insight into basic biological problems.

### *Effects of Medical "Cures" on Gene Frequency*

In hereditary diseases such as those described above, only the symptoms are treated. The defective genes remain unchanged and may be passed on to future generations. Medical practices and miscellaneous environmental control measures thus provide great advantages to individuals and their families, but simultaneously contribute to a deep-seated problem concerning the effect of these genes on the genetic quality of the population in future generations. By preserving individuals with known defective genes and allowing them, indeed often encouraging them, to reproduce and transmit defective genes to their children, we may be creating a population that will be more and more dependent on surgery, drugs and other special treatments for survival. Remarkable things are being done by medicine and surgery and this threat may seem less serious in a society well equipped to take care of the needs of genetically abnormal people. Susceptibility to such diseases as smallpox and plague was once a major problem but this is no longer a health hazard because the diseases are virtually nonexistent in most of the world and environmental control is readily available.

However, when natural consequences are circumvented by man's cleverness, equal ingenuity should be applied to presolving situations which may result. Valid decisions on these points are difficult at present because the mechanics of human genetics are not fully understood. We are also experiencing considerable difficulty in defining the human qualities that should be preserved for future generations. Decisions about human reproduction inevitably require concomitant decisions about what values individuals and the population as a whole should (and may) accept. Some people with known defective genes also carry other highly desirable characteristics which are known or presumed to be hereditary. Relative values, therefore, must be considered for individuals and for the population as a whole with reference to particular combinations of transmittable traits. Then too, more defective genes than those known and expressed are carried by each individual. Many recessive genes remain hidden generation after generation. Estimates have indicated that, on the average, people carry 4 to 8 defective genes which could, in proper combination, render their children incapable of caring for themselves. Every couple producing children bears some risk of having a seriously abnormal child.

*Eugenics*

This line of thought inevitably leads to the practical issue of eugenics, the social behavior which results in an improvement of the genotype of the human population. The first requisites to this behavior are (1) continued study of human genetics and other disciplines designed to understand man, and (2) education, to bring about enlightened public opinion based on sound facts. Accurate knowledge should preceed all important action. This, of all problems, should be based on scientific information. Research and education, however, will be fulfilled only when appropriate action is taken to improve mankind. This aspect of eugenics depends basically on a differential birth rate which must be based on scientific facts with due consideration for moral and ethical principles.

In theory, the procedure seems simple: those with superior genotypes should produce more and those with inferior genotypes less (or none) of the next generation. But in practice, it requires superior wisdom and courage to determine precisely who should and who should not have children. We should probably find it almost equally difficult to decide how and by whom such decisions should be made. Genotypes are, for the most part, not known, and the criteria for selecting types best fitted for environments of the future are not established. Moreover, reproduction cannot be entirely controlled at will. Sterility may interfere with the best planning. Sir Francis Galton, the founder of eugenics, for example, who was unusually gifted and devoted to the principle that the better qualified people should produce at least their share of the children for the next generation, died childless.

Voluntary adherence to any eugenic movement in a free society would require a highly enlightened population that was deeply concerned for the quality of the gene pool. This ideal has been and probably will continue to be very difficult to attain. Most people would agree that severely disabled hereditary defectives should not reproduce, and usually nature takes care of this situation. But the larger segments of the population, those that carry defective genes but fall within the near-normal phenotypic range for basically important traits such as intelligence, ordinarily make their own decisions and naturally cherish that right. One apparently deceiving feature of the statistics, particularly since World War II, is that the average intelligence of the population in the United States has not decreased even though many seemingly less-qualified parents produce a larger share of the children.

In their extensive study of mental retardation, Reed and Reed (1965, p. 79,) have concluded:

> There is a large negative correlation (about −0.3) between the number of children in a family and their average intelligence as measured by any test; this should result in a decrease in the intelligence of the population each generation—but it doesn't. The explanation of the failure of the intelligence of the population to decline is that while a few of the retarded produce exhuberantly large families of low average intelligence, most of the retarded produce only one child or no children at all. The persons at the upper end of the curve of intelligence are consistent in their production of smaller families of more intelligent children; thus the children of the smaller, more intelligent families balance, or perhaps outnumber, the children of

the larger less intelligent families. The net result of eons of evolution has been an increase in intelligence to the present level.

Reed and Reed also showed that only 0.5 percent of the children from normal parents with normal siblings were retarded. On the other hand, five-sixths of the retarded individuals, representing 2.5 percent of the entire population in the United States, have at least one parent or close relative (uncle or aunt) who is retarded. Although environmental as well as hereditary factors are involved in mental retardation of individuals, averages in the population indicate that heredity is important.

### *The Population Explosion*

Since World War II the problem of numbers of people has received more publicity than the problem of quality. The world-wide population increase has become so acute that other aspects of human genetics have been crowded into the background.

Predictions made in the 1940's indicated that the population in the United States would reach 150 million by about 1968 and increase to about 153 million by about 1980. Population analysts of the 1940's were predicting that the population of the United States would stabilize shortly after the year 2000 and that it would remain more or less stationary after that time.

Actually, the population was approaching 200 million in the late 1960's and is increasing at an unprecedented rate. What happened? A tremendous increase in birth rate occurred after World War II. An increase was expected, to make up for delays in reproduction during the war years, but the rapid increase in population was not expected to continue. Several factors now seem to be involved. Support and schooling for war veterans and now for a large segment of the college-age population during the most fertile years of life is certainly one factor. Medical advances which have improved fertility and decreased mortality at both ends of the life span have had their effect on total population. A psychological factor has also been recognized. According to recent surveys, more women want children and larger families than in previous years.

This poses the problem of the relation between population size and available space. Technological advances in food production in the United States allows us to keep pace with a growing population, but limitations of land and water suggest that even here the population cannot increase indefinitely without dire results. It seems obvious that if the present trend persists, education, cultural opportunities, and other "good things of life" will continue to be inaccessible to substantial numbers of people.

The entire world population poses a more urgent problem, especially in terms of the large groups of people that are not now adequately supplied with the basic necessities for life. The world population is now more than three billion and according to estimates of the United Nations it is increasing at the rate of some 50,000,000 per year. The entire history of man on earth up to about 1830 was required to bring the population to one billion (Fig. 21.5). In another century (1830–1930) the population doubled to about two billion. The third billion was added in about 30 years (1930–1960) and the United Nations statisticians estimate that, at the present rate, it will take less than 15 years to add the fourth billion. If the present trend continues, some seven billion people will be living on the earth at the end of the twentieth century. Opinions differ concerning the possibilities for meeting the needs of so many people. Most people, however, acknowledge that in a world with finite supplies of space, land, and water, a time will inevitably come when the limits

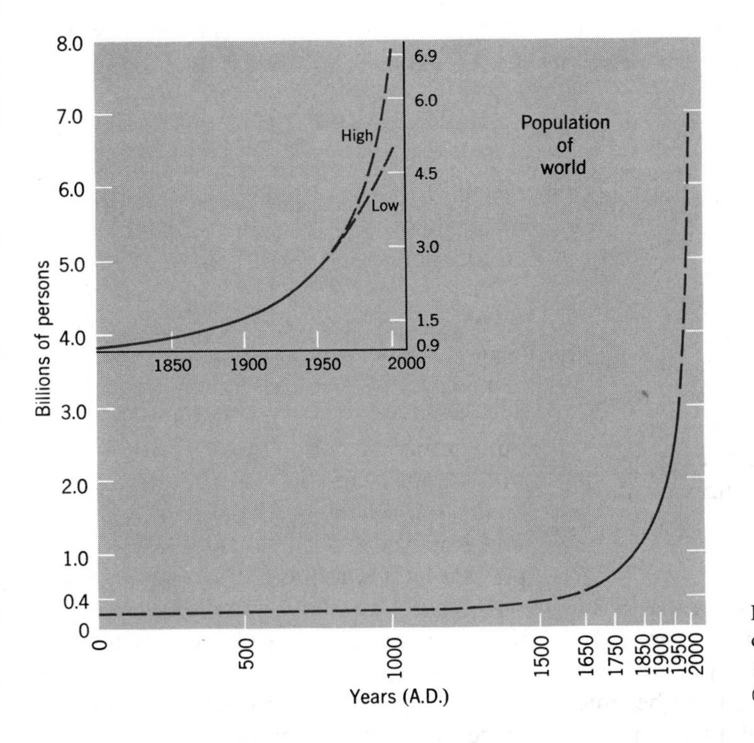


**Fig. 21.5** Estimated population of the world, A.D. 1 to A.D. 2000. (From Dorn, *Science* 135:283–290 © 1962, Amer. Assoc. Adv. Sci.)

of population that can be supported have been reached.

Even now a large proportion, perhaps two-thirds of the people in the world, are hungry. Many are poorly clothed and inadequately sheltered. Large numbers of people in many countries are poorly educated. Moreover, in the increasingly complex culture of the most advanced countries, proportionately more adults are needed to properly educate the children and to provide adequately for the young and old in present-day society. Already there is overcrowding in many places. The problem of controlling the birth rate and increasing the world living standard is so pressing that it must be considered in any evaluation of the future of human genetics, and indeed, the future of man on earth. If we ignore the population problem, we are inviting, for future generations, war, disease, starvation, and the loss of the cultural gains society has won. Man's future on earth depends on man himself.

## REFERENCES

Allard, R. W. 1960. *Principles of plant breeding*. John Wiley and Sons, New York.

Burdette, W. J. (ed.) 1962. *Methodology in human genetics*. Holden-Day, San Francisco.

Burdette, W. J. 1963. *Methodology in mammalian genetics*. Holden-Day, San Francisco.

Darlington, C. D. 1964. *Genetics and man*. The Macmillan Co., New York.

Dorn, H. F. 1962. "World population growth: an international dilemma." *Science,* **135,** 283–290.

Lerner, M., and H. P. Donald. 1966. *Modern developments in animal breeding*. Academic Press, New York.

McKusick, V. A. 1966. *Mendelian inheritance in man*. Johns Hopkins Press, Baltimore.

Moody, P. A. 1967. *Genetics of man*. W. W. Norton and Co., New York.

Reed, E. W., and S. C. Reed. 1965. *Mental retardation: a family study*. W. B. Saunders, Philadelphia.

Reed, S. C. 1963. *Counseling in medical genetics*. W. B. Saunders Co., Philadelphia.

Stern, C. 1960. *Principles of human genetics,* 2nd ed. W. H. Freeman and Co., San Francisco.

Sutton, H. E. 1965. *An introduction to human genetics*. Holt, Rinehart and Winston, New York.

Symposium on Plant and Animal Breeding. 1959.

*Proc. X Int. Cong. Genet.*, **1,** 129–243. (Participants: J. Unrau, H. Kihara, D. F. Jones, C. Larsen, M. S. Navashin. H. Nachtsheim. A. Robertson, C. Stormont, H. P. Donald, and I. Johnson.)

Thompson, J. S., and M. W. Thompson. 1966. *Genetics in medicine.* W. B. Saunders Co., Philadelphia.

Whittinghill, M. 1965. *Human genetics and its foundations.* Reinhold Publ. Corp., New York.

Winters, L. M. 1954. *Animal breeding,* 5th ed. John Wiley and Sons, New York.

*Yearbook of Agriculture.* 1936, 1937, 1943–47, 1953. U. S. Govt. Printing Office, Washington, D. C. (The 1936 and 1937 yearbooks are devoted largely to the breeding of important plant crops. Sections of the yearbooks 1943–47 are also devoted to plant and animal breeding. The 1953 yearbook is concerned with plant pathology, including the breeding of resistant strains.)

## *Problems*

**21.1** Outline a procedure that might be followed in the improvement of domestic animals such as dairy cows.

**21.2** What criteria might be used in choosing animals which have the greatest value for breeding stocks?

**21.3** Why are characteristics other than the production of individual animals considered in selection of dairy cattle when higher production is the ultimate objective for the selection procedure?

**21.4** What is the significance of heritability in breeding for animal characteristics of economic importance?

**21.5** How may resistance to a particular pathogen in a strain or breed of animals be controlled genetically?

**21.6** How do the objectives of the animal breeder compare with those of the plant breeder?

**21.7** Can the expensive research projects now in progress in different experiment stations designed to breed cereal crops which are resistant to rust, smut, and mildew be justified from the practical standpoint?

**21.8** How does natural selection differ from the artificial selection which is controlled by the plant breeder?

**21.9** What are the advantages and disadvantages of (a) mass selection, and (b) pedigree selection in plant breeding? (c) How are the values of these two selection procedures related to the system of mating (that is, self-pollination and cross-pollination) in plants?

**21.10** What limitations are associated with hybridization as a method employed by the plant breeder?

**21.11** How and under what conditions are backcrosses used effectively by plant breeders?

**21.12** Why has human genetics been slow in developing, in spite of its early beginnings and great importance?

**21.13** Why are human traits dependent on dominant genes better known than those dependent on recessive genes?

**21.14** What are the relative values and limitations of (a) pedigree analyses, (b) statistical methods, and (c) twin studies for studying human genetics?

**21.15** How can the statements that human hereditary diseases are curable and are incurable be explained?

**21.16** What effect from widespread medical "cures" of hereditary diseases might be expected on gene frequencies in the population?

**21.17** What is the objective of eugenics?

**21.18** What special problems are involved when eugenic measures are developed in society?

**21.19** How have trends in population in the United States since World War II differed from predictions made in the 1940's?

**21.20** What is the present trend in world population?

# Glossary

(Extended discussions and examples would be helpful to gain appreciation for some of the following terms. The purpose of this glossary is to provide an introduction to the terms employed in the text and an aid in using them. Names of chemical compounds such as amino acids which are identified in the text are omitted in the glossary.)

*Acentric chromosome*. Chromosome fragment lacking a centromere.

*Acquired character*. A modification impressed on an organism by environmental influences during development.

*Adaptation*. Adjustment of an organism or a population to an environment.

*Adenine*. A purine base found in RNA and DNA.

*Agglutinin*. An antibody in blood plasma which brings about clumping (agglutination) of blood cells carrying an incompatible agglutinogen.

*Agglutinogen*. An antigen carried in red blood cells which reacts with a specific agglutinin in the plasma to cause clumping of the cells. A specific antigen when injected into an animal body stimulates the production of a corresponding antibody.

*Agouti*. A grizzled color of the fur of animals resulting from alternating light and dark bands on the individual hairs.

*Albinism*. Absence of pigment in skin, hair, and eyes of an animal. Absence of chlorophyll in plants.

*Alcaptonuria*. An inherited metabolic disorder. Alcaptonurics excrete excessive amounts of homogentisic acid (alcapton) in the urine.

*Aleurone*. The protein matter occurring in the form of minute grains in the endosperm of ripe seeds.

*Aleurone layer*. The outer differentiated layer of cells of the endosperm; named thus because these cells are filled with aleurone grains.

*Allele* (*allelomorph*), *adj*. *allelic* (*allelomorphic*). One of a pair, or series of alternative genes that can occur at a given locus in homologous chromosomes; one contrasting form of a gene. Alleles are symbolized with the same basic symbol (e.g. *D* for tall peas and *d* for dwarf), *see* Multiple alleles.

*Allopolyploid*. A polyploid having chromosome sets from different sources, such as different species. A polyploid containing genetically different chromosome sets derived from two or more species.

*Allotetraploid*. An organism with four genomes derived from hybridization of different species. Usually, in forms that become established, two of the four genomes are from one species and two are from another species.

*Amino acid*. Any one of a class of organic compounds containing the amino ($NH_2$) group and the carboxyl (COOH) group. Amino acids are building blocks of proteins. Alanine, proline, threonine, histidine, lysine, glutamine, phenylalanine, tryptophan, valine, arginine, and leucine are among the common amino acids.

*Amorph*. Mutant allele that has little or no effect on the expression of a trait.

*Amphidiploid*. A species or type of plant derived from doubling the chromosomes in the $F_1$ hybrid of two species; an allopolyploid. In an amphidiploid the two species are definitely known whereas in other allopolyploids they may not be known.

*Anaphase*. The stage of nuclear division during which the daughter chromosomes pass from the equatorial plate toward opposite poles of the cell (toward the ends of the spindle). Anaphase follows metaphase and precedes telophase.

*Androgen.* A substance with male sex hormone activity in vertebrate animals.

*Anemia.* Abnormal condition characterized by pallor, weakness, and breathlessness, resulting from a deficiency of hemoglobin or a reduced number of erthrocytes.

*Aneuploid or heteroploid.* An organism or cell having a chromosome number which is not an exact multiple of the monoploid ($n$) or basic number, hyperploid, higher (e.g., $4n + 1$); hypoploid, lower (e.g., $4n - 1$).

*Anomalous gametes.* Irregular and usually incompatable gametes with chromosome numbers different from those normally produced by members of the species.

*Anther.* Male part of a plant flower in which pollen is produced.

*Anthocyanin.* Glucoside pigment in plants. Anthocyanins range in color from red to blue.

*Anthoxanthine.* Any of a group of yellow pigments found especially in plants.

*Antibody.* Substance in a tissue or fluid of the body which acts in antagonism to a foreign substance (antigen).

*Antigen.* A substance, usually a protein, which stimulates the production of antibodies when introduced into a living organism.

*Antihemophilia globulin.* Blood globulin which reduces the clotting time of hemophilic blood.

*Apomixis.* Development of an individual plant from an egg without fertilization or fusion with pollen nucleus. The egg may be normally reduced (haploid) or, more commonly, through failure of reduction division may remain diploid.

*Ascospore.* One of the spores contained in the ascus of certain fungi such as Neurospora. Following the meiotic sequence, each ascus or sac contains 8 ascospores.

*Ascus, pl. asci.* Reproductive sac in the sexual stage of a type of fungi (Ascomycetes) in which ascospores are produced.

*Asexual reproduction.* Any process of reproduction which does not involve the formation and union of gametes from the two sexes.

*Asynapsis.* The failure or partial failure of pairing of homologous chromosomes during the meiotic prophase; failure of chiasma formation resulting in a high frequency of univalents.

*Atavism. see* Reversion.

*ATP.* Adenosine triphosphate; an energy-rich compound that promotes certain activities in the cell.

*Atrophy.* Decrease in size or wasting away of an organ or tissue.

*Autopolyploid.* A polyploid that has multiple and identical or nearly identical sets of chromosomes (genomes). A polyploid species with genomes derived from the same original species.

*Autoradiograph.* A record or photograph prepared by labeling a substance such as DNA with a radioactive material such as tritiated thymidine and allowing the image to develop on a film over a period of time.

*Autosexing.* A method of distinguishing the sex of young chickens by introducing marker genes into the breeding stock which produce a conspicuous phenotype on the male or female progeny at an early age.

*Autosome.* Any chromosome that is not a sex chromosome.

*Auxotroph.* A mutant organism (bacterium) that will not grow on a minimal medium but requires the addition of some growth factor.

*Backcross.* The cross of a hybrid to one of the parental types. The offspring of such a cross are referred to as the backcross generation or backcross progeny (*see* Test cross).

*Bacteriophage.* Virus that attacks bacteria. Such viruses are called bacteriophages because they destroy their bacterial host.

*Balanced lethal.* Lethal genes on the same pair of chromosomes that remain in repulsion because of close linkage or crossover suppression. Only heterozygotes survive.

*Balanced polymorphism.* Two or more types of individuals maintained in the same breeding population.

*Binomial expansion.* Exponential multiplication of an expression consisting of two terms connected by a + or − such as $(a + b)^n$.

*Bipartite structure* (chromosome). One having two corresponding parts.

*Biometry.* Application of statistical methods to the study of biological problems.

*Biotype.* Distinct physiological race or strain within morphological species. A population of individuals wth identical genetic constitution. A biotype may be made up of homozygotes or of heterozygotes, of which only the former would be expected to breed true.

*Bivalent.* A pair of synapsed or associated homologous chromosomes which may or may not have undergone the duplication process to form a group of four chromatids.

*Blastomere.* Any of the cells formed from the first few cleavages in animal embryology.

*Blastula.* A form of early animal embryo following the morula stage; typically, a single layered, hollow ball stage.

*Blended inheritance.* Inheritance in which the characters of two dissimilar parents appear to be blended in the offspring, and segregation fails to occur in later generations.

*Bud sport or chimera.* A branch, flower, or fruit which differs genetically from the remainder of the plant.

*Carcinogen.* A substance capable of inducing cancer in an organism.

*Carotenoid.* Any of a group of yellow and red pigments found in plants and in the fat of animals.

*Carrier.* An individual which carries a recessive gene that is not expressed (i.e., obscured by a dominant allele).

*Centriole.* Central granule in many animal cells which appears to be the active principle of the centrosome and which undergoes duplication preceding the division of the centrosome proper.

*Centromere or kinetochore.* Spindle-fiber attachment region of a chromosome.

*Centrosome.* A self-propagating cytoplasmic body usually present in animal cells and those of some lower plants, but not present in flowering plants; consisting of a centriole and sometimes a centrosphere (when inactive) or astral rays (when active); located at each pole of the spindle during the process of nuclear division (mitosis).

*Chalcones.* Any of a group of yellow pigments in plants.

*Character (contraction of the word characteristic).* One of the many details of structure, form, substance, or function which make up an individual organism. The Mendelian characters represent the end products of development, during which the entire complex of genes interacts within itself and with the environment.

*Chiasma, pl. chiasmata.* A visible change of partners or crossover in two of a group of four chromatids during the first meiotic prophase. In the diplotene stage of meiosis the 4 chromatids of a bivalent are associated in pairs but in such a way that in one part of their length two chromatids are associated, but in the remainder of their length each is associated with one of the other two chromatids. This point of "change of partner" is the chiasma.

*Chimera.* A mixture of tissues of genetically different constitution in the same part of an organism. It may result from mutation, irregular mitosis, somatic crossing over, or artificial fusion (grafting); may be: periclinical with parallel layers of genetically different tissues; or sectorial.

*Chloroplastid.* Green structure in plant cytoplasm which contains chlorophyll and in which starch is synthesized. A mode of cytoplasmic inheritance independent of nuclear genes has been associated with these cytoplasmic structures.

*Chondriosomes. see* Mitochondria.

*Chondrodystrophic children.* Children with a hereditary abnormality of the bones.

*Chondrodystrophy.* Trait in man characterized by abnormal growth of cartilage at ends and along shafts of long bones.

*Chromatid.* One of the two identical strands resulting from self-duplication of a chromosome during mitosis or meiosis. One of the four strands making up a bivalent during the later meiotic prophase.

*Chromatin.* The nuclear substance which takes basic stain and becomes incorporated in the chromosomes, so called because of the readiness with which it becomes stained with certain dyes (chromaticity).

*Chromatography.* A method of analyzing and comparing chemicals.

*Chromocenter.* Body produced by fusion of the heterochromatin regions of the autosomes and Y chromosome in salivary gland preparations of certain Diptera.

*Chromomeres.* Small bodies described by Belling which he identified by their characteristic size and linear arrangement on the chromosome thread.

*Chromonema, pl. chromonemata.* An optically single thread within the chromosome.

*Chromosome aberration.* Abnormal arrangement of the chromosome complement caused by chromosomal breakage and reunion.

*Chromosomes.* Microscopically observable nucleoprotein bodies, dark-staining with basic dyes, in the cell during cell division. They carry the genes which are arranged in linear order. Each species has a characteristic chromosome number.

*Cilium; pl. cilia; adj. ciliate.* Hair-like locomotor structure on certain cells; a locomotor structure on a ciliate protozoan.

*Cis. see* Coupling.

*Cistron.* A unit of function; a working definition of a gene. One cistron in the DNA specifies one polypeptide in protein synthesis.

*Clone.* All the individuals derived by vegetative propagation from a single original individual.

*Codominant genes.* Alleles, each of which produces an independent effect in heterozygotes.

*Codon.* A set of bases in DNA which will code one amino acid.

*Coenzyme.* A substance necessary for the activity of an enzyme.

*Coincidence.* The ratio of observed double crossovers to expected doubles calculated on the basis of independent occurrence and expressed as a decimal fraction.

*Colchicine.* An alkaloid derived from the autumn crocus which is used as an agent to arrest spindle formation and interrupt mitosis.

*Complementary genes.* Genes which are similar in phenotypic effect when present separately, but which together interact to produce a different character. If two such genes are complementary for a dominant effect, a 9:7 ratio results in $F_2$; if two are complementary for a recessive effect, a 15:1 ratio results in $F_2$.

*Conidium, pl. conidia.* An asexual spore produced by a specialized hypha in certain fungi.

*Conjugation.* Side-by-side association or synapsis of homologous chromosomes, as in meiosis; joining of Paramecia or other protozoans as a part of the fertilization process.

*Continuous variation.* Variation not represented by distinct classes. Individuals grade into each other and measurement data are required for analysis, c.f. discontinuous variation. Multiple genes or polygenes are usually responsible for this type of variation.

*Coordinate repression.* Control of structural genes in an operon by a single operator gene.

*Copolymers.* Mixtures consisting of more than one polymer. *Example:* polymers of two kinds of organic bases such as uracil and cytosine (poly-UC) have been combined for studies of genetic coding.

*"Copy choice."* An explanation for crossing over first suggested by J. Belling in 1930, which assumes that crossing over occurs during the process of chromosome duplication. Duplication or "copying" proceeds partially along one homologue and partially along the other.

*Coupling* or *cis-arrangement.* The condition in linked inheritance in which an individual heterozygous for two pairs of genes received the two dominant members from one parent and the two recessives from the other parent, (e.g., *AABB* × *aabb*). Compare repulsion.

*Crossing over.* A process inferred genetically by new associations of linked factors and demonstrated cytologically from new associations of parts of chromosomes. It results in an exchange of genes and therefore produces combinations differing from those characteristic of the parents. The term "genetic crossover" may be applied to the new gene combinations (*see* Recombination).

*Crossover unit.* A frequency of exchange of 1 percent between two pairs of linked genes; 1 percent of crossing over is equal to 1 unit on a linkage map.

*Cytogenetics.* Area of biology concerned with chromosomes and their implications in genetics.

*Cytokinesis.* Cytoplasmic division and other changes exclusive of nuclear division which are a part of mitosis or meiosis.

*Cytology.* The study of the structure and function of the cell.

*Cytoplasm.* The protoplasm of a cell outside the nucleus in which cell organelles (mitochondria, plastids, etc.) are embedded. All living parts of the cell except the nucleus.

*Cytoplasmic inheritance.* Hereditary transmission dependent on the cytoplasm or structures in the cytoplasm rather than the nuclear genes. Extranuclear inheritance. *Example:* Plastid characteristics in plants may be inherited by a mechanism independent of nuclear genes.

*Cytosine.* A pyrimidine base found in RNA and DNA.

*Dauermodification.* A characteristic induced by the environment which persists and appears to be inherited, sometimes for several successive generations. A type of acquired characteristic.

*Deficiency* (*deletion*). Absence of a segment of a chromosome involving one or more genes.

*Determination.* Process by which embryonic parts become capable of developing into only one kind of adult tissue or organ.

*Deviation.* As used in statistics, a variation from an expected number.

*Diakinesis.* A stage of meiosis just before metaphase I in which the bivalents are shortened and thickened.

*Dicentric chromosome.* One having two centromeres.

*Differentiation.* Modification of different parts of the body for particular functions during development of the organism.

*Dihybrid.* An individual that is heterozygous with respect to two pairs of alleles. The product of a cross between homozygous parents differing in two respects.

*Dimer.* A compound having the same percentage composition as another but twice the molecular weight; one formed by polymerization.

*Dimorphism.* Two different forms in a group as determined by such characteristics as sex, size, or coloration.

*Dioecious plant.* A unisexual plant; each plant is either a male or a female (*see* Monoecious).

*Diploid.* An organism or cell with two sets of chromosomes ($2n$) or two genomes. Somatic tissues of higher plants and animals are ordinarily diploid in chromosome constitution in contrast with the haploid (monoploid) gametes.

*Diplonema, adj. diplotene.* That stage in prophase of meiosis following the pachytene stage, but preceding diakinesis, in which the chromosomes are visibly double; stage characterized by centromere repulsion of bivalents resulting in the formation of loops.

*Discontinuous variation.* Distinct classes such as red vs white, tall vs dwarf, c.f. continuous variation.

*Disjunction.* Separation of homologous chromosomes during anaphase of mitosis or meiotic divisions (*see* Nondisjunction).

*Disome. see* Monosomic.

*Distinguishable hybrid.* A hybrid in which intermediate inheritance is expressed, (i.e., the heterozygous combination is distinguishable by a phenotype).

*Dizygous twins.* Two-egg or fraternal twins.

*DNA.* Deoxyribonucleic acid, the chemical material of which the information-carrying material or gene is composed.

*Dominance.* Applied to one member of an allelic pair of genes which has the ability to manifest itself wholly or largely at the exclusion of the expression of the other member. An inherited trait expressed when the controlling gene is either homozygous or heterozygous.

*Drift or random genetic drift.* Changes in gene frequency in small breeding populations due to chance fluctuations. Appropriately called the "Sewall Wright Effect" because of the basic contributions of Professor Wright in this area.

*Duplication.* The occurrence of a segment more than once in the same chromosome or genome.

*Dysgenic.* A situation that tends to be harmful to the hereditary qualities of future generations (c.f. eugenic).

*Ectoderm.* Outside cellular layer of an early animal embryo that gives rise to the outer skin and nervous system.

*Egg (ovum).* A germ cell produced by a female organism.

*Electrophoresis.* The migration of suspended particles in an electric field.

*Embryo.* A young organism in the early stages of development; in man, first period in uterus.

*Embryo sac.* A large thin-walled space within the ovule of the seed plant in which the egg and, after fertilization, the embryo develop; the mature female gametophyte in higher plants.

*Endoderm.* Inner layer of an early animal embryo which gives rise to the lining of the digestive tract.

*Endomitosis.* Duplication of chromosomes without division of the nucleus resulting in increased chromosome number within cells or endopolyploidy. Chromosome strands separate but the cells do not divide.

*Endoplasmic reticulum.* Network in the cytoplasm to which ribosomes adhere.

*Endosperm.* Nutritive tissue arising in the embryo sac of most angiosperms. It usually follows the fertilization of the two fused primary endosperm nuclei of the embryo sac by one of the two male gametes. In most diploid organisms the endosperm is triploid ($3n$) but in some, for example lily, the endosperm is $5n$.

*Enhancer.* A substance or object that increases a chemical activity or a physiological process, a major or modifier gene which increases a physiological process.

*Environment.* The aggregate of all the external conditions and influences affecting the life and devlopment of the organism.

*Enzyme.* A protein that accelerates a specific chemical reaction in a living system.

*Epigenesis.* The concept that the embryo develops anew from undifferentiated material in each generation, in contrast to preformation.

*Epigenesist.* One who visualizes embryological development as a step-by-step process from a relatively undifferentiated zygote to a complex adult.

*Episome.* A genetic element that may be present or absent in different cells, associated with a chromosome or independent in the cytoplasm. *Example:* Fertility factor (F) in *E. coli.*

*Epistasis.* The suppression of the action of a gene or genes by a gene or genes not allelomorphic to those suppressed. Those suppressed are said to be hypostatic. Distinguished from dominance which refers to the members of one allelomorphic pair.

*Equational or homotypic division.* Mitotic-type division which is usually the second division in the meiotic sequence; somatic mitosis and the nonreductional division of meiosis.

*Equatorial plate.* The figure formed by the chromosomes in the center (equatorial plane) of the spindle in mitosis.

*Estrogen.* Female hormone or estrus-producing compound.

*Euchromatin.* Parts of chromosomes which are genetically active and have characteristic staining properties. Most of the arm-like structures of Drosophila salivary preparations are euchromatin. (Compare heterochromatin.)

*Eugenic.* A situation that tends toward improvement in the hereditary qualities of future generations of mankind, c.f. dysgenic.

*Eugenics.* The science of improving the qualities of the human race; the application of the principles of genetics to the improvement of mankind.

*Euploid.* An organism or cell having a chromosome number that is an exact multiple of the monoploid ($n$) or haploid number. Terms used to identify different levels in an euploid series are: haploid, diploid, triploid, tetraploid, etc. *see* Heteroploid.

*Expressivity.* Degree of expression of a trait controlled by a gene. A particular gene may produce varying degrees of expression in different individuals.

*Extrachromosomal.* Structures that are not a part of the chromosomes; DNA units that control cytoplasmic inheritance.

$F_1$. The first filial generation. The first generation of descent from a given mating.

$F_2$. The second filial generation, produced by crossing *inter se* or by self-pollinating the $F_1$. The inbred "grandchildren" of a given mating. The term is loosely used to indicate any second generation progeny from a given mating, but in controlled genetic experimentation, inbreeding of the $F_1$ (or equivalent) is implied.

*Fertility.* Ability to produce offspring.

*Fertilization.* The fusion of a male gamete (sperm) with a female gamete (egg) to form a zygote.

*Fetal hydrops.* A form of dropsy in the newborn caused by incompatability between an Rh-negative mother and her Rh-positive fetus during pregnancy.

*Fetus.* Prenatal stage of a viviparous animal between the embryonic stage and the time of birth. In man, the final seven months before birth.

*Filial. see* $F_1$ and $F_2$.

*Fitness.* The number of offspring left by an individual as compared with the average of the population, or compared to individuals of different genotype.

*Flagellum; pl. flagella; adj. flagellate.* A whip-like organelle of locomotion in certain cells; locomotor structures in flagellate protozoa.

*Freemartin.* A sexually underdeveloped female calf born twined with a male.

*Gamete.* A mature male or female reproductive cell (sperm or egg).

*Gametogenesis.* The formation of the gametes.

*Gametophyte.* That phase of the plant life cycle that bears the gametes; cells have $n$ chromosomes.

*Gastrula.* An early animal embryo consisting of two layers of cells; an embryological stage following the blastula.

*Gene.* A particulate hereditary determiner; a unit of inheritance; a unit of DNA; located in a fixed location in the chromosome.

*Gene frequency.* The proportion of one allele as represented in a breeding population.

*Gene pool.* Sum total of all genes in a breeding population.

*Genetic drift. see* Drift.

*Genetic equilibrium.* Condition in a group of interbreeding organisms in which particular gene frequencies remain constant through succeeding generations.

*Genetics.* The science of heredity and variation.

*Genoid.* DNA carrying cytoplasmic particle (See Chapter 11).

*Genome.* A complete set of chromosomes (hence of genes), inherited as a unit from one parent.

*Genotype.* The genetic constitution (gene makeup), expressed and latent, of an organism (i.e., *Dd* or *dd*). Individuals of the same genotype breed alike. (Compare with phenotype.)

*Germ cell.* A reproductive cell capable when mature of being fertilized and reproducing an entire organism.

*Germ plasm.* The germinal material or physical basis of heredity. The sum total of the genes.

*Globulins.* Common proteins found in the blood, which are insoluble in water and soluble in salt solutions. Alpha, beta, and gamma globulins can be distinguished in human-blood serum. Gamma globulins are important in developing immunity to diseases.

*Gonad.* A sexual gland, (i.e., ovary or testis).

*Guanine.* A purine base found in DNA and RNA.

*Gynandromorph.* An individual of which one

part of the body is female and another part is male; a sex mosaic.

*Haploid or monoploid.* An organism or cell having only one complete set (*n*) of chromosomes or one genome.

*Haptoglobin.* A serum protein, alpha globulin in the blood.

*Helix.* Any structure with a spiral shape. The Watson and Crick model of DNA is in the form of a double helix.

*Hemizygous.* The condition in which only one allele of a pair is present, as in deletion or sex linkage.

*Hemoglobin.* Conjugated protein compound containing iron, located in erythrocytes of vertebrates; important in the transportation of oxygen to the cells of the body.

*Hemolymph.* The mixture of blood and other fluids in the body cavity of an invertebrate.

*Hemophilia.* A bleeder's disease; tendency to bleed freely from even a slight wound; hereditary condition dependent on a sex-linked recessive gene.

*Heredity.* Resemblance among individuals related by descent; transmission of traits from parents to offspring.

*Heritability.* Degree to which a given trait is controlled by inheritance.

*Hermaphrodite.* An individual with both male and female reproductive organs. *see* Monoecious plant.

*Heterocaryon.* A fungus hypha with two nuclei of different genotypes; the nuclei do not fuse but divide independently and simultaneously as new cells are formed.

*Heterochromatin.* Chromatin staining differently and functioning differently than euchromatin which contains most of the genes. In Drosophila salivary preparations the heterochromatin is mostly in the chromocenter.

*Heterogametic sex.* Producing unlike gametes, particularly with regard to the sex chromosome. In species in which the male is "XY," the male is heterogametic, the female (XX), homogametic.

*Heteroploid or aneuploid.* An organism characterized by a chromosome number other than the true haploid (monoploid) or diploid number ($2n + 1$ or $2n - 1$). *see* Euploid.

*Heteropyknosis, adj. heteropyknotic.* Property of certain chromosomes or of their parts to remain more dense and stain more intensely than other chromosomes or parts during the nuclear cycle.

*Heterosis. see* Hybrid vigor.

*Heterozygote, adj. heterozygous.* An organism with unlike members of any given pair or series of alleles, which consequently produces unlike gametes.

*"Holandric" gene.* A gene carried on the Y chromosome and therefore transmitted from father to son.

*Homogametic sex.* Producing like gametes (*see* Heterogametic sex).

*Homologous chromosomes.* Chromosomes which occur in pairs and are generally similar in size and shape, one having come from the male and one from the female parent.

*Homozygote, adj. homozygous.* An organism whose chromosomes carry identical members of any given pair of genes. The gametes are therefore all alike with respect to this locus and the individual will breed true.

*Homunculus.* Miniature individual imagined by early biologists to be present in the sperm cell.

*Hormone or internal secretion.* An organic product of cells of one part of the body which is transported by the body fluids to another part where it influences activity or serves as a coordinating agent.

*Hybrid.* An offspring of homozygous parents differing in one or more genes.

*Hybrid vigor or heterosis.* Unusual growth, strength, and health of hybrids from two less vigorous parents.

*Hybridization.* Interbreeding of species, races, varieties, etc. among plants or animals. A process of forming a hybrid by cross pollenation of plants or by mating animals of different type.

*Hydrocephalus.* Abnormal increase in the amount of cerebral fluid resulting in enlargement of the head and other symptoms.

*Hypha, pl. hyphae.* A branched filament of a fungus.

*Hypostasis. see* Epistasis.

*Identical twins. see* Twins.

*Idiogram.* A diagrammatic representation of the chromosomes of an individual illustrating their relative sizes and appearance.

*Immunize.* To induce a resistance to a parasite or foreign substance. Noun: immunization.

*Immunoglobulin. see* globulin.

*Inbreeding.* Matings among related individuals.

*Incomplete dominance.* Expression of heterozygous alleles different from those of the parents, producing distinguishable hybrids.

*Independent combinations or independent assortment.* The random behavior of genes in different chromosomes. The distribution of one pair of genes is not controlled by other genes in nonhomologous chromosomes.

*Inhibitor.* Any substance or object that retards a chemical reaction; a major or modifier gene that interferes with a reaction.

*Interference.* Crossing over at one point reduces the chance of another crossover in adjacent regions. Detected by studying crossovers of three or more linked genes.

*Intermediate inheritance.* An alternative to dominance in which the heterozygotes are distinguishable from both homozygotes.

*Interphase.* The stage in the cell cycle when the cell is not dividing; the metabolic stage; the stage following telophase of one division and extending to the beginning of prophase in the next division.

*Intersex.* An organism displaying secondary sexual characters intermediate between male and female; a type that shows some phenotypic characteristics of both males and females.

*Inversion.* A rearrangement of a group of genes in a chromosome in such a way that their order in the chromosome is reversed.

*Isoagglutinogen.* An antigen such as A or B blood-type factor that occurs normally in an individual, that is, without artificial stimulation.

*Karyotype.* The appearance of the metaphase chromosomes of an individual or species; comparative size, shape, and morphology of the different chromosomes.

*Kinetochore. see* Centromere.

*Kinetosome.* Granular body at the base of a flagellum or a cilium.

*Kynurenine.* A compound derived from tryptophan metabolism which occurs in the urine of rabbits and under certain conditions in the urine of other animals.

*Lampbrush chromosomes.* Greatly enlarged chromosomes in the oöcytes of amphibians. They have a main axis and side loops suggesting the name " lampbrush."

*Leptonema, adj. leptotene.* Stage in meiosis immediately preceding synapsis in which the chromosomes appear as single fine threadlike structures.

*Lethal gene.* A gene that renders inviable an organism or a cell possessing it.

*Line breeding.* Mating of selected members of successive generations among themselves to fix desirable characteristics.

*Linkage.* Association of genes that are physically located in the same chromosome. Such a group of linked genes is called a linkage group.

*Locus, pl. loci.* A fixed position on a chromosome occupied by a given gene or one of its alleles.

*Lysis.* Destruction of bacteria as the breaking of cells following infection by bacteriophage.

*Lysogenic bacteria.* Those harboring temperate bacteriophages.

*Macromolecule.* A large molecule; term used to identify such structures as ribosomes in living cells.

*Map units.* One percent of crossing over represents one unit on a linkage map.

*Maternal inheritance* (*maternal effect*). Inheritance from mother to offspring unaffected by inheritance from the father.

*Maturation.* The formation of gametes or spores.

*Mean.* The arithmetic average; the sum of all measurements or values of a group of objects divided by the number of objects.

*Megaspore* (*macrospore*). A spore having the property of giving rise to a gametophyte (embryo sac) bearing only a female gamete. One of the four cells produced by two meiotic divisions of the megaspore-mother-cell called a megasporocyte.

*Megaspore-mother-cell or megasporocyte.* The cell which undergoes two meiotic divisions to produce four megaspores.

*Megasporogenesis.* Process of production of megaspores. *see* Megaspore.

*Meiosis.* The process by which the chromosome number of a reproductive cell becomes reduced to half the diploid ($2n$) or somatic number; results in the formation of gametes in animals, or of spores in plants; important source of variability through recombination.

*Melanin.* Brown or black pigment of animal origin.

*Mendelian population.* A natural interbreeding unit of sexually reproducing plants or animals.

*Merozygote.* Partial zygote produced by a process of partial genetic exchange such as transformation in bacteria.

*Mesoderm.* The middle germ layer that forms in the early animal embryo that gives rise to such parts as bone and connective tissue.

*Messenger-RNA.* A particular kind of RNA that carries information necessary for protein synthesis from the DNA to the ribosome.

*Metabolic cell.* A cell that is not dividing.

*Metabolism.* Sum total of all chemical processes

in living cells by which energy is provided and used.

*Metafemale or superfemales.* In Drosophila, abnormal type of female usually sterile with an overbalance of X chromosomes with respect to autosomes.

*Metamorphosis.* Change of form, structure, or substance.

*Metaphase.* That stage of cell division in which the chromosomes are most discrete and arranged in an equatorial plate.

*Microspore.* One of the four cells produced by the two meiotic divisions of the microspore-mother-cell or microsporocyte. A spore having the property of giving rise to a gametophyte bearing only male gametes.

*Microspore-mother-cell. see* Pollen mother cell.

*Microsporogenesis.* Process of production of microspores. *see* Microspore.

*Mitochondria.* Small bodies in the cytoplasm of most plant and animal cells.

*Mitosis.* Cell division in which there is first a duplication of chromosomes followed by migration of chromosomes to the ends of the spindle and dividing of the cytoplasm.

*Modifier or modifying gene.* A gene that affects the expression of another nonallelic gene.

*Monoecious plant.* Plant with separate staminate (male) and pistillate (female) flowers on the same plant.

*Monohybrid.* An offspring of two homozygous parents differing from one another in only one gene locus.

*Monohybrid cross.* A cross between parents differing in only one trait or in which only one trait is being considered.

*Monomer.* A simple molecule of a compound of relatively low molecular weight.

*Monoploid or haploid.* Individual having a single set of chromosomes or one genome ($n$).

*Monosomic.* A diploid organism lacking one chromosome of its proper complement ($2n - 1$); an aneuploid. Monosome refers to the single chromosome, disome to two chromosomes of a kind, trisome to three chromosomes of a kind.

*Monozygous twins.* One-egg or identical twins.

*Morphology.* Study of the form of an organism. Developmental history of visible structures and the comparative relation of similar structures in different organisms.

*Morula.* A mass of cells formed by repeated cleavage in early animal embryology.

*Mosaic.* An organism part of which is made up of tissue genetically different from the remaining part.

*Mosaic egg.* A fertilized egg (zygote) in which a high degree of organization has already occurred. Parts develop according to a predetermined plan.

*Multiple alleles.* Three or more alternative genes representing the same locus in a given pair of chromosomes.

*Mutable genes.* Those with an unusually high mutation rate (unstable genes).

*Mutagen.* An environmental agent, either physical or chemical that is capable of inducing mutagens.

*Mutant.* A cell or individual organism that shows a change brought about by a mutation. A changed gene.

*Mutation.* A sudden change in the genotype of an organism. The term is used loosely to include point mutations involving a single gene, and chromosomal changes.

*Mutation Pressure.* A constant mutation rate that adds mutant genes to a population.

*Mutator genes.* Those which increase the frequency of mutations in other genes.

*Muton.* The smallest unit of DNA that can undergo change resulting in a mutation.

*Mycelium, pl. mycelia.* Threadlike filament making up the vegetative portion of thallus fungi.

*Natural selection.* Natural processes favoring individuals that are better adapted and tending to eliminate those unfitted to their environment.

*Nondisjunction.* Failure of disjunction or separation of homologous chromosomes in meiosis, resulting in too many chromosomes in some daughter cells and too few in others.

*Notochord.* A longitudinal rod of cells in the embryo of a vertebrate animal that gives rise to the backbone of the adult.

*Nucleic acid.* An acid composed of phosphoric acid, pentose sugar, and organic bases. DNA and RNA are nucleic acids.

*Nucleolus.* Structure within the nucleus of some metabolic cells.

*Nucleoprotein.* Conjugated protein composed of nucleic acid and protein, and making up the chromosomes.

*Nucleotide.* A unit of the DNA molecule containing a phosphate, a sugar, and an organic base.

*Nucleus.* Part of a cell containing genes and surrounded by cytoplasm.

*Nullisomic.* An otherwise diploid cell or organism lacking both members of a chromosome pair (chromosome formula: $2n - 2$).

*Octoploid.* Cell or organism with eight genomes or monoploid sets of chromosomes; a polyploid.

*Ommochrome.* A product of tryptophan metabolism that gives rise to pigments, particularly eye pigments in animals.

*Ontogeny.* The complete developmental history of an organism from egg, spore, bud, etc., to the adult individual.

*Oöcyte.* The egg-mother cell; the cell that undergoes two meiotic divisions (oögenesis) to form the egg cell. Primary oöcyte—before completion of the first meiotic division; secondary oöcyte—after completion of the first meiotic division.

*Oögenesis.* The formation of the egg or ovum in animals.

*Oögonium, pl. oögonia.* A germ cell of the female animal before meiosis begins.

*Operator gene.* A gene making up a part of an operon which controls the activity of one or more structural genes. (See Chapter 15.)

*Operon.* A group of genes making up a functional unit. The unit consists of an operator gene and structural genes.

*Organelle.* Specialized part of a cell with a particular function or functions (e.g., cilium of a protozoan).

*Organizer.* An inductor; a chemical substance in a living system that determines the fate in development of certain cells or groups of cells.

*Otocephaly.* Abnormal development of the head of a mammalian fetus.

*Outbreeding.* Mating of unrelated individuals or of those not closely related.

*Ovary.* The swollen part of the pistil of a plant flower that contains the ovules. The female reproductive gland or gonad in animals.

*Ovist.* Preformationist who considered the egg rather than the sperm to carry the miniature but complete organism.

*Ovule.* The macrosporangium of a flowering plant that becomes the seed. It includes the nucellus and the integuments.

P. Symbolizes the parental generation or parents of a given individual.

*Pachynema, adj. pachytene.* A midprophase stage in meiosis immediately following zygonema and preceding diplonema. In favorable microscope preparations, the chromosomes are visible as long, paired threads. Sometimes four chromatids are observed.

*Paracentric inversion.* An inversion that is entirely within one arm of a chromosome, does not include the centromere.

*Parameter.* A value or constant based on an entire population, c.f. statistic.

*Parthenogenesis.* The development of a new individual from an egg without fertilization.

*Paternal.* Pertaining to the father; set of chromosomes derived from the sperm in animals or pollen in plants.

*Pathogen.* An organism or virus that causes a disease.

*Pedigree.* A table, chart or diagram representing the ancestral history of an individual.

*Penetrance.* The proportion (in percent) of individuals with a particular gene combination that express the corresponding trait.

*Peptide.* A compound containing amino acids. A breakdown or buildup unit in protein metabolism.

*Peptide bond.* A chemical bond holding amino acid subunits together.

*Pericentric inversion.* An inversion including the centromere, hence involving both arms of a chromosome.

*Phage. see* Bacteriophage.

*Phenocopy.* An organism whose phenotype (but not genotype) has been changed by the environment to resemble the phenotype of a different (mutant) organism.

*Phenogroup.* A term used to describe a large number of antigenic responses associated with a particular locus. In cattle a large number of antigenic responses presumably determined by alleles has been associated with the *B* locus.

*Phenotype.* Characteristic of an individual observed or discernable by other means (i.e., tallness in garden peas; color blindness or blood-type in man). Individuals of the same phenotype may appear alike but may not breed alike.

*Pistil.* The female part of the flower consisting of ovary, style, and stigma.

*Plaque.* Clear area on an otherwise opaque culture plate of bacteria where the bacteria have been killed by a virus.

*Plasmagenes.* Self-replicating cytoplasmic particles capable of transmitting traits in inheritance. Units believed to be responsible for extranuclear inheritance.

*Plastid.* A cytoplasmic body found in the cells of plants and some protozoans. Chloroplastids produce chlorophyll which is involved in photosynthesis.

*Pleiotropy, adj. pleiotropic.* Condition in which a single gene influences more than one trait.

*Polar bodies.* In female animals, the smaller cells produced at meiosis that do not develop into egg cells. The first polar body is produced at division I and may or may not go through division II. The second polar body is produced at division II.

*Pollen-mother-cell, microsporocyte or microspore-mother-cell.* The plant-cell that undergoes the meiotic sequence and produces four microspores.

*Pollen parent.* The male plant that produces the pollen. The term is used to designate the pollen-producing parent in a cross.

*Polydactyly.* The occurrence of more than the usual number of fingers or toes.

*Polygene.* One of a series of multiple genes involved in quantitative inheritance.

*Polymer.* A compound composed of two or more units of the same substance; results from a process of polymerization.

*Polymerization.* Chemical union of two or more molecules of the same kind to form a new compound having the same elements in the same proportions, but a higher molecular weight and different physical properties.

*Polymorphism.* Two or more kinds of individuals in a breeding population where the rarer form is maintained by some mechanism other than recurrent mutation.

*Polynucleotide.* A unit of DNA consisting of four nucleotides.

*Polypeptide.* A compound containing two or more amino acids and one or more peptide groups. They are called dipeptides, tripeptides, etc., according to the number of amino acids contained.

*Polyploid.* An organism with more than two sets of chromosomes or genomes (e.g., triploid ($3n$), tetraploid ($4n$), pentaploid ($5n$), hexaploid ($6n$), heptaploid ($7n$), octoploid ($8n$).

*Population.* Entire group of organisms of one kind; an interbreeding group of plants or animals. The infinite group from which a sample might be taken.

*Population genetics.* The branch of genetics which deals with frequencies of alleles in breeding groups of individuals.

*Position effect.* A difference in phenotype that is dependent on the position of a gene or group of genes in relation to other genes.

*Preformationist.* One who considers the embryological process merely as the growth of a miniature but completely formed individual (i.e., a homunculus).

*Prepattern.* An embryonic area or field in which regional differentiation has been predetermined. (See Chapter 16.)

*Prepotency.* Ability of an individual to transmit particular characteristics to the offspring.

*Primary oöcyte. see* Oöcyte.

*Primary spermatocyte. see* Spermatocyte.

*Probability.* Likelihood of occurrence.

*Progeny.* Offspring of animals or plants; individuals resulting from a particular mating.

*Prophage.* Noninfectious stage of a temperate phage in a bacterial cell.

*Prophase.* The stages of mitosis or meiosis from the appearance of the chromosomes following interphase to metaphase.

*Prosthetic group.* An organic component of conjugated proteins. Conjugated proteins are a combination of simple protein and another substance called the prosthetic group. *Example:* Nucleoproteins have as prosthetic groups, nucleic acids.

*Protoplast.* A unit body of protoplasm; the mass of living material within a single cell, including cytoplasm and nucleus.

*Prototroph.* A wild-type organism (bacterium) that will grow on a minimal medium.

*Pseudoalleles.* Closely linked genes that behave ordinarily as if they were alleles but which have been shown by extensive experiments to be separable by crossing over.

*Pseudodominance.* Apparent dominance of a recessive gene in the area opposite a chromosome deficiency. A recessive gene may come to expression because its dominant allele is absent.

*Pure line.* A strain of organisms that is comparatively pure genetically (homozygous) because of continued inbreeding or through other means.

*Quadripartite structure* (chromosome ring). One having four corresponding parts.

*Quadrivalent.* A group of 4 chromosomes of the same kind in a cell. They may be united by chiasmata in the first division prophase of meiosis. Quadrivalents result from chromosome translocations.

*Recessive.* Applied to one member of an allelic pair lacking the ability to manifest itself when the other or dominant member is present. An inherited trait expressed only when the controlling gene is homozygous.

*Reciprocal crosses.* A second cross involving the same strains but carried by sexes opposite to those in the first cross, e.g., a female from strain A × a male from strain B and a male from A × female from B are reciprocal crosses.

*Recombination.* The observed new combinations of traits different from those combinations exhibited by the parents. Percentage of recombination equals percentage of crossing over only when the genes are relatively close together. Cytological chiasma refers to the observed change of partners among chromatids whereas recombination or genetic crossing over refers to the observed genetic result. Random recombination occurs in meiosis.

*Recon.* The smallest unit of DNA capable of recombination; in bacteria, the smallest unit capable of being integrated or replaced in a host chromosome subjected to the transformation process.

*Reduction division or heterotypic division.* Phase of meiosis in which the maternal and paternal elements of the bivalent separate, c.f. equational or homotypic division.

*Regulator gene.* A gene that controls the rate of production of another gene or genes. Example: The operon involved in lactose production in *E. coli* has a regulator, an operator and structural genes.

*Repulsion* or *trans arrangement.* The condition in linked inheritance in which an individual heterozygous for two pairs of linked genes received the dominant member of one pair and the recessive member of the other pair from one parent and the reverse arrangement from the other parent, (e.g., *AAbb* × *aaBB*). Compare coupling.

*Reticulocyte.* A young red blood cell.

*Reversion.* Appearance of a trait expressed by a remote ancestor; a throwback; atavism.

*Ribonucleic acid. see* RNA.

*Ribosome.* Cytoplasmic structure in which proteins are synthesized.

*Roentgen* (*r*). Unit of ionizing radiation.

*RNA—Ribonucleic acid.* The information carrying material in plant viruses. Certain kinds of RNA are involved in the transcription of genetic information from DNA (i.e., m-RNA); transfer of amino acids to the ribosomes for incorporation into proteins (i.e., t-RNA); and the makeup of the ribosome (i.e., r-RNA).

*Secondary oöcyte. see* Oöcyte.

*Secondary spermatocyte. see* Spermatocyte.

*Secretor.* A person with a water soluble form of antigen A or B. In such a person the antigen may be detected in body fluids (i.e., saliva) as well as on the erythrocytes.

*Seed.* The enlarged and matured ovule of a plant embryo in a dormant stage of development.

*Seed parent.* A female parent in a cross between two plants.

*Segregation.* The separation of the paternal from maternal chromosomes at meiosis, and the consequent separation of alleles and their phenotypic differences as observed in the offspring. Mendel's first principle of inheritance.

*Selection.* Any natural or artificial process favoring the survival and propogation of certain individuals.

*Selection Pressure.* Effectiveness of the environment in changing the frequency of alleles in a population of individuals.

*Self-fertilization.* Pollen of a given plant fertilizes the ovules of the same plant. Plants fertilized in this way are said to be selfed.

*Semisterility.* A condition of only partial fertility in plant zygotes (e.g., maize), usually associated with translocations.

*Serology, adj. serological.* The study of interactions between antigens and antibodies.

*Sex chromosomes.* Chromosomes that are particularly connected with the determination of sex.

*Sex-influenced traits.* Those traits in which the dominant expression depends on the sex of the individual (e.g., horns in sheep are dominant in males and recessive in females).

*Sex-limited.* Expression of a trait in only one sex. Examples: milk production, horns in Rambouillet sheep, egg production.

*Sex linkage.* Association or linkage of a hereditary character with sex; the gene is in a sex chromosome.

*Sex mosaic. see* Gynandromorph.

*Sex reversal.* A change in the characteristics of an individual from male to female and vice versa.

*Sexual reproduction.* Reproduction involving the formation of mature germ cells (i.e., eggs and sperm).

*Sib-mating, crossing of siblings.* Matings involving two or more individuals of the same parentage, brother-sister mating.

*Sickle-cell anemia.* An inherited blood abnormality produced by defective hemoglobin. Red blood cells become sickle shaped because of reduced oxygen tension.

*Soma cells.* The cells that make up the body

in contrast with germ cells that are capable of reproducing the organism.

*Somatic cells.* Referring to body tissues; having two sets of chromosomes, one set normally coming from the female parent and one from the male, as contrasted with germinal tissue that will give rise to germ cells.

*Somatoplasm.* The nonreproductive material making up the body of the organism in contrast to germ plasm.

*Species.* A basic category in the classification of plants or animals below the genus level and above the variety or subspecies level. A group of plants or animals that interbreed among themselves but ordinarily not with members of other species.

*Sperm, abb. of spermatozoön, pl. spermatozoa.* A mature male germ cell.

*Spermatids.* The four cells formed by the meiotic divisions in spermatogenesis. Spermatids become mature spermatozoa or sperm.

*Spermatocyte or sperm-mother-cell.* The cell that undergoes two meiotic divisions (spermatogenesis) to form four spermatids; primary spermatocyte, before completion of the first meiotic division; secondary spermatocyte after completion of the first meiotic division.

*Spermatogenesis.* The process by which maturation of the gametes (sperm) of the male takes place.

*Spermatagonium, pl. spermatogonia.* Primordial male germ cell that may divide by mitosis to produce more spermatogonia. A spermatogonium may enter a growth phase and give rise to a primary spermatocyte.

*Spore.* A unit of protoplasm capable of developing asexually into a new individual; in higher plants, the haploid product of meiosis that gives rise to male or female gametes.

*Sporocyte.* The spore mother cell of a plant.

*Sporogenesis.* Formation of the spore or reproductive element in plants.

*Sporophyte.* The spore-forming generation in the life-cycle of plants, normally diploid.

*Stamen.* Male part of the flower which includes the pollen-producing anthers and the filament.

*Standard deviation.* A measure of variability in a population of individuals.

*Standard error.* A measure of variation of a population of means.

*Statistic.* A value based on a sample or samples of a population from which estimates of a population value or parameter may be obtained.

*Step allelism.* The concept of series of alleles with graded effects on the same trait.

*Sterility.* Inability to produce offspring.

*Stigma.* Female part of the flower which receives pollen.

*Structural gene.* A gene that controls actual protein production by determining the amino acid sequence (c.f. operator and regulator genes).

*Style.* Part of the pistil between the stigma and the ovary in a flower through which the pollen tube grows.

*Sublethal gene.* A lethal gene with delayed effect. The gene in proper combination kills its possessor in infancy, childhood, or adulthood.

*Symbiont.* An organism living in intimate association with another dissimilar organism.

*Synapsis.* The conjugation or pairing of homologous chromosomes.

*Syndrome.* A group of symptoms that occur together and represent a particular disease.

*Syngamy.* Union of the gametes in fertilization.

*Telophase.* The last stage of mitosis in which the chromosomes are assembled at the poles of the division spindle.

*Temperate phage.* A phage (virus) that invades but does not destroy the host (bacterial) cell (c.f. virulent phage).

*Template.* A pattern or mold. DNA stores coded information and acts as a model or template from which information is taken by messenger-RNA.

*Terminalization.* Repelling movement of the centromeres of bivalents in the diplotene stages of the meiotic prophase, that tends to move the visible chiasmata toward the ends of the bivalents. The point where the exchange of chromatids or the chiasma occurs is believed to be the point of a genetic crossover, but the chiasmata appear to slip toward the ends of the bivalents, and therefore after the diplotene looping begins there is no longer a relation between the chiasma and the point of crossing over.

*Test cross.* Backcross to the recessive parental type or a cross between genetically unknown individuals with a fully recessive tester to determine whether an individual in question is heterozygous or homozygous for a certain allele. Also used as a test for linkage.

*Tetrad.* The four cells arising from the second meiotic division in plants (i.e., pollen tetrads). The term is also used to identify the quadruple group of chromatids formed by the association of split homologous chromosomes during meiosis, but the term bivalent is preferred in this usage.

*Tetraploid.* An organism whose cells contain four haploid ($4n$) sets of chromosomes or genomes.

*Tetrasomic, noun: tetrasome.* Pertaining to a nucleus or an organism having four members of one of its chromosomes, the remainder of the chromosomes being normally diploid. (Chromosome formula: $2n + 2$).

*Thymine.* A pyrimidine base found in DNA. The other three organic bases, adenine, cytosine and guanine are found in both RNA and DNA but in RNA thymine is replaced by uracil.

*Totipotent cell.* An undifferentiated cell such as a blastomere which when isolated develops into a complete embryo.

*Trans arrangement. see* Repulsion.

*Transduction.* Genetic recombination in bacteria mediated by bacteriophage.

*Transferrin.* Blood serum protein, beta globulin. *see* Globulin.

*Transfer-RNA.* A particular kind of RNA that transports amino acids to the ribosome where they are assembled into proteins.

*Transformation.* Genetic recombination in bacteria brought about by adding foreign DNA to a culture.

*Transgressive variation.* The appearance in the $F_2$ (or later) generations of individuals showing a more extreme development of a character than either parent. Assumed to be due to cumulative and complementary effects of genes contributed by the parents of the original hybrid. Adequate testing of variation in the parents is required to establish its occurrence.

*Translocation.* Change in position of a segment of a chromosome to another part of the same chromosome or to a different chromosome.

*Trihybrid.* The offspring from homozygous parents differing in three pairs of genes.

*Triploid.* An organism with three genomes or sets of chromosomes ($3n$).

*Trisomic.* An otherwise diploid cell or organism which has an extra chromosome of one pair (chromosome formula: $2n + 1$).

*Twins.* Two individuals from the same birth. Identical twins—from the same fertilized egg. Fraternal twins—from different fertilized eggs.

*Unipartite structures* (chromosomes). Single units.

*Univalent.* A chromosome unpaired at meiosis.

*Uracil.* A pyrimidine base found in RNA but not in DNA. In DNA uracil is replaced by thymine.

*Variance.* The square of the standard deviation.

*Variation.* In biology, the occurrence of differences among the individuals of the same species.

*Viability.* Degree of capability to live and develop normally.

*Virulent phage.* A phage (virus) that destroys the host (bacterial) cell (see temperate phage).

*Wild type.* The customary phenotype or standard for comparison.

*X chromosome.* A chromosome associated with sex determination. In most animals the female has two and the male one.

*Xenia.* Immediate effect of pollen on the endosperm, due to the phenomenon of double fertilization in the seed plants.

*Y chromosome.* The mate to the X chromosome in the male of most animal species, usually carries few genes; in Drosophila composed mostly of heterochromatin. In man the Y chromosome carries genes which influence maleness.

*Zygonema, adj. zygotene.* Stage in meiosis during which synapsis occurs; after the leptotene stage and before the pachytene stage in the meiotic prophase.

*Zygote.* The cell produced by the union of two mature sex cells (gametes) in reproduction; also used in genetics to designate the individual developing from such a cell.

# *Answers to Odd-Numbered Problems*

*Chapter 1*

**1.1** With the discovery and understanding of Mendel's paper in 1900 and the work of several investigators who confirmed and extended Mendel's principles, a basic foundation of facts was soon established and genetics became a science.

**1.3** Transmission genetics is accomplished through the reproductive system. Discovery and understanding of sexual reproduction in plants provided a physical basis for inheritance in experimental materials (plants) which lend themselves well to breeding investigations.

**1.5** Mendel chose a self-fertilizing annual plant with well-defined, easily recognizable characteristics that could be investigated individually. Through self-fertilization, garden peas had developed pure lines. One member of each pair of alternative alleles that he studied was dominant over the allele for the contrasting trait. All seven pairs of genes were independent (that is, not linked) with respect to each other.

**1.7** (a) $WW \times ww$; (b) Ⓦ and ⓦ; (c) $Ww$; (d) $Ww \times Ww$; and (e) Ⓦ, ⓦ, and Ⓦ, ⓦ.

(f)

| *Phenotypes* | *Genotypes* | *Genotypic frequency* | *Phenotypic ratio* |
|---|---|---|---|
| round | $WW$ | 1 | 3 |
| | $Ww$ | 2 | |
| wrinkled | $ww$ | 1 | 1 |

**1.9** (a) The 3:1 ratio suggests a single pair of genes with the gene for color dominant over that for white.

(b)

| | |
|---|---|
| $CC \times cc$ | P |
| Ⓒ ⓒ | gametes |
| $Cc$ | $F_1$ |
| $Cc \times Cc$ | $F_1 \times F_1$ |
| Ⓒ ⓒ Ⓒ ⓒ | $F_1$ gametes |
| $1CC{:}2Cc{:}1cc$ | $F_2$ |

| *Phenotypes* | *Observed* | *Calculated* | *Deviation* |
|---|---|---|---|
| Colored | 198 | 202.5 | −4.5 |
| White | 72 | 67.5 | 4.5 |

**1.11** *CCBB* × *ccbb* P
(*CB*) (*cb*) gametes
*CcBb* × *CcBb* $F_1 \times F_1$

| Gametes | (*CB*) | (*Cb*) | (*cB*) | (*cb*) |
|---|---|---|---|---|
| (*CB*) | *CCBB* | *CCBb* | *CcBB* | *CcBb* |
| (*Cb*) | *CCBb* | *CCbb* | *CcBb* | *Ccbb* |
| (*cB*) | *CcBB* | *CcBb* | *ccBB* | *ccBb* |
| (*cb*) | *CcBb* | *Ccbb* | *ccBb* | *ccbb* |

Summary of $F_2$:

| *Phenotypes* | *Genotypes* | *Genotypic frequency* | *Phenotypic ratio* |
|---|---|---|---|
| checkered red | *CCBB* | 1 | 9 |
| | *CCBb* | 2 | |
| | *CcBB* | 2 | |
| | *CcBb* | 4 | |
| checkered brown | *CCbb* | 1 | 3 |
| | *Ccbb* | 2 | |
| plain red | *ccBB* | 1 | 3 |
| | *ccBb* | 2 | |
| plain brown | *ccbb* | 1 | 1 |

**1.13** *Ccbb* × *ccBb*

**1.15** (a) *CCVv* × *ccVv* (b) *CcVv* × *CcVv* (c) *CcVv* × *ccvv*

**1.17** (a) *DDGGWW* × *ddggww* P

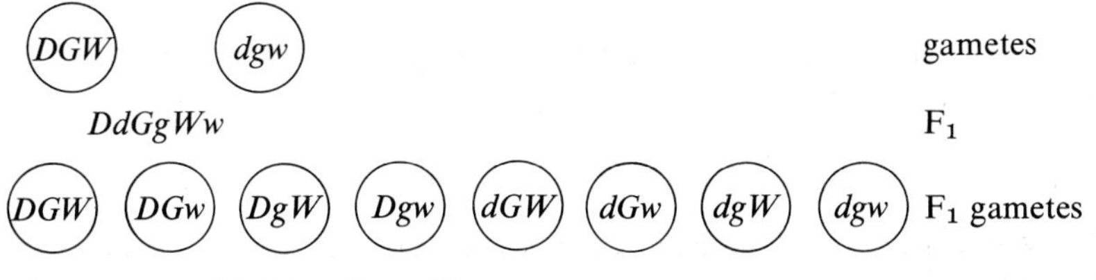


(b) *DdGgWw* × *DdGgWw* $F_1 \times F_1$

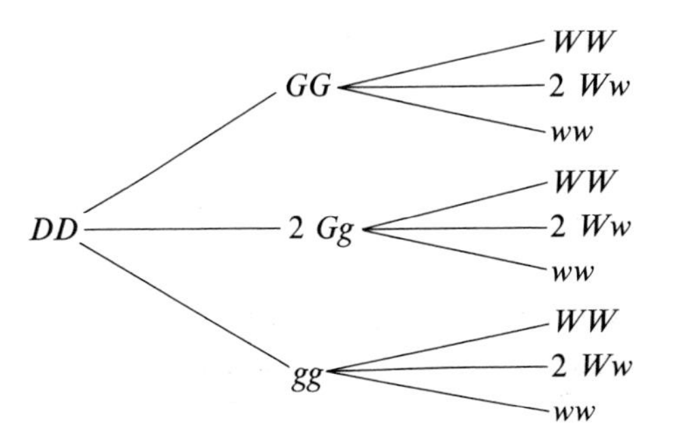

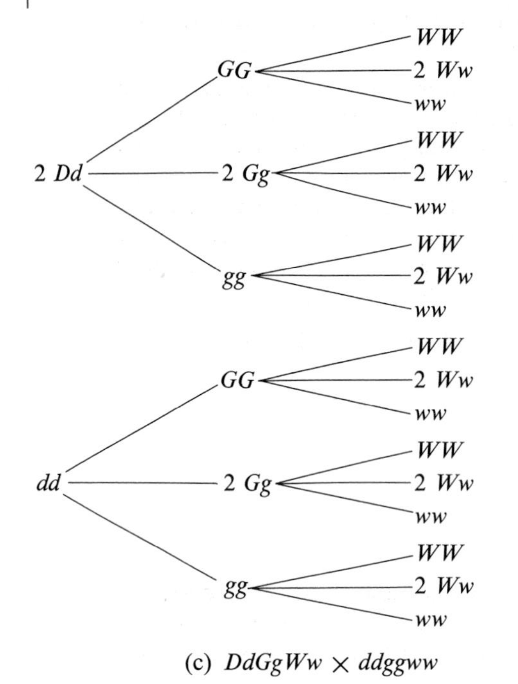


Summary of $F_2$ phenotypes:

27 tall, yellow, round:
9 tall, yellow, wrinkled:
9 tall, green, round:
9 dwarf, yellow, round:
3 tall, green, wrinkled:
3 dwarf, yellow, wrinkled:
3 dwarf, green, round: and
1 dwarf, green, wrinkled.

(c) *DdGgWw* × *ddggww*

Summary of backcross results:

| | | | *Phenotypes* | *Genotypes* | *Genotypic frequency* | *Phenotypic ratio* |
|---|---|---|---|---|---|---|
| *Dd* | *Gg* | *Ww* | tall, yellow, round | *DdGgWw* | 1 | 1 |
| | | *ww* | tall, yellow, wrinkled | *DdGgww* | 1 | 1 |
| | *gg* | *Ww* | tall, green, round | *DdggWw* | 1 | 1 |
| | | *ww* | tall, green, wrinkled | *Ddggww* | 1 | 1 |
| *dd* | *Gg* | *Ww* | dwarf, yellow, round | *ddGgWw* | 1 | 1 |
| | | *ww* | dwarf, yellow, wrinkled | *ddGgww* | 1 | 1 |
| | *gg* | *Ww* | dwarf, green, round | *ddggWw* | 1 | 1 |
| | | *ww* | dwarf, green, wrinkled | *ddggww* | 1 | 1 |

**1.19** *RR* × *R′R′* — P

(*R*) (*R′*) — gametes

*RR′* — $F_1$

*RR′* × *RR′* — $F_1 \times F_1$

(*R*) (*R′*) (*R*) (*R′*) — $F_1$ gametes

Summary of $F_2$

| *Phenotypes* | *Genotypes* | *Genotypic frequency* | *Phenotypic ratio* |
|---|---|---|---|
| red | *RR* | 1 | 1 |
| pink | *R′R* | 2 | 2 |
| white | *R′R′* | 1 | 1 |

**1.21** (a) Segregation is the separation of alleles in the formation of gametes. That is, a zygotic pair such as *Ww* separates to *W* and *w* in the gametes. (b) Independent assortment is the principle of separateness and independence of members of different pairs of alleles with respect to members of other pairs, that is, *Ww* is independent of *Gg* and *W* may combine in the zygote with *G* or *g*. Likewise *w* may enter a gamete with either *G* or *g*.

**1.23** Mendel's work was apparently not understood by the people who knew about it during this period. Although copies of Mendel's paper were in many libraries, people (for example, Darwin) who probably would have appreciated its significance did not know about it. The background in mathematics and cytology that has since supported Mendel's principles was developed during the period 1864 to 1900. DeVries, Correns, and Von Tschermak were all conducting experiments similar to those of Mendel and all three independently discovered and cited Mendel in 1900.

**1.25** Twins, pedigree, statistical, cytological, and biochemical analyses are techniques used in studies of human genetics.

*Chapter 2*

**2.1** (a) 0; (b) 0; (c) 0; (d) 0; (e) 0; (f) +; and (g) +.

**2.3** (a) 200; and (b) 50.

**2.5** Model in text.

**2.7** Meiosis includes a pairing (synapsis) of corresponding maternal and paternal chromosomes. In the cell division that follows, the chromosomes that have previously paired separate. This results in a reduction of chromosome number from $2n$ (diploid) to $n$ (haploid).

**2.9** An egg and an endosperm nucleus are developed in the ovule. Two haploid nuclei are introduced by the pollen tube. One male gamete fuses with the egg and the other with the endosperm nucleus. The fertilized egg is the zygote that develops into an embryo. The endosperm forms the nutrient material that supports the developing embryo.

**2.11** Model in text.

**2.13** 1 *AB*:1 *Ab*:1 *aB*:1 *ab*

**2.15** A parallel was observed independently by Boveri and Sutton between the behavior of genes as interpreted from hybridization experiments and the chromosome cycle in gametogenesis. Boveri and others showed that the nucleus rather than the cytoplasm is involved in inheritance. The four questions (see text) necessary to account for inheritance could be explained on the basis of the chromosome mechanism. (Further support for the chromosome theory is developed in later chapters.)

**2.17** (a) Early primary oöcyte; (b) prophase, first meiotic division; (c) suspended prophase; and (d) first meiotic division is completed just before ovulation of each egg.

*Chapter 3*

**3.1** (a) *DD* × *dd*; (b) *Dd* × *Dd*; and (c) *Dd* × *dd*.

**3.3** (a) spotted; (b) about 8; (c) all 8; (d) 3 spotted: 1 solid; and (e) chance deviation.

**3.5** (a) All recessive; and (b) *aa* for all those expressing trait; *Aa* or *AA* determined from parents or progeny expressions.

**3.7** (a) $\frac{1}{2} \times 1 \times \frac{1}{4} = \frac{1}{8}$; (b) $\frac{1}{16}$; (c) $\frac{1}{6}$; and (d) $\frac{1}{24}$.

**3.9** (a) $X^2 = 0.263$; $P = 0.80 - 0.50$ Not significant
(b) $X^2 = 0.368$; $P = 0.80 - 0.50$ Not significant
(c) $X^2 = 0.450$; $P = 0.80 - 0.50$ Not significant
(d) $X^2 = 0.618$; $P = 0.95 - 0.80$ Not significant
(e) $X^2 = 0.520$; $P = 0.95 - 0.80$ Not significant

**3.11** (a) 1/16, (b) 1/16, (c) 4/16, (d) 4/16, and (e) 6/16.

**3.13** (a) 1/32, (b) 5/32, (c) 10/32, (d) 10/32, (e) 5/32, and (f) 1/32.

**3.15** (a) ½, (b) ½, and (c) 3/8.

**3.17** (a) ¼, (b) ¼, (c) ¼, and (d) ¼.

*Chapter 4*

**4.1** (a) *Dd* × *Dd* — P

(*D*) (*d*) (*D*) (*d*) — gametes

*DD* 2 *Dd* *dd* — progeny

Dies Dichaete Wild type

Summary: 2 dichaete : 1 wild

(b) *Dd* × *dd* — P

(*D*) (*d*) (*d*) — gametes

*Dd* *dd* — progeny

Summary: 1 dichaete : 1 wild

**4.3** *Rrpp* × *RrPp*

**4.5** (a) The forked-line method is illustrated as follows:

*PPRR* × *ppR′R′* — P

(*PR*) (*pR′*) — gametes

*Pp* *RR′* — $F_1$

*PpRR′* × *PpRR′* — $F_1 \times F_1$

*PP* < *RR*, 2 *RR′*, *R′R′*

2 *Pp* < *RR*, 2 *RR′*, *R′R′* — $F_2$

*pp* < *RR*, 2 *RR′*, *R′R′*

Summary of $F_2$:

| *Phenotypes* | *Genotypes* | *Genotypic frequency* | *Phenotypic ratio* |
|---|---|---|---|
| polled, red | *PPRR* | 1 | 3 |
| | *PpRR* | 2 | |
| polled, roan | *PPRR′* | 2 | 6 |
| | *PpRR′* | 4 | |
| polled, white | *PPR′R′* | 1 | |
| | *PpR′R′* | 2 | 3 |

| | | | |
|---|---|---|---|
| horned, red | *ppRR* | 1 | 1 |
| horned, roan | *ppRR'* | 2 | 2 |
| horned, white | *ppR'R'* | 1 | 1 |

**4.7** *CcPP* × *ccpp* or *CCPp* × *ccpp*

**4.9** 12 white:3 yellow:1 green

**4.11** (a) A particular inherited characteristic, sex, was found to be controlled by certain chromosome combinations, supporting the hypothesis that genes are in chromosomes. (b) McClung did not succeed in following oögenesis and concluded that the X body was peculiar to males.

**4.13** An XX female (in female homogametic species) produces eggs with X chromosomes while the XY male produces two kinds of sperm, X and Y, in about equal proportions. Eggs fertilized with X sperm produce females, those fertilized with Y sperm produce males.

**4.15** (a) Bridges postulated that many genes with an accumulative effect and located in the X chromosome influence femaleness whereas genes in the autosomes control maleness. Sex in an individual fly is determined by the margin of sex-producing capacity between the X chromosomes and the autosomes. (b) (1) female, (2) intersex, (3) intersex, (4) metamale, (5) female, and (6) male (sterile if no Y chromosome is present).

**4.17** (a) Male, (b) female, (c) male, and (d) female.

**4.19** (a) Females: ½ normal, ½ intersexes; males: all normal.
(b) Females: ½ normal, ½ intersex; males: all normal.

**4.21** (a) Females: all intersex; males: all normal.
(b) Females: all normal; males: all normal.

**4.23** The single gene (*ba*) removes the female part of the monoecious plant and makes the stalk only staminate. Another gene (*st*) transforms the tassel into a pistillate structure. A plant of the genotype *babastst* would be only pistillate (that is, female) whereas a plant with the genotype $babast^+st^+$ would be only staminate (that is, male).

**4.25** Potential characteristics for both sexes are present in all chickens even though one sex is normally expressed. Manifestation of one sex is suppressed by the hormones of the other sex. If the ovary of the female is destroyed by accident or disease, the suppression of maleness would no longer persist and male characteristics would be expected to develop.

**4.27** (a) ¾; and (b) ¼.

**4.29** (a) ¾; and (b) none.

**4.31** (a) ½$X^{bb}X^{bb}$, bobbed females, ½$X^{bb}Y^{bb^+}$, wild-type males; (b) ½$X^{bb^+}X^{bb^+}$ and $X^{bb}X^{bb^+}$, wild females, ¼$X^{bb^+}Y^{bb}$, wild males, ¼$X^{bb}Y^{bb}$, bobbed males; (c) ½$X^{bb^+}X^{bb^+}$ and $X^{bb}X^{bb^+}$, wild females, ¼$X^{bb^+}Y^{bb}$, wild males, ¼$X^{bb}Y^{bb}$, bobbed males; and (d) ¼$X^{bb^+}X^{bb}$, wild females, ¼$X^{bb}X^{bb}$, bobbed females, ½$X^{bb^+}Y^{bb^+}$ and $X^{bb}Y^{bb^+}$, wild males.

*Chapter 5*

**5.1** Doncaster made reciprocal crosses between lacticolor and typical moths and found that the results could be explained if a recessive gene was carried in the X chromosome.

**5.3** (a) If it breeds true in succeeding generations, it is probably hereditary and may be assumed to have arisen through mutation. (b) The crisscross pattern of inheritance is evidence for sex linkage. (c) Females whose fathers had white eyes could be crossed with white-eyed males. Half of the females would be expected to have white eyes. This would conform to genetic theory based on sex linkage.

**5.5**

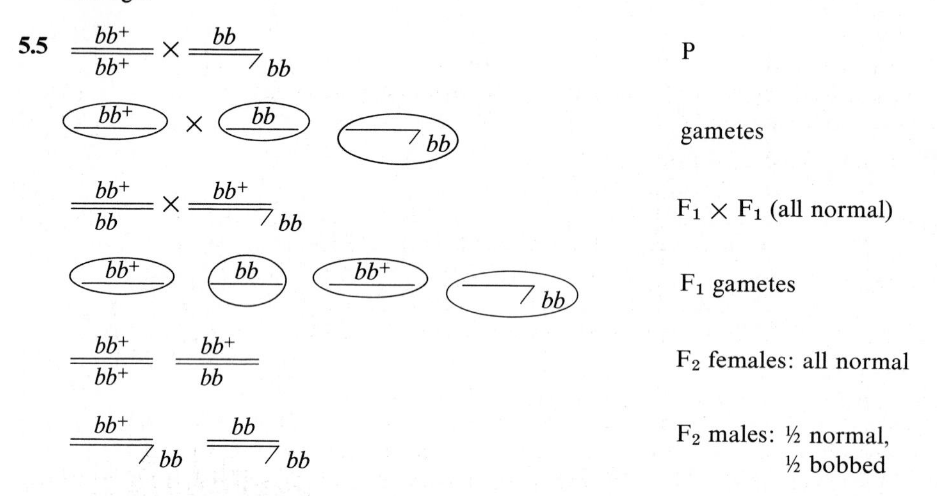


**5.7** (a) A few red-eyed males and white-eyed females were obtained from a cross expected to produce only white-eyed males and red-eyed females. Bridges postulated that the X chromosomes had stayed together in meiosis, upsetting the usual pattern for sex linkage. (b) The hypothesis was proved by cytological observations. The two X chromosomes were observed microscopically in the stages of gametogenesis.

**5.9** (1) $\frac{rg^{+}}{\urcorner}$; (2) $\frac{rg^{+}}{rg}$; (3) $\frac{rg}{\urcorner}$; (4) $\frac{rg^{+}}{rg}$. (5) Probability is $\frac{63}{64}$ for $\frac{rg^{+}}{rg^{+}}$ and $\frac{1}{64}$ for $\frac{rg^{+}}{rg}$; (6) $\frac{rg^{+}}{rg}$; (7) $\frac{rg}{\urcorner}$; (8) $\frac{rg^{+}}{\urcorner}$; and (9) $\frac{rg^{+}}{\urcorner}$.

**5.11** The gene presumably expresses itself whenever it is present in males, but it must be homozygous to come to expression in females.

**5.13**

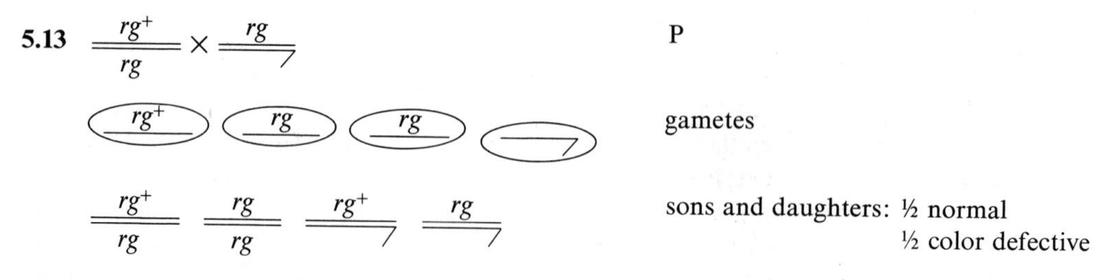


**5.15** ½ chance for each son or ¼ for each child (½ for male X ½ affected).

**5.17** (a) ½; and (b) ½.

**5.19** (a) female male

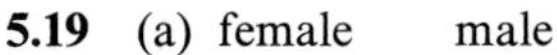

$$\frac{B}{\quad} \quad \frac{B}{B^+}$$
$$\frac{C}{C^+} \times \frac{C}{C^+}$$

Note: In this problem the Y chromosome is symbolized as in Drosophila. Chickens have a small Y chromosome with females heterogametic.

(b) Summary:

| | |
|---|---|
| barred, crested males: | 6 |
| barred, noncrested males: | 2 |
| barred, crested females: | 3 |
| nonbarred, crested females: | 3 |
| barred, noncrested females: | 1 |
| nonbarred, noncrested females: | 1 |

**5.21** (a) 0, (b) 1, (c) 1, (d) 2, and (e) 3.

*Chapter 6*

**6.1** (a) Mendel developed and supported the principle of independent combinations in his paper and he did not discover anything else in the experiments he reported. (b) Boveri might have discovered linkage but the cytological background was not sufficiently established when his work was done. His suggestion that more than one gene was in a chromosome was not remembered but his emphasis on stability of chromosomes is considered by some to have retarded the developments that led to the true explanation. (c) Bateson did not accept the chromosome theory. Although he obtained results that now are interpreted on the basis of linkage and crossing over, he tried to explain them in another way. (d) Morgan related his results from experimental breeding to the chromosome mechanism and arrived at the theory of linkage and crossing over.

**6.3** (a) With most materials, a test cross is easily prepared and the results may be compared with the simple 1:1:1:1 ratio rather than the more complex 9:3:3:1. (b) In self-fertilizing plants it is easier to self the $F_1$ plants and produce an $F_2$ than to emasculate the flowers and make a test cross, but the interpretation of the results requires more involved mathematical calculations.

**6.5** (a) $\dfrac{a^+b^+}{a^+b^+} \times \dfrac{ab}{ab}$ P

$\underline{(a^+b^+)}\underline{(ab)}$ gametes

$\dfrac{a^+b^+}{a\ b}$ $F_1$

(b) $\underline{(a^+b^+)}$ 40%

$\underline{(a^+b\ )}$ 10%

$\underline{(a\ b^+)}$ 10%

$\underline{(a\ b\ )}$ 40%

(c) $\dfrac{a^+b^+}{a\ b}$ 40%

$\dfrac{a^+b}{a\ b}$ 10%

$\dfrac{a\ b^+}{a\ b}$ 10%

$\dfrac{a\ b}{a\ b}$ 40%

(d) coupling

**6.7** The parental gametes would be in the proportion 30% each and the recombinations in the proportion of 20% each. The zygotes from the test cross would be in the same proportion as the $F_1$ gametes.

**6.9** (a) No; (b) –; and (c) $\dfrac{b \quad ts}{b^+ \quad ts^+} \times \dfrac{b \quad ts}{b \quad ts}$

**6.11** (a) Yes; (b) 16.3; and (c) $\dfrac{b^+vg}{b \quad vg^+} \times \dfrac{b \; vg}{b \; vg}$

**6.13** (a) $\dfrac{d^+p^+}{d \quad p}$; (b) $\dfrac{d^+p}{d \quad p^+}$; (c) $54d^+\text{–}p^+\text{–}:21d^+\text{–}pp:21ddp^+\text{–}:4ddpp$

**6.15** (a) Either cataract or polydactyly. The genes would be in repulsion. In the separation at meiosis each gamete would get one or the other. A crossover would be required to produce a gamete with both or neither.

**6.17** The one class which is represented by $^{351}/_{1000}$ is out of proportion for independent assortment. At least two of the three gene pairs must be in the same chromosome.

**6.19** (a) Four kinds in proportion of 5%; 45%; 45%; 5%. (Repulsion)
(b) Wild type, 5%; vestigial, red 45%; long wing, cinnabar 45%; vestigial cinnabar 5%.

**6.21** The classes with the smallest numbers ($++w$ and $y\ ec+$) must be double crossovers. The gene in these classes that differs from the parentals must be in the center, that is, $+w+$ and $y+ec$. With the sequence established, the single crossovers can be identified and percentages calculated.

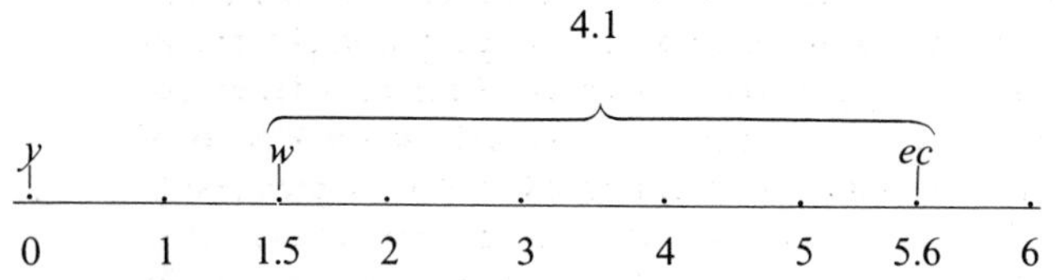

4.1

*y* *w* *ec*

0 1 1.5 2 3 4 5 5.6 6

**6.23** (a)

| | |
|---|---|
| $\underline{a^+b}$ | 45% |
| $\underline{a^+b^+}$ | 5% |
| $\underline{a \; b}$ | 5% |
| $\underline{a \; b^+}$ | 45% |

(b)

| | |
|---|---|
| $a$ | 10% |
| $b$ | 20% |

**6.25**

| | |
|---|---|
| Green, salmon silk, pigmy | 0.81 |
| purple, yellow silk, normal | 0.81 |
| green, yellow silk, normal | 0.09 |
| purple, salmon silk, pigmy | 0.09 |
| green, salmon silk, normal | 0.09 |
| purple, yellow silk, pigmy | 0.09 |
| green, yellow silk, pigmy | 0.01 |
| purple, salmon silk, normal | 0.01 |

These predictions are based entirely on probability assuming equal crossing over in all areas along the chromosome. Interference could curtail the double crossover class.

**6.27**

| | | | |
|---|---|---|---|
| *cpt ch gf* | 0.774 | *cpt ch gf*$^+$ | 0.126 |
| *cpt*$^+$*ch*$^+$*gf*$^+$ | 0.774 | *cpt*$^+$*ch*$^+$*gf* | 0.126 |
| *cpt ch*$^+$*gf*$^+$ | 0.086 | *cpt ch*$^+$*gf* | 0.014 |
| *cpt*$^+$*ch gf* | 0.086 | *cpt*$^+$*ch gf*$^+$ | 0.014 |

*Chapter 7*

**7.1** (a) Point mutation is a change in a single gene whereas a chromosome deficiency is a structural change in which a section of a chromosome is missing. Deficiencies can be seen with the microscope. They grade down in size and undoubtedly occur in a range not detectable by present methods. (b) Germinal mutations are gene changes in the reproductive cells; somatic mutations are changes in the genes of soma cells. (c) Sex-linked mutations occur in the sex chromosomes; autosomal in chromosomes other than sex chromosomes. (d) Spontaneous mutations occur without any known cause; induced mutations are created by some mutagenic agent. (e) Stable genes mutate infrequently; unstable genes have a much higher mutation rate. (f) Mutable genes are genes that mutate more frequently than most genes; mutator genes influence the mutation rate of other genes in the organism.

**7.3** A dominant mutation presumably occurred in the woman in whom the condition was first known to occur.

**7.5** The sheep with short legs could be mated to unrelated animals with long legs. If the trait is expressed in the first generation, it could be presumed to be inherited and to depend on a dominant gene. On the other hand, if it does not appear in the first generation, $F_1$ sheep could be crossed back to the short-legged parent. If the trait is expressed in the backcross progeny it might be presumed to be inherited as a recessive. If two short-legged sheep of different sex could be obtained, they could be mated repeatedly to test the hypothesis of dominance. In the event that the trait is not transmitted to the progeny resulting from the above matings, it might be considered to be environmental or dependent on some complex genetic mechanism that could not be identified by the simple tests used in the above experiments.

**7.7** Mutations in bacteria are least frequent, fruit flies are next, and man has highest mutation rate. When the rates are converted to cell generations, the averages for different organisms are quite similar.

**7.9** Before 1927 attempts were made to induce mutations but techniques were not available to distinguish induced mutations from spontaneous mutations.

**7.11** (a) The *ClB* method requires two generations but the attached-X method can be accomplished in one. (b) *ClB* is designed to detect sex-linked lethals, attached-X, sex-linked visibles.

**7.13** Most induced mutations weaken organisms that are already well adjusted in their environments. Large-scale and well-designed experiments are usually required to induce and detect beneficial mutations. There is also the problem of making the new mutation a part of the gene complement of the organism being improved, without loss in other desirable characters and general viability.

**7.15** Irradiate the nonresistant strain and plate the irradiated organisms on a medium containing streptomycin. Those that survive and produce colonies are resistant. They could be transferred to a medium without streptomycin. Those that survive would be of the first type, those that can live with streptomycin but not without it would be the second type.

**7.17** A balanced lethal could be developed by establishing two homozygous lethal genes in repulsion phase on the same chromosome pair. If the two genes are near each other or a crossover suppressor is present, heterozygosis may be completely enforced.

**7.19** In the seedling stage the results would be approximately 1 white:2 green:1 yellow. The white and yellow seedlings would die and all mature plants would be green.

*Chapter 8*

**8.1** (a) Bateson first used the word allelomorph (abbreviated "allele") meaning "the one or the other" to describe the members of pairs of Mendelian determiners. He clarified and extended the basic concept of paired hereditary elements which Mendel had discovered but had not spelled out in detail. (b) Johannsen coined the word "gene" and made a distinction between the genes responsible for a trait, "genotype," and the expression of the trait "phenotype." (c) Morgan, Bridges, and Sturtevant gave the gene a spatial position called a "locus" in a chromosome, and defined alleles as alternative discrete units in a chromosome.

**8.3** Wild-type alleles can only be postulated when contrasting traits associated with the same locus are discovered. Biochemical studies may be used eventually for detecting wild-type alleles directly, but thus far only phenotypic comparisons have been used for identifying most loci and determining their positions in chromosomes.

**8.5** (a) All colored; (b) 3 colored: 1 albino; (c) 3 colored: 1 chinchilla; (d) 1 chinchilla:1 albino; (e) 3 colored:1 himalayan; and (f) 1 himalayan:1 albino.

**8.7** (a) 1; (b) 2; (c) 2; (d) 10.

**8.9** 60

**8.11** (a) $S_1S_3$, $S_2S_3$; (b) $S_1S_3$, $S_1S_4$, $S_2S_3$, $S_2S_4$, (c) none; and (d) $S_3S_5$, $S_3S_6$, $S_4S_5$, $S_4S_6$.

**8.13** The man with AB-type blood was not the father of the child with O-type blood.

**8.15** They have different quantities of active substances and the terminal residues and linkages of sugar molecules are different.

**8.17** (a) All children would be heterozygous (*Rr*) and Rh-positive. The mother became immunized during the first pregnancy and the next child was affected. (b) All future children would be expected to be affected.

**8.19** (a)

| | | | | | |
|---|---|---|---|---|---|
| $AA$ | $MM$, | $AA$ | $MN$, | $AA$ | $NN$ |
| $AA^B$ | $MM$, | $AA^B$ | $MN$, | $AA^B$ | $NN$ |
| $Aa$ | $MM$, | $Aa$ | $MN$, | $Aa$ | $NN$ |
| $A^BA^B$ | $MM$, | $A^BA^B$ | $MN$, | $A^BA^B$ | $NN$ |
| $A^Ba$ | $MM$, | $A^Ba$ | $MN$, | $A^Ba$ | $NN$ |
| $aa$ | $MM$, | $aa$ | $MN$, | $aa$ | $NN$ |

(b) Many possible combinations are available in these and other blood systems that may be useful in checking identity and paternity.

**8.21** Blood from the sample is almost certainly that of a Negro.

**8.23** (a) In medical practice cross matching of blood is widely used for determining the proper blood type to be used for transfusions. (b) A great amount of variability, useful in human genetics studies, is associated with blood antigens. (c) Blood antigens can be determined and gene frequencies can be evaluated in different living populations as well as in mummies and other remains of ancestral groups. Evidence concerning the ancestral history of human societies may be obtained by studies of blood antigens.

**8.25** Haptoglobins are alpha globulins that bind hemoglobin; transferrins are beta globulins that transport iron and bind this metal in compounds; immunoglobulins are gamma globulins that are useful to human geneticists and anthropologists for studies of human races and ancestral history of present populations. These are serum proteins whereas blood antigens are associated with erythrocytes.

*Chapter 9*

**9.1** (a) A recessive gene presumed to be carried in heterozygous condition came unexpectedly to expression. Bridges postulated that a section in the homologous chromosome carrying the wild-type allele was missing (that is, a chromosome deficiency). On another occasion, Bridges found that a recessive gene presumed to be homozygous did not come to expression. He postulated that a gene acting as a dominant allele must be present elsewhere in the chromosome set (that is, a duplication). (b) It was impossible to distinguish microscopically between the structural parts of homologous chromosomes at the time these genetic results were obtained. (c) The discovery of attached-X chromosomes in Drosophila, meiotic configurations in maize, and salivary chromosomes in Drosophila provided tools for cytological verification.

**9.3** Enlarged size, somatic pairing, identifiable bands, and distinguishable anatomical features along the length of the different chromosomes make salivary gland chromosomes especially useful.

**9.5** The chromonemata duplicate themselves many times but the chromosomes and cells do not divide. Bundles are thus developed. The cross bands represent groups of identical chromomeres.

**9.7** When a section of a chromosome carrying a dominant gene becomes deleted a recessive allele carried in the homologous chromosome may come to expression. See text for illustrations of loop formation caused by deletions.

**9.9** (a) This is not an easy determination. New mutants of a particular kind may occur infrequently at a particular locus and produce phenotypic changes like those associated with a deficiency. A mutation from $v^+$ to $v$ in this case would appear unlikely, but if it did occur the pair of recessive genes would behave in a regular Mendelian pattern. Test cross or $F_2$ results could be predicted and checked. In other animals from which more complete data are available, deficiencies are usually homozygous lethal, resulting in modified $F_2$ ratios. If other recessives in the same chromosome, presumed to be heterozygous, came to expression, the case for a deficiency would be strengthened. (b) Cytological determination in mice is also difficult. There are no enlarged salivary or meiotic chromosomes available for study. If a chromosome could be shown to be shorter or structurally different from its homologue the deficiency hypothesis would gain support.

**9.11** (a) When crossing over occurs in the area of a paracentric inversion, acentric and dicentric chromosomes are formed that do not separate properly to the poles in division. The gametes carrying crossover chromatids are abnormal and inviable. (b) Crossovers within pericentric inversions result in unbalanced chromosome arrangements that make the gametes or zygotes inviable. (c) Crossing over is reduced to some extent, but the main "suppression" results from inviable gametes or zygotes.

**9.13** Unbalanced chromosome arrangements occur in gamete formation making pollen inviable. See text for details.

**9.15** (a) Segment 34 has been deleted; (b) segment 4 duplicated; and (c) segment 876 inverted. See text figures for model illustrations.

**9.17** If a structural alteration in a chromosome can be inseparably related to a phenotypic change, a position effect would be indicated. The phenotypic effect is caused by the change in position of genetic materials rather than addition or deletion.

**9.19** (a) Extensive recombination data may identify exchanges of genetic material within the conventional gene locus. (b) Recombination studies were not large enough and sufficiently well controlled to separate units of fine structure in genetic material.

**9.21** (a) Units of mutation and recombination smaller than those of conventional genes have been detected. (b) The traditional gene concept is valid and useful even though the unit of genetic material called a gene can be subdivided.

*Chapter 10*

**10.1** (a) Chromosome number is a valuable criterion that is available to the taxonomist along with other criteria. It is at least as significant as any well-defined morphological characteristic. (b) Numerical as well as structural differences in chromosomes have been significant in the mechanics of evolution. Analysis and comparison of chromosome numbers within and between taxonomic groups have aided in solving problems of evolution.

**10.3** (a) $\frac{1}{2}$ $2n$ and $\frac{1}{2}$ $2n + 1$, and (b) 11 normal:1 eyeless.

**10.5** Tetrasomics and nullisomics apparently occur in nature but they are less viable and usually die before they are detected.

**10.7** Techniques for preparing slides for critical microscopic observation were not effectively applied to human chromosome studies until about 1956. Better sources of human material from surgical procedures and tissue-culture techniques are now available.

**10.9** (a) XO is basically female, XXY male, and XXX metafemale. The Y carries male-determining capacity. (b) Drosophila Y has no influence on sex determination. Melandrium Y carries male determiners.

**10.11** Nondisjunction of chromosomes in the production of gametes (eggs) seems to be the explanation for most if not all trisomy.

**10.13** (a) $1/490,000$; (b) 6000; and (c) $1/70$.

**10.15** $1/3,500,000$.

**10.17** Individual tissues grow through cell division that can occur regularly among polyploid cells. Sexual reproduction of whole animals requires gamete formation, fertilization, and sex determination. Irregularities associated with polyploidy nearly always result in inviability and sterility.

**10.19** (a) Autopolyploidy is the doubling of a $2n$ complement resulting in 4 similar genomes. Allopolyploidy occurs through hybridization in which two $2n$ complements are involved. (b) Because autopolyploidy results in 4 duplicate sets of chromosomes pairing is irregular; parts of all four similar chromosomes may be paired in different places thus interfering with normal reduction division. This as well as more subtle genetic factors make autopolyploids sterile and incapable of perpetuating themselves. Allopolyploidy on the other hand provides for two pairs of chromosome sets. The chromosomes can pair properly and produce gametes. It has apparently been important in the evolution of many plant groups.

**10.21** Colchicine treatment interferes with spindle formation in cell division and some chromosomes do not reach the poles. The membrane forms independently of the chromosome mechanism and irregular numbers of chromosomes are included in the daughter cells. Sometimes the membrane forms around the entire two sets of chromosomes that normally would separate to two cells and the number in the single cell is thus doubled.

**10.23** Polyploidy associated with hybridization could account for the differences between some known strains of cotton and wheat. The processes through which some modern polyploids may have developed in nature have been reconstructed in the laboratory. See text for details.

**10.25** Poor pairing, also the most obvious cause of sterility, is associated with chromosome irregularity. More subtle genetic factors are also involved.

**10.27** (1) Doubling of chromosomes in the section of the hybrid that grew vigorously. (2) Propagation of cells from polyploid area to reproduce a plant with 2 sets of chromosomes from each parent species.

*Chapter 11*

**11.1** Most inheritance is dependent on nuclear genes. Several examples of cytoplasmic inheritance such as plastid characteristics in plants are now well established. Only a comparatively few of the many cases of inheritance which are on record can be explained on the basis of strict cytoplasmic inheritance.

**11.3** (a) Sex-linked genes are located in the X chromosome and a characteristic crisscross inheritance could be detected from appropriate crosses if sex linkage were involved. (b) Cytoplasmic inheritance would be transmitted through the maternal line because most of the cytoplasm of the zygote comes from the egg. A series of backcrosses could be made from $F_1$ males and females to the appropriate females and males of the two parent types. If the trait is transmitted repeatedly for several generations from the maternal parent to her progeny and not through the paternal parent it may be cytoplasmic. (c) If the trait was transmitted from mother to progeny but did not persist in the maternal line, it might be attributed to the influence of the mother's genes on the developing egg or embryo, that is, a maternal effect. In this case nuclear genes would be involved but they would be the genes of the mother rather than those of the individual itself.

**11.5** Male sterility facilitates crosses involving plants that are ordinarily self-fertilized. Large-scale crossing for obtaining hybrid vigor is more economically accomplished if the plants are male sterile.

**11.7** (a) Genoids have properties of viruses which have become intimately established in Drosophila and (b) kappa particles may be microorganisms that have developed an intimate relation with Paramecia of a particular genotype.

**11.9**

| | |
|---|---|
| $s^+s^+ \times ss$ | P |
| $(s^+)$ $(s)$ | gametes |
| $s^+s$ | $F_1$ all coiled to the right |
| $s^+s \times s^+s$ | $F_1 \times F_1$ |
| $1\ s^+s^+ : 2\ s^+s : 1\ ss$ | $F_2$ genotypes. All $F_2$ snails would coil to right because the $F_1$ mother was $s^+-$. |
| right right left | Phenotypic results from inbreeding the $F_2$ snails. The phenotype depends on the mother's genotype. |

**11.11** The eyes became lighter as the kynurenine that diffused from the *AA* host into the egg was metabolized and broken down by the *aa* individuals that were unable to manufacture more kynurenine.

**11.13** (a) The first step in the analysis might be to determine whether the condition can be removed by environmental changes. If it is maintained in a particular line and cannot be induced or removed by environmental changes in wild stocks, it must be hereditary. (b) Differences in the results of reciprocal crosses but no persistent effect from the maternal line in a series of backcrosses would suggest a maternal effect. (c) A single mutant gene should give monohybrid results from appropriate crosses.

*Chapter 12*

**12.1** They must (1) reproduce or replicate themselves and (2) transfer information necessary for the synthesis of enzymes.

**12.3** Griffith carried out *in vivo* experiments and demonstrated the transformation principle. Avery and others refined the experiments and conducted *in vitro* studies. After long and painstaking investigations, they demonstrated beyond question that the transforming principle was DNA.

**12.5** Type III cells were killed and were not restored to living condition. In later experiments the chemical DNA was extracted and introduced essentially separately as a nonliving chemical entity.

**12.7** The objective was to determine whether DNA or protein was the genetic material. By labeling phosphorus, a constituent of DNA, and sulfur, a constituent of protein in a virus, it was possible to demonstrate that only the labeled phosphorus was incorporated in the host cell during the reproductive cycle of the cell. Therefore, DNA and not protein is the genetic material.

**12.9** (a) DNA has one less atom of oxygen than RNA in the sugar part of the molecule. In DNA, thymine replaces the uracil that is present in RNA. (b) The main function of DNA is to carry information from cell to cell. RNA may also act as an information carrier in some viruses that have no DNA. In cells with both DNA and RNA, m-RNA acts as an intermediary in transcribing the information carried by DNA to the ribosomes where it is used in protein synthesis, t-RNA carries amino acids to the ribosomes where they are assembled into polypeptides and r-RNA makes up an essential part of each ribosome. (c) DNA is located mostly if not entirely in the chromosomes whereas RNA is in the cytoplasm, nucleolus and also in the chromosomes at stages when they are visible in the cell.

**12.11** A spiral pattern was interpreted from X-ray diffraction studies of DNA. Double strands were required to fit the chemical data of pairing of complementary bases and to fit the requirements for replication and stability of the genetic material. Hydrogen bonds were known to hold complementary bases together, to separate readily during replication, and to fit the chemical requirements of the substances and conditions involved.

**12.13** When replication occurs the two strands of the double helix separate. Each unit (nucleotide) directs the synthesis of a complement of itself which is assembled from materials in the substratum. A new double helix is thus produced.

**12.15** Mutations induced by acridine dyes resulted in insertions and deletions of nucleotides which inactivated cistrons by changing the framing pattern. Activity could be restored by compensation of a deletion by an insertion, or by three alterations of one kind. These results indicated that a codon was composed of three bases. Cell-free extract studies indicated that three m-RNA bases such as UUU would code for one amino acid (phenylalanine).

**12.17** A synthetic RNA (polyuridylic acid) was prepared which contained only one base (uracil). This was added to a cell-free extract from *E. coli* together with a mixture of 20 amino acids. A small proteinlike molecule was produced which was shown with radioactive tracers to have only phenylalanine. Uracil was thus shown to code the amino acid, phenylalanine. More efficient means of making and preserving cell-free extracts have been developed along with better methods for preparing synthetic RNAs.

**12.19** It is degenerate because the same amino acid can be coded by more than one base triplet. Each of the 20 common amino acids is coded by two or more codons.

**12.21** (a) 400,000; (b) 20,000; (c) 400,000; and (d) 68,000 Å.

*Chapter 13*

**13.1** Proteins make up the framework of bodies of plants and animals. Enzymes that control metabolic activities are proteins. Information carried by DNA is transcribed for use in protein synthesis. A mechanism through which genes control structural and functional phenotypes is explained on the basis of protein synthesis.

**13.3** Protein synthesis occurs mainly in the ribosomes. Some protein synthesis apparently occurs in the nucleus and the mitochondria are involved to a lesser extent.

**13.5** Ribosomes are from 100 to 200 Å in diameter. They are located in the cytoplasm of the cells of higher organisms. In bacteria and other organisms that do not have a clear separation between nuclear and cytoplasmic material, as well as in higher organisms, they are associated with the endoplasmic reticulum of the cell. Functionally, they are the main centers for protein synthesis. Chemically, they are composed of protein and r-RNA.

**13.7** (a) nucleus, and (b) cytoplasm.

**13.9** Ribosomes held together by m-RNA form a polysome.

**13.11** The t-RNA molecule is much smaller than that of DNA and m-RNA. It is single stranded but folded in such a way that it gives the appearance of being double stranded.

**13.13** Transitions.

**13.15** Ultraviolet light produces mispairing alterations mostly in pyrimidines (for example, cytosine to thymine transitions) during the replicating process. Thymine may be altered to cytosine, which pairs with guanine. A reverse mutation may occur when cytosine is changed to thymine, which pairs with adenine. A T-A base pair may thus be changed to a C-G and the reverse mutation may occur from C-G to T-A.

**13.17** These hemoglobins can be distinguished by (1) mobility of molecules in an electric field, and (2) the amino acid in part 4, position 6 of the beta chain.

**13.19** Mutations.

**13.21** All human chains are basically similar. Differences can be explained by mutations over a period of time. Some 21 homologous sites are recognized on all four human chains and the myoglobin chain.

**13.23** The type of coding and mechanism of protein synthesis is similar for all organisms studied. Evolution of hemoglobin and cytochrome support the view that mechanisms similar to those now being explored were in use a long time ago and have been followed consistently in the evolution of living things.

*Chapter 14*

**14.1** Microorganisms are easily cultured in the laboratory—they multiply rapidly and have large numbers of progeny. They lend themselves well to biochemical studies. Evidence indicates that they have the same general processes as higher organisms but different mechanisms are employed for meeting some requirements. They do not, for example, have a meiotic sequence comparable with that of higher forms but some accomplish gene segregation by other mechanisms. Use of microorganisms has brought great impetus to genetics in recent years.

**14.3** This is a simple virus that reproduces at a rapid rate. The entire biochemical system of such a virus may eventually be understood.

**14.5** Virulent phages go through a cycle that ends in the destruction of the host cells leaving only open spaces or plaques on the culture plate. Temperate phages develop a tolerance with the host and as prophages become incorporated into the host genome. They produce a different kind of plaque with an opaque center.

**14.7** Mixed infections of phage on sensitive bacterial cells have resulted in combinations of markers in the progeny different from those of the parents. During the latent period, when the host DNA disintegrates, the virus DNA apparently undergoes a reorganization. Genetic material of the different viruses may recombine and fragments of DNA from the host cell may be incorporated with that of the virus and may be transmitted to the next host cell invaded.

**14.9** When *r*II mutants are grown on strain K of *E. coli* they do not ordinarily form plaques. Recombination will not occur in strain K. If a mixture of strains K and B is introduced, recombination may occur in B. If plaques are formed, either mutations or recombinations must have occurred. When the strains introduced to the culture are not mixed and the plaques occur in the order of one per $10^8$ phages the most likely explanation for the change is spontaneous mutation.

**14.11** On entering a host cell, the virus loses its protein coat and infectivity. Its DNA becomes incorporated into the genome of the host replicating synchronously with the host.

**14.13** An auxotroph is a mutant that will not live on a minimal medium whereas a prototroph is a wild-type organism that will live on a minimal medium.

**14.15** F factors were demonstrated from recombination studies. When the F factor was attached to the linkage group it was the last marker to enter the recipient cell during conjugation and it behaved as a member of the linkage group. F bodies meet the requirements of "added bodies" or episomes. Such bodies have now been identified in Drosophila, maize, and several other organisms.

**14.17** Viruses can incorporate DNA from a host cell into their own DNA and carry it to other host cells that they later invade. In a new host, it may be transferred to the host's genetic material and expressed in changed traits such as streptomycin resistance.

**14.19** The significance of associating a virus with cancer was not appreciated until recently.

**14.21** Rous sarcoma virus was found to be unable to produce a protein coat but in the presence of a "helper" virus this defect was overcome. Apparently the helper supplied an enzyme necessary to synthesize protein.

**14.23** Many kinds of cancer are known which involve different tissues and have different characteristics. They have one feature in common, the ability to spread or metastasize in the body. It is quite possible that the initial irregularity that makes cells "go wild" may be caused by different factors that influence the biochemistry of single cells.

**14.25** A virus that initiates abnormal multiplication of cells causes an alteration which is perpetuated in succeeding cells but the virus does not remain in the tumor. A tumor from which no virus can be detected may have been initiated by a virus many years before.

*Chapter 15*

**15.1** (a) Understanding of the genetic code is nearly complete whereas information on regulation of gene activity is meager. (b) Much interest and attention is now being given to the latter problem.

**15.3**

| *Gene* | *Function* | *Mechanism* |
|---|---|---|
| (1) Regulator | Controls operator | Turns repressor off when effector is present |
| (2) Operator | Initiates synthesis | Controls structural genes *y* and *z* |
| (3) Structural *y* | Specifies beta-galactosidase | *y* m-RNA |
| (4) Structural *z* | Specifies galactoside permease | *z* m-RNA |

**15.5** (a) Polarity could be demonstrated by inducing inactivating mutations in genes near the operator and determining that the activity of genes in the operon sequence but more distant from the operator was inhibited or decreased. (b) A characteristic adjustment in enzyme level controlled by genes in the operon series beyond an inhibiting mutation would be evidence of modulation. All enzymatic steps beyond gene A would be inhibited or decreased.

**15.7** Clusters of genes functioning as units are probably more common in bacteria than in higher forms which have more elaborate genetic control systems and more recombinations which would break up clusters.

**15.9** The four hormones listed influence the production of RNA in cells. RNA is essential to protein synthesis.

**15.11** Some carcinogens apparently derepress genes for RNA synthesis and thus stimulate gene activity and body growth by cell division. Regulating mechanisms do not keep the growth under proper control and tumor formation results.

**15.13** The gene $v^+$ controls the production of kynurenine and $cn^+$ controls the production of 3-hydroxykynurenine.

**15.15** (a) There may be gradations in the effectiveness of genes and their products in producing visible phenotypes. Modifiers and minor environmental variations may also influence chemical reactions that are reflected in end products. (b) These terms have sometimes been applied to cases in human inheritance where more than one gene is probably involved. Therefore, the explanation should be based on some interaction rather than variable expression of a single gene. The terms have too often been used as a catchall for unexplained deviations from an expected ratio.

**15.17** (a) Wild-type host tissue can apparently compensate for the chemical blocks induced by *v* and *cn* genes. (b) Two steps in the production of wild-type pigment are involved. Discs with *v* can synthesize a material needed for pigment production when supplemented with a substance from the *cn* host. The *cn* discs, however, had their pigment production blocked at a later stage and required a substance that could not be supplied by the *v* host.

**15.19** (a) It has been assumed that environmental agents influence developing phenotypes in the same way as genes. Studies on phenocopies could suggest mechanisms of gene action. (b) They represent one of the few available approaches to physiological genetics. At best they are only suggestive and there is a great distance at present between the phenocopy and an understanding of gene action. (c) Mutations are transmitted in inheritance whereas phenocopies are not inherited.

**15.21** Phenocopies in man are difficult to distinguish from inherited abnormalities dependent on genes that have delayed action.

*Chapter 16*

**16.1** Anatomy is tangible and directly observable. Physiology depends on experimental results that require a background in physics and chemistry. Physiological sciences were not developed until the last century, but anatomy has been successfully investigated for several hundred years.

**16.3** Differentiation provides the necessary cell forms and functions; organization results in appropriate groupings of cells and tissues, and growth, through cell division, determines the ultimate size and shape of the whole organism as well as its various parts.

**16.5** An animal suitable for experimental studies of early development should be adaptable enough to develop under conditions that can be provided in the laboratory. Oviparous animals such as amphibians and birds that develop outside the body of the mother are preferred.

**16.7** Tunicate (Styela) eggs are mosaics already organized before fertilization. Newt eggs are not determined at the time of fertilization but become organized as development proceeds.

**16.9** By transplantation experiments, Spemann showed that particular areas (for example, the dorsal lip of the blastopore) in the amphibian embryo contained organizer substances which directed adjacent areas in differentiation.

**16.11** Genes control the basic pattern of the developing organism. Specific genes or their products must activate each step in the process. If differentiation has occurred in a particular region the changes that depend on other genes becoming active at a later time would be considerably restricted.

**16.13** Cytoplasmic repressor or activator substances such as those suggested in early developmental studies would fit very well into the operon model.

**16.15** Genes are constant but cytoplasm is undergoing chemical change. Genes or operons may be activated by changes in cytoplasmic substances.

**16.17** Animal behavior is the sum total of the animals' responses to its environment. Behavior as well as other more tangible characteristics has a hereditary basis. It is at least partially under genetic control.

**16.19** (a) The round dance performed by returned foragers stimulates other bees to forage in the near vicinity. Locations are identified by odors on the dancer's bodies. (b) For greater distances from the hive, the waggle dance gives information to foragers. (c) The straight portion of the waggle dance gives direction to a distant food source with reference to the position of the sun.

**16.21** Speed of the dance is characteristic of a particular group or geographical race. Members of one race may misinterpret distances represented by the dance of members of a different race because they are familiar with a dance of a different rhythm.

**16.23** (a) Hormones provide chemical coordination and thus influence the general health and temperament as well as the mating behavior of an animal. (b) Glands which produce hormones are under genetic control in development and hormone production in mature animals can be altered by genetic factors. (c) Scott and Fuller showed that genetically determined behavior differences *develop* under the influence of environmental factors.

*Chapter 17*

**17.1** 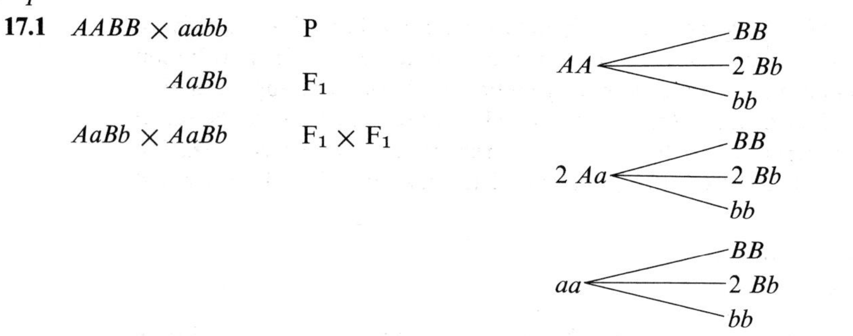


Summary of $F_2$: $1/16$ red; $4/16$ dark; $6/16$ medium; $4/16$ light; $1/16$ white.

**17.3** (a) *Aabbcc* or *aaBbcc* or *aabbCc*; (b) *AaBbcc* or *AabbCc* or *aaBbCc*; and (c) *AaBbCc*.

**17.5** (a) *AaBbcc* × *Aabbcc* or any other combination with two capital letter genes in one parent and one in the other. (b) *AaBbCc*×*AaBbcc* or *AaBbCc*×*AabbCc* or *AaBbCc* × *aaBbCc*; (c) *AaBbCc* × *AaBbCc*.

**17.7** $1/16$ black (*AABB*), $1/16$ white (*aabb*), and $14/16$ with pigmentation intensity between black and white ($4/16$ dark, $6/16$ intermediate, $4/16$ light).

**17.9** (a) There would be more gradations in pigmentation and more than five classes would be required to classify the phenotypes. Individuals homozygous for all pigment-producing genes or all genes for "white" would be considerably more infrequent than the model based on two pairs suggests. (b) Better methods of classifying phenotypes, and more data showing the proportions of different color classes in mixed populations will be required to determine more precisely the number of genes involved. The actual results of matings between large numbers of people with only colored ancestry and those with only white ancestry as well as those of matings involving other particular genotypes would be useful in making such a determination.

**17.11** 2012/8 × 251 or 1 extreme in about 256. 4 pairs of genes were involved.

**17.13** (a) The mean measures the magnitude or average of the sample in the units of measurement. (b) The standard deviation measures the variation within the sample. (c) The standard error of the mean measures the reliability of the sample in terms of sample size and variability in population sampled.

**17.15** (a) $\bar{x} = 10$; (b) $s = 1.3$; (c) $s_{\bar{x}} = 0.29$; and (d) $t = \pm 0.82$

**17.17** (a) $\bar{x} = 11.64$; (b) $s = 1.37$; (c) $s_{\bar{x}} = 0.124$; and (d) $t = \pm 0.25$

**17.19** (a) The mean was near that of the parent that required a short time for maturity. The small standard deviation shows that there is not much variation and the small standard error indicates that a sample of 24 plants was sufficiently large to properly sample the population. (b) The end of the curve representing the shorter time required for maturity. (c) The $F_2$ parent of the sample recorded was probably homozygous.

**17.21** The proportion of individuals similar in phenotype to the parents gives a suggestion as to the number of pairs involved. There are many limitations and it is doubtful that a valid estimate can be obtained when the number of genes is large. It must be assumed that the differences are genetic and cumulative and that all genes contribute equally without dominance, epistasis, hybrid vigor, and other such factors.

*Chapter 18*

**18.1** (a) Hardy and Weinberg independently developed a mathematical theorem to explain how Mendelian determiners behave in a population. This contribution provided a foundation for biometrical genetics but it was not appreciated at the time. (b) Fisher and Wright developed mathematical methods based on Mendelian inheritance that brought a rebirth in biometrical genetics. (c) Dobzhansky interpreted and popularized the mathematics of Fisher and Wright.

**18.3** 0.0126 (about 13 per 1000)

**18.5** *M* 0.53; *N* 0.47

**18.7** Yes. Gene frequencies are *M* 0.54; *N* 0.46. The proportions fit the Hardy-Weinberg equilibrium which assumes random mating.

**18.9** (a) *TT* 0.20, *Tt* 0.50, *tt* 0.30; (b) about $2/7$; and (c) about $5/7$.

**18.11** O-type, 92.16%; A, 5.85%; B, 1.93%; AB, 0.06%.

**18.13**

| *RR* | *Rr* | *rr* |
|---|---|---|
| 0.25 | 0.50 | 0.25 |

**18.15** Hereditary variation is dependent on gene and chromosome differences whereas environmental modifications are not inherited. Natural selection is not effective on environmental modifications.

**18.17** $\Delta q = -.005$ (rate of change against *a*)

**18.19** $-.0003$ (rate of change against *a*)

**18.21** 0.01

**18.23** (a) In bacteria, mutations with adaptive advantage may rapidly become widespread through asexual reproduction, whereas recombinations are not important. (b) In higher organisms with sexual reproduction and limited population size, mutations occur infrequently. Recombinations represent a source of great potential variation.

*Chapter 19*

**19.1** (a) Facts: (1) Tendency for populations to increase geometrically; (2) in spite of this tendency the population remains constant and (3) natural variation exists in populations. Deductions: (1) "Struggle for existence" (2) "Survival of the fit." (b) Darwinism is firmly established, although it has been refined and modified. (c) It has been greatly strengthened by genetics.

**19.3** (a) During long periods of early history, populations were isolated in different parts of the world. Races were formed and, under continued isolation, were moving in the direction of species formation. (b) This trend was changed, however, by invasions and migrations (military and other kinds) which began some 4000 years ago and have occurred almost continuously since that time. The present trend is toward one common gene pool representing all mankind. (c) With improved transportation and communication and better understanding among peoples of the world, the trend will undoubtedly be away from race formation and toward more complete intermixing of peoples unless a major catastrophe disrupts the present trend.

**19.5** The antigens listed are common among the natives of New Guinea. S is not found among Australian natives.

**19.7** (a) Allopolyploidy is restricted to certain groups of plants whereas the Darwinian method is widespread among plants and animals. (b) Allopolyploidy is a rapid method by which new species can be created in a few generations, but long periods of time are usually required for the Darwinian method. (c) Man may induce polyploidy and make appropriate crosses to duplicate species formation that has occurred or that might occur in nature. He can induce mutations and direct selection in domesticated animals and plants, but he has little control over these processes in nature. Some man-made environmental changes have secondarily caused profound alterations in some plant and animal populations.

**19.9** (a) Wingless insects had a selective advantage on an island where those with wings were in danger of being blown out to sea. (b) Those without wings remained in their protected dishes and produced more wingless flies whereas those with wings were blown away.

**19.11** Mutations represent the ultimate source of variation, but in higher forms original mutations are too infrequent to be effective in evolution. Recombination of genes already present in the individuals of the breeding population is an important immediate source of variation. Natural selection is the main directing force and geographic isolation is the factor that builds up boundaries around breeding units and makes reproductive isolation and speciation possible.

*Chapter 20*

**20.1** (a) Inbreeding as such has no effect on gene frequency. (b) It increases homozygosity and decreases heterozygosity.

**20.3** They have already lost essentially all of the deleterious recessives from the breeding population through past inbreeding and selection.

**20.5** (a) Inbreeding tends to bring recessive genes to expression and thus to provide material for natural selection. Outbreeding hides recessives and natural selection has little effect upon them. (b) Inbreeding develops constancy of type and provides a method of perpetuating desirable combinations. Outbreeding breaks up established combinations but is associated with increased hybrid vigor.

**20.7** The expected pure lines would have the following phenotypes: yellow seed, green pod, inflated pod; yellow seed, green pod, constricted pod; yellow seed, yellow pod, inflated pod; yellow seed, yellow pod, constricted pod; green seed, green pod, inflated pod; green seed, green pod, constricted pod; green seed, yellow pod, inflated pod; and green seed, yellow pod, constricted pod.

**20.9** About 1 or 2 (1.5625) plants would be heterozygous at the end of ten generations.

**20.11** The systems are less efficient in order listed (see curves from Wright, in text).

**20.13** (a) Maximum vigor would be transmitted in the seeds from this cross and would be manifest in the $F_1$ progeny. (b) The seed parent would be vigorous and would produce a good quantity of seed but the quality, with reference to hybrid vigor, would be poor. The $F_2$ plants would be variable with only a small proportion as vigorous as the $F_1$ plants. (c) If $A$, $B$, $C$, and $D$ are dominant, this cross should produce as much hybrid vigor as (a). If they are not dominant, the hybrid vigor would be slightly less than that of (a). In any case the parents would be strong hybrid plants on which an abundance of good quality seed could be produced. The $F_1$ plants raised from the seed would be as vigorous or nearly as vigorous and uniform as those from (a).

**20.15** Heterosis probably has great significance for traits with high heritability but it has been difficult to demonstrate. Prospects for the future are good, especially for meat production and beasts of burden.

**20.17** Before the inbreeding process was begun, cancer occurred sporadically in mice. It was impossible to follow hereditary patterns in families and to determine whether some types were due to hereditary or environmental factors. Through inbreeding and selecting for various kinds of cancer, strains have been developed with high incidence of mammary, gastric, and lung cancer, and leukemia. This suggests that there is a genetic basis for these types of cancer and that many genes that can be made homozygous through inbreeding are involved.

**20.19** (a) $1/10,000$, (b) $1/16$, (c) $115/10,000$, (d) $1/128$, and (e) $1/16$.

*Chapter 21*

**21.1** Selection of efficient producers is the best method available for the improvement of domestic animals.

**21.3** General viability, disease resistance, and fertility are related to production over a period of time and should be considered along with production.

**21.5** Resistance may be changed by mutation and may be related to environmental factors. It is usually specific for a given pathogen. New variations in pathogens through mutation may not be covered by the original resistance of the animal. Dynamic relations exist between hosts and parasites.

**21.7** Resistance is the only control available at present against these diseases. Whole crops may be wiped out if a disease for which the plants are not resistant gets started. Experience has shown that projects designed to breed new strains of cereals are necessary to keep ahead of the new pathogens constantly appearing. Thus far, such projects have been amply justified.

**21.9** (a) Mass selection is phenotypic selection where hereditary and environmental influences are not distinguished. The seed is mixed so that the ill effects of inbreeding are avoided. (b) Pedigree selection is confined to individuals and families. It is possible to select within a closely related group in which the genotypes may be known and to separate environmental from genetic variation. Comparisons can be made among different lines. (c) Since pedigree selection involves inbreeding, the advantages of heterosis are not obtained. Mass selection may result in improved strains to the extent that the traits selected are heritable. It favors heterosis.

**21.11** A desirable quality (gene) may be introduced into a standard vegetable crop by hybridization followed by repeated backcrosses with the standard strain as the recurrent parent. This procedure may result in the restoration of the desirable qualities already built up in the standard strain with the addition of a new gene introduced from another strain.

**21.13** Most genes producing gross abnormalities in man are rare. At the same gene frequency, a dominant will be expressed more often than a recessive. A trait dependent on a rare dominant gene will not skip generations (if it is fully penetrant). Thus, its genetic basis is more readily apparent.

**21.15** Human hereditary diseases are incurable in the sense that the genes are already present in the individual and cannot be removed. The symptoms of hereditary diseases can be treated and sometimes prevented or removed. Symptoms of several hereditary diseases respond to environmental treatment and are now being removed or in some cases avoided. With more knowledge of the abnormalities, more effective treatments of the symptoms will be possible.

**21.17** The objective of eugenics is to improve the genetic quality of the human population.

**21.19** Instead of stabilizing at about 150,000,000, the population has continued to rise and is now increasing at an unprecedented rate.

# Index